ANATOMY
AND
PHYSIOLOGY

FOR SPEECH AND LANGUAGE

ANATOMY AND PHYSIOLOGY

FOR SPEECH AND LANGUAGE

John A. Seikel, Ph.D.

Department of Speech and Hearing Sciences
Washington State University
Pullman, Washington

Douglas W. King, Ph.D.

Basic Medical Science
Washington State University
Pullman, Washington

David G. Drumright, B.S.

Computer Programmer
Washington State University at Spokane

Illustrations and Photography by Sarah Moore

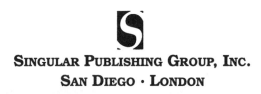

SINGULAR PUBLISHING GROUP, INC.
SAN DIEGO · LONDON

Singular Publishing Group, Inc.
401 West A Street, Suite 325
San Diego, California 92101-7904

19 Compton Terrace
London N1 2UN, U.K.

e-mail: singpub©mail.cerfnet.com
Website: http://www.singpub.com

Typeset in 10/12 Palatino by So Cal Graphics
Printed in the United States of America by McNaughton & Gunn

Library of Congress Cataloging-in-Publication Data

Seikel, John S.
    Anatomy and physiology for speech and language / John A. Seikel,
Douglas W. King, David G. Drumright ; illustrations and photography
by Sarah Moore.
        p.   cm.
    Includes bibliographical references and index.
    ISBN 1-56593-615-9
    1. Speech—Physiological aspects.   2. Human anatomy.   3. Human
physiology.   I. King, Douglas W.   II. Drumright, David G.
III. Title.
    [DNLM: 1. Speech—physiology.   2. Respiratory System—physiology.
3. Phonation—physiology.   4. Neuroanatomy.   5. Nervous System
—physiology.   WV 501S459a 1996]
QP306.S49   1996
612.7'8—dc20
DNLM/DLC
for Library of Congress   96-9818
                                                                        CIP

Contents

P

Preface

Anatomy and physiology provide the bedrock for communication: We feel that to understand human communication processes one must first know the structures that support those processes. Increasingly, speech-language pathologists are faced with assessing communication abilities that have been compromised by illness, trauma, or developmental anomaly. To be effective in this process, you must be able to relate the communication deficit to the structures on which communication depends. Armed with knowledge of the physical systems of speech and language, you will be better equipped to serve those who depend on your knowledge, and your understanding of the physical systems will give you insights into alternatives that might otherwise go unnoticed.

We have tried to provide you with a means of reaching your goal of becoming a competent speech-language pathologist or audiologist by recognizing that learning occurs best when instruction is provided in many different forms. As you will see, the materials we have prepared include text, software, and videotaped lab activities. It is our hope that the text will provide your instructor with support for lecture, and we have found the software to be extremely helpful preparation for labs and tests. Our video experience provides you with the opportunity to examine the actual anatomical structures through a cadaver lab.

We sincerely hope that these materials will help to solidify your knowledge. We join with your instructor in welcoming you to the world of anatomy and physiology for speech and language and trust that this marks only your first stop on a lifetime journey of learning.

Acknowledgment

The authors wish to thank Giri Hegde and Marie Linvill for their continued assistance in this project.

This is dedicated to Paula, Ernestine, Joan, and Russ, and to the memory of Charles Van Riper.

JAS

CHAPTER

Overview of the Text

Human communication is one of the most complex processes known, requiring extraordinary coordination and control of an intensely interconnected sensorimotor system. It is our heart-felt desire that study of the physical system will lead you to an appreciation of the importance of your future work as a speech-language pathologist or audiologist.

We also know that the intensity of your study will work to the benefit of your future clients and that the knowledge you gain through your effort will be applied throughout your career. We appreciate the fact that the study of anatomy is difficult, but we also recognize that the effort you put forth now will provide you with the background for work with the medical community.

A deep understanding of the structure and function of the human body is critical to the individual who is charged with diagnosis and treatment of speech and language disorders. As beginning clinicians you are already aware of the awesome responsibility you bear in clinical management. It is our firm belief that knowledge of the human body and how it works will provide you with the background you need to make informed and wise decisions. We welcome you on your journey into the world of anatomy.

We have organized the text around the four "classic" systems of speech: the respiratory, phonatory, articulatory/resonatory, and nervous systems. The respiratory system (involving the lungs) provides the "energy source" for speech, while the phonatory system (involving the larynx) provides voicing. The articulatory/resonatory system modifies the acoustic source provided by voicing (or other gestures) to produce the sounds we acknowledge as speech. The nervous system lets us control musculature, receive information, and make sense of the information.

There are few areas of study where the potential for choking on detail is greater than in the discipline of anatomy. Our desire with this text and the accompanying software and video labs is to provide a stable foundation upon which detail may be learned. In the text we have tried to provide you with an introductory section that sets the stage for the detail to follow, and we try to bring you back to a more global picture with summaries. We have also provided derivations of words where we thought it would help you to remember technical terms.

We have created companion materials for this text, consisting of video and software activities. The software accompanies the text, and the set of seven videotapes is available separately. These companion materials should be used along with the text. They enhance your understanding of the material presented in the text as well as through lectures from your instructor.

VIDEOTAPED LABS

The set of seven videotaped labs let you examine the structures of the speech mechanism as seen in a cadaver laboratory, in lock-step with the text. We have found that direct examination of specimens is most helpful in understanding anatomy, and this allows you to reinforce your classroom lecture material with a relevant and timely lab experience.

SOFTWARE LABS

We have also created a series of software labs that provide you the opportunity to examine structures and function of the speech mechanism in the more flexible environment of the personal computer. The software closely follows the text, reinforcing identification of the structures presented during lecture, but more importantly illustrating the function of those structures. You will examine speech physiology through interactive manipulation of the structures under study, learning the relationship of the parts and how they function together. The software labs are self-paced, and there are frequent quizzes to help you examine the effectiveness of your study habits. To make the best use of these materials, you will want to pace your video labs so that you work through three per week during the semester. If you spend two or three half-hour sessions per week with the software, you will get the greatest benefit from your class and readings. The software will also provide a great refresher in preparation for quizzes and examinations.

HOW TO USE THIS
INSTRUCTIONAL PACKAGE

We feel that experience is the key to understanding. In the text, we will periodically take you on a guided tour of your own body and its functions. If you take advantage of these "tours," you will get a chance to experience the phenomena under study, setting the stage for a deeper understanding of the processes.

By viewing the video labs as you study the various sections of the text you will have the opportunity to study anatomy from human cadaver specimens. We know that you will view these with the respect owed to individuals who have graciously and selflessly donated their bodies for scientific study and education. Our students have expressed their gratitude over the years for having access to these resources, and we wanted the opportunity to make them available to you.

We have found that anatomy is not a "spectator sport," but that learning is greatly enhanced through active participation. Your understanding of the anatomy and physiology of speech will be greatly enhanced through the interactive software labs as you solidify the concepts of anatomy and physiology presented through the text and video.

As clinicians you want the insight of clinical details, and we have provided Clinical Notes within the text to broaden your appreciation of the importance of anatomy in your clinical practice.

We have attempted to facilitate your work with terminology. Anatomy has its own vocabulary, and you will make it yours before the course is through. As new terms are presented in text, they are highlighted in boldface type and defined on the same page.

If you supplement your reading with the relevant computer and video lab activities, you will have provided yourself with the best opportunity to gain the insight you are seeking. We hope that this text and the accompanying software and video labs serve you well in your career as speech-language pathologists and audiologists.

CHAPTER

$$2$$

Basic Elements of Anatomy

The study of the human body and its parts has a long and rich tradition. Although students of anatomy must still rely on their powers of observation, the task faced by the first anatomists was even more daunting. Modern study of anatomy and physiology is performed with myriad instruments and techniques, but our colleagues from earlier times were not so blessed. If you listen closely you will hear the echoes of the early anatomists' voices as you struggle with terminology that, at times, seems foreign and confusing. It is then that you should open your medical dictionary to see for yourself the roots of the words that seem confusing. Your predecessors chose terms that clarified what they experienced, and the fact that you are unfamiliar with them is a tribute to the long history of which you partake. When you read archaic terminology, recognize that these terms represent the knowledge acquired by your "academic ancestors." The fact that the terminology remains in our lexicon indicates the accuracy with which they studied their field despite extraordinarily limited resources.

In this chapter, we will provide some basic elements to prepare you for your study of anatomy and physiology of speech. To do this, we will provide a broad picture of the field of anatomy, and then introduce you to the basic tissues that make up the human body. When tissues are combined to form structures, those structures must be bound together to form a functioning body, and we will discuss the means of connecting those parts. Finally, we will try to set the stage for your understanding of the new and foreign terminology of anatomy.

ANATOMY AND PHYSIOLOGY

anatomy: Gr., **anatome,** *dissection*

dissect: L., **dissecare,** *to cut up*

physiology: Gr., **physis,** *nature +* **logos,** *study*

The term **anatomy** refers to the study of the structure of an organism. At one time it referred to the actual **dissection** or cutting of parts of the organism, but over time has evolved to encompass a field of study that involves much more than gross separation of body parts. **Physiology** is the study of the function of the living organism and its parts, as well as the chemical processes involved. As science and technology advanced, subspecializations of both anatomy and physiology arose. **Applied anatomy**, also known as **clinical anatomy**, entails application of anatomical study for diagnosis and treatment of disease particularly as it relates to surgical procedures. **Descriptive anatomy**, also known as **systematic anatomy**, is involved in the description of individual parts of the body without reference to disease conditions. Descriptive anatomy views the body as a composite of systems that function together.

Gross anatomy studies structures visible without the aid of microscopy, whereas **microscopic anatomy** examines structures not visible to the unaided eye. **Surface anatomy** is the study of the form and structure of the surface of the body, especially with reference to the organs beneath the surface. **Developmental anatomy** deals with development of the organism from conception to adulthood.

pathological: Gr., **pathos,** *disease +* **logos,** *study*

When your study turns to the pathological entity, you will have entered the domain of **pathological anatomy**. Quite often in anatomy and physiology comparisons are made across species boundaries, because, among other things, knowledge of similarities and differences across the animal kingdom gives insight into the utility of different animal models of research. This study, **comparative anatomy**, provides that wealth of information.

Physiology has undergone similar change as a result of rapidly refined technology. Examination of physiological processes may range from fairly simple methodologies such as measuring the forces exerted by muscles to highly refined **electrophysiological** techniques that measure the electrical activity of single cells or groups of cells, including muscle and nervous system tissue. Indeed, the audiologist will be particularly interested in auditory electrophysiological procedures involved in measurement of the electrical activity of the brain caused by auditory stimuli (**evoked auditory potentials**). **Respiratory physiology** is concerned with all processes involved in breathing.

Teratogens

A **teratogen** or **teratogenic agent** is anything causing **teratogenesis**, the development of a severely malformed fetus. For an agent to be teratogenic, its effect must occur during prenatal development.

Because development of the fetus arises from the proliferation and differentiation of tissue, timing of the teratogen is particularly critical. The heart undergoes its most critical period of development from the third embryonic week to the eighth, while the critical period for the palate begins around the fifth week and ends around the twelfth week. The critical period for neural development stretches from the third embryonic week until birth. These critical periods for development mark the points at which the developing human is most susceptible to insult. Said another way, an agent destined to have an effect on the development of an organ or system will have its greatest impact during that critical period.

Many teratogens have been identified, including organic mercury (which causes cerebral palsy, mental retardation, blindness, cerebral atrophy, and seizures), heroin and morphine (causing neonatal convulsions, tremors, death), alcohol (fetal alcohol syndrome, mental retardation, microcephaly, joint anomalies, maxillary anomalies), and tobacco (growth retardation) to name just a few. Even ingestion of vitamin A, taken during the second to fifth week, may result in cleft palate.

You will sample the fruits of many of these areas during your study of anatomy. We rely heavily on descriptive anatomy to guide our understanding of the physical mechanisms of speech and to aid our discussion of its physiology as well. We will call on pathological anatomy as we deal with the results of conditions, such as emphysema, that change how systems work. Even as we discuss these changes we will need to call on microscopic anatomy to reveal the impact of disease on structures invisible to the unaided eye.

We also must call on knowledge from related fields to support our understanding of anatomy and physiology. **Cytology** is the discipline that examines structure and function of cells, while **histology** is the microscopic study of cells and tissues. **Osteology** is the study of structure and function of bones, while **myology** examines muscle form and function. **Arthrology** studies the joints that unite the bones, and **angiology** is the study of blood vessels and the lymph system. **Neurology** is the study of the nervous system. We will capitalize on all of these disciplines to explain the mechanisms involved in speech production.

cytology: Gr., kytos, cell + logos, study

histology: Gr., histos, web; tissue + logos, study

osteology: Gr., osteon, bone + logos, study

myology: Gr., mys, muscle + logos, study

arthrology: Gr., arthron, joint + logos, study

neurology: Gr., neuron, sinew, nerve + logos, study

To summarize:

■ **Anatomy** is the study of the structure of an organism, whereas **physiology** is the study of function.
■ Several subspecializations of anatomy interact to provide the detail required for understanding the anatomy and physiology of speech.
■ **Descriptive anatomy** relates the individual parts of the body to functional systems.
■ **Pathological anatomy** relates to changes in structure as they relate to disease.
■ **Gross** and **microscopic anatomy** refer to levels of visibility of structures under study.
■ **Developmental anatomy** studies the growth and development of the organism.
■ Disciplines such as **cytology** and **histology** study cells and tissues, and **myology** examines muscle form and function.
■ **Arthrology** refers to study of the joint system for bones, whereas **osteology** is the study of form and function of bones.
■ **Neurology** relates to the study of the nervous system.

In the sections that follow we will present the building blocks of the physical system you are preparing to study. These blocks include the basic tissues, organs, and structures made up of these tissues and the systems made up of the organs. Let us turn our attention to the basic elements of which all bodies are composed.

BUILDING BLOCKS OF ANATOMY: TISSUES, ORGANS, AND SYSTEMS

The body is composed of cells, living tissue that contains a nucleus and a variety of cellular material specialized to the particular function of the individual cell. Cells differ based on the type of tissue they comprise. Our study of anatomy will focus on the product of muscle cells, nerve cells, and bone cells, as these cells combine to form the structures involved in speech production. Four basic tissues comprise the human body, and variants of these combine to make up the structures of the body. These are epithelial, connective, muscular, and nervous.

Each of these tissues is functionally specialized. Epithelium provides a protective lining for the surface of the body and internal surfaces of cavities, while connective tissue is supportive. Muscular tissue is capable of contraction on proper stimulation, and neural tissue is specialized to transmit information. These tissues have numerous subclasses, as shown in Table 2–1. Let us look at each tissue in turn.

Table 2-1. Tissue types.

I. **Epithelial**

 A. **Simple Epithelium: Single layer of cells.**

 Squamous (pavement) epithelium: Single layer of flat cells; linings of blood vessels, heart, alveoli, lymph vessels).

 Cuboidal (cubical) epithelium: Cube-shaped; secretory function in some glands, such as thyroid.

 Columnar epithelium: Single layer, cylindrical cells; inner lining for stomach, intestines, gall bladder, bile ducts.

 Ciliated epithelium: Cylindrical cells with cilia; lining of nasal cavity, larynx, trachea, bronchi.

 B. **Compound Epithelium: Different layers of cells.**

 Stratified epithelium: Flattened cells on bed of columnar cells; epidermis of skin, lining of mouth, pharynx, esophagus; conjunctiva.

 Transitional epithelium: Pear-shaped cells; lining of bladder, etc.

II. **Connective**

 A. **Areolar:** Elastic; supports organs, between muscles.

 B. **Adipose:** Cells with fat globules; between muscles and organs.

 C. **White Fibrous:** Strong, closely packed; ligaments binding bones; periosteum covering bone; covering of organs; fascia over muscle.

 D. **Yellow Elastic:** Elastic; in areas requiring recoil, such as trachea, cartilage, bronchi, lungs.

 E. **Lymphoid:** Lymphocytes; make up lymphoid tissue of tonsils, adenoids, lymph nodes.

 F. **Cartilage:** Firm and solid.

 1. Hyaline cartilage: Bluish white and smooth; found on articulating surfaces of bones, costal cartilage of ribs, larynx, trachea, and bronchial passageway.

 2. Fibro-cartilage: Dense, white, flexible fibers; intervertebral disks, between surfaces of knee joints.

 3. Yellow (elastic) cartilage: Firm elastic; pinna, epiglottis.

 G. **Blood:** Corpuscles (cells: red, white), platelets, blood plasma.

 H. **Bone:** Hardest connective tissue.

 1. Compact bone: Has haversian canal, lamellar structure.

 2. Cancellous (spongy) bone: Spongy appearance, larger haversian canal, red bone marrow producing red and white blood cells and plasma.

III. **Muscular**

 A. **Striated:** Skeletal, voluntary muscle.

 B. **Smooth:** Muscle of internal organs, involuntary.

 C. **Cardiac:** Combination of striated and smooth, involuntary.

(continued)

Table 2–1. *(continued)*

IV. Nervous

    A. Neurons: Transfer information; communicating tissue.

Source: From *Foundations of Anatomy* and *Physiology* by J. S. Ross & K. J. W. Wilson, 1966, pp. 1–32. Baltimore, MD: Williams & Wilkins.

tissue: L., texere, to weave

Epithelial Tissue

Epithelial tissue refers to the superficial layer of mucous membranes and the cells comprising the skin. The hallmark of epithelial tissue is its paucity of intercellular material. This is in contrast to bone, cartilage, and blood, all of which have significant quantities of intercellular matter. The absence of intercellular material lets the epithelial cells form a tightly packed sheet, a protective quality. There may be many layers of epithelium, and some forms of epithelium are secretory (glandular epithelium); others have **cilia** or hair-like protrusions that actively beat to remove contaminants from the epithelial surface (beating ciliated epithelia). We are most familiar with the surface covering of our body, but epithelial tissue lines nearly all of the cavities of the body as well as the tubes that connect them.

Connective Tissue

Connective tissue is perhaps the most complex of the categories, a tribute to the vast amount of connective tissue within the body. This tissue is specialized for the purpose of support. Unlike epithelium, connective tissue is composed predominantly of intercellular material, known as the **matrix**, within which the cells of connective tissue are bound. Connective tissue may be solid, liquid, or gel-like. The matrix is the defining property of a specific connective tissue, as you shall see.

Areolar tissue, also referred to as loose connective tissue, is supportive in nature. This elastic material is found between muscles and as a thin, membranous sheet between organs. It fills the **interstitial** space between organs, and its fibers form a mat or weave of flexible collagen. **Adipose** tissue is areolar tissue that is highly impregnated with fat cells. **Lymphoid tissue** is specialized connective tissue found in tonsils and adenoids.

interstitial: L., interstitium, space or gap in tissue

Fibrous tissue binds structures together, and may contain combinations of fiber types. **White fibrous** tissue is strong, dense, and highly organized. It is found in ligaments that bind bones together, as well as in the fascia that encase muscle, as will be described shortly. **Yel-**

low elastic tissue is found where connective tissue must return to its original shape after being distended, such as in the cartilage of the trachea or bronchial passageway. The characteristics of these tissues are determined by their properties. **Collagenous** and **reticular fibers** provide a flexible structure to fibrous connective tissue, while **elastic fibers** provide tissue recoil to this tissue where needed.

Cartilage is a particularly important tissue, because it has unique properties of strength and elasticity. Cartilage has two qualities that make it ideally suited for some structural purposes. The **tensile strength** of cartilage is the quality which keeps the fibers from being easily separated when pulled, while the **compressive strength** of cartilage lets it retain its form by being resistant to crushing, compressing forces. **Hyaline cartilage** is smooth and has a glassy, blue cast. It provides a smooth mating surface for the articulating surfaces of bones, as the cartilaginous portion of the rib cage, making up the larynx, trachea, and bronchial passageway. **Fibro-cartilage** contains collagenous fibers, providing the cushion between the vertebrae of the spinal column, as well as the mating surface for the temporomandibular joint between the lower jaw and the skull. Fibro-cartilage acts as a shock absorber and provides a relatively smooth surface for gliding. **Yellow (elastic) cartilage** has less collagen, endowed rather with elastic fibers. It is found in the pinna, nose, and epiglottis.

It might surprise you to know that **blood** is connective tissue. The fluid component of blood is called plasma, and blood cells (including red and white corpuscles) are suspended in this matrix. The blood cells arise from within the marrow of another type of connective tissue, bone.

Bone is the hardest of the connective tissues. The characteristic hardness of bone is a direct function of the inorganic salts that make up a large portion of bone. Bone is generally classified as being compact or spongy. **Compact** bone is characterized microscopically by its lamellar or sheet-like structure, whereas **spongy** bone looks porous. Spongy bone contains the marrow that produces red and white blood cells as well as the blood plasma matrix.

Muscle

Muscle is specialized contractile tissue. Although the connective tissues discussed previously have important supportive roles, they have no ability to contract. Muscle fibers are capable of being stimulated to contract.

Muscle is generally classified as being striated, smooth, or cardiac (Figure 2–1). **Striated** muscle is so-called because of the striped appearance it takes on microscopic examination. Striated muscle is

Muscle function is described in Chapter 10.

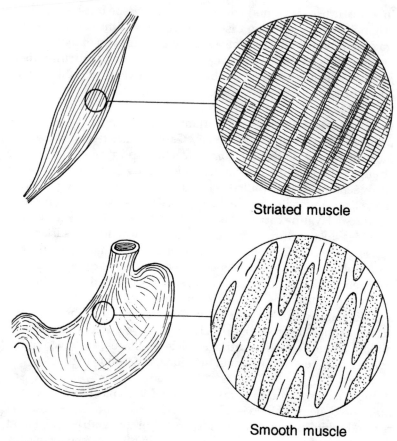

Striated muscle

Smooth muscle

FIGURE 2–1. Striated *(upper)* and smooth muscle *(lower)*.

striated: L., stria, striped, streaked

autonomic: Gr., autos, self + nomos, law; self-regulating

somatic: Gr., soma, body

known as **skeletal muscle** as well, because it is the muscle used to move skeletal structures. Likewise, it is known as **voluntary** or **somatic muscle**, because it can be moved in response to conscious, voluntary processes. This is in contrast to **smooth** muscle, which includes the muscular tissue of the digestive tract, blood vessels, and so forth. Smooth muscle is generally sheet-like, with spindle-shaped cells. **Cardiac muscle** is composed of cells that interconnect in a net-like fashion. Smooth and cardiac muscle are generally outside of voluntary control, relegated to the **autonomic** or involuntary nervous system, which will be discussed in Chapter 10.

Nervous Tissue

Nervous tissue structure is described in Chapter 9.

Nervous tissue is highly specialized communicative tissue. Nervous tissue consists of **neurons** or nerve cells that take on a variety of forms. The function of nervous tissue is to transmit information from one neuron to another, from neuron to muscle, or from sensory receptors to other neural structures.

To summarize:

- Four **basic tissues** comprise the human body: epithelial, connective, muscular, and nervous.
- **Epithelial tissue** includes the surface covering of the body and linings of cavities and passageways.
- **Connective tissue** varies as a function of the intercellular material (matrix) surrounding it.
- **Areolar connective tissue** is loose and thin, and **adipose tissue** is areolar tissue with significant fat deposits.
- White and yellow **fibrous connective tissue** is found in ligaments, tendons, and cartilage.
- **Cartilage** has both tensile and compressive strength and is elastic (fibers of cartilage resist being torn apart or crushed, and cartilage tends to return to its original shape upon being deformed).
- Hyaline cartilage is smooth, while fibro-cartilage provides a collagenous cushion between structures.
- Yellow cartilage is highly elastic.
- **Blood** is a fluid connective tissue, whereas **bone** is a highly dense connective tissue.
- **Muscle** is the third type of tissue, consisting of **voluntary** (striated), **involuntary** (smooth), and **cardiac** muscle.
- **Nervous tissue** is specialized for communication.

Tissue Aggregates

The basic body tissues (epithelial, connective, muscular, nervous) are used to form larger structures. For instance, **organs** are aggregates of tissue with **functional unity**, by which we mean that the tissues of the organ all serve the same general purpose. In the same sense, we speak of **muscles** (such as the diaphragm) as being structures made up of muscular tissue, and the muscles must be attached to bone or cartilage in some fashion. Let us examine some of the larger organizational units.

Fascia. As mentioned in the previous section, fascia surrounds organs, being a sheet-like membrane that may either be dense or filmy, thin or thick. Striated muscle is surrounded by **perimysium**, fascia sufficiently thick that the muscle cannot be seen clearly through it.

fascia: L., band

ligament: L., ligamentum, a band

viscera: L., body organs

Ligaments. The term "ligament" refers specifically to "binding." **Visceral ligaments** bind organs together or hold structures in place. **Skeletal ligaments** must withstand great pressure, as they typically bind bone to bone. To achieve this, the connective tissue fibers course in the same direction, giving ligaments great tensile strength. Most ligaments have little stretch, although some (such as the posterior spinal cord ligaments) are endowed with elastic fibers to permit limited stretching. Ligaments that stretch will appear yellow, while the collagen of inelastic ligaments will give them a white cast.

Tendons. Tendons provide a means of attaching muscle to bone or cartilage (see Figure 2–2). The fibers of tendons are arrayed longitudinally (as opposed to interwoven or matted), giving them great tensile strength but reduced compressive strength. Because tendon is actually part of the muscle, it always binds muscle to another structure (typically bone), attaching to the connective tissue of that skeletal structure. Tendons tend to have the **morphology** (or form) of the muscles they serve. Compact, tubular muscles tend to have long, thin tendons. Flat muscles, such as the diaphragm, will have flat tendons. The microscopic structure of a tendon makes it quite resistant to damage. Because the collagenous fibers intertwine, the forces placed on the tendon are distributed throughout the entire bundle of fibers.

aponeurosis: Gr., **apo,** *from +* **neuron,** *nerve; tendon*

When a tendon is sheet-like, it is called an **aponeurosis**. Aponeuroses greatly resemble fascia, but are much denser. In addition, an aponeurosis will retain the longitudinal orientation of the connective tissue fibers, whereas fascia are made up of matted fibers. It is this homogeneous orientation, by the way, that gives tendons their shiny appearance, as compared with the duller-looking fascia.

The dense packing of longitudinal fibers makes tendons quite strong. A tendon can withstand pulling over 8000 times the stretching force that a muscle the same diameter can. In fact, the tendon for a given muscle will be able to withstand at least twice the pulling force of the muscle itself. That is to say, a sudden pull on a muscle will damage the muscle itself or the musculo-tendinous junction well before actually damaging the tendon.

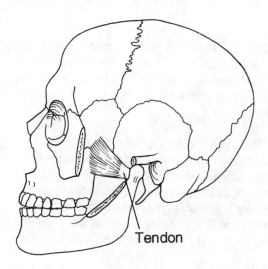

Tendon

FIGURE 2–2. Tendon attaching muscle to bone.

Bones. Bones and cartilage have an interesting relationship. Developing bone typically has a portion that is cartilage, and all bone begins as a cartilaginous mass. Many points of **articulation** or joining between bones retain this relationship, because cartilaginous surfaces are smoother and will glide across each other more freely than surfaces of bone. Likewise, cartilage will replace bone where elasticity is beneficial. We will see this in the cartilaginous portion of the rib cage (Chapter 3), in the cartilage of the larynx (Chapter 5), and in the nasal cartilages (Chapter 7). As cartilage becomes impregnated with inorganic salts it begins to harden, ultimately becoming bone.

Cartilage becomes quite important as we discuss the respiratory system (Chapter 3), the phonatory system (Chapter 5), and the articulatory/resonatory system (Chapter 7).

Bones provide rigid skeletal support and protect organs and soft tissue. Thirty percent of a bone is collagen, providing great tensile strength. The rigidity and compressive strength of bone tissue comes from the even greater proportion of calcium deposited within it. Indeed, bones of the aged become more susceptible to compression as a result of loss of calcium through aging.

Bones are broadly characterized by length (long or short), shape (flat), or generally as having irregular morphology. The periosteum covering of a bone extends along its entire surface, with the exception of regions endowed with cartilage. This outer periosteum layer is most tightly bound to the bone at the tendinous junctures. Although the outer periosteum layer is tough and fibrous, the inner layer of periosteum contains cells that facilitate bone repair, **fibroblasts**.

Bone growth and development is a classic example of "use it or lose it." The density of bone and its conformation are directly related to the amount of force placed on it. Use of muscles actually causes bone to strengthen and become more dense in regions stressed by that activity. Males tend to have greater muscle mass than females, and the bones of males will often have more readily identifiable landmarks.

fibroblast: L., fibra, fibrous + Gr., blastos, germ

Joints. The union of bones with other bones or cartilage with other cartilage is achieved by means of **joints** (see Figure 2–3). Joints take a variety of forms, many of which will be important to you in your studies. Generally, joints are classified based on the degree of movement they permit: high mobility (**diarthrodial joints**), limited mobility (**amphiarthrodial**), or no mobility (**synarthrodial**) (Table 2–2). The joints are classified in parallel form based on the primary component involved in the union between bones. Synarthrodial joints are anatomically classified as **fibrous joints**, while amphiarthrodial joints are **cartilaginous joints**, and diarthrodial joints are **synovial joints**, or joints containing synovial fluid within a joint space.

*joint: L., **junctio**, a joining*

Fibrous Joints. There are three major types of fibrous or synarthrodial joints: syndesmosis, suture, and gomphosis. **Syndesmosis** joints are bound by fibrous ligaments but have little movement. **Sutures** are joints between bones of the skull that are not intended to move at

syndesmosis: Gr., syndesmos, ligament + osis, condition

*suture: L., **sutura**, seam*

Osteoporosis

Osteoporosis is a condition wherein bone becomes increasing porous due to loss of calcium. The reduction in calcium may be the result of aging or may arise from vitamin D deficiency, as in **osteomalacia.** Loss of calcium may also arise from disuse, as found in individuals confined to bed during illness. Individuals with osteoporosis are particularly susceptible to bone fractures arising from what would be considered normal application of force. The elderly individual who has fallen and broken his or her hip may actually have broken the hip prior to the fall. An individual with osteoporosis may break ribs while coughing.

Osteoporosis may be localized, as seen in the bones of the skull in **Paget's disease** (osteitis deformans).

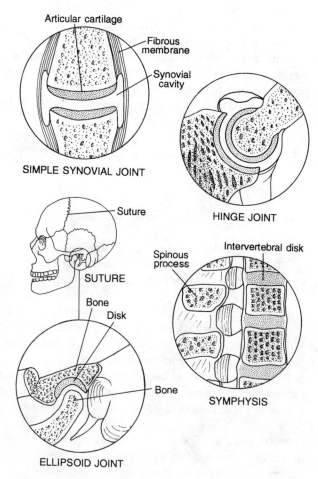

FIGURE 2–3. Different types of joints.

Table 2-2. Types of joints.

I. Fibrous Joints (Immobile).
    A. Syndesmosis: Banded by ligament.
    B. Suture: Skull bone union.
    C. Gomphosis: Tooth in alveolus.
II. Cartilaginous Joints (Limited movement).
    A. Synchondrosis: Cartilage that ossifies through aging.
    B. Symphysis: Bone connected by fibrocartilage.
III. Synovial Joints (Highly mobile).
    A. Plane joint (gliding joint; arthrodia): Shallow or flat surfaces.
    B. Spheroid (cotyloid).
    C. Condylar joint: Shallow ball-and-socket joints.
    D. Ellipsoid joint: "Football" shaped ball-and-socket joint.
    E. Trochoid joint (pivot).
    F. Sellar joint.
    G. Ginglymus (hinge) joint.

---

all. The mating surfaces of the bones forms a rough and jagged line that enhances the strength of the joint. A **gomphosis** is a type of joint in which a structure is bound within a cavity, as in the union of a tooth root to the hole that holds it, the alveolus.

gomphosis: *Gr., bolting together*

Cartilaginous Joints. As the name implies, cartilaginous or amphiarthrodial joints are those in which cartilage provides the union between two bones. Considering that bone arises from cartilage during development, it makes sense that in some cases cartilage would persist. In **synchondrosis** the cartilaginous union is maintained, as in the junction of the manubrium sterni and the corpus sterni, although it ossifies as the individual ages. The second type of cartilaginous joint is a **symphysis**, as found between the pubic bones (pubic symphysis) or between the disks of the vertebral column.

synchondrosis: *Gr.,* **syn,** *together +* **chondros,** *cartilage +* **osis,** *condition*

symphysis: *Gr., growing together*

Synovial Joints. The distinguishing feature of synovial or diarthrodial joints is that they all include some form of joint cavity within which is found **synovial fluid**, a lubricating substance, and around which is an articular capsule. The **articular capsule** is made up of an outer fibrous membrane of collagenous tissue and ligament to which binds the bone and an inner synovial membrane lining. Hyaline cartilage covers the surface of each bone of the joint, providing a smooth, strong mating surface.

Synovial joints are either simple or composite, depending on whether there are two bone surfaces being joined or more than two, respectively. **Plane synovial joints** (gliding joints; arthrodial) are

Craniosynostosis

As the infant develops, the sutures of the skull become ossified, a process called **synostosis.** Complete synostosis normally occurs well into childhood, but in some instances synostosis may occur prenatally. Continued normal growth of the brain, especially during the first postnatal year, places pressure on the skull. The effects of premature synostosis or **craniosynostosis** on skull development are quite profound. With **premature sagittal synostosis**, the child's head becomes peaked along the suture and elongated in back. In **Apert syndrome**, a genetic condition, the affected child's stereotypic "peaked head" is the result of premature closure of the coronal suture, resulting in pronounced bulging along that articulation.

cotyloid: Gr., kotyloeides, cup-shaped

those in which the mating surfaces of the bone are more or less flat. Bones joined in this manner are permitted some gliding movement. **Spheroid** (or **cotyloid**) **joints** are **reciprocal** in nature (as are all but plane joints), in that one member of the union has a convex portion that mates with a concave portion of the other member. The spheroid joint is a ball-and-socket joint, in which a convex ball or head fits into a cup or **cotylica**. This joint permits a wide range of movement, including rotation.

condylar: Gr., kondylos, knuckle

sellar: L., sella, Turkish saddle

ginglymus: Gr., ginglymos, hinge

Condylar joints are more shallow versions of the ball-and-socket joint, and these joints permit more limited movement. **Ellipsoid joints** capitalize on an elliptical (football-shaped) member. These joints permit a wide range of movement, but obviously not rotation. A **trochoid joint** (**pivot joint**), on the other hand, is designed for rotation, and little else. It consists of a bony process protruding into a space. A **saddle joint** (or **sellar joint**) is perhaps the most descriptive of the joint names. One member of the saddle joint is convex, like a saddle, while the other convex member "sits" on the saddle. A **hinge joint** (**ginglymus**) acts like the hinge of a cabinet door: One member rotates on that joint with a limited range, permitting only flexion and extension.

To summarize:

■ Tissues combine to form larger structures.
■ **Fascia** is a sheet-like membrane surrounding organs.
■ **Ligaments** bind organs together or hold bones to bones or cartilage.
■ **Tendons** attach muscle to bone or to cartilage, and if the tendon is flat it is referred to as an **aponeurosis.**

■ Bones and cartilage provide the structure for the body, articulating by means of joints.

■ **Diarthrodial** (synovial) **joints** are highly mobile, **amphiarthrodial** (cartilaginous) **joints** permit limited mobility, and **synarthrodial** (fibrous) **joints** are immobile.

■ **Fibrous joints** bind immobile bodies together, **cartilaginous joints** are those in which cartilage serves the primary joining function, and **synovial joints** are those in which lubricating synovial fluid is contained within an articular capsule.

■ Among synovial joints are **plane** (gliding) joints, **spheroid, condylar, trochoid, sellar,** and **ellipsoid** joints (all variants of ball-and-socket joints), as well as **hinge** joints.

Muscles. The combination of muscle fibers into a cohesive unit is both functionally and anatomically defined. Anatomically, muscles are bound groups of muscle fibers with functional unity. A fascia of connective tissue termed the **epimysium** surrounds muscles, and muscles are endowed with a tendon to permit attachment to skeletal structure. Muscles have a nerve supply to provide stimulation of the contracting bundle of tissue, and muscles have a vascular supply to meet the nutrient needs. Muscle **morphology** or form varies widely, depending on function. Fibers of wide, flat muscles tend to radiate from a broad point of origination to a more focused insertion. More cylindrical muscles will have unitary points of attachment on either end. In all cases, the orientation of the muscle fibers defines the region on which force will be applied, because muscle fiber can only actively shorten.

epimysium: Gr., epi, upon, over + mys, muscle

morphology: Gr., morphe, form + logos, study

Although we discuss muscle physiology in Chapter 10, some points bear note. A muscle can contract to approximately one half its original length, and thus long muscles can contract greater distances than short muscles. The diameter of a muscle is directly related to its strength, because that represents the number of muscle fibers allocated to perform the task.

See Chapter 9 for a discussion of neuromuscular function.

The work performed by the body is widely varied between extremes of muscular effort (very little to great amounts) and extremes of muscle rate of contraction (very rapid to slow and sustained). Although muscle morphology accounts for much of the variation in function, the physical relationship between muscle and bone provides a great deal of flexibility in muscle use.

Muscles can exert force only by shortening the distance between two points and can contract only in a straight line (with the exception of sphincteric muscles). By convention, the point of attachment of the least mobile element is termed the **origin**, and the point of attachment that moves as a result of muscle contraction is termed the **insertion**. When referring to limbs, the insertion point is more distant from the body. Muscles that move a structure are referred to as **ago-**

nists or prime movers, whereas those that oppose a given movement are called **antagonists**. Thus, an agonist for one movement may become an antagonist for the opposite movement. Muscles used to stabilize structures are termed **synergists**.

As you can see in Figure 2–4, the points of muscle attachment have a great deal to do with how much force can be exerted by muscle contraction to achieve work. If, for a moment, we hold muscle length constant, then a muscle attached closer to a joint will move the bone farther and faster than one attached farther from the joint. In contrast, the muscle farther from the joint will be able to exert more force through its range because of the leverage advantage. Thus, the more distally placed muscle will have an advantage for lifting, while the muscle closer to the joint will provide greater range to the bone to which it is attached.

*afferent: L., **ad,** to + **ferre,** carry*

*efferent: L., **ex,** from + **ferre,** carry*

Muscles are **innervated** or supplied by a single nerve. Innervation can be sensory (generally termed **afferent**) or excitatory (**efferent**) in nature. A **motor unit** consists of one efferent nerve fiber and the muscle fibers to which it attaches. Every muscle fiber will be innervated. In addition, muscles have sensory components providing information to the central nervous system concerning the state of the muscle.

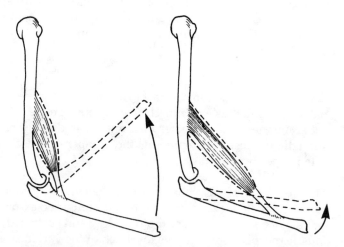

FIGURE 2–4. Mechanical advantage derived from point of insertion. On the left, the muscle inserts closer to the point of rotation and the movable point will undergo a greater excursion on contraction of the muscle. On the right, the muscle is attached a greater distance from the point of rotation so that the bone will move a smaller distance, but the muscle is capable of exerting greater force in the direction of movement.

Neuromuscular Diseases

A host of neuromuscular conditions prey on the muscular system and the nerve components that supply it. **Amyotrophic lateral sclerosis** is a condition in which the myelin sheath surrounding the nerve axon is progressively destroyed, resulting in loss of muscle function. A similar but less predictable myelin destruction occurs in **multiple sclerosis**, although the course and severity of the disease are markedly different from amyotrophic lateral sclerosis. **Myasthenia gravis** is a condition in which the nerve-muscle junction is destroyed as a result of an immune system response. The result is weakness and loss of muscle range due to inability of the nerve and muscle to communicate.

To summarize:

- **Muscle** is contractile tissue, with muscle bundles capable of shortening to about half their length.
- The point of attachment with the least movement is termed the **origin,** while the **insertion** is the point of attachment of relative mobility.
- Muscles that move a structure are **agonists** and those that oppose movement are called **antagonists.**
- Muscles that stabilize structures are termed **synergists.**
- Muscles are innervated by a single nerve, and **innervation** can be **afferent** or **efferent.**
- A **motor unit** is the efferent nerve fiber and muscle fibers it innervates.

Body Systems

Much as tissues combine to form organs, organs combine to form functional systems. **Systems** of the body are groups of organs with functional unity. That is, the combination of organs performs a basic function, and failure or deficiency of an organ will result in a change in function of the system. Because systems are functionally defined, organs can belong to more than one system. Similarly, we can define the physical communication systems of the human organism through combinations of organs.

The basic systems of the body are fairly straightforward. The **muscular system** includes the smooth, striated, and cardiac muscle of the body, and the **skeletal system** includes the bones and cartilages that form the structure of the body. The **respiratory system** includes the passageways and tissues involved in gas exchange with the environment, including the oral, nasal, and pharyngeal cavities, the trachea and bronchial passageway, and lungs. The **digestive system** also includes the oral cavity and pharynx, in addition to the esophagus, liver, intestines, and associated glands. The **reproductive system** includes the organs involved with reproduction (ovaries; testes), and the **urinary system** includes the kidneys, ureters, bladder, and urethra. The **endocrine system** involves production and dissemination of hormones, so it includes glands, such as the thyroid gland, testes, and ovaries. The **nervous system** includes the nerve tissue and structures of the central and peripheral nervous systems.

Systems of Speech

Speech is an extraordinarily complex process that capitalizes on these systems. The functionally defined systems of speech combine organs and structures in a unique fashion.

A classical categorization of the systems of speech includes respiratory, phonatory, articulatory, resonatory, and nervous systems. The **respiratory system** is a precise match with the anatomical respiratory system, including the respiratory passageway, lungs, trachea, and so forth. The **phonatory system** is the system involved in production of voiced sound and utilizes components of the respiratory system (the laryngeal structures). The **articulatory system** is the combination of structures that are used to alter the characteristics of the sounds of speech, including parts of the anatomically defined digestive and respiratory systems (the tongue, lips, teeth, soft palate, etc.). The **resonatory system** includes the nasal cavity and soft palate and portions of the anatomically defined respiratory and digestive systems. Although some speech scientists view the resonatory system as separate from the articulatory system, we take an alternate view in this text, defining rather the articulatory/resonatory system of speech production.

The logic of combining the articulatory and resonatory systems will become clear in Chapter 7.

Our definition of systems of speech is truly a convenience. Do not think for a minute that any of the systems operates in isolation. Speech requires the integrated action of all of the systems, and the level of coordination involved in this task is sobering.

To summarize:

■ Organs combine to form **functional systems,** including the system concerned with muscles (**muscular system**), with the framework of the body (**skeletal system**), breathing (**respiratory system**), digestion (**digestive system**), reproduction (**reproductive system**), the **urinary** and **endocrine systems,** and **nervous system**.
■ Within the discipline of speech pathology we have functionally defined four systems.
■ The **respiratory system** is the system concerned with respiration, the **phonatory system** is made up of the components of the respi-

ratory and digestive systems associated with production of voiced sounds (the larynx), the **articulatory system** (including the structures of the face, mouth and nose), and the **nervous system** (related to central and nervous system control of speech processes).

TERMINOLOGY OF ANATOMY

We talk about the structures in anatomy through modifying terms. Clarity of terminology lets us accurately represent structures, and is of the utmost importance in the study of anatomy. Terminology also links us to the roots of this field of study. To the budding Latin or Greek scholar learning the terms of anatomy will be an exciting reminder of our linguistic history. To the rest of us, the terms we are about to discuss may be less easily digested, but are nonetheless important.

As you prepare for your study of anatomy, please realize that this body of knowledge is extremely hierarchical. What you learn today will be the basis for what you learn tomorrow. Not only are the terms the bedrock for understanding anatomical structures, mastery of their usage will let you gain the maximum benefit from new material presented.

Parts of the Body

The human body can be defined in terms of specific regions. The **thorax** is the chest region, the **abdomen** is the region represented externally as the anterior abdominal wall. Together, these two components make up the **trunk** or **torso**. The **dorsal trunk** is the region we commonly refer to as the back. The area of the hip bones is known as the **pelvis**. Resting atop the trunk is the head or **caput**. The **cranium** is the portion of the skull housing the brain.

abdomen, L., belly

The upper and lower extremities are appended to the trunk. The **upper extremity** consists of the arm (from the shoulder to the elbow), the forearm, wrist, and hand. The **lower extremity** is made up of the thigh, leg, ankle, and foot.

Terms of Orientation

Anatomical terms deal with ways of looking at structures (orientation) and the form of those structures (morphology). We discuss position and orientation with reference to the living body, and thus the anatomical position refers to a standing body. In the **anatomical position**, the body is erect, the palms, arms, and hands face forward, as shown in Figure 2–5. Discussion of terms of direction assumes this position.

Intrinsic to this discussion is the concept of axis. The body and brain (and many other structures) are seen to have axes or midlines from

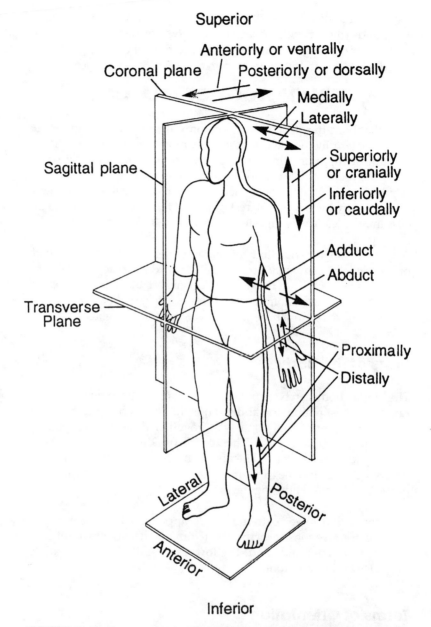

FIGURE 2–5. Terms of orientation and planes of reference.

which other structure arise. The **axial skeleton** is the head and trunk, with the spinal column being the axis, while the **appendicular skeleton** includes the lower and upper limbs. The **neuraxis** or axis of the brain is slightly less straightforward, due to morphological changes of the brain during development. The embryonic nervous system is essentially tubular, but as the cerebral cortex develops, a flexure occurs and the telencephalon (the region that will become the cerebrum) folds forward. As a result, the neuraxis takes a T-formation.

The spinal cord and brainstem have dorsal and ventral surfaces corresponding to those of the surface of the body. Because the cerebrum folds forward, the dorsal surface is also the superior surface, and the ventral surface is the inferior surface. Most anatomists avoid this confusing state by referring to the superior and inferior surfaces.

Some terms are sensitive to the physical orientation of the body (such as "vertical" or "horizontal"). Other terms (such as "frontal," "coronal," and "longitudinal") refer to planes or axes of the body, and are therefore insensitive to the position of the body.

With the anatomical position in mind, let us turn to planes of reference. You may think of the following planes as referring to sections of a standing body, but they are actually defined relative to imaginary axes of the body. If you were to divide the body into front and half sections you would have produced a **frontal section** or **frontal view**. (Realize that a frontal view is the product of a frontal section but, in practice, frontal section often refers to the view.) On the other hand, if you cut the body into left and right halves you would have **midsagittal sections**. A **sagittal section** is any cut that divides the body into left and right portions, and the cut is in the sagittal plane. A **transverse section** produces upper and lower halves of a body. Figure 2–5 illustrates these sections.

A **frontal** or **coronal section** results in front and back portions of a body, and is so called because the plane is parallel to the coronal suture of the skull which roughly divides the body in half along that axis. Recognize that these are midline sections, which provide equal halves, but sections are also made off midline. Armed with these basic planes of reference, you could rotate a structure in space and still discuss the orientation of its parts.

The term **anterior** refers to the front surface of a body. (Those of you who play cards may remember "ante up," meaning, "put your money up front!" You may remember the term "antebellum," meaning "before the war.") **Ventral** and anterior are synonymous for the standing human, but have different meanings for a quadruped. The ventral aspect of a standing dog includes its abdominal wall, which happens to be directed toward the ground. The anterior of the same dog would be the portion including the face.

The opposite of anterior is **posterior**, meaning "toward the back," and the synonym for bipeds is **dorsal**. Again, the posterior of a four-footed animal differs from that of humans. Thus you may refer to a muscle running toward the anterior surface, or a structure having a specific landmark in the posterior aspect. These terms are "body-specific:" No matter what the position of the body is, anterior is "toward the front" of that body. The term **rostral** is often used to mean "toward the head." If the term is used to refer to structures within the cranium, rostral refers to a structure anterior to another.

sagittal: L., sagittalis, arrow-like

anterior: L., front

The term "quadruped" refers to four-footed animals. The term "biped" refers to two-footed animals.

rostral: L., rostralis, beak-like

When discussing the course of a muscle, we often need to clarify its orientation with reference to the surface or level within the body. Thus, a structure may be referred to as **peripheral** ("away from the center") to another. A structure is **superficial** if it is confined to the surface.

external: L., externus, outside

When we say one organ is "**deep** to another", we mean it is closer to the axis of the body. A structure may also be referred to as being **external** or **internal**, but these terms are generally reserved for cavities within the body. Likewise, you may refer to an aspect of an appendicular structure (such as arms and legs) as being **distal** (away from midline) or **medial** (toward the midline).

A few terms refer to the actual present position of the body rather than a description based on the anatomical position. **Superior** (above, farther from the ground) and **inferior** (below, closer to the ground) are used in situations where gravity is important. The terms **prone** (on the belly) and **supine** (on the back) are also commonly used in describing the present actual position.

proximal: L., proximus, next

Often we must describe the orientation of a structure relative to another structure, and subsequently disregarding the anatomical position. Some term that will assist you are **lateral** (related to the side, as in football's "lateral pass"), **proximal** (nearest to the point of attachment or some point of reference, as in "approximate"). These two terms are usually reserved for discussion of the relationship between limbs and trunk.

flexion: L., flexio, bending
extension: Gr., ex, out + L., tendere, to stretch

There are specialized terms associated with movement. **Flexion** refers to bending at a joint, usually toward the ventral surface. That is, flexion usually results in two ventral surfaces coming closer together. Thus, sit-ups would be an act of flexion, because you are bending at the waist. **Extension** is the opposite of flexion, being the act of pulling two ends farther apart. Again, having completed a sit-up you return to the extended condition. **Hyperextension**, as in arching your back at the end of your sit-up, is sometimes referred to as **dorsiflexion**.

inversion: L., in, in + versio, to turn

eversion: L., ex, from, out + versio, to turn

Use of flexion and extension with reference to feet and toes is a little more complex. **Plantar** refers to the sole of the foot, the flexor surface. If you rise on your toes, you are extending your foot, but the gesture is referred to reasonably as **plantar flexion**. A **plantar grasp reflex** would be one in which stimulation of the sole of the foot causes the toe of the feet to "grasp." The term **dorsiflexion** may be used to denote elevation of the dorsum (upper surface) of the foot. You may turn the sole of your foot inward, termed **inversion**. A foot turned out is termed **eversion**.

The term **palmar** refers to the palm of the hand, that is, the ventral (flexor) surface. The side opposite the palmar side is the dorsal side.

If the hand is rotated so that the palmar surface is directed inferiorly it is **pronated** (remembering that in the prone position one is lying on his or her stomach or ventral surface). **Supination** refers to rotating the hand so that the palmar surface is directed superiorly. A **palmar grasp reflex** is elicited by lightly stimulating the palm of the hand. The response is to flex the fingers to grasp.

These and other useful terms and their definitions may be found in Appendixes A and B at the end of the book, as well as in the Glossary. A good medical dictionary will be an invaluable aid in the process of sorting out anatomical terminology.

The names of muscles, bones, and other organs were mostly set down at a time in history when medical people spoke Latin and Greek as universal languages. The intention was to name parts unambiguously rather than to make things mysterious. Many of the morphemes left over from Latin and Greek are worth learning separately. When you come across a new term, you will often be able to determine its meaning from these components. For instance, when a text mentions an **"ipsilateral"** course for a nerve tract, you can see **"ipsi"** (same) and **"lateral"** (side) and conclude that the nerve tract is on the same side as something else. Your study of the anatomy and physiology of the human body will be greatly enhanced if it includes memorization of some of the basic forms found in the appendix.

While you are studying the nomenclature of the field, do not let the plurals get you down. Fortunately, Latin is a well-organized language with a few general rules that will assist you in sorting through terminology. If a singular word ends in "-a" the plural will most likely be "-ae" (pleura; pleurae). If the word ends in "-us" (such as "locus") the plural will be "-i". When the singular form ends in "-um" (as in "datum" or "stratum"), the plural will have "-a" ("data" or "strata").

Often you can feel comfortable using the Anglicized version ("hiatuses", but never "datas") but do not assume everyone will. Many combined forms involve a possessive form, denoting ownership (the genitive case, in linguistic jargon): "corpus"—body; "corporum"—of the body.

The English pronunciation of these forms is unfortunately less predictable; the dictionary often does not agree with the pronunciations common among medical personnel.

In summary:

■ The **axial skeleton** consists of the trunk and head, whereas the **appendicular skeleton** is that related to the upper and lower extremities.
■ The **trunk** consists of the abdominal and thoracic regions.

■ Anatomical terminology is the specialized set of terms used to define position and orientation of structures.

■ A **frontal section** is one in which there are front and back halves, whereas a **sagittal section** divides the body into right and left halves.

■ A **transverse section** divides the body into upper and lower portions.

■ **Anterior** and **posterior** refer to the front and back surfaces of a body, as do **ventral** and **dorsal** for the erect human.

■ **Superficial** refers to the surface of a body, while **peripheral** and **deep** refer to directions toward and away from the surface.

■ **Distal** and **medial** refer to being away from or toward the midline of a free extremity, respectively.

■ **Superior** refers to an elevated position, whereas **inferior** is closer to the ground.

■ **Prone** and **supine** refer to being on the belly or back, respectively.

■ **Lateral** refers to the side, **proximal** refers to a point near the point of attachment of a free extremity, and **distal** refers to a point away from the root of the extremity.

■ **Flexion** and **extension** refer to bending at a joint, where flexion refers to bringing ventral surfaces closer together and extension is moving them farther apart.

■ **Plantar** refers to the sole of the foot, while **palmar** refers to the palm of the hand, both ventral surfaces.

CHAPTER SUMMARY

Anatomy and **physiology** are the study of structure and function of an organism. Subspecializations of anatomy interact to provide the detail required for understanding the anatomy and physiology of speech. **Descriptive anatomy** relates the individual parts of the body to functional systems and **pathological anatomy** relates to changes in structure from disease. Disciplines such as **cytology** and **histology** study cells and tissues, and **myology** examines muscle form and function. **Arthrology** refers to the study of the joint system for bones, while **osteology** is the study of form and function of bones. **Neurology** relates to the study of the nervous system.

The four basic tissues of the human body are **epithelial, connective, muscular,** and **nervous. Epithelial** tissue provides the surface covering of the body, and linings of cavities and passageways. **Connective tissue** provides the variety of tissue linking structures together, those comprising **ligaments, tendons, cartilage, bone,** and **blood. Muscular** tissue is contractile in nature, comprised of **striated, smooth,** and **cardiac. Nervous** tissue is specialized for communication.

Tissue combine to form structures and organs. **Fascia** surrounds organs, **ligaments** bind bones or cartilage, **tendons** attach muscle to bone or to cartilage, and **bones** and **cartilage** provide the structure for the body. **Joints** between skeletal components may be **diarthro-**

dial (**synovial;** highly mobile), **amphiarthrodial** (**cartilaginous;** slightly mobile), and **synarthrodial** (**fibrous;** immobile). **Fibrous joints** bind immobile bodies together, **cartilaginous joints** are those in which cartilage serves the primary joining function, and **synovial joints** are those in which lubricating synovial fluid is contained within an articular capsule.

Muscle bundles are capable of shortening to about half their length. The **origin** is the point of attachment with the least movement, and the **insertion** is the relatively mobile point of attachment. **Agonists** are muscles that move a structure, **antagonists** oppose movement, and **synergists** stabilize a structure. Muscles are **innervated** by a single nerve, and innervation can be **afferent** or **efferent.** A **motor unit** is the efferent nerve fiber and muscle fibers it innervates.

Systems of the body include the **muscular, skeletal, respiratory, digestive, reproductive, urinary, endocrine,** and **nervous** systems. Systems of speech production include the **respiratory, phonatory, articulatory/resonatory,** and **nervous** systems.

The **axial skeleton** is that supporting the trunk and head, and the **appendicular skeleton** is related to the extremities. Anatomical terminology relates position and orientation of the body and its parts. A **frontal plane** is that involving a cut providing front and back halves of a body, a **sagittal plane** is produced by a cut dividing the body into left and right halves, and a **transverse plane** is that produced by dividing the body into upper and lower halves. **Anterior** and **posterior** refer to front and back of a body, as do **ventral** and **dorsal** for the human. **Peripheral** refers to a direction toward the surface or superficial region, while **deep** refers to direction away from the surface. **Distal** and **proximal** refer to away from and toward the root of a free extremity, respectively. **Superior** and **inferior** refer to upper and lower regions. **Lateral** and **medial** refer to the side and midline, respectively. **Flexion** refers to bending at ventral surfaces toward each other at a joint, and **extension** is moving those surfaces farther apart. **Plantar** and **palmar** refer to ventral surfaces of the feet and hands, respectively.

Study Questions

1. _____ is the study of the structure of an organism.

2. ___ _____ is the study of the function of a living organism and its parts.

3. _____ anatomy is anatomical study for diagnosis and treatment of disease.

4. _____ anatomy is involved in the description of individual parts of the body without reference to disease conditions, viewing the body as a composite of systems that function together.

5. _____ is the study of structure and function of cells.

6. _____ is the study of structure and function of bones.

7. _____ is the study of form and function of muscle.

8. _____ is the study of the nervous system.

9. Skin and mucous membrane are made up of _____ tissue.

10. _____ is a particularly important connective tissue because it is both strong and elastic.

11. _____ is contractile tissue.

12. _____ bind organs together or hold bones to bone or cartilage.

13. _____ is a sheet-like membrane surrounding organs.

14. _____ attach muscle to bone or to cartilage.

15. The relatively immobile point of attachment of a muscle is termed the _____.

16. The relatively mobile point of attachment of a muscle is termed the _____.

17. Identify the systems defined below:

   a. _____ This system includes smooth, striated, and cardiac muscle of the body.

   b. _____ This system includes the bones and cartilages that form the structure of the body.

   c. _____ This system includes the passageways and tissues involved in gas exchange with the environment, including the oral, nasal, and pharyngeal cavities, the trachea and bronchial passageway, and lungs.

   d. _____ This system includes the esophagus, liver, intestines, and associated glands.

   e. _____ This system includes the nerve tissue and structures of the central and peripheral nervous system.

18. Identify the systems of speech defined below.

   a. _____ This system includes the passageways and tissues involved in gas exchange with the environment, including the oral, nasal, and pharyngeal cavities, the trachea and bronchial passageway, and lungs.

   b. _____ This system is involved in production of voiced sound and utilizes components of the respiratory system (the laryngeal structures).

c. _____ This system is the combination of structures that is used to alter the characteristics of the sounds of speech, including parts of the anatomically defined digestive and respiratory systems (the tongue, lips, teeth, soft palate, etc.).

d. _____ This system includes the nasal cavity and soft palate and portions of the anatomically defined respiratory and digestive systems.

19. Terms of orientation: On the figure below, identify the descriptive terms indicated.

a. _____ plane

b. _____ plane

c. _____ plane

d. _____ aspect

e. _____ aspect

f. _____ (movement away from midline)

g. _____ (movement toward midline)

h. _____ (located away from midline)

i. _____ (located near midline)

j. _____ (related to the side)

k. _____ (above)

l. _____ (below)

Study Question Answers

1. <u>ANATOMY</u> is the study of the structure of an organism.

2. <u>PHYSIOLOGY</u> is the study of the function of a living organism and its parts.

3. <u>CLINICAL OR APPLIED</u> anatomy is anatomical study for diagnosis and treatment of disease.

4. <u>SYSTEMIC ANATOMY</u> is involved in the description of individual parts of the body without reference to disease conditions, viewing the body as a composite of systems that function together.

5. <u>CYTOLOGY</u> is the study of structure and function of cells.

6. <u>OSTEOLOGY</u> is the study of structure and function of bones.

7. <u>MYOLOGY</u> is the study of form and function of muscle.

8. <u>NEUROLOGY</u> is the study of the nervous system.

9. Skin and mucous membrane are made up of <u>EPITHELIAL</u> tissue.

10. <u>CARTILAGE</u> is a particularly important connective tissue because it is both strong and elastic.

11. <u>MUSCLE</u> is contractile tissue.

12. <u>LIGAMENTS</u> bind organs together or hold bones to bone or cartilage.

13. <u>FASCIA</u> is a sheet-like membrane surrounding organs.

14. <u>TENDONS</u> attach muscle to bone or to cartilage.

15. The relatively immobile point of attachment of a muscle is termed the <u>ORIGIN</u>.

16. The relatively mobile point of attachment of a muscle is termed the <u>INSERTION</u>.

17. Identify the systems defined below:

    a. <u>MUSCULAR SYSTEM</u> This system includes smooth, striated, and cardiac muscle of the body.

    b. <u>SKELETAL SYSTEM</u> This system includes the bones and cartilages that form the structure of the body.

    c. <u>RESPIRATORY SYSTEM</u> This system includes the passageways and tissues involved in gas exchange with the environment, including the oral, nasal, and pharyngeal cavities, the trachea and bronchial passageway, and lungs

    d. <u>DIGESTIVE SYSTEM</u> This system includes the esophagus, liver, intestines, and associated glands.

    e. <u>NERVOUS SYSTEM</u> This system includes the nerve tissue and structures of the central and peripheral nervous system.

18. Identify the systems of speech defined below.

    a. <u>RESPIRATORY SYSTEM</u> This system includes the passageways and tissues involved in gas exchange with the environment, including the oral, nasal, and pharyngeal cavities, the trachea and bronchial passageway, and lungs.

    b. <u>PHONATORY SYSTEM</u> This system is involved in production of voiced sound and utilizes components of the respiratory system (the laryngeal structures).

    c. <u>ARTICULATORY SYSTEM</u> This system is the combination of structures that are used to alter the characteristics of the sounds of speech, including parts of the anatomically defined digestive and respiratory systems (the tongue, lips, teeth, soft palate, etc.).

    d. <u>RESONATORY SYSTEM</u> This system includes the nasal cavity and soft palate and portions of the anatomically defined respiratory and digestive systems.

19. Terms of orientation: On the figure below, identify the descriptive terms indicated.

    a. <u>TRANSVERSE</u> plane

    b. <u>SAGITTAL</u> plane

    c. <u>CORONAL OR FRONTAL</u> plane

    d. <u>ANTERIOR OR VENTRAL</u> aspect

    e. <u>POSTERIOR OR DORSAL</u> aspect

    f. <u>ABDUCT</u> (movement away from midline)

g. <u>ADDUCT</u> (movement toward midline)

h. <u>DISTAL</u> (located away from midline)

i. <u>MEDIAL</u> (located near midline)

j. <u>LATERAL</u> (related to the side)

k. <u>SUPERIOR</u> (above)

l. <u>INFERIOR</u> (below)

REFERENCES

Barnett, H. L. (1972). *Pediatrics*. New York: Appleton-Century-Crofts.

Basmajian, J. V. (1975). *Grant's method of anatomy*. Baltimore, MD: The Williams & Wilkins Company.

Bateman, H. E. (1977). *A clinical approach to speech anatomy and physiology*. Springfield, IL: Charles C. Thomas.

Bateman, H. E., & Mason, R. M. (1984). *Applied anatomy and physiology of the speech and hearing mechanism*. Springfield, IL: Charles C. Thomas Publishers.

Duffy, J. R. (1995). *Motor speech disorders*. St. Louis, MO: Mosby.

Fink, B. R., & Demarest, R. J. (1978). *Laryngeal biomechanics*. Cambridge, MA: Harvard University Press.

Gosling, J. A., Harris, P. F., Humpherson, J. R., Whitmore, I., Willan, P. L. T. (1985). *Atlas of human anatomy*. Philadelphia, PA: J. B. Lippincott.

Grobler, N. J. (1977). *Textbook of clinical anatomy* (Vol. 1). Amsterdam: Elsevier Scientific.

Kaplan, H. (1960). *Anatomy and physiology of speech*. New York: McGraw-Hill.

Kuehn, D. P., Lemme, M. L., & Baumgartner, J. M. (1989). *Neural bases of speech, hearing, and language*. Boston, MA: Little, Brown.

Moore, K. L. (1988). *The developing human*. Philadelphia, PA: W. B. Saunders.

Ross, J. S., & Wilson, K. J. W. (1966). *Foundations of anatomy and physiology*. Baltimore, MD: Williams & Wilkins.

Williams, P., & Warrick, R. (1980). *Gray's anatomy* (36th Brit. ed.). Philadelphia, PA: W. B. Saunders.

Zemlin, W. R. (1988). *Speech and hearing science: Anatomy and physiology*. Englewood Cliffs, NJ: Prentice-Hall.

CHAPTER

3

Anatomy of Respiration

"Breathe! You are alive!"

—Thich Nhat Hanh, Zen Master

We *must* breathe with great regularity to maintain bodies that are dependent on efficient oxygen exchange. In parallel with this process we, as humans, have "hijacked" the respiratory system to provide the energy source for oral communication. As you will see in our discussion of respiratory physiology, we exercise a great deal of external control over the respiratory mechanism while still working within the bounds of the biological requirements for life. First, let us discuss respiration as it is needed to sustain life.

Respiration is defined as the exchange of gas between an organism and its environment. We bring oxygen to the cells of the body to sustain life by breathing in, the process of **inspiration**, and eliminate waste products by breathing out, or **expiration**. A close look at the mechanics of gas exchange also will provide an understanding of how significantly a deficit in this area will impair speech.

inspiration: Gr. **spiro,** *breath*

Gas exchange happens within the minute air sacs known as the **alveoli**, located deep within the lungs, only after gas has been drawn into the system. The process of bringing air into the lungs is muscular in nature. It capitalizes on the fact that all forces in nature seek balance and equilibrium. The basic mechanism for inspiration may be likened to a hypo-

alveolus: L., small hollow or cavity

dermic needle. If the plunger on the hypodermic needle in Figure 3–1 is pulled down, whatever is near the opening will enter the tube and be drawn into the awaiting chamber. If you envision the respiratory system as a hypodermic needle, with your mouth or nose as the tip of the needle, you will realize that pulling on the plunger (your diaphragm) causes air to enter the chamber (your lungs). What you also will remember from playing with bicycle pumps and the like is that, if you were to hold your finger over the opening as you pull back the plunger, you would feel the suction of the device on your finger. This suction is the product of lowering the relative air pressure within the chamber, producing an imbalance in relation to atmospheric pressure. Although the rest of the chapter will be devoted to the structures and function involved in the respiratory process, let us examine the physical principles involved a little more deeply before proceeding.

Before we can talk about the forces driving respiration, you need an intuitive feel for what air pressure really is. **Air pressure** is the force exerted on walls of a chamber by molecules of air. Due to the molecular charge, air molecules tend to keep their distance from other air molecules. If the chamber is opened to the atmosphere, the pressure exerted on the inner walls of the chamber is the same as that exerted on the outer walls, or on the ceiling of the room you are in, for that matter.

FIGURE 3–1. Comparison of the action of the diaphragm with that of a plunger on a hypodermic needle. As the diaphragm pulls down, air enters the lungs, just as it enters the chamber of the hypodermic needle.

The action starts when you close off the chamber and change the volume. Making the chamber smaller does not change the forces that are keeping molecules apart. What it does, however, is let those forces be manifest on the walls of the chamber. Although the forces have not changed, the area on which they can exert themselves has (you made it smaller, remember?) and that results in an increase in pressure. That is, **Pressure** is *Force* exerted on *Area*, or **P = F/A**. You have just increased pressure by decreasing area.

Boyle's law states that, given a gas of constant temperature, if you increase the volume of the chamber in which the gas is contained, pressure will decrease. If you increase the size (volume) of the chamber of the hypodermic needle, the air pressure within that chamber will decrease. The opposite also is true: If you decrease the volume of the chamber, the pressure will increase. Once again we see that forces seek stability and equilibrium. When volume increases, pressure decreases, and natural law says that air will flow to equalize that pressure. Thus, air flows into the chamber, in our case, the lungs.

Figure 3–2 shows the same effect graphically. The chamber has 11 molecules in it in both cases. On the left, the volume of the chamber has

Positive Pressure   Negative Pressure

FIGURE 3–2. The piston on the left has been depressed, compressing the air in the chamber and increasing the air pressure. On the right, the piston has been retracted, increasing the space between the molecules and creating a relatively positive pressure.

been reduced, the 11 molecules are much closer together, and the pressure has increased (known as **positive pressure**). Likewise, when you pull the plunger back so the molecules are farther apart than the forces dictate, the pressure decreases, and the pressure is now referred to as **negative pressure**. The beauty of this arrangement is that it provides all the principle we need to discuss respiratory physiology at the macro- or microscopic level. The forces that draw air into the lungs also are responsible for drawing carbon dioxide out.

In summary:

- **Pressure** is defined as force distributed over area.
- **Boyle's law** tells us that, as the volume of a container increases, the air pressure within the container will decrease.
- This relatively **negative pressure** will cause air to enter the container until the pressure is equalized.
- If volume is decreased, pressure increases and air flows out until the pressure inside and outside are equal.
- This principle forms the basis for movement of air into and out of the lungs.

THE SUPPORT STRUCTURE OF RESPIRATION

Overview

A Guided Tour

The respiratory system consists of a gas-exchanging mechanism supported and protected by a bony cage (see Table 3–1). In this case, gas

Table 3-1. Structures of respiration.

Bony Thorax
  Vertebrae and vertebral column
  Ribs and their attachment to vertebral column
  Pectoral girdle
    scapula and clavicle
  Sternum
  Pelvic girdle
    ischium
    pubic bone
    sacrum
    ilium

Visceral Thorax
  Respiratory passageway
    mouth and nose
    trachea and bronchi

Table 3–1. *(continued)*

Lungs
Mediastinum

Muscles of Respiration
Diaphragm
Accessory muscles of inspiration
Accessory muscles of expiration
Muscles of postural control

exchange is carried out by the lungs, while the rib cage performs the protective function (and more, as you shall see).

Before we get to the details of how the mechanism works, it might help to take a guided tour of your respiratory system. To begin, pay attention to your own breathing. Try the following. Sit up straight and close your eyes while taking 10 quiet breaths through your nose. First, concentrate attention on your nose, feeling the air entering and leaving your nostrils. Then feel your abdominal region stretch out a little with each inspiration, and then become aware that your **thorax** (rib cage) is expanding a little with each inhalation. Now take a good, deep breath (still through your nose) and feel your whole chest rise and your shoulders straighten out a little.

Besides relaxing you, attending to your breathing has given you a sense of the parts of your body that are activated for inspiration and expiration. At first you attended to your nostrils, the part of the respiratory passageway that warms and moistens air going into the lungs. Then you noticed your abdomen protruding, which is a natural process associated with inspiration, because the diaphragm is pushing against the abdomen when it contracts to bring air in. Then you noticed your thorax was expanding a little as you breathed in quietly, and then you noted that your thorax expanded markedly as you breathed in deeply. If you missed any of these things happening, take a minute and breathe a little more. This will set the stage for understanding what is going on with the bones and muscles of respiration.

Developing an understanding of respiratory function requires knowledge of the skeletal system. The lungs are housed within the thorax or rib cage, an area bounded in the superior aspect by the **first rib** and **clavicle**, and in the inferior by the twelfth rib (see Figure 3–3). The lateral and anterior aspects are composed of the **ribs** and **sternum**. The entire thorax is suspended from the **vertebral column** (a.k.a. spinal column), a structure which doubles as the conduit for the **spinal cord**, the nervous system supply for the body and extremities.

sternum: L., sternum, breastplate

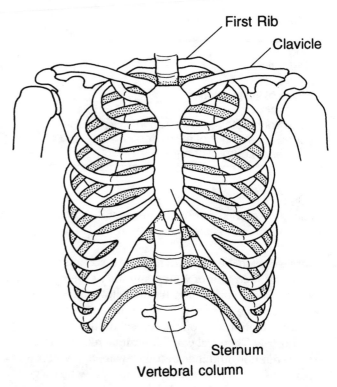

First Rib

Clavicle

Sternum

Vertebral column

FIGURE 3–3. Anterior view of the thorax.

Vertebral Column

The functional unit of the spinal column is the **vertebra** (plural, vertebrae) or spinal column segment. The vertebral column is divided into five divisions: cervical, thoracic, lumbar, sacral, and coccygeal (see Figure 3–4). The anatomical shorthand associated with the vertebral column and spinal nerves is worth paying attention to. The **vertebrae** are numbered sequentially from superior to inferior by section, so that the uppermost **cervical vertebra** is C1, the second is C2, and so forth to C7. Likewise, the first **thoracic vertebra** is T1, and the last is T12. **Lumbar vertebrae** include L1 through L5, **sacral vertebrae** include S1 through S5, and the **coccygeal vertebrae** are considered to be a fused unit, known as the **coccyx**.

The vertebral column is composed of 33 segments of bone with a rich set of fossa and protuberances clearly designed for function. Although vertebrae have roughly the same shape, their form and landmarks vary depending on location and area they serve, their attachments (such as ribs), and their neural payload. The area serving the head requires more security for the vertebral artery, so there is the addition of protected **foramina** (or openings) for that purpose. In lower regions, there is a great deal more bone in the **corpus** or body of the vertebra,

foramen, foramina, L.,
opening

corpus, L., body

reflecting the power of the muscles used for lifting. The vertebral canal will be larger in areas serving the legs and arms, because these regions must carry more nerve fibers than other regions.

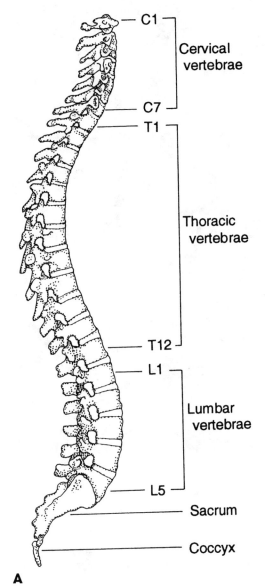

A

FIGURE 3–4. a. Components of the vertebral column, consisting of 7 cervical (C), 12 thoracic (T), and 5 lumbar (L) vertebrae, as well as the 5 fused vertebrae of the sacrum (S), and the coccyx. *(continued)*

B

FIGURE 3–4. b. Articulated cervical and thoracic vertebrae.

There are 7 cervical vertebrae, 12 thoracic vertebrae (paralleling the 12 ribs of the thorax), 5 massive lumbar vertebrae, 5 sacral vertebrae, and 3 (or 4) fused coccygeal vertebrae.

Cervical Vertebrae

The general structure of the vertebrae includes a prominent **spinous process** (the collection of which can be felt by rubbing the spine of your friend's back) and **transverse processes** on both sides (see Figure 3–5).

These two processes are excellent structures on which to attach muscles. The corpus of the vertebra makes up the anterior, with a prominent hole or **vertebral foramen** just posterior to that. It is through this foramen that the tracts of the nervous system (spinal cord) that supply the body's periphery pass. The spinal nerves must somehow exit and enter the spinal cord, and this happens through the **intervertebral foramina** on either side of the vertebra. Vertebral segments ride one

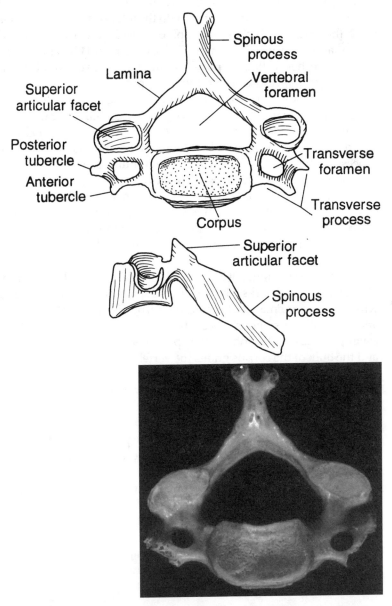

FIGURE 3–5. Superior and lateral views of cervical vertebra.

tubercle: **tuberculum,** *L., little swelling*

facet: **facette,** *Fr., small face*

dens: *L, tooth*

atop another to form the vertebral column, and this articulation is completed by means of the **superior** and **inferior articular facets**. These facets provide the mating surfaces for two adjacent vertebrae, limiting movement in the anterior-posterior dimension (and thus protecting the spinal cord), permitting limited rotatory and rocking motion. We must be able to move freely, but not *too* freely, considering the importance of the spinal cord within that column.

The uppermost cervical vertebra, C1, is the **atlas,** so-named for its singular role in supporting the skull for rotation (after the mythical figure supporting the earth). Articulating with the inferior surface of the atlas is C2, the **axis,** on which the skull pivots (see Figure 3–6). C1 and C2 differ markedly from C3 through C7. The posterior of C1 has a reduced prominence, here called the **posterior tubercle.** The **superior articular facet** is larger than those of C3 through C7, providing increased surface area for vertebra-skull articulation. Similarly, the vertebral foramen is larger than those in the lower cervical vertebrae, reflecting the transition from spinal cord to brainstem that begins at that level. C1 also has a significantly enlarged vertebral foramen, accommodating the **dens** process of the axis (also known as the **odontoid process**) which will protrude through it. This loose lock-and-key arrangement is protective, because unchecked movement could result in damage to the spinal cord at this level, which would be life-threatening. You might notice that the axis (C2) has a rudimentary spinous process, although the atlas does not. The articulation of C1 and C2 is shown in Figure 3–6.

As you can see in Figure 3–5, a typical cervical vertebra has a number of interesting landmarks. The corpus and spinous process provide you with a clue to orientation, because the corpus is in the anterior aspect and the posterior spinous process will slant downward. The vertebral canal provides protection for the spinal cord that passes through it, and the bulk of the corpus grants the vertebra its strength.

pedicle: **pedalis,** *L., foot*

palpate: **palpare,** *L., to touch*

Examination of Figure 3–5 also will reveal lateral wings known as the **transverse processes,** which are directed in a posterolateral (*postero* = back; *lateral* = side) direction. The superior surface is marked by a **superior articular facet** which rests atop the **pedicle.** The inferior surface retains an **inferior articular facet**. In the articulated vertebral column, these facets mate. The paired transverse foramina shown in Figure 3–5 are found only in the cervical vertebrae and may even be absent in C7. Figure 3–7 shows that the vertebral artery passes through this foramen. You can **palpate** (to examine through touching) the seventh cervical vertebra by bending your head forward so that your chin touches your chest. The first prominent spinous process you feel on your neck is C7. You can also palpate the large transverse processes of atlas, inferior to the mastoid process of the temporal bone.

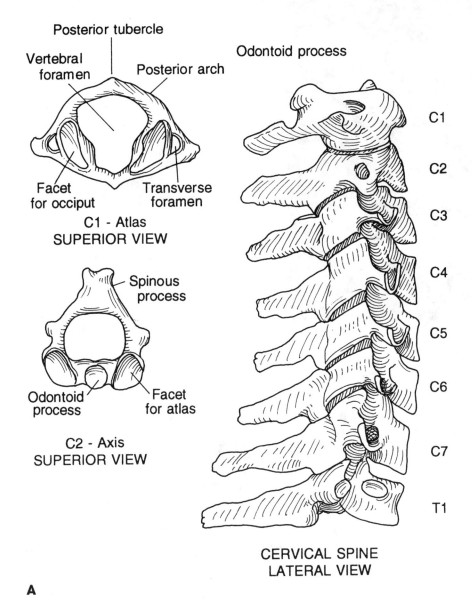

Posterior tubercle

Vertebral foramen

Posterior arch

Facet for occiput

Transverse foramen

C1 - Atlas
SUPERIOR VIEW

Spinous process

Odontoid process

Facet for atlas

C2 - Axis
SUPERIOR VIEW

Odontoid process

C1
C2
C3
C4
C5
C6
C7
T1

CERVICAL SPINE
LATERAL VIEW

A

FIGURE 3–6. a. Cervical vertebrae. On left are atlas (C1, *upper*) and axis (C2, *lower*). On the right are the articulated cervical vertebrae. *(continued)*

C1-Atlas
SUPERIOR
VIEW

Facet
for occiput

C2-Axis
SUPERIOR
VIEW

Spinous
process

Facet
for atlas **B**

Odontoid process

FIGURE 3-6. *(continued)* **b.** Superior view of at-las and axis.

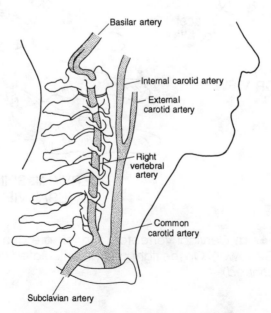

Basilar artery

Internal carotid artery

External carotid artery

Right vertebral artery

Common carotid artery

Subclavian artery

FIGURE 3-7. Course of vertebral artery through the transverse foramina of cervical vertebrae.

Thoracic Vertebrae

The twelve thoracic vertebrae (T1 to T12) provide the basis for the respiratory framework, because they form the posterior point of attachment for the ribs of the bony thorax. As seen in Figure 3–8, the thoracic vertebrae have larger spinous and transverse processes, which is highly appropriate because significant musculature and bone are attached to them. Between vertebrae is the **intervertebral foramen**, the product of the inferior and superior **vertebral notches** of articulating vertebra, through which spinal nerves communicate with the spinal cord in life. You should pay particular attention to the superior and inferior costal facets, because these are the points of attachment for the ribs, as seen in Figures 3–9.

The articulation of rib and thoracic vertebrae is complicated. Although it would have been simpler for us had the second rib been attached to the second vertebra, had the third rib been attached to the third vertebra, and so forth, only the first rib and the last three ribs (1, 10, 11, 12) have this nice one-to-one arrangement. Each of the remaining ribs (2 through 9) attaches to the transverse process and corpus of its vertebra number and also attaches to the body of the rib above it (e.g., rib 2 attaches to transverse process of T2 and body of T1 and T2). The utility of this articulation will become apparent as we discuss movement of the rib cage for respiration.

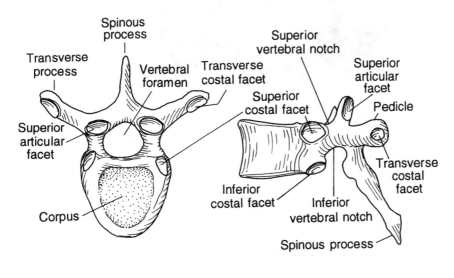

SUPERIOR VIEW   LATERAL VIEW

A

FIGURE 3–8. a. Superior and lateral view of thoracic vertebra. *(continued)*

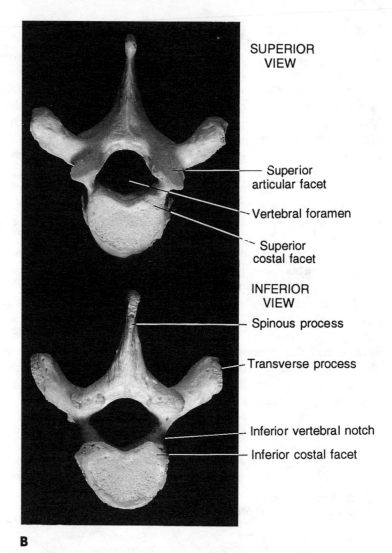

SUPERIOR
VIEW

— Superior
articular facet

— Vertebral foramen

— Superior
costal facet

INFERIOR
VIEW

— Spinous process

— Transverse process

— Inferior vertebral notch

— Inferior costal facet

B

FIGURE 3–8. *(continued)* **b.** Superior *(upper)* and inferior *(lower)* view of thoracic vertebra.

Lumbar Vertebrae

The five lumbar vertebrae are quite large by comparison with those of the thoracic or cervical region, reflecting the stresses placed on them during lifting and **ambulation** (walking). They provide direct or indirect attachment for a host of back and abdominal muscles, as well as for the posterior fibers of diaphragm. The transverse and spinous processes are relatively smaller, and the corpus is much larger than in the thoracic and cervical vertebrae.

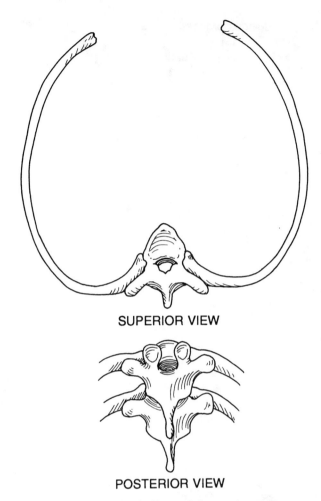

SUPERIOR VIEW

POSTERIOR VIEW

FIGURE 3-9. Articulation of rib and vertebrae.

Sacrum and Coccyx

The five sacral vertebrae are actually a fused mass known as the sacrum. The sacrum and its ossified intervertebral discs retain vestiges of the vertebrae from which they are formed, with remnants of spinous and transverse processes. The sacral foramina perform the function of the intervertebral foramina, providing the passage of the sacral nerves (see Figure 3–10).

The coccyx is composed of the fused coccygeal vertebrae. It is so named because of its beak-like appearance, and it articulates with the inferior sacrum by means of a small disc.

sacrum: **sacralis,** *L., sacred*

coccyx: **kokkus,** *Gr., cuckoo (shaped like cuckoo's beak)*

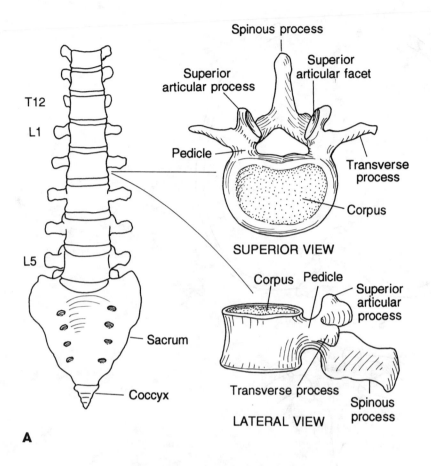

SUPERIOR VIEW

LATERAL VIEW

A

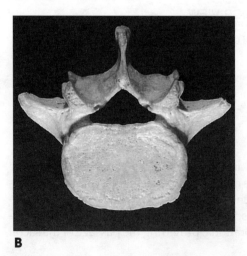

B

FIGURE 3-10. a. Lumbar vertebrae articulated with sacrum and coccyx (*left*). Upper right shows superior view of lumbar vertebra, and lower right shows lateral view. **b.** Superior view of lumbar vertebra.

To summarize:

■ The **vertebral column** is composed of vertebral segments combined to form a strong but flexible column.
■ **Vertebrae** are labeled, based on their level: C1 to C7 (**cervical**), T1 to T12 (**thoracic**), L1 to L5 (**lumbar**), S1 to S5 (**sacral**).
■ The fused **coccygeal** vertebrae are referred to as the *coccyx*.
■ This spinal column provides the points of attachment for numerous muscles by means of the **spinous** and **transverse processes**.
■ It also houses the **spinal cord,** with **spinal nerves** emerging and entering the spinal cord through spaces between the vertebrae.
■ The ribs of the rib cage articulate with the spinal column in a fashion that permits the rib cage some limited movement for respiration.

Pelvic and Pectoral Girdle

The vertebral column and rib cage is central to the body, and if we are to interact physically with our environment we must attach appendages to this column. The lower extremities are attached to this axis by means of the **pelvic girdle**, and the upper extremities are attached through the **pectoral girdle**.

The pelvic girdle attaches to the lower portion of the vertebral column and is comprised of the ilium, sacrum, pubic bone, and ischium (see Figure 3–11). The combination provides an extremely strong structure capable of bearing a great deal of translated weight from use of the legs.

The pectoral girdle is the superior counterpart to the pelvic girdle. This structure permits attachment of the upper extremities to the vertebral column, a feat attained through a balancing act among bones of the girdle.

Pelvic Girdle

The pelvic girdle provides a strong structure for attaching the legs to the vertebral column (see Figure 3–11). By means of this structure, forces generated through movement of the legs are distributed across a mass of bone which, in turn, is attached to the spinal column.

The pelvic girdle is made up of the ilium, sacrum, pubic bone, and ischium. The **ilium** is a large, wing-like bone (similar in this way to the **scapula** or shoulder blade of the upper body) which provides the bulk of the muscular support for the abdominal musculature and the prominent hip bone on which many parents carry their children. The iliac crest of the superior-lateral surface is an important landmark as the superior point of attachment for the inguinal ligament which runs from the crest of the iliac to the joining of the two pubic bones at the **pubic symphysis**. Deep to this bone is the massive medial structure,

symphysis: *Gr., growing together*

the sacrum. As may be seen in Figure 3–11, the sacrum actually consists of five fused vertebrae, with the upper vertebra articulating with the fifth lumbar vertebra. The iliac bones articulate with the sacrum laterally, forming the sacroiliac joints. (The structure comprised of the iliac, ischium, and pubis bones is referred to as the innominate or hip bone: "innominate" means, literally, "unnamed.") The coccyx is the inferiormost segment of spinal column, consisting of four fused vertebrae articulating at the inferior aspect of sacrum.

Pectoral Girdle

pectoralis: L., pertaining to the chest

clavicle: clavicula, L., little key

The **pectoral or shoulder girdle** includes the **scapula** and **clavicle**, bones that support the upper extremities. The clavicle, also known as the collarbone, is attached to the superior sternum, running from that attachment laterally to join with the wing-like scapula. The clavicle provides the anterior support for the shoulder by its articulation with the scapula (see Figure 3–12). The wing-like scapula has its only skeletal attachment via the clavicle, which in turn has its only skeletal attachment at the sternum. From the scapula are slung several muscles that hold it in a dynamic tension that facilitates flexible upper body movement while not compromising strength in the balance. The down side of this "smoke and mirrors" arrangement is the vulnerability of the junction of the scapula and clavicle. Disarticulation of these two bones will cause a collapse of the structure so that the shoulder rotates forward and in.

A

FIGURE 3–11. **a.** Pelvic girdle, consisting of the ilium, pubis, and ischium.

Inguinal ligament

B

FIGURE 3-11. b. Anterior view of pelvis. Lower view shows location of the inguinal ligament.

A

B

FIGURE 3–12. **a.** Anterior view of skeleton, showing components of pelvic and pectoral girdle. **b.** posterior view.

PECTORAL GIRDLE

C

PELVIC AND PECTORAL GIRDLES

D

FIGURE 3–12. c. Isolated pectoral girdle. **d.** Photograph of articulated thorax with pelvic and pectoral girdles.

Although at first this configuration would appear tenuous for a structure designed to support the arms in physical labor, the design is actually rather economical. The physical arrangement provides another "A-frame" of support to distribute force through relatively solid articulation at the scapula and muscular attachment in the form of the massive muscles of the thorax and back.

When taken together, one can view the human skeleton as a tube with two A-frames attached at the ends. The tube provides a flexible-yet-strong support for the trunk, even as the A-frames give that trunk the opportunity to explore its environment by means of the arms and legs. The A-frame design provides maximum strength for these extremities with a minimum of bone mass.

To summarize:

■ The bony support structure of the respiratory system is composed of the **rib cage** and **vertebral column.**

■ At the base of the vertebral column is the **pelvic girdle,** composed of the **ilium, sacrum, pubic bone,** and **ischium.**

■ The **pectoral girdle** is comprised of the **scapula** and **clavicle,** which attach to the **sternum.**

■ These structures provide the points of attachment for the lower and upper extremities.

Ribs and Rib Cage

Ribs are capable of a degree of movement, so that the rib cage can rock up in front, hinged on the vertebral articulation with the rib cage. The rib cage is made up of 12 ribs, with all but the lowest two attached by means of cartilage to the sternum in the front aspect of the rib cage. If you look at Figure 3–13, you can see that the sternum provides a focal point for the rib cage, and it turns out to be a significant structure in respiration.

Another thing you might notice in Figure 3–13 is that the rib cage tends to slant down in front. With the mobility of the rib cage granted by the articulation of the vertebrae and ribs, the rib cage is quite capable of elevating during inspiration to increase the size of the thorax.

Ribs

There are 12 pairs of **ribs** in the human **thorax,** with each rib consisting generally of four components; the **head, neck, shaft,** and **angle** (see Figure 3–14). The head provides the articulating surfaces with the spinal column, and the angle represents the point at which the rib begins the significant curve in its course forward. The shaft is the largest and most anterior component of the rib. The barrel shape of the thorax is created by the relatively small superior and inferior ribs as compared with the longer middle ribs. The rib cage provides attachment for numerous muscles that provide strength, rigidity, continuity, and mobility to the rib cage.

Ribs are of three general classes: **true ribs, false ribs,** and **floating ribs.** The true (or vertebrosternal) ribs consist of the upper ribs (1 through 7), all of which form more or less direct attachment with the sternum. Their actual attachment is by means of a cartilaginous union through the **chondral** (i.e., cartilaginous) portion of the rib (see Figure 3–15). The false or vertebrochondral ribs (ribs 8, 9, and 10) also are attached to the sternum through cartilage, although this chondral portion must run superiorly to attach to the sternum. The floating or vertebral ribs (ribs 11 and 12) articulate only with the vertebral column.

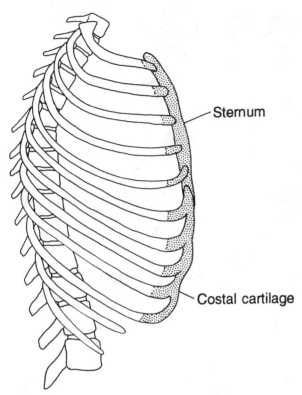

FIGURE 3-13. Lateral view of rib cage showing relationship among ribs and sternum. Note that the rib cage slants down in the front.

FIGURE 3-14. Schematic of second rib with landmarks.

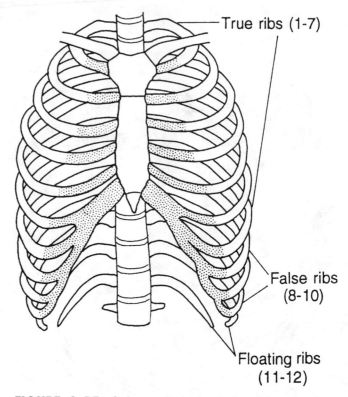

True ribs (1-7)

False ribs (8-10)

Floating ribs (11-12)

FIGURE 3-15. Schematic of relationships among true, false, and floating ribs.

The chondral attachment mentioned earlier is particularly useful, because the elastic properties of cartilage permit the ribs to be twisted on the long axis (torqued) without breaking. Thus, the rib cage is quite strong (being made up predominantly of bone), but capable of movement (being well-endowed with resilient cartilage).

The rib cage gives a marked advantage to the organ buried deep within it (i.e., the heart). The protection it provides is a triumph of nature. The rib cage also provides the basis for respiration, and the general structure of the "barrel" deserves some attention at this juncture.

As you can see in Figure 3–16, the ribs make their posterior attachment along the vertebral column. If a fly were to walk along the superior surface of a rib, starting from the tip of the head and walking to the point of attachment at the sternum, it would start out by walking in a postero-lateral direction, but would quickly round a curve that would aim it toward the front. Its hike would be along a great, sweeping arc ending when it reached the cartilaginous portion of the sternal attachment. In short, the rib's course running postero-lateral and then arcing around to the anterior aspect of the body provides the bony structure for most of

FIGURE 3-16. Lateral view of rib cage. The downward tilt of the rib cage in front provides one of the mechanisms for increasing the volume of the thorax during respiration.

the posterior, lateral, and anterior aspects of the thorax. In addition, the fly would have hiked downhill, because the ribs slope downward when the rib cage is inactive and at equilibrium. The beauty of the rib cage, the vertebral attachments, and the chondral (cartilaginous) portion of the sternal attachment is that the rib cage can elevate, providing an increase in lung capacity for respiration. We will talk more about that.

The posterior attachment of the rib is made through a gliding (arthrodial) articulation with the thoracic vertebrae, thus permitting the rib to rock up during inspiration. As mentioned, most of the ribs actually attach to two vertebrae.

Sternum

The sternum is composed of three components: The **manubrium sterni**, the **corpus** (body), and the **xiphoid** or **ensiform process** (see Figure 3–17). The sternum has articular cavities for costal attachment,

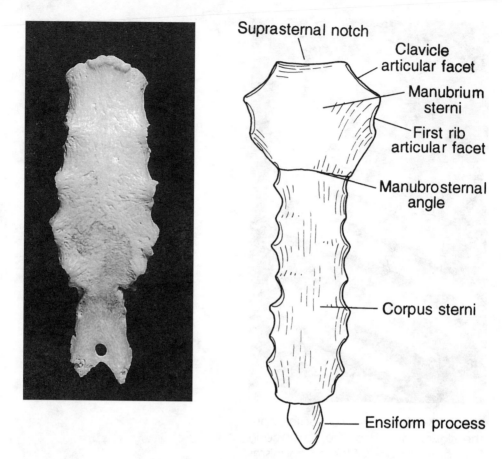

FIGURE 3–17. Schematic and photo of sternum. Note that the manubrium has been removed from the sternum on the left.

chondral: chondros, Gr., cartilaginous

manubrium sterni: L., handle, of sternum

corpus: L., body

xiphoid: Gr., sword

ensiform: L., sword-like

with the manubrium sterni providing the attachment for the **clavicle** and first rib, and the second rib articulating at the juncture of the manubrium and corpus, known as the **manubrosternal angle**. The corpus provides articulation for five more ribs by means of relatively direct costal cartilage, and the remaining (false) ribs 8, 9, and 10 are attached by means of more indirect costal cartilage. The floating (11, 12) ribs are free in the anterior.

The sternum provides an excellent opportunity to investigate anatomy with your own hands. As you look at Figure 3–17 of the sternum, you can palpate your own sternal structures. First, find your "Adam's apple" (actually, the thyroid cartilage of the larynx), then bring your finger downward until you reach the significant plateau at about the level of your shoulders. This is the superior surface of the manubrium sterni, and is known as the **suprasternal** or **sternal notch**. Ignoring the tendon which you can feel on either side, palpate the bone which is directed laterally. This is the clavicle. If you can feel the place that the clavicle articulates with the manubrium, you can probably find the articulation of the first rib immediately inferior to it. If you once again find the sternal notch and draw your finger downward about 2 inches you may feel a very prominent bump, which is the **manubrosternal angle** or **junction**. Now if you draw your finger downward another 4 or 5 inches you can find the point at which the sternum and xiphoid process articulate, an important landmark for individuals performing cardiopulmonary resuscitation (CPR). You have also found the anterior-most attachment of your diaphragm.

In summary:

■ The **rib cage** is composed of 12 ribs (7 true ribs, 3 false ribs, and 2 floating ribs).

■ The **cartilaginous attachment** of the ribs to the sternum permits the rib to rotate slightly during respiration, allowing the rib cage to elevate.

■ The construction of the rib provides the characteristic curved barrel shape of the rib cage.

■ At rest the ribs slope downward, but they **elevate** during inspiration.

Soft Tissue of the Thorax and Respiratory Passageway

Deep to the rib cage lies the core of respiration. Gas exchange for life occurs within the lungs; spongy, elastic tissue which is richly perfused with vascular supply and air sacs. Healthy, young lungs are pink, while older lungs that have undergone the stresses of modern, polluted life are distinctly gray. Communication from the lungs with the external environment is by means of the respiratory passageway, which includes the oral and nasal cavities, larynx, trachea, and bronchial tubes.

The **trachea** is a flexible tube, approximately 11 cm in length and composed of a series of 16 to 20 hyaline cartilage rings that are open in the posterior aspect. This tube runs from the inferior border of the larynx for about 11 cm, where it bifurcates (divides) at a point known as the **carina trachea** to become the left and right **mainstem bronchi** (or **bronchial tubes**) which serve the left and right lungs, respectively (see Figure 3–18).

trachea: **tracheia,** *Gr., rough*

carina: L., Keel of boat

bronchi: **bronchos,** *Gr., windpipe*

The tracheal rings are 2 to 2.5 cm in diameter, and .4 to .5 cm wide. They are connected by a continuous mucous membrane lining, which provides both continuity and flexibility. The ring is discontinuous in the posterior aspect, allowing for expansion and contraction of the diameter of the ring, an action largely controlled by the trachealis muscle. The gap between the rings is spanned by smooth muscle which is in a steady state of contraction until oxygen needs of the individual increase, at which time the muscle relaxes. That is, the tube is in a state

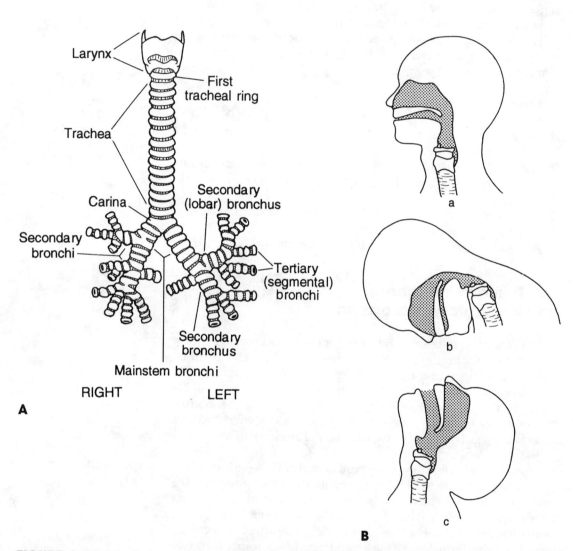

FIGURE 3-18. a. Bronchial passageway, including trachea, mainstem bronchi, secondary (lobar) bronchi, and tertiary (segmental) bronchi. **b.** Effect of head posture on airway patency (modified from data and views of Moser and Sprang, 1982).

C

FIGURE 3-18. c. Respiratory passageway from oral cavity to segmental bronchi. Note that lungs have been dissected to reveal the bronchi within.

of slight constriction until oxygen needs are sufficiently great that the muscle action is inhibited, at which time the diameter of the trachea increases to improve air delivery to the lungs. The inner mucosal lining of the trachea is infused with submucosal glands that assist in the cleaning process of the trachea.

The cartilaginous rings of the trachea are particularly well-suited for the task of air transport. Because the process involves drawing air into the lungs and expelling it, pressures (negative and positive) must be generated to get that gas moving, but same pressures will tend to collapse or expand tissue that is not reinforced for strength. On the other hand, a strictly rigid tube would not permit the degree of flexibility dictated by an active life (i.e., differential head and thorax movement). Thus, the trachea must be both rigid and flexible. In response to this need, the trachea is built of hyaline cartilage rings connected by fibroelastic membrane. The cartilage provides support, while the membrane permits freedom of movement.

bolus: *L., lump*

Posterior to the trachea is the **esophagus**. The esophagus is a long, collapsed tube running behind and adjacent to the trachea and providing the conduit to the digestive system. It retains its collapsed condition except when occupied with a **bolus** of food being propelled by gravity and peristaltic contractions to the waiting stomach.

The trachea bifurcates to form right and left **mainstem** (or main) bronchi. The right side forms a 20–30° angle relative to the trachea, and the left forms a 45–55° angle. (This explains why the right lung is most often the landing site for the errant peanut that makes it past the protective laryngeal structure!)

The lungs are a composite of the tissues of which they are made— blood, arterial and venous network, connective tissue, respiratory pathway, and tissue specialized for gas exchange.

The **bronchial tree** is characterized by increasingly smaller tubes as one progresses into the depths of the lungs, but the total surface area at any given level of the tree is greater than the level before it. There are 28 generations of the bronchial tree, beginning with the single trachea, followed by bifurcation of the main mainstem bronchi to serve the left and right lungs, **lobar** (intermediate) bronchi to supply the lobes of the lungs, and further branchings down to the final, **terminal respiratory bronchioles**. This division process is shown in Table 3–2. Within the cartilaginous passageway, there are one trachea, two mainstem bronchi, 5 lobar bronchi, 19 segmental bronchi, 38 subsegmental bronchi, and so forth.

mediastinum: medius, *L., middle*

The lobar or secondary divisions serve the lobes of the lungs. The right lung is composed of three lobes, separated by fissures. The left lung has only two lobes (see Figure 3–19). Space on the left is taken up by

Keeping the Airway Open in Respiratory Emergency

In times of respiratory emergency it sometimes becomes necessary to ensure that the respiratory pathway remains patent ("open"). In a conscious patient the normal head and neck orientation places the mouth at a 90° angle from the airway above the larynx (pharynx). If an unconscious individual's head drops forward (see Figure 3–18) the airway may become occluded and limit respiration.

   In some cases there may be concern that the vocal folds or airway above that level will not remain open and an emergency tracheostomy will be performed (*tracheo* = trachea; *stoma* = mouth). This medical procedure involves opening an artificial passageway into the region between the thyroid and cricoid cartilage, a location chosen because of the limited blood supply in that region. A surgical tracheostomy will typically be placed 1–3 cm below the cricoid cartilage.

the heart and **mediastinal** or "middle space" structures. The right mainstem bronchus divides to supply the superior, middle, and inferior lobes of the right lung. The left mainstem bronchus bifurcates to serve the superior and inferior lobes of the left lung, although there is a vestigial middle lobe (called the lingula). The space vacated by the missing lobe is taken up by the heart on the left side (see Figure 3–20).

The third level of branching serves the segments of each lobe. At this third level of division, the bronchi divide repeatedly into smaller and smaller cartilaginous tubes, with the final tube being the **terminal** (end) **bronchiole** (see Figure 3–21).

This repeated branching has an important effect on respiratory function. Examination of Table 3–2 reveals that there are 27 generations of subdivisions in the respiratory tree, providing a truly amazing amount of surface area for respiration. Although the cross-sectional area of the trachea is about 5 cm^2 (about the diameter of a quarter), the cross-sectional area of the 300,000,000 alveoli would equal 70 M^2, or the area of a throw rug large enough to cover a 10' × 24' room!

The first nine divisions of the bronchial tree (technically referred to as "dead space") are strictly conductive and cartilaginous, being designed only to transport gas between environment and lungs. Successive divisions of the noncartilaginous airway reach a minimal diameter of 1 mm. This conducting zone, which includes the conducting regions of both the upper and lower respiratory tracts and terminates with the terminal bronchioles, makes up approximately 150 ml in the adult, a

Gastroesophageal Reflux

The esophageal orifice is situated in the inferior laryngopharynx and is enveloped by the musculature of the inferior pharyngeal constrictors. The cricopharyngeus muscle, which is actually part of the inferior constrictor, controls the size of the orifice by contracting to constrict the opening. In speech and hearing science, we are little concerned with the esophagus, except for its use in esophageal speech in patients who have undergone laryngectomy. In this case, the cricopharyngeus is the muscle which will be set into vibration by the controlled "belch" used for speech. Another concern is with **esophageal reflux**, the condition in which digestive acids are expelled into the region above the superior orifice of esophagus, causing irritation to the delicate laryngeal tissue.

Gastroesophageal reflux refers to the reintroduction of gastrointestinal contents into the esophagus and respiratory passageway. This condition may be found in the newborn and very young child who has a weak esophageal sphincter or hypersensitivity of the esophageal sphincter, resulting in reflux, inability to retain nourishment, and life-threatening malnutrition. It is not uncommon among children with cerebral palsy, typically resulting in frequent vomiting and loss of nutrition and aspiration pneumonia (see clinical note on aspiration).

The size of the esophageal opening may be reduced surgically through a procedure known as Nissen fundoplication ("sling"), thereby inhibiting regurgitation of stomach contents. Nissen fundoplication involves surgical narrowing of the esophageal opening by releasing a flap of tissue from the stomach, followed by elevation and suturing of the flap to the esophageal orifice. The child may receive nutrition through a tube run through the nasal cavity into the esophagus (nasogastric tube; *naso* = nose; *gastric* = stomach) or through orogastric (oral feeding tube; a.k.a. "gavage") feeding, again via tube.

Surgical placement of a gastronomy tube may be required if reflux cannot be controlled adequately to guarantee nutrition. This procedure, referred to as "gastronomy" results in surgical placement of a feeding tube into the stomach wall. Similarly, "jejunostomy" is placement of a feeding tube into the small intestine. For a more detailed discussion, see Langley and Lombardino (1991).

volume known as dead air because air that does not descend below the space cannot undergo gas exchange with the blood.

The final seven divisions are actual respiratory zones comprised of the respiratory bronchioles, alveolar ducts, and alveoli. The respira-

Aspiration

Although not directly related to respiratory anatomy or physiology, aspiration *is* an issue in maintaining respiratory function. Aspiration refers to entry or removal of liquid or solid materials from a cavity by means of suction, although more often removal of the foreign matter through suctioning is referred to as "performing a bronch" (as in "bronchoscopy"—instrumental entry into the bronchi). Fluid or solids may enter the lungs as a result of some failure in coordination, sensation, or awareness (aspiration). The process of removing the foreign matter through suction is also referred to as aspiration. Patients who are intubated to support respiration during crisis are *also* at risk for aspiration because their airway is artificially kept open: Vomitus or reflux from the stomach (logically via the esophageal opening at the level of the larynx) readily enters the unprotected lungs through the larynx. Aspiration of foreign matter into the lungs is a very real danger in cases of neurological deficit, and the individual suffering stroke, cerebral palsy, or other compromising condition is particularly vulnerable. Aspiration results from loss of sensation that would otherwise trigger a protective coughing or "clearing" response. The patient may also demonstrate diminished or ineffective (nonproductive) cough, as well as reduced muscular strength and control of the muscles of deglutition, and perhaps diminished ability to recognize the threat involved. In children with cerebral palsy, reduction in coordinated movement ability may also arise from the neurological deficit.

Because the client with neurological deficit may not be aware or competent to seek help, it is wise to know symptoms of aspiration. If the client's voice sounds wet or gurgly or if the client has a history of respiratory illnesses, the client is at risk for aspiration pneumonia. Likewise, the client may have a weak, breathy vocalization or cry, indicating laryngeal muscle weakness and the potential for lack of adequate protective function.

tory bronchioles ("little bronchi") are the terminal bronchioles, serving the alveoli.

The terminal bronchiole is small (about 1 mm in diameter) and at its end becomes the alveolar duct, which in turn communicates with the alveolus. The alveoli are extremely small (approximately 1/4 mm in diameter) but extremely plentiful, with approximately 300 million in the mature lungs.

You might think of the final respiratory exchange region as a series of apartment houses. As you can see in Figure 3–20, the respiratory bron-

FIGURE 3–19. a. Bronchial tree within lungs (modified from data and view of DesJardins, 1984). **b.** Lung dissected to reveal bronchial passageway.

Mainstem bronchus

Secondary bronchi

Tertiary bronchi

Trachea

Carina

A

B

chioles are the entryways for each apartment building, and the alveolar duct is the passageway to the individual "apartment," the alveolus.
Each of these alveoli is between 200 and 300 microns in diameter,
which is quite small because a micron is one thousandth of a millimeter. Put another way, you could place five alveoli in the space between
the millimeter marks on your ruler.

This "apartment house" analogy will serve you as you read about the
devastating effects of emphysema on respiration. Among other things,
emphysema removes the "walls" within individual "apartments,"
greatly reducing the surface area which can participate in gas exchange.)

The alveoli at this terminal point do the real work of respiration by virtue
of their architecture and relationship with the vascular supply (see Figure 3–21). The alveolus is an extremely thin membrane (about one third
the thickness of a red blood cell) which is permeable to both oxygen and
carbon dioxide when provided with the proper circumstances.

Each alveolus is an exquisitely thin-walled structure which is completely covered with a bed of over 2,000 capillaries. The alveolar lining
is made up of two types of cells, Type I and Type II pneumocytes. Type
I pneumocytes (membranous pneumocytes) are flat cells that are
directly involved in gas exchange. Type II cells (cuboidal cells) are the
source of the surfactant, a substance which reduces surface tension,
that is released into the alveolus and alters the surface tension to keep
the alveoli from collapsing during respiration. When Type I cells are
damaged, Type II cells will proliferate, becoming Type I cells as a
regenerative process.

The alveolar wall is extraordinarily thin, ranging from 0.35 to 2.5
microns (by comparison, a red blood cell is 7 microns in diameter),
and this quality promotes rapid transfer of gas across the membrane.
The capillaries in the lungs are the most dense in the body, being
approximately 10 microns long and 7 microns wide. Their extremely
small size and prolific presence permit 100 to 300 ml of blood to be
spread over 70 square meters of surface. Moser and Spragg (1982)
note that this is the equivalent of spreading 1 teaspoon of blood over
a square meter of surface.

The rich investment with alveoli make the lungs spongy, because the
surfactant (a substance that lowers surface tension) at that level promotes inflation of the alveoli. Each alveolus is richly supplied with blood
for gas exchange from over 2,000 capillaries. A little multiplication will
reveal that there are over 600,000,000,000,000 (600 trillion) capillaries
involved in gas exchange, reminding us of the amount of vascular tissue
in the lungs. The lungs also have an intricate lacework of cartilage,
because the bronchial tree is invested with this supportive tissue, and
because most of the levels of branching of this tree contain cartilage.

FIGURE 3-20. a. Schematic representation of lungs, showing lobes and segments.

B

FIGURE 3-20. b. Anterior and medial view of lungs.

FIGURE 3-21. Schematic representation of cluster of alveoli with capillary bed. Lower portion shows a cross section through alveoli and terminal bronchiole.

pulmonary: **pulmonarius,** *L., pertaining to the lungs*

During normal quiet respiration the blood spends only about 0.5 seconds in the capillaries, with gas exchange occurring within the first quarter of its transit through the pulmonary system. The **pulmonary artery** branches to follow the bronchial tree, ultimately serving the gas exchange process at the alveolar level. There is a parallel vascular sup-

Table 3–2. Divisions of the bronchial tree. From Moser & Spragg, (1982). p. 15.

	Generation From			Number	Diameter	Cross Section
	Trachea	Segmental Bronchus	Terminal Bronchiole			
Trachea	0			1	2.5 cm	5.0 cm^2
Main bronchi	1			2	11–19 mm	3.2 cm^2
Lobar bronchi	2–3			5	4.5–13.5	2.7 cm^2
Segmental	3–6	0		19	4.5–6.5 mm	3.2 cm^2
Subsegmental bronchi	4–7	1		38	3–6 mm	6.6 cm^2
Bronchi		2–6		variable	variable	variable
Terminal bronchi		3–7		1000	1.0 mm	7.9 cm^2
Bronchioles		5–14		variable	variable	variable
Terminal bronchioles		6–15	0	35,000	0.65 mm	116 cm^2
Respiratory bronchioles			1–8	variable	variable	variable
Terminal respiratory bronchioles			2–9	630,000	0.45 mm	1,000 cm^2
Alvoelar ducts and sacs			4–12	14×10^6	0.40 mm	1.71 M^2
Alveoli				300×10^6	0.24–.3 mm	70 M^2

Source: From *Respiratory Emergencies* by K. M. Moser & R. G. Spragg. 1982. p. 15. St. Louis, MO: C. V. Mosby. Copyright 1982 C. V. Mosby Co. Reprinted with permission.

ply to oxygenate the lung tissue (the bronchial arteries), providing a safeguard for the times when oxygen may not be adequate. The maintenance of lung tissue via the bronchial arteries requires only about 50 ml per minute, whereas the pulmonary system will process approximately 5000 ml per minute.

At this end point in the bronchial tree, the marvel of gas exchange takes place. Attached to the final cartilaginous bronchiole is the alveolus or air sac, the point at which oxygen and carbon dioxide are translated to and from the blood stream.

The bronchial tree and trachea are obvious conduits for contaminants as well as air. The nasal and oral passageways provide some protection from respiratory contamination, but nature has not caught up with a modern society so heavily polluted. The respiratory pathway has multiple filtering functions to safeguard the lungs against pollutants. The nostril hairs provide a first line of defense, catching most particulate matter greater than 10 microns (a micron is one millionth of a meter) before they enter the trachea, and the moist mucous membrane of the upper respiratory system provides another receptacle for foreign matter. Goblet cells within the mucosal lining and submucosal glands secrete lubricant into the respiratory tract that traps pollutants as they enter the trachea and larynx. The respiratory passageway from the nose to the beginning of the bronchi is lined with tall columnar epithelium covered by **cilia** (hair-like processes) that beat over 1000 times per minute. In the lower pathway, the beating action drives pollutants upward, and beating drives nasal passage contaminants posteriorly.

The beating epithelia slowly, progressively move the material up the bronchi to the level of the vocal folds in the larynx, at which time the breathing person feels the stimulation of secretion at the vocal folds and "clears her throat." That "ahem" is just enough force to blow the mucus off the folds (**mucus** is the dense fluid product of mucous membrane tissue), where it can be swallowed without further ado. Unfortunately, these beating epithelia may be damaged by pollutants such as cigarette smoke, resulting in the failure of this system. Particles in the 2 to 10 micron range will settle on the walls of the bronchi, where they are eliminated by these beating epithelia. If a particle is less than 2 microns it will generally reach the alveolus but will be eliminated by microphages, cells that destroy foreign matter.

The lymphatic system provides a final cleaning stage for the respiratory tissue. The upper respiratory passageway effectively removes normal levels of particulate pollution down to diameters of approximately 5 microns, but smaller particles will not be filtered. These particles are eliminated by means of the lymphatic system which serves down to the level of the terminal bronchiole. Pollutants are suspended in mucus and migrate to the bronchioles through coughing where they can be eliminated by the lymphatics and macrophages.

Emphysema

Emphysema is generally considered to be a product of a modern society that has not solved its pollution problems. Often the disease results from tobacco smoking, but it may apparently arise from living in an industrial environment. Its progression is slow and may be arrested to some degree by altering the respiratory environment.

The mechanism for emphysema appears to be as follows. You will recall that the bronchial passageway is richly infused with ciliated epithelia that beat continuously to remove contaminants from the respiratory tract. This continuous waste removal process is seriously hampered by pollutants that, in the early stages of emphysema, destroy the epithelia.

The absence of epithelia greatly reduces the cleaning ability of the respiratory system and removal of waste products, promoting deposition of pollutants within the alveoli. The alveoli undergo a significant morphological ("form") change: The walls of the alveoli break down and alveoli recombine so that clusters of alveoli become a single sac. Although this may seem benign, it has a devastating effect in that the surface area for gas exchange is greatly reduced as a result.

A second morphological change arises as a compensation to the first. The individual with emphysema is faced with an ongoing shortage of oxygen and is forced to attempt continually deeper inspirations to accommodate, and a characteristic "barrel chest" results from these efforts. (The thorax must be greatly expanded to accommodate the compromised alveolar surface area.)

This second morphological change causes a third pathological response. You will recall that the lower margin of the rib cage marks the point of attachment of the diaphragm. Because the rib cage is flared out due to emphysema, contraction of the diaphragm (which pulls on the rib cage) causes the rib cage to pull down and in, which actually *reduces* the size of thorax rather than increases it.

The final morphological change arising from this trilogy of tragedy is respiratory failure. The respiratory mechanism is highly compromised, leaving the individual susceptible to respiratory diseases such as pneumonia.

The respiratory passageway also protects the lungs by warming and humidifying the air as it enters. The mucous membrane is highly vascularized permitting rapid transfer of heat from blood to air.

To summarize:

- The respiratory system is composed of right and left **lungs** having three and two **lobes,** respectively.
- Communication between the external and internal environments is by means of the **trachea** and **bronchial tree**.
- Repeated subdivisions of this bronchial tree end with the **alveoli,** the site of gas exchange.
- These highly vascularized alveoli provide the mechanism by which oxygen enters the blood stream and carbon dioxide is removed.
- Pollutants entering the respiratory tract will be removed through the cleansing action of **beating epithelia** which line the bronchial passageway.

MOVEMENT OF AIR THROUGH THE SYSTEM

The lung tissue is particularly prepared to process the gases of life by nature of their construction. Such great design, however, would be useless without a mechanism for bringing air into and out of those lungs.

We have already discussed the mechanics of the system, so you should be familiar with the idea that the lungs expand as a result of enlarging the structure surrounding them. We contract the diaphragm to enlarge the **vertical dimension** (superior-inferior dimension), and elevate the rib cage to enlarge the **transverse dimension** (antero-posterior and lateral dimensions). You might be curious about *how* these changes cause the lungs to expand. The key is having a closed system.

You will recall that the cavity holding the lungs is supported by muscle and bone which covers every centimeter of the thoracic wall. Likewise, the bottom of the thoracic cavity is completely sealed by the diaphragm, making the thorax almost impervious to the outside world, were it not for the respiratory passageway. The only way air can enter or leave the lungs is by means of the tubes connected to them (the bronchial tree, continuous with the upper respiratory passageway).

Now comes the tricky part. The lungs are simply placed inside this cavity, not held to the walls by ligaments or cartilage. It is as if you placed a too-small sponge in a too-large bottle, because the thoracic volume is *greater* than that of the lungs at rest.

pleural: **pleura,** *Gr., a side*

costal: **costae,** *L., coast*

The lungs and inner thoracic wall are completely covered with a **pleural lining** (Figure 3–22), and this lining provides a means of smooth contact for rough tissue, as well as a mechanism for translating the force of thorax enlargement into inspiration. The lungs are encased in linings referred to as the **visceral pleurae,** and the thoracic linings are the **parietal pleurae.** The regions of the parietal pleurae are identified by location: mediastinal, pericardial, diaphragmatic, parietal, and api-

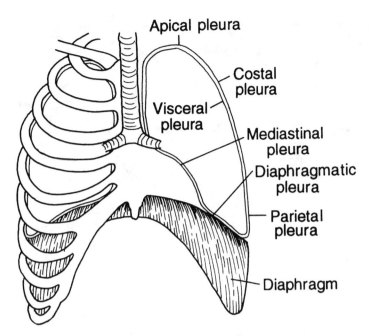

FIGURE 3-22. Pleural linings of the lungs and thorax. Parietal pleurae include costal, diaphragmatic, mediastinal, and apical pleurae. Visceral pleurae line the lungs.

cal pleurae. The **mediastinal pleura** covers the mediastinum and the **diaphragmatic pleura** covers the diaphragm. The **costal pleurae** cover the inner surface of the rib cage. The **apical pleurae** cover the superior-most region of the rib cage.

The pleural membranes are composed of elastic and fibrous tissue and endowed with **venules** and lymphocytes. Although it is convenient to think of the pleural linings as being separate entities, the visceral and parietal pleurae are actually continuous with each other. These wrappings completely encase both the lungs and inner thorax, with the reflection point being the hilum (root of lung, at about the level of T4 or T5). This continuous sheet provides the airtight seal required to permit the lungs to follow the movement of the thorax.

venules: **venula**, *L., tiny veins*

To understand how these pleura help us breathe will take a little thought. You have probably experienced the difficulty involved in separating two pieces of plastic food wrap, especially if there is fluid between the two sheets. There is a degree of surface tension arising from the presence of fluid and highly conforming surfaces that helps keep the sheets together. Cuboidal cells within the pleural lining produce a mucous solution that is released the space between the parietal and visceral pleurae. This surfactant reduces the surface tension in the lungs and provides a slippery interface between the lungs and the thoracic wall permitting easy, low-friction gliding of the lungs within the

Pleurisy

Pleurisy is a condition in which the pleural linings of the thoracic cavity are inflamed. When the inflammation results in "dry pleurisy," the patient will experience extreme pain upon breathing as a result of the loss of lubricating quality of the intrapleural fluid. "Adhesions" may result, in which portions of the parietal pleurae adhere to the visceral pleurae. (The patient may experience "breaking up" of these adhesions for quite some time following his or her bout with pleurisy.) Pleurisy may be unilateral or bilateral and may result in excessive fluid (potentially purulent) into the pleural space.

thorax. The presence of surfactant keeps the two sheets from clinging to each other. If you were to wrap the lungs in sheets of similar quality (we will call them pleurae) and line the thoracic cavity with the same, you would have an analogous situation. The two surfaces conform to each other as a result of the fluid bond between them, and a negative pressure is maintained by lack of contact with the outside atmosphere. The down-side of this is that, if you puncture a lung, the bond is broken.

When you contract the **diaphragm**, the pleural lining of the diaphragm (diaphragmatic pleura) maintains its contact with the visceral pleurae of the two lungs above it, and the lungs will expand. Likewise, if you expand the thorax transversely by elevating the rib cage you will find that the lungs will follow faithfully. In this manner, the lungs are able to follow the action of the muscles without actually being attached to them.

The pleural linings serve another function as well. Because the mating surfaces of the two linings are infused with a liquid serous secretion, the friction of movement of the two linings is greatly reduced, making respiration much more efficient. When this fluid is lost or reduced, as through the disorder known as dry pleurisy, the friction is greatly increased and pain results. As a protection, each lung is separately endowed with pleural lining. If the lining of one lung is damaged through disease or trauma, we still have the other lung in reserve.

We have discussed the lungs and hinted at the second most important muscle of the body (the diaphragm) but have glossed over the fact that the most important muscle of the body (the heart) is located deep within the thorax, in a region known as the **mediastinum**. The heart is encased in the mediastinal pleurae, along with nerves, blood vessels, the esophagus, and lymph vessels (see Figure 3–23).

The mediastinum is the most important and protected region of the body. This space is occupied primarily by the heart, as well as the trachea, major blood vessels, nerves, thymus gland, lymph nodes, and the conducting portion of the gastrointestinal tract known as the esophagus.

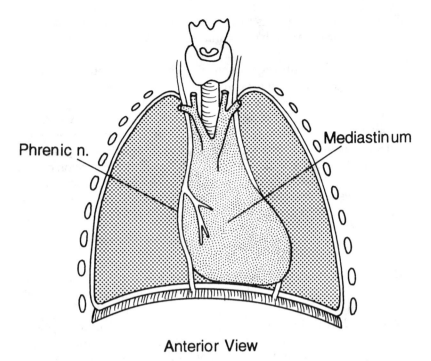

Phrenic n.

Mediastinum

Anterior View

FIGURE 3-23. Relationship among mediastinum, diaphragm, and lungs. Note the phrenic nerve innervation of the diaphragm.

The mediastinum lies deep to the bony thorax and its muscular coverings and is nestled deep to the lungs. Its central location in the body belies its importance to all regions, and its critical placement surrounded by lung tissue guarantees efficient transfer of gas to (and from) the blood pumped by the heart.

Because the heart is such an important muscle, it is located deep within several layers of thick muscle and bone. In the posterior are the vertebrae and massive muscles of the back, and the anterolateral aspect of the thorax is a strong wall of bone and muscle. The heart is well protected against most trauma, with the exception of romantic disappointment!

The organs and structures of the mediastinum are encased by a continuation of the parietal pleurae. This lining provides a low-friction mating surface between the lungs and the middle space. The visceral pleural lining of the lungs adjacent to the mediastinum is termed the mediastinal pleurae.

The left and right phrenic nerves pass anterior to the root structures of the lungs, coursing along the lateral surfaces of the pericardium to innervate the diaphragm. The two vagi enter the posterior mediastinum to innervate the heart, first passing behind the root structures of the lung, coursing inferiorly to the anterior and posterior surfaces of the esophagus. They descend through the diaphragm adjacent to the esophagus through the esophageal **hiatus** to innervate the abdominal viscera. The vagal pulmonary branches provide parasympathetic nerve supply for

hiatus: *L., an opening*

the lungs, with nerve fibers found even in the smallest bronchioles. The vagus mediates the cough reflex and control of airway diameter.

Movement of the rib cage for inspiration requires muscular effort. Muscles of respiration may be divided into muscles of inspiration and expiration (see Table 3–3). Before delving into these muscles, we should give you a word of caution. The primary muscles of respiration are relatively easy to identify, but we will inevitably make some assumptions about function of secondary muscle groups based on muscle attachment. It also is wise to explain at the start that expiration can be either forced or passive and is much more often a passive process. Thus, the muscles of expiration are not always active and depend on some other forces to help us eliminate carbon dioxide-laden air.

In summary:

■ The lungs are covered with **pleural linings** which, in conjunction with the lungs, provide the mechanism for air movement through muscular action.
■ When the diaphragm contracts, the lungs are pulled down due to the association between the pleurae and the diaphragm.
■ **Diaphragmatic contraction** expands the lungs, drawing air into them through the bronchial passageway.

MUSCLES OF INSPIRATION

As with many voluntary bodily functions, inspiration is a graded activity. Depending on the needs of your body, you are capable of **quiet inspiration**, which requires only one muscle, and **forced inspiration**, which calls on many more muscles. We enlist the help of increasingly larger numbers of muscles as our respiratory needs increase. You may wish to refer to the Appendix C for a summary of the muscles of respiration.

If the lungs are to expand and fill with air, the thorax must increase in size as well. As mentioned, there are only two ways this can happen. The first way to expand the thorax is to increase its **vertical** (superior-inferior) dimension, a process which will occur for both quiet and forced inspiration. First, picture the lungs encased in bone around the barrel-shaped mid-section of the rib cage, and bounded above by the clavicle and first rib. Remember that the rib cage is open at the bottom (look back at that drawing of the skeleton if your memory fails).

A thin but strong muscle placed across the bottom margin of the rib cage, configured like a drum-head, would be an economical means of expanding the size of the rib cage without having to manipulate the bony portion at all. The thorax and abdominal cavity below are separated by one of the most important muscles of the body, the diaphragm.

Table 3-3. Muscles of respiration.

Inspiration

Muscles of Trunk
  Primary of Thorax
    Diaphragm
  Accessory of Thorax
    Anterior
    External intercostal
    Interchondral portion, internal intercostal
    Posterior
    Levatores costarum (brevis and longis)
    Serratus posterior superior
  Muscles of Neck
    Sternocleidomastoid (superficial neck)
    Scalenus (anterior, middle, posterior)
    Trapezius
  Muscles of Thorax, Back, and Upper Limb
    Pectoralis major
    Pectoralis minor
    Serratus anterior
    Subclavius
    Levator scapulae
    Rhomboideus major
    Rhomboideus minor

Expiration

Muscles of Trunk
  Muscles of Thorax, Back, and Upper Limb
    Anterior
    Internal intercostal (interosseous portion)
    Transversus thoracis
    Posterior
    Subcostal
    Serratus posterior inferior
    Innermost intercostal
    Latissimus dorsi
  Abdominal Muscles
    Anterolateral
    Transversus abdominis
    Internal oblique abdominis
    External oblique abdominis
    Rectus abdominis
    Posterior
    Quadratus lumborum

The diaphragm takes the form of an inverted bowl, with its attachments along the lower margin of the rib cage, sternum, and vertebral column. It forms a reasonably complete separation between the upper (thoracic) and lower (abdominal) chambers, and when it contracts the force of contraction is directed downward toward the abdominal viscera. This contraction results in elongation of the cavity formed by the ribs, so that the lungs expand and air enters through the respiratory passageway.

Primary Inspiratory Muscle of Thorax

Diaphragm

The primary muscle of inspiration is the diaphragm. As seen in Figure 3–24, the diaphragm completely separates the abdominal and thoracic cavities (with the exception of vascular and esophageal hiatuses). This striated muscle takes the form of a large inverted bowl. The edges of this irregular bowl attach along the inferior boundary of the rib cage, xiphoid process, and to the vertebral column in the posterior aspect. The intermediate region is made up of a large, leafy aponeurosis called the **central tendon**. When the muscle contracts, muscle fibers shorten

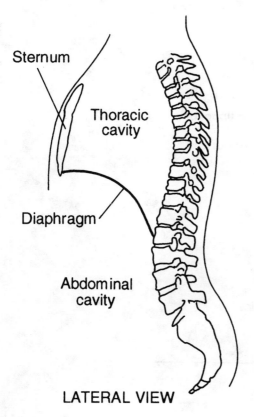

Sternum

Thoracic
cavity

Diaphragm

Abdominal
cavity

LATERAL VIEW

FIGURE 3-24. Lateral view schematic of diaphragm and thorax. Notice that the diaphragm courses markedly down from the sternum to the vertebral attachment, completely separating the thorax from the abdomen.

and the diaphragm pulls the central tendon down and forward. Let us look at this extremely important muscle in detail.

The muscle fibers of the diaphragm radiate out from the leafy mid-region aponeurosis referred to as the central tendon, forming the sternal, costal, and vertebral attachments. The anterior-most sternal attachment is made at the xiphoid process, with fibers coursing up and back to insert into the anterior central tendon. Lateral to the xiphoid, the fibers of the diaphragm attach to the inner border of ribs 7 through 12 and to the costal cartilages to form the costal attachment. In the posterior aspect, the vertebral diaphragmatic attachment is made with the corpus of L1 through L4 and transverse processes L1.

The fibers from these attachments course upward and inward to insert into the central tendon (see Figure 3–25). The posterior vertebral

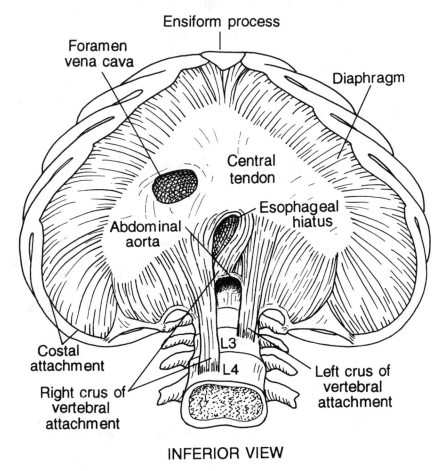

FIGURE 3–25. Inferior view schematic of diaphragm, as seen from the abdominal cavity.

crura: *L., crosses*

attachment also provides support for the esophageal hiatus. The vertebral attachment is accomplished by means of two **crura**. The right crus arises from attachment at L1 through L4, wherein the fibers ascend and separate to encircle the esophageal hiatus. Fibers of the left crus support this endeavor by passing to the left of the hiatus.

Although the diaphragm separates the thorax from the abdomen, the need for nutrients dictates that there be communication between the oral cavity and abdominal region. The region below the diaphragm also has vascular needs, and these require supply routes through the diaphragm.

There are three openings (diaphragmatic hiatuses) through which structures pass. As seen in Figure 3–25, the descending aorta passes through the aortic hiatus located adjacent and lateral to the vertebral column. The esophageal hiatus, through which the esophagus passes, is found immediately anterior to the aortic hiatus, while the inferior vena cava traverses these two cavities by means of the foramen vena cava which is in the right-central aspect of the diaphragm as viewed from above.

The actual muscle fibers of the diaphragm radiate out from the imperfect center formed by the central tendon. Careful examination of the forces of muscular contraction will be most helpful in later discussion of muscular contraction and action. Realize, again, that muscle can perform only one task, and that is to shorten. If a muscle is attached to two points, shortening will tend to bring those two points closer together, or simply tense the muscle if neither point is capable of moving. The diaphragm will stretch your understanding of this basic muscle function somewhat. Although the principles of muscle action and result still hold, movement of the diaphragm will not make a great deal of sense until you realize where the points of attachment really are.

Figure 3–26 is a schematic drawing of the diaphragm and central tendon. First, look at the upper portion of the figure. If you choose some subset of those fibers and shorten them, the end result will be that the central tendon would move toward the point of firm attachment, the origin. But when the diaphragm contracts, all fibers contract together which means that all fibers will pull more-or-less equally on the central tendon. Now look at the second part of the figure, and trace the same effect. If you contract (shorten) one fiber, the central tendon will move down toward the origin for the fiber. If you contract the entire diaphragm, the net result will be that the diaphragm is pulled down as a unit. Notice that the fibers in the front are longer than those in the back. Because a muscle can shorten to about one half of its original length, it stands to reason that the diaphragm will pull down farther in the front than in the back, and that is what happens. *Contraction of the diaphragm has the result of pulling the central tendon down and forward.*

The prominent **central tendon** is the last element of the diaphragm that we need to consider. Look again at Figure 3–26 and notice that the

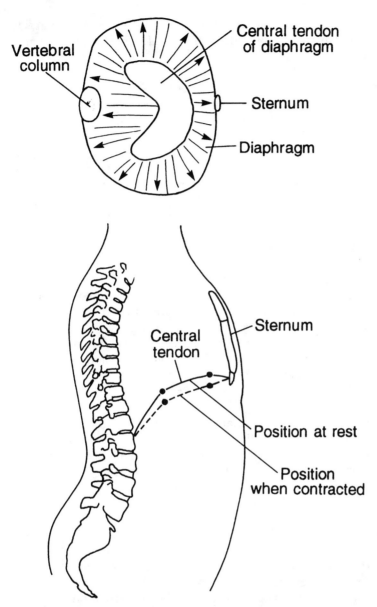

FIGURE 3-26. *Top:* Schematic of diaphragm with central tendon. The arrows depict the direction of force on contraction of the diaphragm. *Bottom:* This lateral view of the diaphragm shows that contraction of the diaphragm pulls the central tendon down.

central tendon is a crescent-shaped aponeurosis that is white and translucent. The tendon tends to conform to the prominence of the vertebral column in the thoracic cavity, so its shape mimics the curvature of the transverse thoracic cavity. It has the flexibility of aponeurosis, but has no contractile qualities. It depends on the radiating fibers of the diaphragm to account for movement. Above the central tendon is the heart, and this tendon provides a strong and secure floor for that mediastinal organ.

Innervation. Innervation of the diaphragm is by means of the **phrenic nerves** (see Figure 3–23). The diaphragm can be placed under voluntary control (you can hold your breath), but it is under primary control of the autonomic system (you have no choice but to breathe eventually). Nature has provided bilateral innervation of the diaphragm, supporting the notion that this is an exceptionally important unpaired muscle. The phrenic nerves originate in the **cervical plexus** (a plexus is a group of nerves coming together for a common purpose) from spinal nerves C3, C4, and C5 of both sides of the spinal cord.

The phrenic nerve descends deep to the omohyoid and sternocleidomastoid muscles and superficial to the anterior scalenus muscle, into the mediastinal space on the left and right sides of the heart. The fibers descend and divide to innervate the superior surface of the diaphragm. One branch (the left and right phrenicoabdominal) descends deep to innervate the inferior surface. The left branch is longer than the right, because it has a greater distance to travel around the mediastinum. The phrenic nerve mediates both motor and sensory information. The lower intercostal nerve serves the inferior-most boundary of the diaphragm.

One final comment is warranted on the diaphragm and its action. Throughout this description we have ignored the abdominal viscera, but beneath the diaphragm are numerous organs which undergo continual cycles of compression during respiration, a fact that will work to the advantage of anyone wishing to forcefully exhale (or perform the Heimlich maneuver, as we shall see).

To summarize:

■ The primary muscle of inspiration is the **diaphragm,** the dividing point between the thorax and the abdomen.
■ The fibers of the diaphragm pull on the **central tendon,** resulting in downward motion of the diaphragm during inspiration, and this movement expands the lungs in the **vertical dimension.**

Accessory Muscles of Inspiration

Although the diaphragm is the major contributor to inspiration, it needs help to meet the needs of your body for **forced inspiration.** If you take a look at Figure 3–27 you will see the rib cage from the side. Direct your attention first to the way the ribs run: They are directed distinctly downward as they make their path to the front of the skeleton. Next, imagine raising the ribs in front, and realize that when you do that the front of the

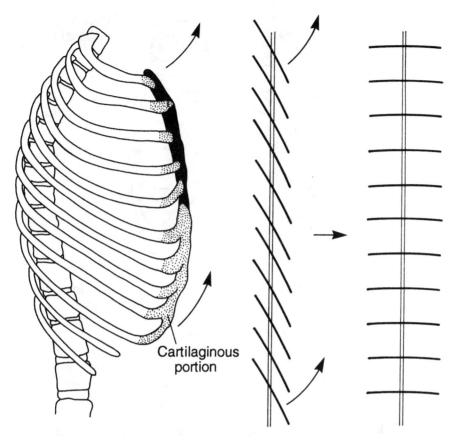

FIGURE 3–27. Schematic of rib cage from the side. Notice that the ribs slant down as they run forward. During inspiration the rib cage will elevate, as shown by the arrows. On the right side, the venetian blinds shown from the side demonstrate the change in volume achieved by elevation of the rib cage.

rib cage expands as a result. Swinging those ribs up means that they will swing out a bit, thereby increasing the volume of the rib cage.

To put this function in everyday terms, look at Figure 3–27 showing venetian blinds from the side. When they are closed they are similar to the rib cage at rest, and when they are tilted so that you can see through them it is similar to the point of elevation of the ribs. That elevation brings them more nearly horizontal, just like the blinds, and that change increases the overall front-back dimension.

Because the goal is to raise all of the ribs and *all* parts of the ribs, we would have to attach muscles to broad areas of the ribs to achieve this. The **external intercostals** (see Figure 3–28) are positioned so that when they contract the entire rib cage elevates, with most of the distance moved being in the front aspect.

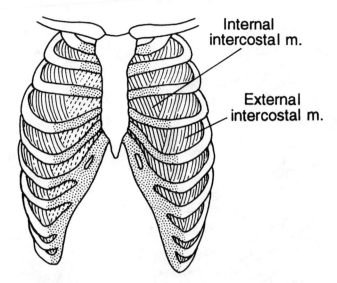

FIGURE 3–28. Rib cage with external and internal intercostal muscles. Note that on the left rib cage the fascia covering the internal intercostals has been removed, whereas it remains present and translucent on the right. External intercostals are absent near the sternum, and thus one can see the deeper internal intercostals within that region.

By labeling these muscles as "accessory muscles" of inspiration, we are acknowledging the simple fact that you could perform the respiratory act without them. They provide a significant increase in the amount of air we are able to process, but one is capable of surviving on diaphragmatic support in absence of the accessory muscles. Most assuredly you are not using the accessory muscles as you quietly read this text, but you would probably invoke them to help you discuss this chapter in front of the class. We will differentiate these based on region of the body: anterior and posterior thoracic muscles, neck muscles, and muscles of the arm and shoulder.

Anterior Thoracic Muscles of Inspiration

■ External Intercostal
■ Interchondral Portion, Internal Intercostal

External Intercostal and Interchondral Portion, Internal Intercostal Muscles. The external intercostal muscles are among the most significant respiratory muscles for speech. They not only provide a significant proportion of the total respiratory capacity, but they also perform functions that are uniquely speech-related, as will become clear.

As you can see in Figure 3–28, the 11 external intercostal muscles reside between the 12 ribs of the thorax, providing the ribs with both unity and mobility. The external intercostal muscles originate on the lower surface of each rib (except rib 12), course downward and inward, to insert into the upper surface of the rib immediately below. These muscles provide a unified surface of diagonally slanting striated muscle on all costal surfaces of the rib cage *with the exception of the region near the sternum*, because contraction of external intercostal fibers in that region would provide little benefit (and perhaps some negative effect) to the job of increasing cavity size. Later we will see that the internal and external intercostals play a very important role in control of respiration for speech.

The external intercostal muscles are covered with the translucent intercostal membrane which separates them from the internal intercostal muscles.

The internal intercostal muscles (to be discussed) are predominantly muscles of expiration, with the exception of the chondral portion. The **parasternal** ("near the sternum") portion of the external intercostal muscles encompassing the chondral aspect of the ribs has been shown to be active during forced inspiration. The musculature is quite capable of segmental activation so that one portion of this muscle can contract while contraction of the rest of the muscle is inhibited. The cross-laced effect of external and internal intercostal muscles forms a strong protective barrier for the lungs and heart and an impervious cavity for the forces of gas exchange.

Functionally, the external intercostal muscles elevate the rib cage. When the rib cage is elevated, the flexible coupling of the costo-sternal attachment permits the chondral portion of the ribs to rotate as they elevate. The net result is that the sternum remains relatively parallel to the vertebral column even as the rib cage expands, increasing the anterior dimension and thus the volume of the lungs (see Figure 3–27). The effort involved in raising the ribs twists (torques) the elastic cartilaginous portion of the ribs, and when that force is relaxed, the cartilage returns to its original form. Inspiration is an active process: Expiration can simply involve letting nature take its course, but it may be active as well.

> *Innervation* Innervation of the external intercostal muscles is achieved by the anterior divisions of the 12 pairs of thoracic spinal nerves, identified by the location of the region they innervate. The thoracic intercostal nerves arise from T1 through T6, and the thoracoabdominal intercostal nerves which pass into the abdominal wall arise from T7 through T11. T1 is a small but present intercostal nerve. Most of T1 fibers go into the brachial plexus. The subcostal nerve arises from T12. These intercostal nerves supply not only the intercostal muscles but also a number of other muscles of respiration located in the anterior abdominal wall (see Figure 3–29).

Although the external intercostals account for most of the second dimensional change (the anterior-posterior dimension), there are other muscles which, by virtue of their arrangement, are assumed to be of help. Any muscle that attaches to the rib cage or sternum and could feasibly elevate either could assist in the process of inspiration.

Some other possible assistants in respiration are the **levatores costarum** (brevis and longis), and **serratus posterior superior**, as shown in Figure 3–30. You can imagine that they would elevate the rib cage on contraction, as would the **serratus posterior superior**. You might be less inclined to accept the **trapezius** in this role!

trapezius: **trapezium,** *Gr., small table*

Posterior Thoracic Muscles of Inspiration

■ **Levatores Costarum (Brevis & Longis)**
■ **Serratus Posterior Superior**

Levator Costarum (Brevis & Longis). If you examine the course of the levator costarum ("elevators of the ribs") shown in Figure 3–30, you will see that shortening these muscles tends to elevate the rib cage. Although these muscles would appear to be muscles of the back, they are considered to be thoracic muscles. The **brevis** ("brief") portions of the levator costarum originate on the transverse processes of vertebrae C7 through T11, for a total of 12 levator costarum brevis muscles. Fibers course obliquely down and out to insert into the tubercle of the rib below.

The **longis** portions originate on the transverse processes of T7 through T11, with fibers coursing down and obliquely out. The fibers bypass the rib below the point of origin, inserting rather into the next

External intercostal m.   Intercostal n.

Innermost intercostal m.

Internal intercostal m.

External intercostal m.

Sympathetic trunk

FIGURE 3–29. Schematic of intercostal nerves, as seen from within the thoracic cavity.

rib. You can see that the longis portion will have a greater effect on elevation of the rib cage.

Innervation. Much as the intercostal muscles, the levatores costarum take their innervation from the dorsal rami (branches) of the intercostal nerves arising from spinal nerves T2 through T12. Upon exiting the spinal column, the dorsal rami course abruptly back, dividing into medial and lateral branches. The lateral branch of the dorsal ramus provides innervation of the levatores costarum.

Serratus Posterior Superior. In Figure 3–30, you can see that, given their course, contraction of the serratus posterior superior muscles could easily contribute to elevation of the rib cage.

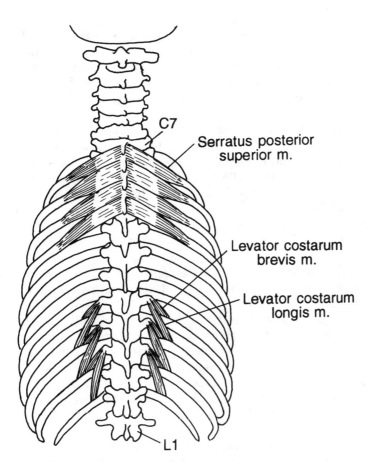

FIGURE 3–30. Posterior thoracic muscles of inspiration. Note that the levatores costarum have been shown only in the lower thorax for clarity although the brevis are present on all ribs.

The serratus posterior superior muscles take their origins on the spinous processes of C7 and T1 through T3. Fibers from these muscles course down and laterally to insert just beyond the angles of ribs 2 through 5. This more lateral insertion provides significant enhancement of the mechanical advantage afforded this muscle, as compared with the levatores costarum brevis or longis.

> *Innervation.* Innervation of the serratus posterior superior is completed by means of the ventral intercostal portion of the spinal nerves T1 through T4 or T5.

Accessory Muscles of Neck

■ Sternocleidomastoid
■ Scalenes (Anterior, Middle, Posterior)

There are several neck muscles that may assist in inspiration (Figure 3–31). The **sternocleidomastoid** muscle makes a direct attachment to the sternum and certainly could elevate that structure and the rib cage with it. Other potential muscles of inspiration are the **scalenus anterior, medius,** and **posterior** muscles, which are muscles of the neck. When they contract, they will elevate the first and second ribs.

scalenus: *L., uneven*

As with virtually all anatomical structures involved in speech, the muscles of the neck serve double duty. Although the muscles that will be discussed in this section are important for respiration, they are also sources of stability and control of neck flexion and extension. As an infant develops, it is the early control of neck musculature that marks the shift from the neonatal flexion position to one of balance between flexion and extension. When flexion and extension are balanced, the infant is well on the road toward the whole-body stability required for speech.

Sternocleidomastoid. The sternocleidomastoid courses from origin on the mastoid process of the temporal bone to its insertion at the sternum (sterno) and clavicle (cleido) (Figure 3–31). This muscle is prominent and its outline is easily visible on an individual, especially when the head is turned toward one side. When contracted separately, the sternocleidomastoid will rotate the head toward the side of contraction. When both left and right sternocleidomastoid muscles are simultaneously contracted the thoracic cavity will be the beneficiary, because these muscles have the capacity to elevate the sternum and subsequently the anterior rib cage.

> *Innervation.* The sternocleidomastoid and trapezius muscles derive their innervation from the eleventh cranial nerve, spinal branch (XI) accessory. The spinal portions of the accessory nerves originate from rootlets which arise from the side of the spinal cord in the regions of C2 through

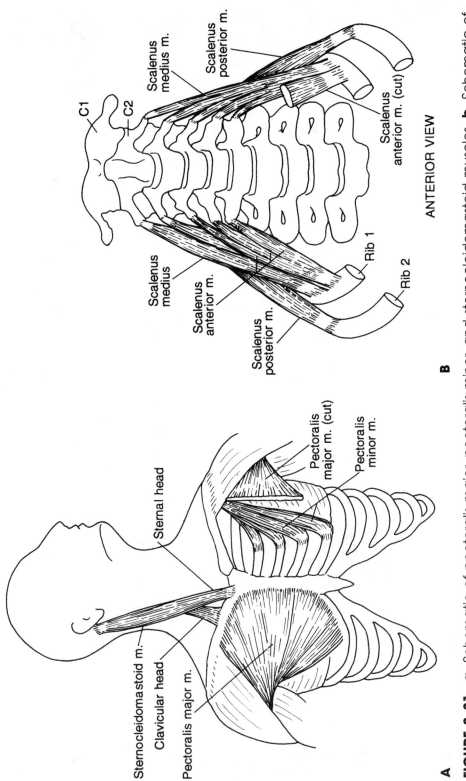

FIGURE 3-31. **a.** Schematic of pectoralis major, pectoralis minor, and sternocleidomastoid muscles. **b.** Schematic of scalenus anterior, medius, and posterior muscles.

93

C4 or C5. These fibers join to become the spinal root, ascending within the vertebral column behind the denticulate ligament. The spinal root enters the skull via the foramen magnum where it joins with the cranial root to exit the skull through the jugular foramen. The spinal and cranial branches separate, with the spinal branch coursing to innervate the sternocleidomastoid. It is supported in this by interconnection with C2 spinal nerve, which also innervates the muscle. This branch continues, descending deep to the trapezius muscle and above the clavicle, finally communicating with C3 and C4 to form a pseudoplexus, subsequently innervating the trapezius. The fibers of the cranial parts of the accessory nerve join the vagi to be distributed to skeletal muscles as vagal fibers.

Scaleni Anterior, Middle, Posterior. The scaleni (or "scalenes," as they also are called) are muscles of the neck which provide stability to the head and facilitate rotation and, by virtue of their attachment on the first and second ribs, have the potential of increasing the superior-inferior dimension of the thorax (Figure 3–31). Neck stability and control are essential ingredients for normal development of speech.

The anterior scaleni originate on the transverse processes of vertebrae C3 through C6, with fibers coursing down to insert into the superior surface of the first rib. The middle scaleni take their origin on transverse processes of vertebrae C2 through C7, also inserting into the first rib. The posterior scaleni insert into the second rib, having coursed from the transverse processes of C5 through C7.

> *Innervation.* The scaleni anterior are innervated by spinal nerves C4 through C6. The middle scalenes are innervated primarily by the cervical plexus derived from C3 and C4 (although spinal nerves C5 through C8 also are involved in their innervation). Spinal nerves C5 through C8 innervate the posterior scalenes.

Muscles of Upper Arm and Shoulder

The accessory muscles of the arm may assist the external intercostal in elevation of the thorax by virtue of their attachment to the sternum and ribs. Although not all have been confirmed through physiological study, the action of each of the following muscles has the potential of increasing the anterior-posterior dimension of the thorax.

serratus: serratus, *L.,* toothed, notched

rhomboideus: rhombus + oid, *L. parallelogram + like*

- ■ **Pectoralis Major**
- ■ **Pectoralis Minor**
- ■ **Serratus Anterior**
- ■ **Subclavius**

Clavicular Breathing

Clavicular breathing is a form of respiration in which a major source of thorax expansion arises from elevation of the rib cage via contraction of the accessory muscles of inspiration, most notably the sternocleidomastoid. Clavicular breathing often is an adaptive response by an individual to some previous or present pathological condition which prohibits use of other means to expand the thorax, such as chronic obstructive pulmonary disease. Because elevation of the sternum results in only a small increase in thorax size, clavicular breathing is a less-than-perfect solution to the problem of respiration.

Use of accessory muscles of inspiration to augment diminished respiratory support most typically will include the anterior, middle, and posterior scalene muscles (to elevate the first and second ribs) and the sternocleidomastoid (to elevate the sternum and increase the antero-posterior dimension of the rib cage). You may have seen patients with severe respiratory difficulties stretch out their arms and hold onto the back of a chair to breathe: When they do this, they give the pectoralis major muscles something to work against, thus allowing these muscles to increase the antero-posterior dimension. You may have also seen "shrugging" action by these patients, a sure sign that the trapezius muscle is in use to raise the rib cage.

■ **Levator Scapulae**
■ **Rhomboideus Major**
■ **Rhomboideus Minor**
■ **Trapezius**

Pectoralis Major and Minor. The pectoralis major is a large, fan-shaped muscle that originates from two heads (see Figure 3–31). The sternal head attaches along the length of the sternum at the costal cartilages, while the clavicular head is attached to the front of the clavicle. The muscle converges at the crest of the greater tubercle of the humerus. In respiration, the pectoralis major elevates the sternum and thus increases the transverse dimension of the rib cage.

The pectoralis minor originates on the anterior surface of ribs 2 through 5, with fibers coursing up to converge on the coracoid process of scapula. As with the pectoralis major, respiratory function would involve elevation of the rib cage, although this function has not been verified for either muscle.

Innervation. Innervation of the pectoralis major and pectoralis minor is by the pectoral nerves arising from the medial and lateral cords of the brachial plexus, a formation of C5 through C8 and T1 spinal nerves (see Figure 3–32).

Serratus Anterior. Fibers of the serratus anterior arise from ribs 1 through 9 along the side of the thorax, coursing up to converge on the inner vertebral border of the scapula. The saw-like fingers of this muscle give it its name ("serratus" as in "serrated knife"), and contraction of the muscle may elevate the ribs to which it is attached and subsequently the rib cage.

> *Innervation*: As with the pectoralis major and minor, serratus anterior receives innervation from the brachial plexus. The long thoracic nerve arises from C5 through C7 and passes between the middle and posterior scalene neck muscles to descend to the level of the serratus anterior.

Subclavius. As the name implies, the subclavius muscle courses under the clavicle, originating from the inferior margin of clavicle and taking an

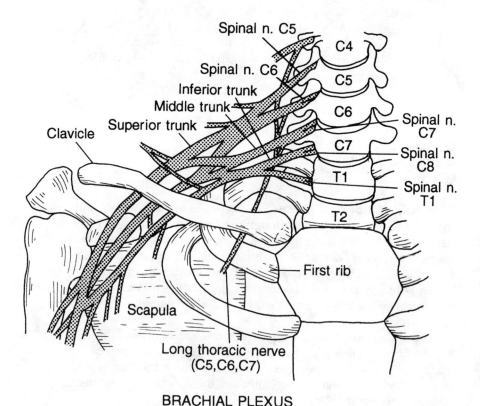

BRACHIAL PLEXUS

FIGURE 3–32. Schematic of brachial plexus arising from C5 through C8 and T1 spinal nerves. (Modified from data and view of Twietmeyer and McCracken, 1992.)

oblique and medial course to insert into the superior surface of the first rib at the chondral margin. It is a small muscle which may elevate the first rib during inspiration, although there is scant evidence of this.

Innervation. The subclavius muscle is innervated by branches from the brachial plexus, with fibers originating in the fifth and sixth spinal nerves.

Levator Scapulae. The levator scapulae provides neck support secondarily as a result of its function as an elevator of the scapula. This muscle originates from the transverse processes of C1 through C4, and courses down to insert into the medial border of the scapula (Figure 3–33).

Innervation. As with the scaleni anterior, middle, and posterior, the levator scapulae derives its innervation from C3 through C5 of the cervical plexus.

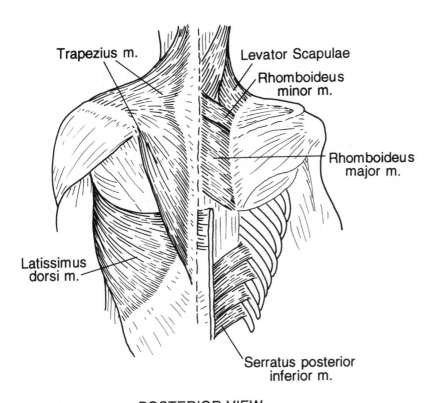

POSTERIOR VIEW

FIGURE 3–33. Accessory muscles of respiration: Trapezius, levator scapulae, rhomboideus minor, rhomboideus major, serratus posterior inferior, and latissimus dorsi. (Modified from data and view of Netter, 1989.)

Rhomboideus Major and Minor. The rhomboids (major and minor) lie deep to the trapezius, originating on the spinous processes of T2 through T5 (rhomboideus major) and from C7 and T1. The muscle courses down and laterally to insert into the medial border of the scapula. Primary speech function of the rhomboids is the support they provide for the upper body, and especially for the stability of the shoulder girdle.

Innervation. The rhomboids receive their innervation from the dorsal scapular nerves off the upper roots of the brachial plexus (C5). The dorsal scapular nerves pass through the scaleni medius muscles in their course to the rhomboids.

Trapezius. The trapezius muscle (Figure 3–33) is a massive muscle making up the superficial upper back and neck, originating along the spinous processes of C2 to T12 by means of fascial connection. (The trapezius is alternately considered a muscle of the arm.) Fibers of this muscle fan laterally to insert into the acromion of scapula and superior surface of clavicle. Contraction of this muscle clearly plays a significant role in elongation of the neck and head control.

Innervation: XI Accessory: See innervation of sternocleidomastoid, discussed previously.

For respiration, support is the primary function of the back muscles, although there are distinct respiratory actions, as we shall see. Back muscles provide a dense, multilayered mass of tissue that supports and protects (see Figure 3–33). Perhaps the most important function of these muscles is maintenance of the delicate balance of upper body mobility in the face of required stability. To experience this firsthand, place both feet firmly on the ground while sitting erect, and then with one arm reach straight ahead as if you were about to grasp an object beyond your reach. You will need to overextend when you do this, but if you attend to the musculature of your head, shoulders, and back you will feel them tighten to support your efforts. Your shoulders rotated while the rest of your trunk remained relatively stable.

In the "big picture" of trunk control the following back muscles are key players. The trapezius and levator scapulae muscles serve clear roles in neck elongation and head stability. Support for the vertebral column is provided by the trapezius muscle and the rhomboideus major and minor muscles, and this support serves respiration in a stabilizing manner. The clinical note on development of motor coordination emphasizes the importance of trunk and back muscle development from an oral motor perspective.

In summary:

■ The **diaphragm** is an exceptionally important muscle of inspiration but there are many **accessory muscles** of inspiration and expiration that also serve respiration.

Trunk Stability and Upper Body Mobility

Infant motor development is a process of increasing control of motor function and control of speech musculature depends in large part on development of trunk control. It is truly a "for want of a nail" situation: If the infant fails to develop neck extension, he or she will not develop the ability to balance neck extensors and flexors. Once the normal extension begins development, the back muscles begin to come under control, again becoming dynamically opposed by anterior trunk muscles. Through this interplay of antagonist and agonist trunk muscles the infant develops the ability to rotate the trunk, stabilize the hips (and, of course, walk), and elevate the head in preparation for speech. Once controlled, the infant can rotate his or her head, differentiate mandible movement from head movement, and tongue from mandible. All the while, the infant is developing the dynamic aspects of laryngeal control which permit the larynx to descend and tongue to become controlled.

This is a long-winded ways of saying that, although respiratory function of back muscles is open to question, absence of controlled use of the back muscles most certainly would result in loss of head control for speech, reduced differentiation of facial muscle control, and lack of laryngeal control due to the tonic imbalance of the torso. The indirect effects of muscle imbalance within the trunk are innumerable.

■ Generally, muscles of the thorax and neck which elevate the rib cage will serve some accessory function for inspiration.

In the next section we shall see that muscles that compress the abdomen or pull down on the rib cage will assist in expiration.

MUSCLES OF FORCED EXPIRATION

Active expiration requires that musculature act on the lungs indirectly to "squeeze" the air out of them. This is achieved in two ways. Because the rib cage expands in two dimensions, it makes sense that it will contract in two dimensions as well. The front-to-back dimension was expanded by elevating the rib cage, so active expiration should reduce that dimension. The rib cage can be pulled down by the **internal intercostal muscles**, the **innermost intercostal muscles,** and the **transversus thoracis** muscles. The second means of expanding the volume of the thorax was by increasing the vertical dimension through contraction of the diaphragm. If you examine Figure 3–34, you will realize that relaxing the diaphragm will return it to its original posi-

Resting
position

Contracted
position

LATERAL VIEW

FIGURE 3–34. Lateral view schematic of diaphragm.

tion, and no farther. If you note the viscera of the abdomen below the diaphragm, you can now see the second means of active expiration. If I could somehow squeeze my abdominal viscera, I could push my diaphragm higher into the thorax and remove more air from my lungs. (If you want to verify this, have one of your friends perform a gentle version of the Heimlich maneuver on you and feel what happens with your respiration. Do you inhale or exhale?)

We can forcefully expire by contracting the muscles of the abdominal region which, in turn, squeeze the abdomen and force the viscera upward, reducing the size of the thorax. This is half of the reason you "get the wind knocked out of you" when someone punches you in the abdomen. See the clinical note for the other half of that story.

If you examine the abdominal muscles of expiration (Figure 3–35), you will see that they are very much like a cumberbund, wrapping the abdomen into a neat package in the front, side, and back. The major players in the anterior abdomen are the **internal** and **external oblique**

"Getting the Wind Knocked Out of You"

Why *does* a blow to the abdomen result in your losing your breath? Logic would dictate that you would lose your breath from being hit in the chest. You'll want to take a look at the explanation of reflexive responses in the clinical note entitled "paradoxical respiration" because that will go a long way toward explaining this response as well.

Try to recall what happened the last time you had the wind knocked out of you. First, something hit you in the abdominal region. From what you now know, forced expiration depends in large part on contraction of the abdominal muscles which, in turn, causes the abdominal viscera to push the diaphragm upward and pull the thorax down. Both of these gestures remove air forcefully from the lungs.

This doesn't explain the agony you experience trying to regain respiratory control, however. When those muscles are passively moved (stretched) a stretch reflex is triggered which causes the muscle to contract involuntarily. This contraction only serves to increase the effect of being hit in the abdomen, because it is essentially doing the same thing the blunt force did. To cap it all off, your attempts to contract your diaphragm add a third dimension to the problem, because that will once again stretch the abdominal muscles and promote further reflexive contraction.

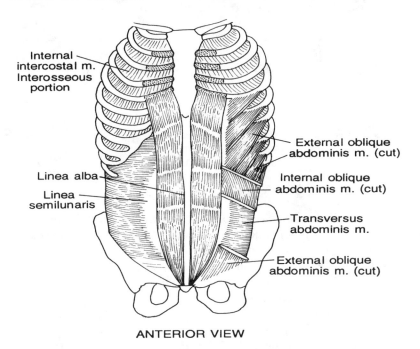

ANTERIOR VIEW

FIGURE 3–35. Accessory muscles of expiration.

Use of Abdominal Muscles for Childbirth and Other Biological Functions

Nature has a way of getting the most use out of structures, and the abdominal muscles are a great example. Clearly, we use the abdominal muscles to force air out of the lungs, but they serve several other worthwhile (even vital) functions. The act of vomiting requires evacuation of the gastric or even intestinal contents, and to do so necessitates forceful action from the abdominal muscles.

A less obvious function has to do with thoracic fixation. For the muscles of the upper body to gain maximum benefit, they need to pull against a relatively rigid structure. The thorax can be made rigid by inhaling and then capturing the respiratory charge by closing off the vocal folds. To demonstrate this process, take a very deep breath and hold it: To do this you must close off the folds.

This thoracic fixing gives leverage for lifting (notice that you "grunt" when you lift because some air is escaping past the vocal folds, having been compressed by your muscular effort), but it also gives leverage in the other direction. Defecation requires compression of the abdomen and increase in abdominal pressure, and that process also demands thoracic fixation for efficiency.

Another not immediately obvious use for abdominal muscle contraction is childbirth. Although you may not have experienced this directly, you are probably familiar with midwives, nurses, or spouses whose job it was to remind the mother-to-be to "breathe." It shouldn't surprise you to realize that mother has not forgotten this basic biological process, but rather she has an overwhelming, deep biological urge to "push." The person who is doing the cheerleading is doing so to keep her from closing the vocal folds (you can't breathe through closed folds), because if she does, she will start pushing the baby to its new home before the time has come.

abdominis, **transversus abdominis**, and the **rectus abdominis** muscles. In the posterior abdomen, the **quadratus lumborum, iliacus**, and **psoas major** and **minor** muscles serve this function. If you look at the drawing in Figure 3–35 you will see that the **latissimus dorsi** muscles also could support expiratory efforts, although studies on function of this muscle are contradictory.

The layers of abdominal muscles provide excellent support for the rib cage during lifting and other body gestures. These gestures virtually demand fixing the thorax by inflating the lungs and closing off the vocal folds, and the abdominal muscles help to compress the viscera while simultaneously stabilizing the thorax.

Muscles of Thorax: Anterior/Lateral Thoracic Muscles

■ Internal Intercostal (Interosseous Portion)
■ Transversus Thoracis
■ Innermost Intercostals

Internal Intercostal. The internal intercostal muscles are significant contributors to forced expiration. As seen earlier in Figure 3–28, the internal intercostal muscles are pervasive throughout the thorax, originating on the inferior margin of each rib (except the twelfth) and running up and medially to insert into the superior surface of the rib below. They are conspicuously absent in the posterior aspect of the rib cage near the vertebral column. Because the external intercostal muscles run at nearly right angles to the internals, these two sets of muscles provide significant support for the rib cage and protection of the ribs within, as well as maintenance of rib spacing.

The course of the muscle fibers is constant from front to side to back of rib cage. That is, while the fibers run up and medially in front, that translates to running up and laterally in the dorsal aspect.

Besides their support function, the internal intercostal muscles also provide a mechanism for depressing the rib cage. As you can see from the schematic of Figure 3–36, when the interosseous portion of the internal intercostal contract and shorten, the direction of movement is down, and the expanded rib cage will become smaller.

> *Innervation.* Intercostal nerves: See external intercostal, discussed previously.

Innermost Intercostal (Intercostales Intimi). The innermost intercostal muscles are the deepest of the intercostal muscles, with fibers coursing between the inner costal surfaces of adjacent ribs. The innermost intercostals have a course parallel to those of the internal intercostal muscles, with fibers originating on the surface of the lower rib and coursing obliquely up to insert into the rib above. As with the external intercostals, the innermost intercostals are absent in the chondral portion of the ribs, becoming apparent first in the lateral aspect of the inner rib cage. The innermost intercostals are absent near the vertebral and sternal borders, and are sparse in the upper thorax, and parallel the morphology of the internal intercostals. The innermost intercostals interdigitate with the subcostal muscles.

> *Innervation.* Intercostal nerves: See external intercostals, discussed previously.

Transversus Thoracis. As the name implies, the Transversus Thoracis ("transverse muscles of thorax") muscles are found on the inner surface of the rib cage. The muscles originate on the margin of the sternum, with fibers coursing to the inner chondral surface of ribs 2 through 6. As seen in Figure 3–37, contraction of the muscles would

Effect of contraction
of internal intercostal muscles

FIGURE 3–36. Effects of contraction of the interosseous portion of the internal intercostals is to pull the rib cage down, thereby decreasing the volume of the lungs.

tend to resist elevation of the rib cage and decrease the volume of the thoracic cavity.

> *Innervation.* Considering the proximity of the transversus thoracis to the internal intercostal muscles, it should not be surprising that the transversus thoracis takes its innervation from the same source (the thoracic intercostal nerves), as well as from the thoracoabdominal intercostal nerves and subcostal nerves derived from T2 through T2 spinal nerves.

Posterior Thoracic Muscles

■ **Subcostals**
■ **Serratus Posterior Inferior**

Subcostals. The subcostals are widely variable, but generally take a course parallel to the internal intercostal and thus have the potential of serving expiration. The subcostals are found on the inner posterior wall of the thorax. Unlike the intercostal muscles, the subcostals may span more than one rib.

> *Innervation.* The subcostals are innervated by the intercostal nerves of thorax, arising from the ventral rami of the spinal nerves.

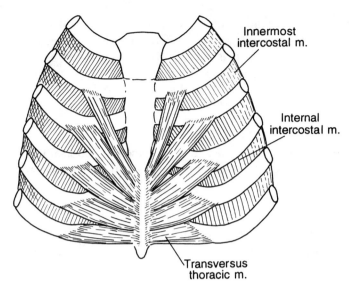

Innermost
intercostal m.

Internal
intercostal m.

Transversus
thoracic m.

VIEW FROM WITHIN THORACIC CAVITY

FIGURE 3–37. Transversus thoracis muscles, as viewed from within the thoracic cavity.

Serratus Posterior Inferior. The serratus posterior inferior muscles originate on the spinous processes of the T11, T12, L1 through L3 and course up and laterally to insert into the lower margin of the lower five ribs. Contraction of these muscles would tend to pull the rib cage down, supporting expiratory effort.

> *Innervation.* The serratus posterior inferior derive their innervation from the intercostal nerves arising from T9 through T11 and subcostal nerve from T12.

Abdominal Muscles of Expiration

If you examine once again the skeleton in Figure 3–3 and imagine placing muscles in the region between the rib cage and the pelvis, you will realize that there are few places from which muscles can originate. Clearly one could attach muscles to the rib cage, vertebral column, and the pelvic girdle to give some structure, but that leaves a great deal of territory to cover in the anterior aspect. To deal with this, nature has provided a tendinous structure, the **abdominal aponeurosis**. Let us examine how it is constructed and then attach some muscles to that structure.

Figure 3–38 shows a schematic representation of the abdominal aponeurosis from the front, as well as in transverse section.

The **linea alba** ("white line") runs from the xiphoid process to the pubic symphysis, forming the midline structure for muscular attach-

linea alba: *L., white line*

ment. Looking at the schematic of a transverse section you will see that as the linea alba progresses laterally, it differentiates into two sheets of aponeurosis, between which is placed the rectus abdominis. This aponeurotic wrapping comes back together to form another band of tendon, the linea semilunaris. This tendon once again divides, but this time into three sheets of aponeurosis, which will provide us with a way to attach three more muscles to this structure.

rectus: *L., straight (not crooked)*

In the posterior aspect, the fascia join to form the lumbodorsal fascia. This structure provides the union of three abdominal muscles (**transversus abdominis, internal** and **external oblique abdominis**) with the vertebral column.

The external oblique aponeurosis communicates directly with the fascia covering the **rectus abdominis**, forming a continuous layer of connective tissue from the linea alba to the external oblique muscle.

Anterolateral Abdominal Muscles

The abdominal muscles of expiration function by compression of the abdominal viscera. This compression function is not only useful in respiration, but also aids in defecation, vomiting, and childbirth (with vocal folds tightly adducted).

- ■ **Transversus Abdominis**
- ■ **Internal Oblique Abdominis**
- ■ **External Oblique Abdominis**
- ■ **Rectus Abdominis**

Transversus Abdominis. Lateral to the rectus abdominis is the transversus abdominis, the deepest of the anterior abdominal muscles (Figure 3–38). The transversus abdominis runs laterally (that is, horizontally; hence the name "transversus"), originating in the posterior aspect at the vertebral column via the thoracolumbar fascia of the abdominal aponeurosis. Its anterior attachment is to the transversus abdominis aponeurosis, as well as to the inner surface of ribs 6 through 12, interdigitating at that point with the fibers of the diaphragm. Its inferior-most attachment is at the pubis. Contraction of the transversus will significantly reduce the volume of the abdomen.

> *Innervation.* Innervation of the transversus abdominis is via the thoracic and lumbar nerves, specifically from the lower thoracoabdominal nerves (derived from T7 to T12) and first lumbar nerve, iliohypogastric and ilioinguinal branches.

Internal Oblique Abdominis. The internal oblique abdominis is located between the external oblique abdominis and the transversus abdo-

TRANSVERSE VIEW

A

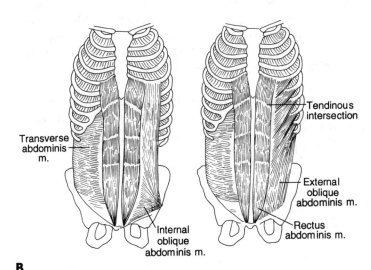

B

FIGURE 3-38. a. Schematic of abdominal aponeurosis as related to the abdominal muscles of expiration. **b.** Transversus abdominis, rectus abdominis, external and internal oblique abdominis muscles.

minis. As seen in Figure 3–35, this muscle fans out from its origin on the inguinal ligament and iliac crest to the cartilaginous portion of the lower ribs and the portion of the abdominal aponeurosis lateral to the rectus abdominis, and thus, by association, inserts into the linea alba. Contraction of the internal oblique abdominis assists in rotation of the trunk if unilaterally contracted or flexion of the trunk when bilaterally contracted.

> *Innervation.* See transversus abdominis innervation.

External Oblique Abdominis. The external oblique abdominis are the most superficial of the abdominal muscles, as well as the largest of this group. These muscles originate along the osseous portion of the lower seven ribs, and fan downward to insert into the iliac crest, inguinal ligament, and abdominal aponeurosis (lateral to rectus abdominis). Bilateral contraction of these muscles will flex the vertebral column, while unilateral contraction results in trunk rotation.

> *Innervation.* This muscle receives innervation from the thoracoabdominal nerve arising from T7 through T11 and subcostal nerve from T12.

Rectus Abdominis. The rectus abdominis muscles are the prominent midline muscles of the abdominal region with origin at the pubis inferiorly (see Figure 3–35). The superior attachment is at the xiphoid process of sternum and the cartilage of the last true rib (rib 7) and the false ribs.

These "rectangular" (i.e., rectus) muscles are manifest in a series of four or five segments connected (and separated) by tendinous slips known as tendinous intersections. Use of this muscle is a "must" if your are to succeed at your sit-ups, because contraction will draw the chest closer to the knees, and the only way to do this is to bend. Contraction of the rectus abdominis also compresses the abdominal contents.

> *Innervation* Innervation derives from T7 through T11 intercostal nerves (thoracoabdominal) and subcostal nerve from T12. This segmented muscle is segmentally innervated as well: T7 supplies the uppermost segment, T8 supplies the next section, and the remaining portions are supplied by T9.

Posterior Abdominal Muscles

■ Quadratus Lumborum

Quadratus Lumborum. As seen in Figure 3–33, the quadratus lumborum is located in the dorsal aspect of the abdominal wall. These muscles originate along the iliac crest and fan up and in to insert into the transverse processes of the lumbar vertebrae and inferior border of the twelfth rib. Unilateral contraction of the quadratus lumborum would assist lateral movement of the trunk, whereas bilateral contraction would fix the abdominal wall in support of abdominal compression.

Innervation. This muscle is innervated by the lowest thoracic nerve T12 and the first four lumbar nerves.

There are other abdominal muscles supporting abdominal wall fixation. The psoas major and minor muscles and the iliacus may provide abdominal support for forced expiration, but there is little evidence for this function due to the difficulty involved in taking physiological recordings from these muscles.

Muscles of Upper Limb

■ Latissimus Dorsi

latissimus: L., widest

Latissimus Dorsi. The latissimus dorsi muscle (Figure 3–33) originates from the lumbar, sacral, and lower thoracic vertebrae, with fibers rising fan-like to insert into the humerus. Its primary role is in movement of the upper extremity, but it clearly plays a role in chest stability, and perhaps expiration. With the arm immobilized, contraction of the latissimus dorsi would stabilize the posterior abdominal wall, performing a function similar to that of quadratus lumborum.

> *Innervation.* Innervation for this muscle arises from the posterior branch of the brachial plexus. Fibers from the regions C6 through C8 of this plexus form the long subscapular nerve to supply the latissimus dorsi.

In summary:

■ To inflate the lungs, you need to expand the cavity that holds them so air can rush in.
■ To do this you can either increase the long dimension fairly easily by contracting the **diaphragm** or you can elevate the rib cage with just a little bit more effort.
■ **Forced expiration** reverses this process by pulling the thorax down and in and by forcing the diaphragm higher into the thorax.
■ The next chapter will provide insight into these processes.

CHAPTER SUMMARY

Respiration is the process of gas exchange between an organism and its environment. The **rib cage,** made up of the **spinal column** and **ribs,** houses the lungs which are the primary mechanisms of respiration. By means of the cartilaginous **trachea** and **bronchial tree,** air is brought into the lungs for gas exchange within the minute **alveolar sacs.** Oxygen enters the blood and carbon dioxide is removed, to be expired.

Air is drawn into the lungs through muscular effort. The **diaphragm,** placed between the thorax and abdomen, contracts during inspiration. The **lungs** expand when the diaphragm contracts, drawn by **pleurae** linked through surface tension and negative pressure. When lungs expand, the air pressure within the lungs becomes negative with respect to the outside atmosphere, and **Boyle's law** dictates that air will flow from the region of higher pressure to fill the lungs. **Accessory muscles** also provide added expansion of the rib cage for further inspiration.

Expiration may occur passively, through the forces of **torque, elasticity,** and **gravity** acting on the ribs and rib cage. It also may be **forced,** utilizing muscles of the abdomen and those that depress the rib cage to evacuate the lungs.

Study Questions

1. _____ is defined as force distributed over area.

2. _____ pressure causes air to enter the container until the pressure is equalized.

3. How many of each of the following vertebrae are there?

   _____ cervical vertebrae

   _____ thoracic vertebrae

   _____ lumbar vertebrae

   _____ sacral vertebrae (fused)

4. On the figure below please identify the landmarks indicated.

   a. _____ process

   b. _____ process

   c. _____

   d. _____ facet

   e. _____ facet

   f. _____ facet

   g. _____ foramen

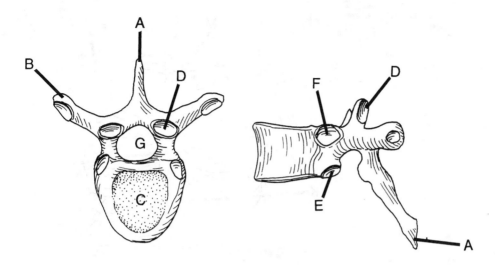

5. The _____ passes through the vertebral foramen.

6. On the figure below please identify the landmarks indicated.

a. _____(bone)

b. _____(bone)

c. _____(bone)

d. _____

e. _____

f. _____

g. _____

h. _____(bone)

i. _____(bone)

j. _____

k. _____

l. _____

m. _____

7. On the figure below please identify the landmarks indicated.

a. _____

b. _____

c. _____

d. _____

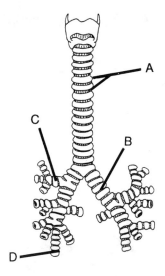

8. On the figure below please identify the muscles and structures indicated.

a. _____

b. _____

c. _____

d. _____

e. _____

f. _____ ligament

g. _____

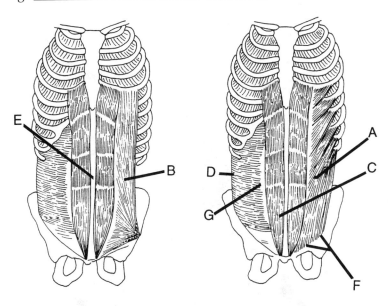

9. On the figure below please identify the muscles indicated.

a. _____

b. _____

c. _____

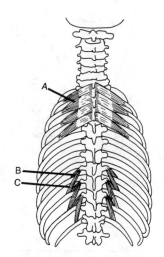

10. Please identify the muscles indicated below.

a. _____

b. _____

c. _____

11. Please identify the muscles and portions of muscles indicated below.

a. _____

b. _____ head

c. _____ head

d. _____

e. _____

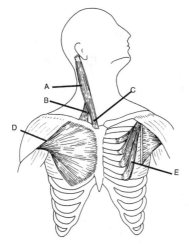

12. Contraction of the diaphragm increases the _____ dimension of the thorax.

13. Contraction of the accessory muscles of inspiration increase the _____ dimension of the thorax.

14. Contraction of the muscles of expiration _____ the volume of the thorax.

Study Question Answers

1. <u>PRESSURE</u> is defined as force distributed over area.

2. <u>NEGATIVE</u> pressure causes air to enter the container until the pressure is equalized.

3. How many of each of the following vertebrae are there?

   <u>7</u> cervical vertebrae

   <u>12</u> thoracic vertebrae

   <u>5</u> lumbar vertebrae

   <u>5</u> sacral vertebrae (fused)

4. On the figure below please identify the landmarks indicated.

   a. <u>SPINOUS</u> process

   b. <u>TRANSVERSE</u> process

   c. <u>CORPUS</u>

    d. SUPERIOR ARTICULAR facet

    e. INFERIOR COSTAL facet

    f. SUPERIOR COSTAL facet

    g. VERTEBRAL foramen

5. The SPINAL CORD passes through the vertebral foramen.

6. On the figure below please identify the landmarks indicated.

    a. ILIUM

    b. ISCHIUM

    c. PUBIC BONE

    d. SACRUM

    e. ILIAC CREST

    f. PUBIC SYMPHYSIS

    g. COCCYX

    h. CLAVICLE

    i. SCAPULA

    j. MANUBRIUM STERNI

    k. XIPHOID or ENSIFORM PROCESS

    l. CORPUS STERNI

    m. STERNAL NOTCH

7. On the figure below please identify the landmarks indicated.

    a. TRACHEA

    b. MAINSTEM BRONCHUS

    c. SECONDARY BRONCHUS

    d. TERTIARY BRONCHUS

8. On the figure below please identify the muscles and structures indicated.

    a. EXTERNAL OBLIQUE ABDOMINIS

    b. INTERNAL OBLIQUE ABDOMINIS

    c. RECTUS ABDOMINIS

    d. TRANSVERSUS ABDOMINIS

    e. LINEA ALBA

    f. INGUINAL LIGAMENT

    g. LINEA SEMILUNARIS

9. On the figure below please identify the muscles indicated.

    a. SERRATUS POSTERIOR SUPERIOR

    b. LEVATOR COSTARUM BREVIS

    c. LEVATOR COSTARUM LONGIS

10. Please identify the muscles indicated below.

    a. SCALENUS ANTERIOR

    b. SCALENUS MEDIUS

    c. SCALENUS POSTERIOR

11. Please identify the muscles and portions of muscles indicated below.

    a. STERNOCLEIDOMASTOID

    b. CLAVICULAR head

    c. STERNAL head

    d. PECTORALIS MAJOR

    e. PECTORALIS MINOR

12. Contraction of the diaphragm increases the VERTICAL dimension of the thorax.

13. Contraction of the accessory muscles of inspiration increase the TRANSVERSE dimension of the thorax.

14. Contraction of the muscles of expiration DECREASE the volume of the thorax.

REFERENCES

Arnott, W. M. (1973). *Disorders of the respiratory system.* Oxford, England: Blackwell Scientific Publications.

Baken, R. J. (1987). *Clinical measurement of speech and voice.* Austin, TX: Pro-Ed.

Basmajian, J. V. (1975). *Grant's method of anatomy.* Baltimore, MD: Williams & Wilkins.

Bateman, H. E., & Mason, R. M. (1984). *Applied anatomy and physiology of the speech and hearing mechanism.* Springfield, IL: Charles C. Thomas.

Beck, E. W. (1982). *Mosby's atlas of functional human anatomy.* St. Louis, MO: C. V. Mosby Company.

Bergman, R., Thompson, S., & Afifi, A. (1984). *A Catalog of human variation.* Baltimore, MD: Urban & Schwarzenberg.

Burrows, B., Knudson, R. J., & Kettel, L. J. (1975). *Respiratory insufficiency.* Chicago, IL: Year Book Medical Publishers.

Bly, L. (1994). *Motor skills acquisition in the first year.* Tucson, AZ: Therapy Skill Builders.

Campbell, E., Agostoni, E., & Davis, J. (1970). *The respiratory muscles, mechanics and neural control.* Philadelphia, PA: W. B. Saunders.

Chusid, J. G. (1979). *Correlative neuroanatomy and functional neurology* (17th ed.). Los Altos, CA: Lange Medical Publications.

Des Jardins, T. (1984). *Clinical manifestations of respiratory disease.* Chicago, IL: Year Book Medical Publishers.

Draper, M., Ladefoged, P,. & Whitteridge, D. (1959). Respiratory muscles in speech. *Journal of Speech and Hearing Research, 2,* 16–27.

Ganong, W. F. (1981). *Review of medical physiology.* Los Altos, CA: Lange Medical Publications.

Gordon, M. S. (1972). *Animal physiology: Principles and adaptations.* New York: Macmillan.

Gosling, J. A., Harris, P. F., Humpherson, J. R., Whitmore, I., & Willan, P. L. T. (1985). *Atlas of human anatomy.* Philadelphia, PA: J. B. Lippincott.

Grobler, N. J. (1977). *Textbook of clinical anatomy* (Vol. 1). Amsterdam: Elsevier Scientific.

Kahane, J. C., & Folkins, J. F. (1984). *Atlas of speech and hearing anatomy.* Columbus, OH: Charles E. Merrill.

Kao, F. F. (1972). *An introduction to respiratory physiology.* Amsterdam: Exerpta Medica.

Kaplan, H. (1960). *Anatomy and physiology of speech.* New York: McGraw-Hill.

Kuehn, D. P., Lemme, M. L., & Baumgartner, J. M. (1989). *Neural bases of speech, hearing, and language.* Boston, MA: Little, Brown.

Langley, M. B., & Lombardino, L. J. (1991). *Neurodevelopmental strategies for managing communication disorders in children with severe motor dysfunction.* Austin, TX: Pro-Ed.

Lee, D. H. K. (1972). *Environmental factors in respiratory disease.* New York: Academic Press.

Logemann, J. (1983). *Evaluation and treatment of swallowing disorders.* Boston, MA: College-Hill Press.

McMinn, R. M. H., Hutchings, R. T., & Logan, B. M. (1994). *Color atlas of head and neck anatomy.* London: Mosby-Wolfe.

McReynolds, L., Northern, J. & Yoder, D. (Eds.) *Speech, language, and hearing* Vol. I. *Normal processes.* Philadelphia, PA: W. B. Saunders.

Mohr, J. P. (1989). *Manual of clinical problems in neurology.* Boston, MA: Little, Brown.

Moser, K. M., & Spragg, R. G. (1982). *Respiratory emergencies.* St. Louis, MO: C. V. Mosby.

Murray, J. F. (1976). *The normal lung. The basis for diagnosis and treatment of pulmonary disease.* Philadelphia, PA: W. B. Saunders.

Netter, F. H. (1983a). *The CIBA collection of medical illustrations. Vol. 1. Nervous system. Part I. Anatomy and physiology.* West Caldwell, NJ: CIBA Pharmaceutical Company.

Netter, F. H. (1983b). *The CIBA Collection of medical illustrations. Vol. 1. Nervous system. Part II. Neurologic and neuromuscular disorders.* West Caldwell, NJ: CIBA Pharmaceutical Company.

Netter, F. H. (1989). *Atlas of human anatomy.* West Caldwell, NJ: CIBA Pharmaceutical Company.

Pace, W. R. (1970). *Pulmonary physiology.* Philadelphia, PA: F. A. Davis.

Peters, R. M. (1969). *The mechanical basis of respiration.* Boston, MA: Little, Brown.

Rohen, J. W., & Yokochi, C. (1993). *Color atlas of anatomy.* New York: Igaku-Shoin.

Snell, R. S. (1978). *Gross anatomy dissector.* Boston, MA: Little, Brown.

Spector, W. S. (1956). *Handbook of biological data*. Philadelphia, PA: W. B. Saunders Company.

Taylor, A. (1960). The contribution of the intercostal muscles to the effort of respiration in man. *Journal of Physiology, 151*, 390.

Tokizane, T., Kawamata, K., & Tokizane, H. (1952). Electromyographic studies on the human respiratory muscles. *Japan Journal of Physiology, 2*, 232.

Williams, P., & Warrick, R. (1980). *Gray's anatomy. (36th British ed.)*. Philadelphia, PA: W. B. Saunders.

Zemlin, W. R. (1988). *Speech and hearing science. anatomy and physiology*. Englewood Cliffs, NJ: Prentice-Hall.

CHAPTER

4

Physiology of Respiration

Respiration requires muscular effort, and the degree to which an individual can successfully control that musculature determines, in large part, the efficiency of respiration itself. Respiratory function (physiology) changes as we exercise, age, or suffer setbacks in health. Considering its importance in speech, it is no wonder that as the respiratory system goes, so goes communication.

We are capable of both quiet and forced inspiration. There is a parallel to this in expiration, because we are capable of **passive** and **active expiration**. In passive expiration, we let the forces inherent to the tissues restore the system to a resting position after inspiration. In active expiration, we use muscular effort to push just a little farther. Let us examine these forces.

The process of expiration is one of eliminating the waste products of respiration. Attend to your own respiratory cycle to learn an important aspect of quiet expiration. Close your eyes while you breathe in and out 10 times, quietly and in a relaxed manner. Pay particular attention to the area of your body around your diaphragm, including your rib cage and your abdomen.

What you experienced is the active contraction of the diaphragm, followed by a simple relaxing of the musculature. You actively contract to breathe in, and then simply let nature take its course for expiration. It is a little like blowing up a balloon, because the balloon will deflate as soon as you let go of your grip. The forces on the balloon that cause it to lose its air are among those that cause your lungs to deflate, and here is how that story goes. The forces we need to talk about are torque, elasticity, and gravity.

Torquing refers to twisting of a shaft while not permitting one end to move. Take hold of a wooden or plastic ruler by the end in one hand, and grasp the other end of the ruler and twist it around its long axis (see Figure 4–1). When you perform this task, you will feel the ruler return to its original state, the product of a restoring force contributed by the elastic qualities of the material from which the ruler is made.

Think of the "shafts" we could twist in the rib cage. If you thought "rib," you thought right. Unfortunately, bone is poorly designed in the area of

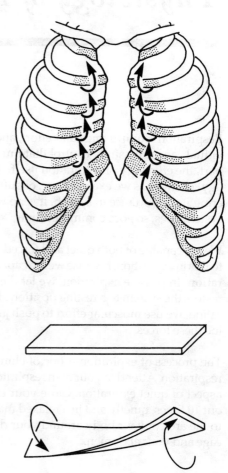

FIGURE 4-1. When the rib cage is elevated the cartilage of the ribs is torqued or twisted. Because cartilage is highly elastic it tends to return to its original condition after being torqued.

restoring forces (forces that tend to return a body to its original position) because it is quite inelastic. There is an elastic element, however, in the chondral portion of the rib cage, and we do take advantage of that.

Return to our earlier discussion of the elevation of the rib cage by the external intercostals and the accessory muscles of inspiration to recognize that, when those muscles pull the rib cage up and out, the anterior cartilage comes under some torquing strain. As soon as you stop pulling on the rib cage, it will return to its original shape, thanks to restoring forces of the elastic cartilage, and that will cause the rib cage to drop back down to its resting state.

Elevation of the rib cage occurs during moderate to great inspiratory effort but is not necessary for quiet inspiration. We must account for passive expiration during quiet respiration in another way, but that involves tissue elasticity as well.

You will recall that the lungs are highly elastic, porous tissue. They are sponge-like, and when they are compressed will tend to expand. Likewise, if you were to grab a sponge by its edges and stretch it, the sponge will tend to return to its original shape and size when you release it.

You can think of the lungs as small sponges in a large bottle. The lungs truly will not fill up that "bottle" of the chest cavity when they are left to their own devices (i.e., permitted to deflate to their natural resting condition). In the adult body, the lungs are actually stretched beyond their resting position, but this is not so with the infant.

During early development, the lungs completely fill the thorax, so that they are not stretched to fit the relaxed rib cage. As the child develops the rib cage grows at a faster rate than the lungs, and the pleural linings and increased negative intrapleural pressure provide a means for the lungs to be stretched out to fill that space.

The result of this stretching is greatly increased capacity and reserve in adults, but not in infants. Because the thorax and lungs are the same size, infants must breathe two to three times as often as an adult for adequate respiration. The adult's lungs are stretched out and *never* are completely compressed, so there is always a reserve of air within them that is not at the moment undergoing gas exchange.

Upon increasing the thorax size, the lungs expand just as if you had grabbed them and stretched them out. When the muscles that are expanding the rib cage relax, the lungs tend to return to their original shape and size. In addition, when you inhale and your abdomen protrudes, you are stretching the abdominal muscles. Relaxing the inspiratory process will let those muscles return to their original length. That is, the abdominal muscles will tend to push your abdominal viscera back in and to force the diaphragm up.

A final force acting in support of passive expiration is gravity. When standing or sitting erect, gravity acts on the ribs to pull them back after they have been expanded through the effort of the accessory muscles of inspiration. Gravity also works in favor of maximizing your overall capacity, because it pulls the abdominal viscera down, leaving more room for the lungs. We will talk about this more because body position becomes a significant issue in the efficiency of respiration.

To summarize:

■ We are capable of quiet respiration as well as forced inspiration and expiration.
■ **Quiet inspiration** will utilize the diaphragm and often the external intercostals, but **forced** inspiration will use many of the accessory muscles.
■ Expiration may be passive, driven by the forces of **torque, elasticity**, and **gravity**.
■ We also may use muscles that reduce the size of the thorax by compressing the **abdomen** or pulling the rib cage down, and this will force air out of the lungs beyond that which is expired in passive expiration.

THE MEASUREMENT OF RESPIRATION

The quantity of air processed through respiration is dictated primarily by bodily needs, and speech physiology operates within these limits. We will discuss respiration in terms of rate of flow in respiration, volume and lung capacities, and pressure.

Respiratory flow, volumes, and capacities are measured using a **spirometer** (see Figure 4–2). The classical wet spirometer involves a tube connected to a container opened at the bottom. This container is placed inside another container that is full of water.

To measure lung volume, an individual will breathe into the tube, causing a volume of water to be displaced. The amount of water displaced will give you an accurate estimate of the air that was required to displace it. (We are ignoring the *pressure* required to raise the container and the effort involved in this process.)

The classic U-tube **manometer** is one means of measuring pressure, as shown in Figure 4–3. A subject is asked to place the tube in his or her mouth and to blow. The force of the subject's expiration is exerted on a column of water that rises as a result. The more force the person uses, the higher the column rises. We can measure the effects of that force in inches or in centimeters of water (i.e., barometric pressure is often reported in millimeters of mercury, which refers to how many millimeters of mercury were elevated by the pressure). Because water is

WET SPIROMETER

FIGURE 4–2. Wet spirometer used to measure lung volumes. When the individual exhales into the tube, gas entering the air chamber displaces the water, causing the chamber to rise. These changes are charted on the recording drum.

FIGURE 4–3. U-tube manometer for measurement of respiratory pressure.

considerably less dense than mercury, the same amount of pressure will elevate a column of water much higher than a similar column of mercury. For this reason we measure the rather small pressures of respiration with the water standard, although mechanical and electronic techniques are eliminating the water-filled tube.

Breathing requires that gas be exchanged in an ongoing basis. The body has specific needs that must be met continually, so we will need to discuss respiration in terms of the **rate of flow** of air in and out of the lungs (measured as cubic centimeters per second or minute). We also need to speak of the quantities or **volumes** that are involved in this gas exchange (measured in liters [L], milliliters [ml], cubic centimeters [cc], or on occasion, cubic inches).

RESPIRATION FOR LIFE

What is by now obvious to you is that respiration is vital. As a swimmer you probably remember staying under water a little too long, discovering the limits of your respiratory system and the panic you felt when you reached those limits. Let us examine why those limits are reached and how we work within those limits for speech.

When you breathe in, you are engaged in a simple gesture with very complex results. The goal of respiration, of course, is oxygenation of blood and elimination of carbon dioxide.

The basic process of gas exchange involves four stages: Ventilation, distribution, perfusion, and diffusion. **Ventilation** refers to the actual movement of air in the conducting respiratory pathway. This air is **distributed** to the 300,000,000 alveoli where the oxygen-poor vascular supply from the right pulmonary artery is **perfused** to the 6,000,000,000 capillaries that supply those alveoli. The actual gas exchange across the alveolar-capillary membrane is referred to as **diffusion**.

The ventilation process is a direct function of the action of the diaphragm and muscles of respiration. As discussed earlier, contraction of muscles of inspiration causes expansion of the alveoli that results in a negative alveolar pressure and air being drawn into the lungs. Understanding the pressure changes in this process is critical.

Effects of Turbulence on Respiration

When lungs expand, pressure throughout the system drops as a result of expansion of the alveoli. Air courses through the large diameter conducting bronchi, that, being comprised of cartilage, resist the negative pressure to collapse. In healthy lungs this results in relatively low resistance, laminar flow or air. A slight turbulence occurs at bifurcations such as where the trachea splits to become the right and left mainstem bronchi, but generally the flow is unimpeded. This is not a trivial notion, because even a small irregularity in the airway (such as mucus) greatly increases the resistance to airflow and also the difficulty of respiration.

The expiratory act, of course, is performed by decreasing the thoracic volume, thus eliminating carbon dioxide. Gas that was previously captive in the blood has migrated across the alveolar-capillary membrane and is expelled into the atmosphere.

Respiratory Cycle

During quiet respiration adults will complete between 12 and 18 cycles of respiration per minute (see Figure 4–4). A cycle of respiration is defined as one inspiration and one expiration. This quiet breathing pattern, known as **quiet tidal respiration** (because it can be visualized as a tidal flow of air into and out of the lungs) involves about 500 ml (1/2 liter) of air with each cycle. (You can visualize this by imagining a 2-liter bottle of soda being one quarter full.) A quick calculation will reveal that we process something in the order of 6,000 to 8,000 ml (6–8 liters) of air every minute. (The volume of air that is involved in one minute of respiration is referred to as the **minute volume**.)

Because these values are based on quiet, sedentary breathing, it will not surprise you to learn that they increase during strenuous work. An adult male will increase his oxygen requirements by a factor of 20 on increasing work output. As you can see in Table 4–1, as work increases the ventilation requirements are met by increased respiratory flow.

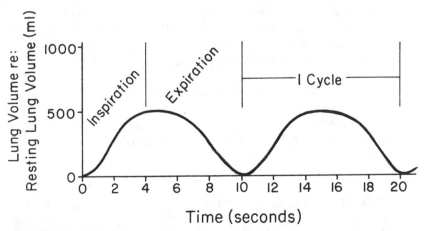

FIGURE 4-4. Volume display of two cycles of quiet respiration.

Table 4–1. Respiratory volume as a function of work intensity.

	Work Intensity (Kg m/min)	Ventilation (ml)
Female	600	3470
	900	5060
Male	900	4190
	1200	5520
	1500	7090

Source: Data from *Handbook of Biological Data* by W. S. Spector, 1956, p. 352. Philadelphia, PA: W.B. Saunders.

Developmental Processes in Respiration

There are developmental effects on respiration as well. The lungs undergo a great deal of prenatal development, as seen in Figure 4–5. By the time the infant is born, the cartilaginous conducting airway is complete, although the number of alveoli will increase from about 25 million at birth to over 300 million by 8 years of age. We retain that number throughout life.

The conducting airways will grow steadily in diameter and length until thorax growth is complete, although the thorax will expand to a greater degree than the lungs. As the thorax expands, the lungs are stretched to fill the cavity, a fact that helps to explain two differences between adults and children. As we mentioned earlier, adults breathe between 12 and 18 times per minute while at rest, but the newborn will breathe an average of 40 to 70 cycles per minute. By 5 years, the child is down to about 25 breaths per minute (bpm), and that number drops to about 20 bpm at 15 years of age. The adult has a considerable volume of air that is never expelled, but the infant does not have this reserve. In essence, the thorax expands during growth and development and stretches the lungs beyond their natural volume.

As a result of this expansion there is a volume of air in the adult lung that cannot be expelled (residual volume), and this volume helps to account for the reserve capacity of adults relative to infants: Infant lungs have yet to undergo the proliferation of the alveoli seen during childhood, and infants must breathe more frequently to meet their metabolic needs.

Volumes and Capacities

Respiration is the product of a number of forces and structures, and for us to make sense of them, we need to define some volumes and capac-

A

A

B

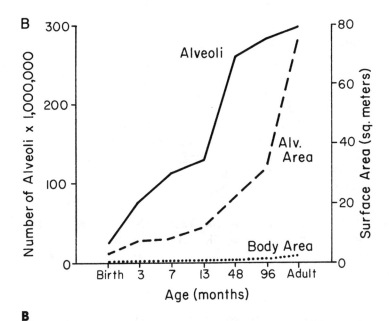

B

FIGURE 4-5. a. Changes in lung weight as a function of age. Notice that males and females are essentially equivalent in lung weight until puberty, at which time the increased thoracic cavity size of the male is reflected in larger lung weight. **b.** Changes in lung tissue with age. The number of alveoli increases radically through the fourth year of life, and the total alveolar area stabilizes around puberty when the thorax approximates its volume. (Data from *Handbook of Biological Data* by W.S. Spector, 1956, pp. 162, 176–180, 353. Philadelphia, PA: W. B. Saunders.)

ities of the lungs. When we refer to volumes we are partitioning off the respiratory system so that we may get an accurate estimate of the amount of air each compartment can hold. (For instance, we could conceivably talk about the volume of a single alveolus, which is about 250 microns in diameter, or about 250 millionths of a meter, although this might not produce a very useful number.) We also might speak of **capacities**, which are more functional units. Capacities refer to combinations of volumes that express physiological limits. Volumes are discrete, whereas capacities represent functional combination of volumes.

Both volumes and capacities will be measured in milliliters (ml, which are thousandths of a liter) or cubic centimeters (cc, which is another name for the same thing). To get an idea of what these volumes and capacities really amount to, look at a 2-liter soda bottle for a reference. One liter is 1000 ml, which is also 1000 cc.

There are five volumes that we should consider: Refer to Tables 4–2 and 4–3, as well as Figure 4–6 as we discuss these.

Volumes

Tidal Volume (TV). The volume of air that we breathe in during a respiratory cycle is referred to as Tidal Volume (TV). The definition of tidal volume makes precise measurement difficult, because tidal volume varies as a function of physical exertion, body size, and age. **Quiet tidal volume** (tidal volume at rest) has an average for adult males of around 600 cc, and for adult females, approximately 450 cc. This works out to an average of 525 cc for adults, or approximately one quarter of the volume of a 2-liter soda bottle every 5 seconds. You will fill up three of these bottles every minute. As shown in Table 4–1, tidal volume increases markedly as effort increases.

Inspiratory Reserve Volume (IRV). The second volume of interest is inspiratory reserve volume (IRV). Inspiratory reserve volume is that volume that can be inhaled after a tidal inspiration. It is the volume of air that is in reserve for use *beyond* the volume you would breathe in tidally.

To help remember the inspiratory reserve volume, do the following exercise. Sit quietly and breathe in and out tidally until you become aware of your breath, and tag each breath mentally with the word "in" and "out." After a few "outs and ins" stop breathing at the end of one of your inspirations. This is the peak of the tidal inspiration. Instead of breathing out (which is what you want to do) breathe in as deeply as you can. The amount you inspired after you stopped is the inspiratory reserve volume, and if you are an average adult the volume is about 2475 cc (2.475 liters).

Table 4–2. Respiratory volumes and capacities.

Volumes

Tidal Volume (TV): Volume of air exchanged in one cycle of respiration.

Inspiratory Reserve Volume (IRV): Volume of air that can be inhaled after a tidal inspiration.

Expiratory Reserve Volume (ERV): Volume of air that can be expired following passive, tidal expiration. Also known as **resting lung volume**.

Residual Volume (RV): Volume of air remaining in the lungs after a maximum exhalation.

Dead Air: Volume of air within the conducting passageways that cannot be involved in gas exchange (included as a component of residual volume).

Capacities

Vital Capacity (VC): The volume of air that can be inhaled following a maximal exhalation (includes inspiratory reserve volume, tidal volume, and expiratory reserve volume (VC = IRV + TV + ERV).

Functional Residual Capacity (FRC): The volume of air in the body at the end of passive exhalation, including expiratory reserve and residual volumes (FRC = ERV + RV).

Total Lung Capacity (TLC): The sum of inspiratory reserve volume, tidal volume, expiratory reserve volume, and residual volume (TLC = IC + FRC).

Inspiratory Capacity (IC): The maximum inspiratory volume possible after tidal expiration (IC = TV + IRV).

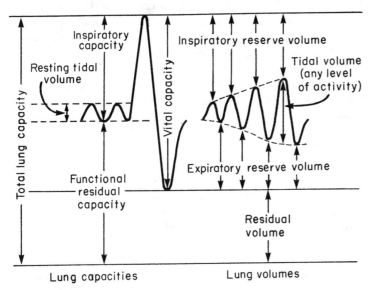

FIGURE 4–6. Lung volumes and capacities as displayed on a spirogram. (Modified from data of Pappenheimer et al., 1950)

Expiratory Reserve Volume (ERV). The parallel volume for expiration is the expiratory reserve volume (ERV). Expiratory reserve volume is the amount of air that can be expired following passive, tidal expiration. To experience this, breathe as you did before, but this time stop before you breathe in following expiration. (This point is easier to reach, because you can just *relax* your muscles and air will flow out without muscular effort.) Expire as completely as you can and you will have experienced expiratory reserve volume: It is the amount of air you could expire after that tidal expiration, amounting to about 1000 cc (1.0 liters). This volume is referred to as **resting lung volume** (RLV) as well because it is the volume present in the resting lungs after a passive exhalation.

Residual Volume (RV). A third volume of interest is residual volume (RV). Residual volume is the volume remaining in the lungs after a maximum exhalation. No matter how forcefully or completely you exhale there is a volume or air (about 1.1 liters) that cannot be eliminated. This volume exists because the lungs are stretched as a result of the relatively expanded thorax, so it should come as no shock to know that it is not present in the newborn. You might think of it as an "acquired space." By the way, this does not mean we do not use that air, but rather simply that it is a *volume* that is not eliminated during expiration.

Dead Space Air. We have accommodated the major volumes, but we must deal with the volume that cannot be involved in gas exchange. The air in the conducting passageways cannot be involved in gas exchange because there are no alveoli there. You will recall that the conducting passageways of the lung are constructed largely of cartilage, and the upper respiratory passageway of the mouth, pharynx, and nose certainly do not have alveoli. The volume that cannot undergo gas exchange in the lungs is referred to as dead space air and in the adult has a volume of about 150 cc. This varies also with age and weight, but is approximately equal (in cubic centimeters) to your weight in pounds. The volume associated with dead air is included in residual volume, because both are volumes associated with air that cannot be expelled.

The concept of dead air (and its importance) may become more vivid if you consider a swimmer using a tube or snorkel to breathe from underwater. This person has additional dead air associated with the tube, and the longer the tube is the greater is the volume he or she will have to inhale to pull air from the surface into the lungs. In pathological conditions the term "dead space" takes on new meaning. In the healthy individual **anatomical dead space** (that described previously) and **physiological dead space** (wasted ventilation) are the same. As you will find in the clinical notes of Chapter 3, there are conditions that contribute to increased physiological dead space; that is, pathological conditions of the respiratory system often result in wastage of respiratory effort and air.

Capacities

The volumes may be combined in a number of ways to characterize physiological needs. The following four capacities are useful combinations of volumes.

Vital Capacity (VC). Of the capacities, vital capacity (VC) is the most often cited in speech and hearing literature, because it represents the capacity available for speech (see Figure 4–7). Vital capacity is the combination of inspiratory reserve volume, expiratory reserve volume, and tidal volume. That is, vital capacity represents the total volume of air that can be inspired after a maximal expiration. Because VC = IRV + ERV + TV, you can quickly see that it is approximately 4000 cc in the average adult.

Functional Residual Capacity (FRC). Functional residual capacity is the volume of air remaining in the body after a passive exhalation (FRC = ERV + RV). In the average adult this comes to approximately 2550 cc.

Total Lung Capacity (TLC). Total lung capacity is the sum of all the volumes (TLC = TV + IRV + ERV + RV), totaling approximately 5100 cc.

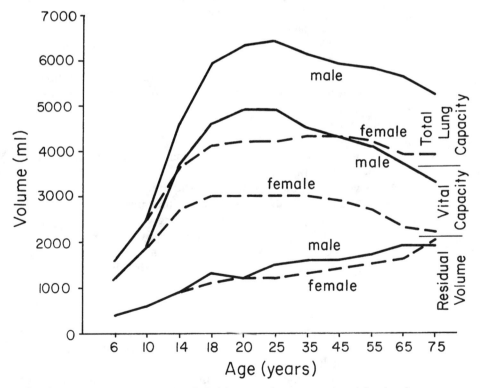

FIGURE 4-7. Vital capacity, total lung volume, and residual volume as a function of age. (Data from *Handbook of Biological Data* by W. S. Spector, 1956, p. 267. Philadelphia, PA: W. B. Saunders.)

Note that this is different from vital capacity. Vital capacity represents that volume of air that is involved in a maximal respiratory cycle, whereas total lung capacity includes the residual volume. Residual volume serves as a buffer in respiration because it is not immediately involved with interaction with the environment. Oxygen-rich air is diluted by mixing with the air of the residual volume, so that during brief periods of fluctuating air quality relatively constant oxygenation will occur.

Inspiratory Capacity (IC). Inspiratory capacity is the maximum inspiratory volume possible after tidal expiration (IC = TV + IRV). This refers to the capacity of the lungs for inspiration and represents a volume of approximately 3000 cc in the adult.

Effect of Age on Volumes

As we age, tissue changes, information that will probably not come as a surprise. What may shock you is how rapidly your body reaches its peak function and how steady is the decline. Vital capacity is a function of body weight, age, and height, the relationship for which can be expressed mathematically as seen in Table 4–3 and graphically in Figure 4–8.

What you can see from the formula is that as age increases vital capacity decreases by about 100 ml per year in adulthood. What the formula also shows is that vital capacity increases steadily with body growth up to about 20 years of age, holds constant through about age 25, and then begins a steady decline. What might be apparent also from the formula is that females will have smaller vital capacity throughout the life span, as reflected in the height element (males tend to be taller).

To summarize:

■ There are several volumes and capacities of importance to your study of respiration.
■ The volumes indicate arbitrary partitioning of the respiratory system and include **tidal volume** (the volume inspired and expired in a cycle of respiration), **inspiratory reserve volume** (air inspired beyond tidal inspiration), **expiratory reserve volume** (air expired beyond tidal expiration), **residual volume** (air that remains in the lungs after maximal expiration), and **dead air**, which cannot undergo gas exchange.
■ **Vital capacity** is the volume of air that can be inspired after a maximal expiration.
■ **Functional residual capacity** is the air that remains in the body after passive exhalation, while **total lung capacity** represents the sum of all lung volumes.
■ **Inspiratory capacity** is the volume that can be inspired from resting lung volume.

Table 4–3. Typical respiratory volumes and capacities in adults. From Baldwin, Cournand, and Richards, 1948, in Kao, 1972, p. 39 and Peters (1969), p. 49.

Volume/Capacity	Males (in cc)	Females (in cc)	Average (in cc)
Resting tidal volume	600 cc	450 cc	525 cc
Inspiratory reserve volume	3000	1950	2475
Expiratory reserve volume	1200	800	1000
Residual volume	1200	1000	1100
Vital capacity	4800	3200	4000
Functional residual capacity	2400	2700	2550
Inspiratory capacity	3600	2400	3000
Total Lung capacity	6000	4200	5100

Note: Volumes and capacities vary as a function of body size, gender, age, and body height. These volumes represent approximate values for healthy adults between 20 and 30 years of age. Vital capacity is estimated by accounting for age (in years) and height (in cm):

Males:
VC in ml = 27.63 – (0.112 × age in yrs.) × ht. in cm

Females:
VC in ml = 21.78 – (0.101 × age in yrs.) × ht. in cm

Source: Data from Baldwin, Cournand, and Richards, (1948) as cited in *An Introduction to Respiratory Physiology* by F. F. Kao, 1972. Amsterdam: Excerpta Medica and *The Mechanical Basis of Respiration* by R. M. Peters, 1969, p. 49. Boston: Little, Brown.

Pressures of the Respiratory System

There are five specific locations for pressure measurement for non-speech and speech: Alveolar pressure, intrapleural pressure, subglottal pressure, intraoral pressure, and atmospheric pressure (see Figure 4–9).

The atmosphere surrounding the earth and within which we live exerts a sizable pressure on the surface of the earth (760 mm Hg; that is, sufficient pressure to elevate a column of mercury 760 mm against gravity). Atmospheric pressure (P_{atm}) is actually our reference in discussions of the respiratory system, and so we will treat it as a constant zero against which to compare respiratory pressures. **Intraoral** or

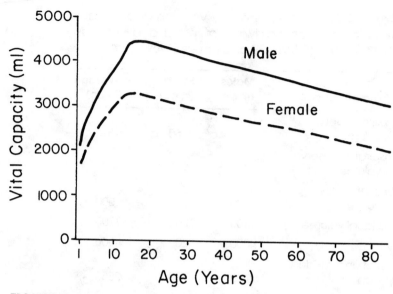

FIGURE 4–8. Mathematically predicted changes in vital capacity based on age and gender.

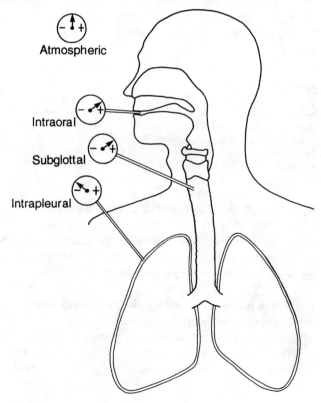

FIGURE 4–9. Pressures of respiration.

mouth pressure (P_m) is the pressure that could be measured within the mouth, while **subglottal pressure** (P_s) is the pressure below the vocal folds. During normal respiration with open vocal folds we may assume that subglottal and intraoral pressures are equal to alveolar pressure. As we progress more deeply into the lungs we can estimate **alveolar** or **pulmonic pressure** (P_{al}), the pressure that is present within the individual alveolus. If we were to measure the pressure in the space between parietal and visceral pleurae we would refer to it as **pleural** or **intrapleural pressure** (P_{pl}). Intrapleural pressure will be negative throughout respiration. Recall that the lungs, inner thorax, and diaphragm are wrapped in a continuous sheet of pleural lining. When one attempts to separate the visceral from parietal pleurae, a negative pressure ensues.

These pressure measurements are all made relative to atmospheric pressure. When we refer to alveolar pressure as being, for instance, +3 cm H_2O, it means that, through muscular effort, we have generated +3 cm H_2O pressure above and beyond atmospheric pressure (if atmospheric pressure is 1,033 cm H_2O, then alveolar pressure would be 1,036 cm H_2O). Alveolar pressure may be indirectly estimated by having an individual swallow a balloon and breathe. Because the trachea and esophagus are adjacent structures sharing a common wall, the pressure changes within the trachea produce analogous changes in the esophagus, and a pressure sensor in the balloon will permit estimation of air pressure below the level of the vocal folds.

When the diaphragm is pulled down for tidal inspiration, Boyle's law predicts that alveolar pressure will drop (relative to atmospheric pressure), and it does. In quiet tidal inspiration, alveolar pressure drops to approximately –2 cm H_2O until equalized with atmospheric pressure by inspiratory flow. Likewise, during expiration the pressure at the alveolar level becomes positive with reference to the atmosphere, increasing to +2 cm H_2O during quiet tidal breathing.

The work of expanding the lungs is one of overcoming resistance within the lungs. Surface active solution (surfactant) is released into the alveoli, and the result is greatly reduced surface tension. This decrease in surface tension reduces the pressure of the alveoli, keeps the alveolar walls from collapsing, and keeps fluid from the capillaries from being drawn into the lungs. Pressure in any network of tubes is greatest at the source of the pressure, which would be at the alveolus.

The surfactant protects the alveolus, promotes airflow, and facilitates effort-free respiration. During respiration oxygen is perfused into the bloodstream across the alveolar-capillary membrane barrier, while carbon dioxide is perfused into the alveolus.

When the thorax is expanded by means of muscular contraction, the lungs will follow faithfully with the result being expansion of the

300,000,000 alveoli within the lungs. Secreting cells within the visceral pleurae release a lubricating fluid into the potential space between visceral and parietal pleurae, and presence of this fluid lets the lungs and thorax make a slippery, extremely low-friction contact. At the alveolus, oxygen and carbon dioxide diffuse across the alveolus-capillary boundary.

Figure 4–10 is a schematic of the alveolar pressures, intrapleural pressures, and change in lung volume during quiet tidal breathing. This figure shows the alveolar pressure associated with a cycle of respiration and illustrates what we have been talking about. We have placed markers on it so that we can discuss how this whole system of pressures and flows works together.

Look at the "volume" portion of the graph and notice the periodic function representing tidal respiration. Point "A" represents the peak of that inspiration, and the lungs have about 500 cc of air in them. Point "B" represents the end of the expiratory cycle, where our subject has relaxed the forces of inspiration and the lungs have passively evacuated down to resting lung volume. The point marked "C" represents the electromyographic activity recorded from the diaphragm as it contracts. Putting these two traces together, you can see that as the diaphragm contracts the volume increases to a maximum, ending at the point where the diaphragmatic contraction is complete.

Let us examine the "flow" component. As the diaphragm contracts there is a fairly steady flow of air into the lungs (measured in cc/second), indicated by point "D." When the inspiratory effort is completed (represented by the termination of the diaphragm activity and the volume peak at "A"), the flow of air into the lungs ends. That is, when the diaphragm stops contracting, air stops flowing. As air leaves the lungs, the airflow becomes negative at point "E" (which simply means that the air is flowing in a different direction). The pressure goes positive (+2 cm H_2O) during expiration, a change you would predict from what you know about the lungs. To summarize, when the diaphragm contracts airflow begins and is fairly steady throughout the inspiratory cycle; when the diaphragm stops contracting, the air begins to flow out of the lungs.

This is a good point to examine the pressures driving this process. Recall that contraction of the diaphragm causes the alveolar pressure to drop and the point marked "F" will make sense: When the diaphragm is active ("C"), pressure deep within the lungs drops. At this point alveolar pressure reaches its maximum negativity during this tidal respiration (–2 cm H_2O relative to atmospheric pressure), because the negative pressure is responsible for airflow into the lungs. Looking at "G" will explain why that pressure drops. You will recall that intrapleural pressure is constantly negative relative to atmospheric pressure, arising from the fact that the lungs are in a state of con-

Pneumothorax

Pneumothorax (*pneumo* = air) is aggregation of air in the pleural space between the lungs and the chest wall with subsequent loss of the negative intrapleural pressure. It can arise through one of several means, but the product is always "collapsed" lung. In "open" pneumothorax, air is introduced into the space through a breech of the thoracic wall, typically by means of a puncture wound (knife wound; automobile accident, etc.) When air is introduced (or collects) into the intrapleural space, the result is a loss of the constant negative intrapleural pressure. If you recall it is this pressure which maintains the close bond between the visceral pleural lining of the lungs and that of the inner thorax, it may not surprise you to learn that, when that bond is broken by the open wound, the lungs will collapse. This collapse arises from the fact that the lungs are in a state of constant distension, arising from the difference between adult thorax size and adult lung size (see detail on lung development).

tinued expansion within the thoracic cavity. This is reflected in the fact that the highest pressure on the intrapleural plot is negative.

When the diaphragm contracts, the intrapleural pressure becomes even more negative as the diaphragm attempts to pull the diaphragmatic pleurae away from the visceral pleurae. During the entire period of contraction of the diaphragm, the pressure continues to drop: The diaphragm is pulling farther away from its resting point and the pressure between the pleurae increases proportionately. As the diaphragm reaches the end of its contraction, intrapleural pressure reaches a maximum negativity ("H") that reverses upon relaxation of the diaphragm. When the diaphragm contracts, the volume (space) between the two pleural linings increases; and Boyle's law dictates that pressure will drop, and it does.

Depression of the diaphragm for quiet tidal inspiration results in an intrapleural pressure of approximately -10 cm H_2O, but relaxing the diaphragm during quiet expiration does not return the pressure to atmospheric, but rather returns it to a constant rest pressure of -6 cm H_2O. In the normal, healthy individual intrapleural pressure remains negative at all times, becoming increasingly negative as muscles of inspiration act on the lungs.

The fact that this intrapleural pressure remains negative underscores two important notions. First, the lungs are in a state of continual expansion because the thorax is larger than the lungs that fill it. Sec-

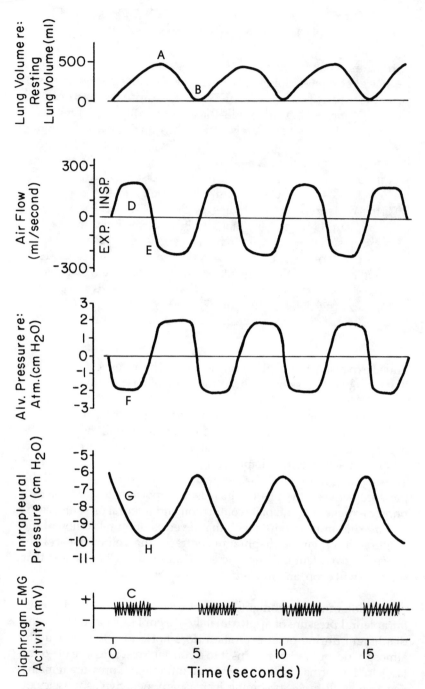

FIGURE 4-10. Relationships of pressures, flows, and volumes to diaphragm activity. Contraction of the diaphragm causes a drop in intrapleural and alveolar pressure which results in an increase in airflow and lung volume. (Data from *Physiology of Respiration* by J. H. Comroe, 1965. Chicago, IL: Year Book Medical Publishers.)

ond, the lungs are never completely deflated under normal circumstances, giving rise to the residual volume discussed earlier.

During inspiration and expiration two more pressures are of interest to us. Subglottal pressure is the pressure measured beneath the level of the vocal folds (glottis refers to the space between the vocal folds). Above the vocal folds the respiratory pressure measured within the oral cavity is referred to as intraoral pressure. When the vocal folds are open, intraoral pressure, subglottal pressure, and alveolar pressure are the same.

The pressure beneath and above the vocal folds is directly related to what is happening in the lungs, as long as the vocal folds are open for air passage. If the lungs are drawing air in, there will be a negative pressure at both of these locations. If the lungs are in expiration, the pressure will be relatively positive. Things get dicier when the vocal folds are closed.

When we close vocal folds for phonation (voicing), we place a significant blockage in the flow of air through the upper respiratory pathway. Closing the vocal folds causes an immediate increase in the subglottal air pressure as the lungs continue expiration. At the same time, closing the vocal folds causes the intraoral pressure to drop to near atmospheric, resulting in a large difference in pressure between the supraglottal (above vocal folds) and subglottal regions. If this increased pressure exceeds 3–5 cm H_2O the vocal folds will be blown open and voicing will begin. This turns out to be a critical pressure in itself, because it marks the minimal requirement of respiration for speech.

You can now view these critical pressures as a system: We are continually playing the respiratory system against the relatively stable **atmospheric pressure**. Contraction of the diaphragm and muscles of inspiration causes the **intrapleural pressure** to decrease markedly, which in turn causes the lungs to be expanded. When the lungs expand, **alveolar pressure** drops relative to atmospheric pressure, causing air to enter the lungs. Relaxing the muscles of inspiration permits the natural recoil of the lungs and cartilage to draw the chest back to its original position, and the relaxed diaphragm again returns to its relatively elevated position in the thorax. When this happens, intrapleural pressure increases (but still stays negative) and alveolar pressure becomes positive relative to atmospheric pressure. Air leaves the lungs.

In summary:

■ Volumes and pressures vary as a direct function of the forces acting on the respiratory system.
■ With the vocal folds open, **oral pressure**, **subglottal pressure**, and **alveolar pressure** are roughly equivalent.
■ **Intrapleural pressure** will remain constantly negative, increasing in negativity during inspiration.

■ These pressures are all measured relative to **atmospheric pressure**.
■ During inspiration, expansion of the thorax decreases the already negative intrapleural pressure, and the increased lung volume results in a **negative alveolar pressure**.
■ Air from outside the body will flow into the lungs as a result of the pressure difference between the lungs and the atmosphere.
■ During expiration, this pressure differential is reversed, with air escaping the lungs to equalize the **positive alveolar pressure** with the relatively negative atmospheric pressure.

Pressures Generated by the Tissue

At this point we should address the forces of expiration in earnest. The process of inspiration is one of exerting force to overcome gravity. Inspiration is generally active, requiring muscular action to complete it.

Expiration capitalizes on torque, elasticity, and gravity to reclaim some of the energy expended during inspiration. When muscles of inspiration contract they stretch tissue, torque cartilage of the ribs, and distend the abdomen. When these muscles relax during expiration, the stretched tissues tend to return to their original dimension due to their elastic nature, the chondral portions of the ribs returns to their original positions due to the elastic restoration following **torquing**, and **gravity** works to depress the rib cage. To breathe in you have to move all of these muscles and bones, and as you relax they return to their original positions.

These restoring forces actually generate pressures themselves. Recoil of the chest during exhalation obeys the laws of any other elastic material: The greater you distend or distort the material, the greater is the force required to hold it in that position, and the greater is the force with which it returns to rest.

You have common sense validation of this if you recall loading a stapler with staples. As you pull back the spring that holds the staples you reach a point where the spring almost wins. The force required to hold the spring back is much greater as it gets farther from its point of rest. You know also the force with which your finger can get whacked if you do not get out of the way in time, and the farther you have pushed the spring, the more it hurts when it is inadvertently released.

The same elastic forces govern how much effort is required to inhale. Close your eyes and breathe in as deeply as you can and hold it for a few seconds. Feel how much pressure you are fighting to hold your chest in that position. Next, take in a quiet breath and hold it: Do you feel the difference in pressure?

This relationship is described in the curve of Figure 4–11. What this figure shows is the result of pressure generated by all that force (remem-

FIGURE 4-11. Relaxation pressure curve representing pressures generated by the passive forces of the respiratory system.

ber that pressure is force exerted over an area). The farther the rib cage is expanded, the greater is the force that is trying to return the rib cage to rest.

This curve is called the relaxation pressure curve, and it was generated by asking people to do what you just did with your eyes closed. Subjects were told to inhale to some percentage of their vital capacity and then to relax their musculature while their intraoral pressure (which approximates both subglottal and alveolar pressure) was measured using a manometer. Repeated measures of this sort at various percentages of vital capacity resulted in the upper positive portion of the curve. It is positive because the tissue is attempting to return to rest. This is a measure of the strength of those physical restoring forces. Note that you are capable of generating some reasonably large forces with this tissue recoil. Pressures on the order of 60 cm H_2O are fairly significant, considering that phonation requires only about 5 cm H_2O.

The bottom half of the curve is produced in much the same way, only this time people were asked to exhale down to a percentage of their vital capacity. The dashed line is the relaxation point, the point where no pressure is generated, because all parts of the system are at equilibrium. (Breathe out and then do not breathe in again: This "relaxation" point before you inhale a new breath is one of three times during a respiratory cycle when atmospheric pressure equals alveolar pressure.) The dashed relaxation point of zero pressure represents about 38% of vital capacity. When you relax entirely with open airway, the lungs still have 38% of the total exchangeable volume left, and this could be forcefully exhaled. Said another way, from this point you can actively inhale 62% of your vital capacity.

Examine the bottom portion of the curve in Figure 4–11 and you will recognize that the pressures generated are not as great, and that they are negative. These negative pressures are predominantly the result of the recoil of the chest wall attempting to return to stasis, whereas the positive pressures are governed by the contribution of lung elasticity arising from the recoil of the muscles and cartilage in bronchi, bronchioles, and blood vessels, as well as elastic tissue throughout the lung. Agostoni and Mead (1964) demonstrated that above about 55% of vital capacity the chest wall does not add anything to the pressure of the curve, while below about 55% the elasticity of the lungs contribute little to the curve. That is, the lungs compress the air nicely above resting lung volume (RLV), while the chest works very hard below RLV to pull air into the system. Likewise, below 55% you start to use the muscles of expiration to maintain constant subglottal pressure.

The relaxation pressures reveal the recoil forces of respiration without considering active muscular contraction. You can generate a similar set of responses by asking people to completely deflate their lungs and then inflate them to a specific percentage of VC, and then have them either exhale or inhale as forcefully as they can. This measures the result of forces that can be generated by actual work associated with muscular contraction.

Look at Figure 4–12 to see that the respiratory system works as you would expect. On the right side is the expiratory pressure. This is the result of trying to breathe out when you have achieved a specific lung volume. The greater your lung volume is, the more force you can generate for exhalation. On the left side, notice that your ability to draw air in is also intimately related to the amount of air in the lungs: The less air there is in your lungs, the greater is the force you can generate to bring air in. What is that curve in the middle? It is the same one we just looked at—the relaxation curve!

In summary:

■ The process of contracting musculature deforms the cartilage and connective tissue, and **recoil forces** will drive the respiratory system back to equilibrium after inspiration or expiration.
■ **Relaxing** the musculature after inspiration results in a **positive alveolar pressure** that decreases as volume approaches resting lung volume.
■ When the pressure is measured following forced expiration, a **negative relaxation pressure** is found, increasing to equity at resting lung volume.

FIGURE 4-12. Pressure-volume relationship for muscular activity by percentage of vital capacity. Pi = Pressure from muscles of inspiration; Pe = Pressure from muscles of expiration; Pr = Pressure from relaxation of muscles of inspiration and expiration. (Based on data from The Pressure-Volume Diagram of the Thorax by H. Rahn, A. Otis, L. E. Chadwick, & W. Fenn, 1946, p. 164. *American Journal of Physiology, 146,* 161–178.)

■ The negative pressures are a function of the chest wall recoil, while the positive pressures arise from the expanded lungs and torqued cartilage.

Effects of Posture on Speech

Body posture is a significant contributor to efficiency of respiration, and any condition that compromises posture also compromises respiration (see Figure 4–13). As the body is shifted from an erect, sitting posture to supine, the relationship between the physical structures of respiration and gravity changes. In the sitting posture, gravity is pulling the abdominal viscera down (supporting inspiration), as well as pulling the rib cage down (supporting expiration). When the body achieves the supine position, gravity is pulling the abdominal viscera toward the spine. The result of this is spread of the viscera toward the thorax and further distension of the diaphragm into the thoracic cavity. In supine, gravity supports neither expiration nor inspiration: Muscles of inspiration must elevate both abdomen and rib cage against gravity.

Although vital capacity is not affected, the ability to completely inflate the lungs is. The resting lung volume is significantly reduced from approximately 38% of vital capacity in sitting position to 20% in supine, arising from the shift in viscera and effects of gravity on the rib

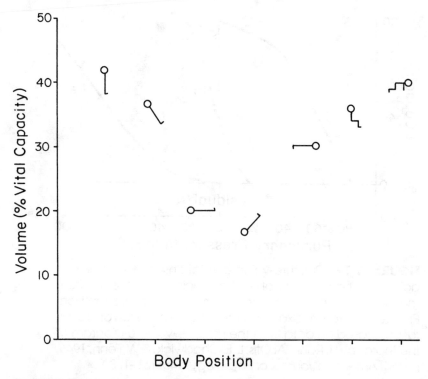

FIGURE 4-13. Vital capacity changes resulting from postural adjustment. (Data from *Respiratory Function in Speech* by T. J. Hixon, 1973, p. 165. In F. D. Minifie, T. J. Hixon, & F. Williams, *Normal Aspects of Speech, Hearing,* and *Language.* Englewood Cliffs, NJ: Prentice-Hall.

cage. The elastic forces that would normally inflate the lungs to that 38% point only inflate them to to 20%, leaving muscular effort to account for the additional 18%.

You can demonstrate the effects of posture easily for yourself. First, stand up, take a deep breath, and hold a sustained vowel as long as you can. You will want to keep track of the duration of the vowel. Next, lie on your back (in supine), take a deep breath, and perform the same task. What you will notice is that you were not able to sustain the vowel for as long. Finally, lie in prone (on your "stomach") and sustain the vowel again.

If you did all three of these activities you found the most efficient posture for respiration is erect, while the reclining positions required more effort for the same gesture and were less efficient for sustained phonation.

You may have already realized the danger this poses to a person whose illness requires that he or she stay in bed for long periods of time. It should not surprise you that pneumonia is a major complication in conditions that immobilize a person.

Muscular Weakness and Respiration

Individuals with diseases that weaken the muscles of inspiration are at significant respiratory risk for a number of reasons. Although gravity is the friend of respiration in a person with normal function, we must realize that inspiration requires muscular effort and that effort is aimed very specifically at overcoming gravity.

Individuals in the later stages of demyelinating diseases such as amyotrophic lateral sclerosis (ALS) suffer from extreme muscular weakness as a result of the disease but are still faced with the oxygenation demands typically met with respiratory work. If the patient is placed in the supine position (on the back), gravity will conspire against their respiratory effort, and this "resting" position will actually put them at risk for respiratory distress. Here's why: When lying in supine, gravity is pushing on the abdominal viscera, forcing them toward the patient's back. When the individual attempts to take a breath in, the abdomen *should* protrude, but with compromised muscular strength that will require more effort than the person is capable of. When in supine the abdominal viscera are one more thing to overcome, and it turns out to be one thing too many.

To overcome this, patients in the later stages of ALS will often remain in a semi-reclined position to permit rest but capitalize on gravity to assist with respiration. By the way, this might also give you a clue as to why individuals with weakened musculature are more prone to pneumonia than healthy individuals: It takes a great deal of work to clear the lungs and to keep them clear.

To summarize:

- **Posture** and **body position** play an important role in volumes for respiration.
- When the body is placed in a reclining position, the abdominal contents shift rostrally as a result of the forces of gravity.
- Aside from reducing the resting lung volume, the force of **gravity** on the abdomen increases the effort required for inspiration.

Pressures of Speech

The respiratory system operates at two levels of pressure virtually simultaneously. The first level is the relatively constant supply of subglottal pressure required to drive the vocal folds, a topic with which you will become familiar in the next chapter. To produce sustained voicing of a given intensity, this pressure is relatively constant. As we will see, the minimum driving pressure to make the vocal folds move would elevate a column of water between 3–5 cm (3–5 cm H_2O), with conversational speech requiring between 7 and 10 cm H_2O. Loud speech requires a concomitant increase in pressure.

The second level of pressure is one requiring micro-control. Even as we maintain the constant pressure needed for phonation, we are also quite capable of rapidly and briefly changing the pressure for linguistic purposes such as syllable stress. With quick bursts of pressure (and laryngeal adjustments) we can have rapid and brief increases in vocal intensity and vocal pitch. These bursts are small and fast: We will increase subglottal pressure by about 2 cm H_2O to add stress, but we will return to the previous subglottal pressure within one tenth of a second. We will see that these two modes of pressure control use the same mechanical structures.

To maintain that constant pressure for speech we must first charge the system. During normal respiration, inhalation takes up approximately 40% of the cycle, while expiration takes up about 60%. When you realize that you speak only on expiration you will realize also that it would not take many minutes of talking like this to drive you (and your communication partner) to distraction! Imagine every 6 seconds of speaking followed by 4 seconds of silence while you inhale, and you will see why we have modified this plan for speech (see Figure 4–14).

In fact, the respiratory cycle for speech is markedly different. You need a long, drawn out expiration to produce long utterances, and you need a very short inspiration to maintain the smooth flow of communication. When you breathe in for speech you actually spend only 10% of the respiratory cycle on inspiration, and about 90% breathing out.

This does not change the amount of air we breathe in and out. We will still breathe exactly the volume we need for our metabolic processes (too much and we take in too much oxygen, or hyperventilate; too little and we take in too little oxygen and become **hypoxic**). All we need to do is alter how long we spend in either stage of the process.

Earlier we said that we need to hold a reasonably constant subglottal pressure to maintain phonation, but we did not say *how* we achieve *it*. You already have all the pieces, so let us pose the puzzle to you. If you take in a deep breath as if you were about to speak but just let the air flow out unimpeded you run out of air within one or two quick words. That burst of air is not going to work for speech.

Instead of letting the air out through total relaxation, let the air out slowly. As you do this pay attention to the fact that you are using muscles to restrain the airflow. If you remember that the lungs are attempting to empty as a result of their being stretched for inspira-

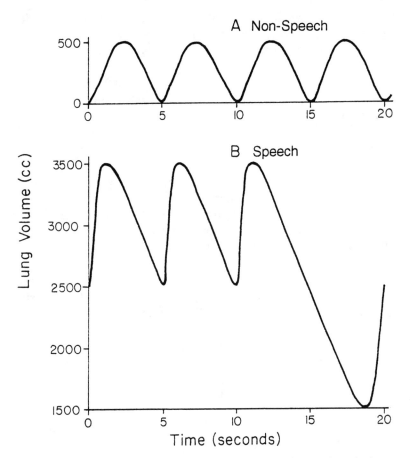

FIGURE 4-14. Modification of respiratory cycle during speech compared with nonspeech respiratory cycle. **a.** This trace represents quiet tidal respiration, with volume related to resting lung volume. **b.** This trace is related to total lung capacity. The speaker rapidly inhales a markedly larger volume than during quiet tidal inspiration and then slowly exhales the air during speech. Note that inspiration occurs with the same timing in both speech and nonspeech, but that the expiratory phase is proportionately longer during speech. In the final portion of the trace, the speaker is called on to speak on expiratory reserve volume.

tion, then you might realize that if you were to *hold* that inspiration position you would impede the outflow of air. This process is called *checking action*. That is, you "check" (impede) the flow of air out of your inflated lungs by means of the muscles that got it there in the first place—the muscles of inspiration.

Checking action is an extremely important concept for respiratory control for speech, because it directly addresses a person's ability to restrain the flow of air. When a person has a deficit associated with checking action (as in paralysis), the person is at a tremendous disadvantage, because he or she will be restricted to extremely short bursts of speech.

Checking action permits us to maintain the constant flow of air through the vocal tract and that in turn lets us accurately control the pressure beneath vocal folds which have been closed for phonation. We will see that this is very important when it comes to maintaining constant vocal intensity and frequency of vibration.

There is an expiratory parallel to checking action, and that is the process of speaking on expiratory reserve. Take another look at Figure 4–11 and examine the relaxation pressure curve. Checking action lets us stay within the upper portion of the curve for quite a while, making maximum use of our respiratory charge for speech.

What happens when we get down to that resting lung volume point of 38% during speech? If we have more to say before we inhale, we simply keep talking. Instead of using the muscles of inspiration we used to keep the air from flowing out, we have to enlist the muscles of *expiration* to push beyond that resting lung volume. Using the muscles of expiration we continue talking beyond the point where we would normally take another breath, letting us control when we break for inspiration so that our speech is fluid and nicely controlled.

A graphic demonstration of how well we perform this feat is fairly simple. Do the following steps and note the times:

Take a maximally deep breath, and time yourself as you hold a sustained vowel as long as you can only using your chest muscles (do not force using your abdominal muscles, but rather just let your inspiratory muscles do all the work).

Take another breath, but this time sustain the vowel just as long as you can by running all the way into the region of expiratory reserve. If you continue your vowel to the point where you are forcing with muscles of expiration, you will find that the duration has increased 40 to 50%. Of course, you do not normally speak as far down on your respiratory charge as that, but your teacher regularly gets into expiratory reserve while lecturing, we guarantee.

It is wise to say, one more time, that the speaker will always take care of business first: The body's needs will be met in a constant fashion in the face of using respiration for communication. The next time your instructor is lecturing count the number of breaths she or he takes per minute and you will see that it is right around 15. Despite what you may have heard teaching *is* work, so respiration may be a little faster than the 12 breaths per minute of quiet tidal respiration.

Remember, however, that this checking action and speaking on expiratory reserve do not come without a cost. We have to work to overcome the recoil forces in each case, and the deeper our inhalation or the farther we go below resting lung volume, the greater is the force we have to overcome. If you are a cheerleader you know exactly what we mean: Speaking loudly and with continuity requires effort. Look again at that relaxation pressure curve and realize that the effort you must exert in the upper part of the curve to keep the air from rapidly leaving the lungs is directly proportional to the pressure those forces generate. Likewise, it requires a great deal of effort to squeeze the last bit of expiratory reserve air out of the lungs.

To summarize:

■ During speech we modify our respiratory activities to balance both bodily needs and those of communication.
■ During respiration for speech we spend markedly less time in **inspiration** than in **expiration**, thus capitalizing on the positive pressures generated.
■ We also will meter out that respiratory charge through **checking action**, using the muscles of inspiration to restrain expiration.
■ We will use our muscles of expiration to capitalize upon the expiratory reserve volume for speech.
■ Even as we maintain this **relatively constant subglottal pressure** through muscles of inspiration and expiration, we also will use those muscles to produce small surges in pressure for syllable stress during speech.

Muscular Activity During Respiration

Electromyography is the process of measuring and recording the electrical activity associated with muscular contraction. Figure 4–15 is a schematic representation of some classical data from Draper, Ladefoged, and Whitteridge (1959) showing the electrical activity of musculature during several phases of respiration for speech.

The recordings were made directly from muscle fibers rather than through surface electrodes, and muscle activity is represented by spikes of activity during contraction. It should be noted also that some muscles are not amenable to recording, because it is difficult to make positive identification of deep muscles.

Examination of Figure 4–15 supports the concepts we have been discussing throughout the chapters on respiration. During inspiration there is clear evidence of diaphragm and external intercostal activity. What also should be evident is the continued activity of these muscles even during expiration: This is clear evidence of checking action. Look closely at figure 4–15 and you will see that the diaphragm ceases activ-

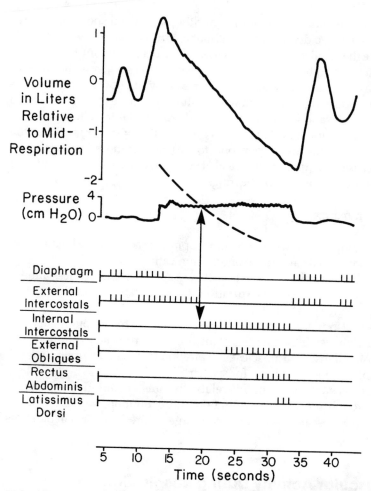

FIGURE 4–15. Muscular activity as it relates to alveolar pressure and lung volume. (Redrawn from data of from Respiratory Muscles in Speech by M. Draper, P. Ladefoged, & D. Whitteridge, 1959, p. 20. *Journal of Speech and Hearing Research, 2.*)

ity earlier than the external intercostals, but both of these muscles become silent by the time resting lung volume is achieved.

As the speaker continues to speak, he or she is using expiratory reserve and must exert the muscles of forced expiration to capitalize on that reserve. As the speaker reaches deeper and deeper into expiratory reserve, the internal intercostals, external oblique, and rectus abdominis are called into duty in that order. This is an important point: The musculature is recruited as needed to develop increasingly greater abdominal pressure (and, subsequently, alveolar pressure). To plumb the depths of the respiratory system increasing numbers of expiratory muscles are needed. Remember that not all muscles are represented here.

If you look back on this discussion, you will find a common thread: Respiration is work. Generating pressure requires muscular activity, and restraining that pressure for speech requires even more effort. Respiration is truly the battery of the speech production mechanism, and it provides the energy source for our oral communication. Our next task is to see how respiration is used to produce a major component of this speech signal—voicing.

CHAPTER SUMMARY

Respiration requires the balance of **pressures**. Decreased **alveolar pressure** is the product of expansion of the thorax. When the thorax expands, the pressure between the pleurae decreases as the thorax and diaphragm are pulled away from the lungs. The force of the distended lungs will increase the **negative intrapleural pressure**, and the expansion will cause a drop in alveolar pressure as well. The relatively lower alveolar pressure represents an imbalance between pressures of the lungs and the atmosphere, and air will enter the lungs to equalize the imbalance. **Expiration** requires reduction in thorax size that results in a **positive pressure** within the alveoli, with air escaping through the oral cavity. The **intrapleural pressure** becomes less negative during expiration, but never reaches atmospheric pressure.

Several **volumes** and **capacities** may be identified within the respiratory system. **Tidal volume** is the volume inspired and expired in a cycle of respiration, while **inspiratory reserve volume** is the air inspired beyond tidal inspiration. **Expiratory reserve volume** is air expired beyond tidal expiration, and **residual volume** is air that remains in the lungs after maximal expiration. **Dead** air space contains air that cannot undergo gas exchange. **Vital capacity** is the volume of air that can be inspired after a maximal expiration, and **functional residual capacity** is the air that remains in the body after passive exhalation. Inspiratory capacity is the volume that can be inspired from resting lung volume. **Total lung capacity** is the sum of all lung volumes.

For speech we must work within the confines of pressures and volumes required for life function. We alter the respiratory cycle to capitalize on expiration time and restrain that expiration through **checking action**. We also generate pressure through contraction of the muscles of expiration when the lung volume is less than resting lung volume. With these manipulations we will maintain a respiratory rate to match our metabolic needs, and even use the accessory muscles of inspiration and expiration to generate small bursts of pressure for **syllabic stress**.

Study Questions

1. Passive expiration involves the forces of _____, _____, and _____.

2. Identify the indicated volumes and capacities described below.

   a. _____volume: The volume of air that we breathe in during a respiratory cycle.

   b. _____volume: The volume that can be inhaled after a tidal inspiration.

   c. _____volume: The volume that can be exhaled after a tidal expiration.

   d. _____volume: The volume remaining in the lungs after a maximal exhalation.

   e. _____capacity: The combination of inspiratory reserve volume, expiratory reserve volume, and tidal volume.

   f. _____capacity: The volume of air remaining in the body after a passive exhalation.

   g. _____capacity: The sum of all the volumes.

3. _____ is the volume of air that cannot undergo gas exchange.

4. _____ pressure is the air pressure measured within the oral cavity.

5. _____ pressure is the air pressure measured below the vocal folds.

6. _____ pressure is the pressure within the alveolus.

7. _____ pressure is the pressure between the visceral and parietal pleural membranes.

8. When the diaphragm contracts, pressure within the alveolus _____ (increases/decreases).

9. When air pressure within the lungs is lower than that of the atmosphere, air will _____ (enter/leave) the lungs.

10. When the body is placed in a reclining position, the resting lung volume _____ (increases/decreases).

11. Use of the muscles of inspiration to impede the outward flow of air during speech is termed _____.

Study Question Answers

1. Passive expiration involves the forces of <u>TORQUE, ELASTICITY,</u> and <u>GRAVITY</u>.

2. Identify the indicated volumes and capacities described below.

   a. <u>TIDAL VOLUME</u>

   b. <u>INSPIRATORY RESERVE</u> volume

   c. <u>EXPIRATORY RESERVE</u> volume

   d. <u>RESIDUAL</u> volume

   e. <u>VITAL</u> capacity

   f. <u>FUNCTIONAL RESIDUAL</u> capacity

   g. <u>TOTAL LUNG</u> capacity

3. <u>DEAD AIR SPACE</u> is the volume of air that cannot undergo gas exchange.

4. <u>INTRAORAL</u> pressure is the air pressure measured within the oral cavity.

5. <u>SUBGLOTTAL</u> pressure is the air pressure measured below the vocal folds.

6. <u>ALVEOLAR</u> or <u>PULMONIC</u> pressure is the pressure within the alveolus.

7. <u>INTRAPLEURAL</u> or <u>PLEURAL</u> pressure is the pressure between the visceral and parietal pleural membranes.

8. When the diaphragm contracts, pressure within the alveolus <u>DECREASES</u>.

9. When air pressure within the lungs is lower than that of the atmosphere, air will <u>ENTER</u> the lungs.

10. When the body is placed in the supine position, the resting lung volume <u>DECREASES</u>.

11. Use of the muscles of inspiration to impede the outward flow of air during speech is termed <u>CHECKING ACTION</u>.

REFERENCES

Agostoni, E., & Mead, J. (1964). Statics of the respiratory system. In W. Fenn, & H. Rahn, (Eds.), *Handbook of physiology, respiration* (Vol. 1, Sect. 3). Washington DC: American Physiological Society. Baltimore, MD: Williams & Wilkins.
Baken, R. J. (1987). *Clinical measurement of speech and voice.* Austin, TX: Pro-Ed.

Baken, R., & Cavallo, S. (1981). Prephonatory chest wall posturing. *Folia phoniatrica, 33*, 193–202.

Baken, R., Cavallo, S., & Weissman, K. (1979). Chest Wall movements prior to phonation. *Journal of Speech & Hearing Research, 22*, 862–872.

Burrows, B., Knudson, R. J., & Kettel, L. J. (1975). *Respiratory insufficiency.* Chicago, IL: Year Book Medical Publishers.

Campbell, E. (1958). An electromyographic examination of the role of the intercostal muscles in breathing in man. *Journal of Physiology, 129*, 12–26.

Campbell, E., Agostoni, E., & Davis, J. (1970). *The respiratory muscles, mechanics and neural control.* Philadelphia, PA: W. B. Saunders.

Comroe, J. H. (1974). *Physiology of respiration.* Chicago, IL: Year Book Medical Publishers.

Des Jardins, T. (1984). *Clinical manifestations of respiratory disease.* Chicago, IL: Year Book Medical Publishers, Inc.

Draper, M., Ladefoged, P., & Whitteridge, D. (1959). Respiratory muscles in speech. *Journal of Speech & Hearing Research, 2*, 16–27.

Ganong, W. F. (1981). *Review of medical physiology.* Los Altos, CA: Lange Medical Publications.

Hixon, T. J. (1973). Respiratory function in speech. In F. D. Minifie, T. J. Hixon, & F. Williams (Eds.), *Normal aspects of speech, hearing, and language* (pp. 73–126). Englewood Cliffs, NJ: Prentice-Hall.

Kahane, J. (1982). Anatomy and physiology of the organs of the peripheral speech mechanism. In N. Lass, L. McReynolds, J. Northern, & D. Yoder (Eds.), *Speech, language, and hearing* (Vol. 1, pp. 109–155 *normal processes.* Philadelphia, PA: W. B. Saunders.

Kao, F. F. (1972). *An introduction to respiratory physiology.* Amsterdam: Exerpta Medica.

Kaplan, H (1960). *Anatomy and physiology of speech.* New York: McGraw-Hill.

Konno, K., & Mead, J. (1968). Measurement of the separate volume changes of rib cage and abdomen during breathing. *Journal of Applied Physiology, 22*, 407–422.

McReynolds, L., Northern, J., & Yoder, D. (Eds.). *Speech, language, and hearing. Vol. I: Normal processes.* Philadelphia, PA: W. B. Saunders.

Moser, K. M., & Spragg, R. G. (1982). *Respiratory emergencies.* St. Louis, MO: C. V. Mosby.

Murray, J. F. (1976). *The normal lung. The basis for diagnosis and treatment of pulmonary disease.* Philadelphia, PA: W. B. Saunders.

Pace, W. R. (1970). *Pulmonary physiology.* Philadelphia, PA: F. A. Davis Company.

Pappenheimer, J. R., Comroe, J. H., Cournand, A., Ferguson, J. K. W., Filley, G. F., Fowler, W. S., Gray, J. S., Helmholtz, H. F., Otis, A. B., Rahn, H., & Riley, R. L. (1950). Standardization of definitions and symbols in respiratory physiology. *Federation proceedings, Federation of the American Society for Experimental Biology* (pp. 602–605).

Peters, R. M. (1969). *The mechanical basis of respiration.* Boston, MA: Little, Brown.

Rahn, H., Otis, A., Chadwick, L. E., & Fenn, W. (1946). The pressure-volume diagram of the thorax and lung. *American Journal of Physiology, 146*, 161–178.

Spector, W. S. (1956). *Handbook of biological data.* Philadelphia, PA: W. B. Saunders.

Taylor, A. (1960). The contribution of the intercostal muscles to the effort of respiration in man. *Journal of Physiology, 151*, 390.

Tokizane, T., Kawamata, K., & Tokizane, H. (1952). Electromyographic studies on the human respiratory muscles. *Japan Journal of Physiology, 2*, 232.

Zemlin, W. R. (1988). *Speech and hearing science. Anatomy and physiology.* Englewood Cliffs, NJ: Prentice-Hall.

CHAPTER

5

Anatomy of Phonation

Spoken communication uses both voiceless and voiced sounds, and this chapter is concerned with that critical distinction. **Voiceless** phonemes or speech sounds are produced without use of the vocal folds, for example, the /s/ or /f/ sounds. **Voiced** sounds are produced by action of the vocal folds, for example, the /z/ and /v/ sound. **Phonation**, or voicing, is the product of vibrating vocal folds, and this occurs within the larynx. Just as we referred to respiration as the source of *energy* for speech, phonation is the source of voice for speech. Respiration is the energy source that permits phonation to occur, and without respiration there would be no voicing.

The vocal folds are actually five layers of tissue, with the deepest layer being muscle. The space between the vocal folds is called the **glottis (or rima glottidis)**, and the area below the vocal folds is the **subglottal** region. The vocal folds are located within the airstream at the superior end of the trachea. As the airstream passes between the vocal folds, they may be made to vibrate, much as a flag flaps in the wind. Try this: Place your hand on the side of your neck and hum. You will feel a tickling vibration. This is the mechanical correlate of the sound you hear. If you alternately produce /a/ and /h/, you will feel your vocal folds as they start vibrating and stop, because /a/ is a voiced sound and /h/ is voiceless.

rima glottidis: *L., "slit of the glottis"*

Biological Functions of the Larynx

Although we capitalize on the larynx for phonation, it has a much more important function in nature. The larynx is an exquisite sphincter, in that the vocal folds are capable of a very strong and rapid clamping of the airway in response to threat of intrusion by foreign objects. As evidence of this primary function, there are six laryngeal muscles responsible for either approximating or tensing the vocal folds, although there is only one muscle responsible for opening them. The vocal folds are "wired" to close immediately on stimulation by outside agents, such as food or liquids, a response which is followed quickly by a rapid and forceful exhalation. This combination of gestures is designed to stop intrusion by foreign matter and to rapidly expel that matter away from the opening of the airway.

It has other important functions as well. Because the vocal folds provide an excellent seal to the respiratory system, they permit you to hold your breath, thus capturing a significant respiratory charge for such activities as swimming.

Holding your breath serves other functions as well. Lifting heavy objects requires you to "fix" your thorax by inspiring and clamping your laryngeal sphincter (vocal folds). This gives the muscles of the upper body a solid framework with which to work. You'll also note from the margin notes in Chapter 3 that tightly clamping the vocal folds plays an important part of childbirth and defecation.

When you felt the vibrations of the vocal folds, you also might have noted a very important aspect of phonation. You were able to turn your voice on and off to produce the alternating voiced and voiceless sounds. When you alternated those two sounds, you were actually moving the vocal folds into and out of the airstream to cause them to start or stop vibrating. The vocal folds are bands of tissue set into vibration, and you may wish to read the note at the end of this chapter on the mechanics of vibration so you can truly appreciate this exquisite mechanism. If you are already familiar with these concepts, you are ready to look at the aerodynamic processes which control vocal fold vibration.

THE BERNOULLI EFFECT

Vocal folds are masses that may be set into vibration. The **larynx** is the cartilaginous structure housing the two bands of tissue we call the vocal folds. The paired vocal folds are situated on both sides of the larynx so that they actually intrude into the airstream, as you can see from the schematic in Figure 5–1. This figure is a view from above and a

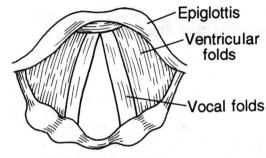

Epiglottis

Ventricular folds

Vocal folds

A   SUPERIOR VIEW

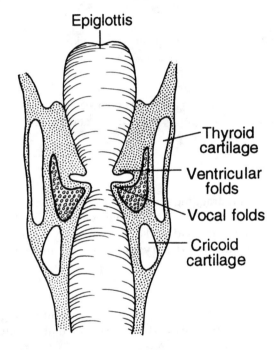

Epiglottis

Thyroid cartilage

Ventricular folds

Vocal folds

Cricoid cartilage

B   FRONTAL SECTION

FIGURE 5-1. a. Vocal folds from above. **b.** Frontal view of larynx, showing constriction in laryngeal space caused by the vocal folds.

view from behind. From above, you can see that the vocal folds are bands of tissue that are actually visible from a point immediately behind your tongue, looking down toward the lungs. From behind, you can see that the vocal folds also are a constriction in the airway, a critical concept for phonation.

You will remember from our discussion of respiratory physiology that any constriction in the airway greatly increases airway turbulence. If you are the passenger in a car and put your hand out the window, you

Bernoulli Effect in Everyday Life

Examples of the Bernoulli effect are apparent throughout daily life. If you are a baseball fan, you will appreciate the amazing curve ball of your favorite pitcher more when you realize that the Bernoulli effect is the driving force behind it. In this case, the pitcher ensures that the ball *begins* its flight with the smooth surface toward the front and that the seam on the ball rotates to the side of the ball sometime during its brief flight. The seam acts as a constriction: The pressure on the seam side is lower than on the opposite smooth side, and the ball is "sucked" toward the seam.

You might want to trade in your airplane tickets before your next flight. The wing of an airliner with its hundreds of passengers is designed so that there is a slight elevation on the upper surface of the wing. Air must travel faster over the elevation, causing a drop in pressure. Yes, that's correct: The wing is "sucked" upward by that negative pressure. For an excellent discussion of this effect, see Adair (1995).

will feel the force of the wind dragging against your hand and you will hear the turbulence associated with it. You can rotate your hand so that the turbulence is reduced or increased, and as the force on your hand increases it becomes more difficult to keep your hand in the airstream.

See Chapter 4 for a discussion of respiratory physiology.

The vocal folds also are a source of turbulence the in vocal tract. Without them, air would pass relatively unimpeded out of the lungs and into the oral cavity. The addition of the vocal folds results in air having to make a detour around the folds, and the result of that detour invokes a discussion of the Bernoulli effect.

Daniel Bernoulli, a 17th century Swiss scientist, recognized the effects of constricting a tube during fluid flow. The **Bernoulli effect** states that, given a constant volume flow of air or fluid, *at a point of constriction there will be a decrease in air pressure perpendicular to the flow and an increase in velocity of the flow.* If you put a constriction in a tube, air flows faster as it detours around the constriction, and the pressure on the wall at the point of constriction will be lower than that of the surrounding area. Let us examine this statement.

Air Flow Increase

Figure 5–2 shows a tube with a constriction in it representing the vocal folds. If you have placed your thumb over a garden hose, you know

FIGURE 5-2. Rate of airflow through the tube will increase at the point of constriction, and air pressure will decrease at that point as well.

that the rate of water flow increases as a result of that constriction. Likewise, if you have ever been white-water rafting you will immediately recognize that the white water comes from constriction in the flow of the river, in the form of boulders. As the water flows through the constriction the rate of flow increases, giving you the thrill as you speed uncontrollably toward your fate.

Air Pressure Drop

To get an intuitive feel for the pressure drop, you must think about the flow in terms of molecules of air. Look again at Figure 5–2. We have drawn it so that you can count the number of molecules of air in the tube relative to the tube's length. In the unconstricted regions, you can count 10 molecules of air. Where the tube becomes narrower, there will be fewer air molecules because there is less space for them to occupy, and you only count five in that area. Where the constriction ends, you once again see 10 molecules.

When air is forced into a narrower tube, the same total volume of air has to squeeze through a smaller space. Because each unit mass of air becomes longer and narrower, it covers a longer stretch of the tube's walls. The pressure exerted by this mass, although the same in an overall sense, is now distributed over more of the wall. The result is that each atom of the wall feels less force from the air molecules, and the narrow part of the tube is more likely to collapse. This effect only occurs when the air is forced to move; air without any forced movement will sooner or later equalize its pressure everywhere. If you remember that pressure is force exerted on an area ($F = P/A$), a drop in pressure makes perfect sense.

See the Introduction of Chapter 3 for a discussion of force, pressure, and area.

These two elements are the heart of the Bernoulli effect and help us to understand vocal fold vibration. Return to the notion of vocal folds being a constriction in a tube, as illustrated in Figure 5–3. You will want to refer to this figure as we discuss the Bernoulli principle applied to phonation.

The vocal folds are soft tissue, made up of muscle and mucous membrane. Because of this, the folds are also capable of *moving* when sufficient force is exerted on them, as in the case of your hand extended out the moving car window.

By examining Panel A in Figure 5–3 you will see that the vocal folds are closed. In the next panel (B) the air pressure generated by the respiratory system is beginning to force the vocal folds open, but there is no transglottal flow because the folds are still making full contact. By Panel D the vocal folds have been blown open. Because the vocal folds are elastic, they will tend to return to the point of equilibrium, which is the point of rest. They cannot return to equilibrium, however, as long as the air pressure is so great that they are blown apart. When they are in that position, however, there is a drop in pressure at the point of constriction (the Bernoulli effect), and we already know that if there is a drop in pressure, something is going to move to equalize that pressure.

In the last three panels (E, F, and G) you can see the result of the negative pressure: The vocal folds are being sucked back toward midline (E) as a result of the negative pressure and tissue elasticity. The final panels (F and G) show the folds again making contact, with airflow completely halted. The vocal folds are, in essence, sucked back to midline by the pressure drop at the constriction. When the vocal folds are pulled back toward midline by their tissue-restoring forces, they completely block the flow of air for an instant as they make contact. When they are in contact, air has stopped flowing briefly, and therefore the negative pressure related to flow is gone also. Instead, there is the force of respiratory charge beneath the folds ready to blow them apart once again. By the way, the minimum subglottal pressure that will blow the vocal folds apart to sustain phonation is approximately 3–5 cm H_2O, although much larger subglottal pressures will be required for louder speech.

What you hear as voicing is the product of the repeated opening and closing of the vocal folds. The motion of the tissue and airflow disturb the molecules of air, causing the phenomenon we call sound.

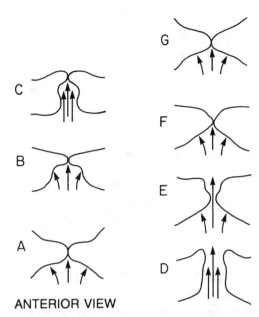

ANTERIOR VIEW

FIGURE 5–3. One cycle of vocal fold vibration as seen through a frontal section. **a.** Air pressure beneath the vocal folds arises from respiratory flow. **b.** Air pressure causes the vocal folds to separate in the inferior. **c.** Superior aspect of vocal folds begins to open. **d.** Vocal folds are blown open, flow between the folds increases, and pressure at the folds decreases. **e.** Decreased pressure and elastic quality of vocal folds causes folds to move back toward midline. **f.** Vocal folds make contact inferiorly. **g.** The cycle of vibration is completed.

The act of bringing the vocal folds together for phonation is referred to as **adduction**, and the process of drawing the vocal folds apart to terminate phonation is called **abduction**. As we shall see, both of these movements are achieved using specific muscles, but the actual vibration of the vocal folds is the product of airflow interacting with the tissue *in absence of repetitive muscular contraction.*

If you have followed this introductory discussion of the principles governing vocal fold vibration, you are prepared to examine the structures of the larynx.

In summary:

■ **Phonation**, or voicing, is the product of vibrating vocal folds within the larynx.

■ The **vocal folds** vibrate as air flows past them; the Bernoulli phenomenon and tissue elasticity help maintain phonation.

■ The **Bernoulli principle** states that, given a constant volume flow of air or fluid, at a point of **constriction** there will be a **decrease** in air **pressure** perpendicular to the flow and an **increase** in **velocity** of the flow.

■ The interaction of **subglottal pressure**, **tissue elasticity**, and **constriction** within the airflow caused by the vocal folds produces sustained phonation as long as pressure, flow, and vocal fold approximation are maintained.

A TOUR OF THE PHONATORY MECHANISM

This is a good opportunity to walk you through the vocal mechanism. We will get into details soon enough, but for now let us look at the larger picture.

Framework of the Larynx

The larynx is a musculo-cartilaginous structure located at the superior (upper) end of the trachea. It is comprised of three unpaired and three paired cartilages bound by ligaments and lined with mucous membrane.

If you will examine Figure 5–4 you can see the relation between the trachea and larynx. As you recall, the trachea is composed of a series of cartilage rings, connected and separated by fibroelastic membrane. As seen in Figure 5–4, the larynx sits as an oddly shaped box atop the last ring of the trachea. It is adjacent to cervical vertebrae 4 through 6 in the adult, but the larynx of an infant will be higher. The average length of the larynx in males is 44 mm; in females it is 36 mm.

cricoid: Gr., krikos, ring; "ring-form"

arytenoid: Gr., arytaina, ladle; "ladle-form"

corniculate: L., cornu, horn; "little horn"

epiglottis: Gr., epi, over; "over glottis"

The **cricoid cartilage** is a complete ring resting atop the trachea and is the most inferior of the laryngeal cartilages. From the side, the cricoid cartilage takes on the appearance of a signet ring, with its back arching up relative to the front. The **thyroid cartilage** is the largest of the laryngeal cartilages, articulating with the cricoid cartilage below by means of paired processes that let it rock forward and backward at that joint. With this configuration, the paired **arytenoid cartilages** ride on the high-backed upper surface of the cricoid cartilage, forming the posterior point of attachment for the vocal folds (or plicae vocalis). The **corniculate cartilages** ride on the superior surface of each arytenoid and are prominent landmarks in the aryepiglottic folds. The inner surface of the thyroid cartilage provides the anterior point of attachment for the vocal folds.

Laryngectomy

Patients who undergo **laryngectomy** (surgical removal of the larynx) lose the voicing source for speech. The larynx is removed and the oral cavity is sealed off from the trachea and lower respiratory passageway as a safeguard, because the protective function of the larynx is also lost. **Laryngectom***ees* (individuals who have undergone laryngectomy) must alter their activities, because they now breathe through a **tracheostoma**, an opening placed in the trachea through a surgical procedure known as a **tracheostomy**.

Loss of the ability to phonate is but one of the difficulties facing the laryngectomee. This patient will have difficulty with **expectoration** (elimination of phlegm from respiratory passageway) and coughing, and will no longer able to enjoy swimming or other activities that would expose the **stoma** to water or pollutants. The air entering the patient's lungs is no longer humidified or filtered by the upper respiratory passageway, and a filter must be kept over the stoma to prevent introduction of foreign objects. The flavor of foods is greatly reduced, because the patient may no longer breathe through his or her nose and our perception of food relies heavily on the sense of smell. Depending on pre- and postoperative treatment, patients may experience extreme dryness of oral tissues arising from damage to salivary glands from radiation therapy.

The thyroid cartilage articulates with the **hyoid bone** by means of a pair of superior processes. Medial to the hyoid bone and thyroid cartilage is the **epiglottis**, a leaf-like cartilage. The epiglottis is potentially a protective structure, in that it will drop to cover the **orifice** of the larynx during swallowing. Although there is debate among physiologists and speech scientists as to whether the epiglottis protects the airway in humans, there is no doubt that it serves this function in animals walking on four feet.

An orifice is an opening.

To summarize:

- The **larynx** is a musculo-cartilaginous structure located at the upper end of the trachea, being comprised of the **cricoid, thyroid**, and **epiglottis cartilages**, as well as the paired **arytenoid, corniculate**, and **cuneiform cartilages.**
- The thyroid and cricoid cartilages articulate by means of the **cricothyroid joint** that lets the two cartilages come closer together in front.
- The **arytenoid** and **cricoid cartilages** also articulate with a joint that permits a wide range of arytenoid motion.

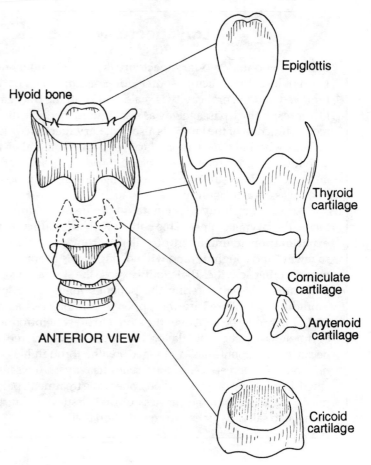

FIGURE 5–4. Larynx *(left)* and cartilages making up the larynx *(right)*.

■ The **corniculate cartilages** rest on the upper surface of the arytenoids, while the **cuneiform cartilages** reside within the **aryepiglottic folds.**

INNER LARYNX

When these cartilages are combined with the trachea and the airway above the larynx, the result is a rough tube-like space with a constriction caused by the cartilages. This construction is unique, however, in that it is an *adjustable* constriction. The vocal folds are bands of mucous membrane, connective tissue, and muscle that are slung between the arytenoid cartilages and the thyroid cartilage so that they may be moved into and out of the airstream. (Alternately, some anatomists refer to the vocal folds as the mucous membrane and connective tissue, excluding the thyrovocalis muscle.) Muscles attached to the arytenoids provide both adductory and abductory functions, with which we control the degree of air flow by means of muscular contraction.

Laryngeal Membranes. The cavity of the larynx is a constricted tube with a smooth and reasonably aerodynamic surface (see Figure 5–5). This tube is created by developing a deep structure of cartilages, connecting those cartilages through sheets and cords of ligament and membrane, and lining the entire structure with a wet, smooth mucous membrane. Let us work from the inside out to identify these connective structures. The extrinsic ligaments attach the hyoid or trachea to the cartilages of the larynx. The **thyrohyoid membrane** stretches across the space between the greater cornu of hyoid and the lateral thyroid. Posterior to this is the **lateral thyrohyoid ligament**, which runs from the superior cornu of thyroid to the posterior tip of greater cornu hyoid. A small **triticial cartilage** may or may not be found here. In front, running from the corpus hyoid to the upper border of the ante-

FIGURE 5–5. Cavity of the larynx with landmarks.

rior thyroid is the **median thyrohyoid ligament**. Together, the median thyrohyoid ligament, thyrohyoid membrane, and lateral thyrohyoid ligament connect the larynx and the hyoid bone. There are other extrinsic ligaments. The **hyoepiglottic ligament** and **thyroepiglottic ligament** attach the epiglottis to the corpus hyoid and the inner thyroid cartilage, just below the notch, respectively. The epiglottic attachment to the tongue is made by means of the **lateral** and **median glossoepiglottic ligaments**, and the overlay of mucous membrane on these ligaments produces the "little valleys" or **valleculae** between the tongue and the epiglottis. The trachea must attach to the larynx, as well, and this is performed through the **cricotracheal membrane**.

The **intrinsic ligaments** connect the cartilages of the larynx and form the support structure for the cavity of the larynx, as well as that of the vocal folds themselves. The **fibroelastic membrane** of the larynx is composed of the upper **quadrangular membranes** and **aryepiglottic folds**, the lower **conus elasticus**, and the **vocal ligament**, which is actually the upward free extension of the conus elasticus.

quadrangular membrane:
L., quadri, four; angulus,
right; "right-angled"

conus elasticus: *L., elastic*
cone

The quadrangular membranes are the undergirding layer of connective tissue running from the arytenoids to the epiglottis and thyroid cartilage and forming the false vocal folds. They originate at the inner thyroid angle and sides of epiglottis, and form an upper cone that narrows as it approaches and terminates in a free margin at the arytenoid and corniculate cartilages. The **aryepiglottic muscles** course from the side of epiglottis to the arytenoid apex, forming the upper margin of the quadrangular membrane and laterally, the **aryepiglottic folds**. These folds are simply the ridges marking the highest elevation of these membranes and muscles slung from the epiglottis to arytenoids.

To summarize:

- The **cavity** of the **larynx** is a constricted tube with a smooth surface.
- Sheets and cords of ligaments connect the cartilages, while smooth **mucous membrane** covers the medial-most surface of the larynx.
- The **thyrohyoid membrane, lateral thyrohyoid ligament**, and **median thyrohyoid ligament** cover the space between the hyoid and thyroid.
- The **hyoepiglottic** and **thyroepiglottic ligaments** attach the epiglottis to the corpus hyoid and the inner thyroid cartilage, respectively.
- The **valleculae** are found between the tongue and the epiglottis, within folds arising from the lateral and median glossoepiglottic ligaments.
- The **cricotracheal ligament** attaches the trachea to the larynx.
- The **fibroelastic membrane** is composed of the upper **quadrangular membranes** and **aryepiglottic folds**, the lower **conus elasticus**, and the **vocal ligament**, which is actually the upward free extension of the conus elasticus.

■ The **aryepiglottic folds** course from the side of the epiglottis to the arytenoid apex.

Fine Structure of the Vocal Folds. The vocal folds are composed of five layers of tissue. Figure 5–6 shows the most superficial layer to be an extremely thin (less than 0.1 mm thick) sheet of squamous epithelium. This layer gives the vocal folds the glistening white appearance seen during laryngoscopic examination (use of a **laryngoscope**, a device typically used by **laryngologists** or speech-language pathologists to view the larynx).

Deep to this layer is the **lamina propria**, which is composed of three different tissues. The first layer of the lamina propria (which is the second layer of vocal fold tissue), approximately 0.5 mm thick, is made up of elastin fibers, so named because of their physical elastic qualities which permit them to be extensively stretched. Moving medially, the next layer (1–2 mm thick) encountered is composed also of elastin fibers as well, but these fibers have an anterior-posterior orientation as compared with the more-or-less random orientation of the first layer of lamina propria. The final and deepest layer of the lamina propria (also 1–2 mm thick) shares the anterior-posterior orientation of the second layer, but is composed of collagen fibers which, in contrast to elastin, prohibit extension.

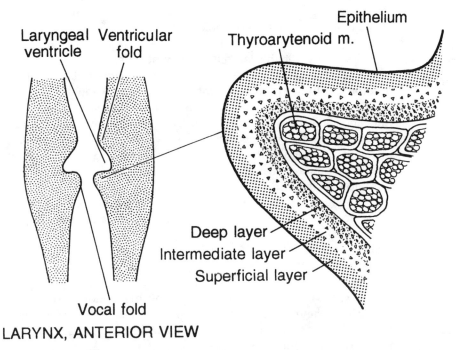

LARYNX, ANTERIOR VIEW

FIGURE 5-6. Microstructure of vocal folds. (From Titze, 1994.)

Deep to the lamina propria is the fifth layer of the vocal folds, the **thyrovocalis muscle**. This makes up the bulk of the vocal fold. Because the muscle course is anterior-posterior, the fibers are arranged in this orientation.

The **mucosal lining** of the vocal folds is actually a combination of the epithelial lining and the disorganized first primary lamina propria layer. The second and third layers (elastin and collagen) comprise the **vocal ligament**, a structure giving a degree of stiffness and support to the vocal folds. Some authors refer alternately to the **cover** of the vocal folds (superficial epithelium, primary and secondary layers of lamina propria) and the **body** (third layer of lamina propria and thyrovocalis) of the vocal folds.

aditus laryngis: L., entrance; "laryngeal entrance"

aryepiglottic fold: ary(tenoid) + epiglottis

If you will look at the profile of the larynx in Figure 5–7, you will appreciate some of the relationships among the structures. The **aditus laryngis** or **aditus** is the entry to the larynx from the pharynx above. (Some anatomists define the aditus as the first space of the larynx; others view it simply as the entryway to the first cavity—the vestibule—to be discussed.) You may think of the aditus as the door frame through which you would pass when entering a house. The anterior boundary of the "frame" of the aditus is the epiglottis, with the fold of membrane and muscle slung between the epiglottis and the arytenoids (the **aryepiglottic folds**) comprising the lateral margins of aditus. In Figure 5–8 you can see two "bumps" under the aryepiglottic folds. These are caused by the cuneiform cartilages embedded within the folds. The second set of prominences posterior to the first two are from the corniculate cartilages on the arytenoids.

The first cavity of the larynx is the **vestibule**, or entryway. The vestibule is the space between the entryway or aditus and the **ventricular** (or **vestibular**) folds. The ventricular folds are known also as the **false vocal folds**, because they are not used for phonation except in rare (and clinically significant) cases. The vestibule is wide at the aditus but narrows at the ventricular folds. The lateral walls are comprised of the **aryepiglottic folds**, and the posterior walls are made up of the membrane covering the arytenoid cartilages which project superiorly to the false folds. The false vocal folds are made up of mucous membrane and a fibrous **vestibular ligament**, but not muscular tissue. The space between the false vocal folds is termed the **rima vestibuli**.

rima vestibuli: L., "slit of the vestibule"

In apes the laryngeal saccules are so well developed that they contribute to the resonance of the voice!

The middle space of the larynx is that between the margins of the false vocal folds and the true vocal folds below. This space is the **laryngeal ventricle** (or **laryngeal sinus**), and the anterior extension of this space is the **laryngeal saccule**. The saccule (or pouch) is endowed with over 60 mucous glands that secrete lubricating mucus into the laryngeal cavity. These sacs are actually endowed with muscle to squeeze the mucus out for lubrication.

FIGURE 5-7. a. Larynx, as seen from behind and above. **b.** Larynx which has been cut sagittally and the sides reflected, revealing the two halves of larynx.

FIGURE 5–8. Vocal folds as seen from above.

The glottis is the space between the vocal folds, inferior to the ventricle and superior to the conus elasticus. This is the most important laryngeal space for speech, because it is defined by the *variable sphincter* that permits voicing. The length of the glottis is approximately 20 mm in adults at rest from the **anterior commissure** (anterior-most opening) to the **posterior commissure** (between the arytenoid cartilages). The glottis area is variable, dependent upon the moment-by-moment configuration of the vocal folds. At rest the posterior glottis will be approximately 8 mm wide, although that dimension will double during times of forced respiration.

The lateral margins of the glottis are the vocal folds and the arytenoid cartilage. The anterior three-fifths of the vocal margin is made up of the soft tissue of the vocal folds. (You will see this referred to as the **membranous glottis**, because some anatomists define the glottis as the entire vocal mechanism.) In adult males, the free margin of the vocal folds will be approximately 15 mm in length, and in females it will be approximately 12 mm. This free margin of the vocal folds is the vibrating element that provides voice. The posterior two-fifths of the vocal folds is comprised of the cartilage of the arytenoids. (This is often referred to as the **cartilaginous glottis**, because "glottis" can refer also to the entire vocal mechanism.) This portion of the vocal folds is between 4 and 8 millimeters long, depending on gender and body size.

The conus elasticus begins at the margins of the true vocal folds and extends to the inferior border of the cricoid cartilage, widening from the vocal folds to the base of the cricoid.

Vocal Fold Hydration

The vocal folds are extremely sensitive to internal and external environment. Although the effects of smoking and other pollutants are known to cause irritation to the tissues of the vocal folds, the internal environment appears to have an impact as well.

When the vocal folds are subject to abuse, several problems may arise, among them contact ulcers and vocal nodules. Hydration therapy is a frequent prescription to counteract the problems of irritated tissue. Dry tissue does not heal as well as moist tissue, so the client will be told to increase the environmental humidity, drink fluids, or even take medications to promote water retention. This type of therapy makes more than medical sense. Verdolini, Titze, and Fennell (1994) found that the *effort* of phonation increased as individuals became dehydrated, and decreased when they were hydrated beyond normal levels. Indeed, the airflow required to produce the same phonation is greatly increased by a poorly lubricated larynx. In addition, the vocal folds vibrate much more periodically (they have greatly reduced **perturbation**, or cycle-by-cycle variation) when lubricated (Fukida et al., 1988). When the relative periodicity of the vocal folds decreases, the voice sounds "hoarse," a perception that you will agree with if you think of the last time you had laryngitis.

In summary:

■ The **vocal folds** are made up of five layers of tissue.
■ Deep to the thin **epithelial layer** is the **lamina propria**, made up of two layers of elastin and one layer of collagen fibers, the thyrovocalis being the deepest of the layers.
■ The **vocal ligament** is made of elastin. The **aditus** is the entryway of the larynx, marking the entry to the **vestibule**.
■ The **ventricular** and **vocal folds** are separated by the **laryngeal ventricle**.
■ The **glottis** is the variable space between the vocal folds.

STRUCTURE OF THE LARYNX

Cricoid Cartilage

The unpaired cricoid cartilage can be viewed as an expanded tracheal cartilage (Figure 5–9). As the most inferior cartilage of the larynx, the

FIGURE 5–9. Cricoid cartilage and landmarks.

cricoid cartilage is the approximate diameter of the trachea. It is higher in the back than in the front.

There are several important landmarks on the cricoid. The low, anterior cricoid arch provides clearance for the vocal folds that will pass over that point, while the posterior elevation, the superior surface of the **posterior quadrate lamina**, provides the point of articulation of the arytenoid cartilages. On the lateral surfaces of the cricoid are articular **facets** or "faces," marking the point of articulation of the inferior horns of the thyroid cartilage. This **cricothyroid joint** is a diarthrodial, pivoting joint that permits rotation of the two articulating structures.

*facets: Fr., **facette**, small face*

One more note on the cricoid. The figures and photographs are quite misleading concerning the size of laryngeal structures. For perspective, your cricoid cartilage would fit loosely upon your little finger which is about the diameter of your trachea. The laryngeal structures are *small*.

Thyroid Cartilage

The unpaired thyroid cartilage is the largest of the laryngeal cartilages. As you can see in Figure 5–10, the thyroid has a prominent anterior surface made up of two plates called the thyroid laminae, joined at the midline at the **thyroid angle**. At the superior-most point of that angle you will see the **thyroid notch** that you can palpate if you will do the following. Place your finger under your chin and on your throat, and bring it downward to the point you might refer to as your adam's apple (more prominent in males than females, for a good reason). When you have found the top of that structure you have identified the thyroid notch. Look at the drawing as you feel the indentation in your own thyroid. Now draw your finger down the midline a little until you feel the angle. If you put your index finger on the angle and your thumb and second finger on the sides, you will have digits on the angle and both laminae. Do take a moment to discover these regions on yourself, because they provide you with a reference that is near and dear to you. By the way, when you had your finger on the notch you were as close as you could be to touching your vocal folds, because they attach to the thyroid cartilage just behind that point.

Drawing your attention back to Figure 5–10, on the lateral superficial aspect of the thyroid laminae you will see the **oblique line**. This marks the point of attachment for two of the muscles we will talk about shortly.

The posterior aspect of the thyroid is open, and is characterized by two prominent sets of **cornu** or horns. The **inferior cornua** project downward to articulate with the cricoid cartilage, while the **superior cornua** project superiorly to articulate with the hyoid. In some individuals a small, **triticial cartilage** *(cartilago triticea)* may be found between the superior cornu of the thyroid cartilage and the hyoid bone.

cornu, L., horn (as in cornucopia, the "horn of plenty"

triticial: L., triticeus, wheat; "wheat-like"

Arytenoid and Corniculate Cartilages

The paired arytenoid cartilages are among the most important of the larynx. They reside on the superior posterolateral surface of the cricoid cartilage, and provide the mechanical structure that permits onset and offset of voicing. The form of the arytenoid may be likened to a pyramid to aid in visualization (see Figure 5–11). Each cartilage has two processes and four surfaces.

The apex is the truncated superior portion of the pyramidal arytenoid cartilage, and on the superior surfaces of each arytenoid is a **corniculate cartilage**, projecting posteriorly to form the peak of the distorted pyramid. The inferior surface of the cartilage is termed the **base**, and

FIGURE 5-10. Thyroid cartilage and landmarks.

Labels in figure:

ANTERIOR VIEW
- Triticial cartilage
- Superior cornu
- Laryngeal prominence
- Lamina
- Angle
- Inferior cornu
- Notch

POSTERIOR VIEW
- Superior cornu
- Inferior cornu

LATERAL VIEW
- Superior cornu
- Oblique line
- Inferior cornu
- ANTERIOR
- POSTERIOR

Corniculate cartilage
Apex
Muscular process
Vocal process
Cricoid cartilage

ANTERIOR VIEW

Vocal process
Muscular process
ANTERIOR
POSTERIOR
Cricoid cartilage

LATERAL VIEW

Apex
Muscular process
Cricoid cartilage

POSTERIOR VIEW

FIGURE 5-11. Arytenoid cartilages articulated with cricoid cartilage.

its concave surface is the point of articulation with the convex arytenoid facet of the cricoid cartilage.

The names of the two processes of the arytenoid give a hint as to their function. The **vocal processes** project anteriorly toward the thyroid notch, and it is these processes to which the posterior portion of the vocal folds themselves will attach. The **muscular process** forms the lateral outcropping of the arytenoid pyramid and, as its name implies, is the point of attachment for muscles that adduct and abduct the vocal folds.

Epiglottis

The unpaired epiglottis is a leaflike structure that arises from the inner surface of the angle of the thyroid cartilage just below the notch, being attached there by the thyroepiglottic ligament. The sides of the epiglottis are joined with the arytenoid cartilages via the aryepiglottic folds, which are the product of the membranous lining draping over muscle and connective tissue.

The epiglottis projects upward beyond the larynx and above the hyoid bone and is attached to the root of the tongue by means of the median **glosso-epiglottic fold** and the paired **lateral glosso-epiglottic folds**. This juncture produces the valleculae, landmarks which will become important in your study of swallowing and swallowing deficit. During swallowing, food passes over the epiglottis, and from there laterally to the **pyriform** (also piriform) sinuses, which are small fossa or indentations between the aryepiglottic folds medially and the mucous lining of the thyroid cartilage. Together, the pyriform sinuses and valleculae are called the **pharyngeal recesses** (see Figure 5–8).

See Chapter 9 for a discussion of the X vagus nerve.

vagus: L., wandering

The epiglottis is attached to the hyoid bone via the **hyo-epiglottic ligament**. The surface of the epiglottis is covered with mucous membrane lining, and beneath this lining on the posterior, concave surface may be found branches of the internal laryngeal nerve of the X **Vagus** that conduct sensory information from the larynx.

Cuneiform Cartilages

cuneiform: L., cuneus, wedge; "wedge-shaped"

The cuneiform cartilages are small cartilages embedded within the aryepiglottic folds. They are situated above and anterior to the corniculate cartilages, and cause a small bulge on the surface of the membrane that looks white under illumination. These cartilages apparently provide support for the membranous laryngeal covering.

Hyoid Bone

Although not a bone of the larynx, it is the union between the tongue and the laryngeal structure. This unpaired small bone articulates with the superior cornu of the thyroid cartilage, and has the distinction of being the only bone of the body that is not attached to other bone (see Figure 5–12).

As you can see from the view of the hyoid bone from above, this structure is U-shaped, being open in the posterior. There are three major ele-

SUPERIOR VIEW

POSTERIOR VIEW

FIGURE 5–12. Hyoid bone as seen from above and behind. Note that points of attachment of muscles and membranes are indicated in parentheses.

ments of the hyoid bone. The corpus or body of the hyoid is the prominent shield-like structure forming the front of the bone, and is a structure you can palpate. If you will place your finger on your thyroid notch and push *lightly* back toward your spine you will feel the hard structure of the corpus near your fingernail. As you are doing this, take one more look at the figure (Figure 5–11) showing the structures together, to become acquainted with the relationship of these structures.

The front of the corpus is convex, while the inner surface is concave. The corpus is the point of attachment for six muscles, no small feat for such a small structure.

The **greater cornu** arises on the lateral surface of the corpus, projecting posteriorly. At the junction of the corpus and greater cornu you can see the **lesser cornu**. Three additional muscles will be attached to these two structures.

Movement of the Cartilages

The cricothyroid and thyroarytenoid joints are the only functionally mobile points of the larynx, and both of these joints serve extremely important laryngeal functions.

The cricothyroid joint is the junction of the cricoid cartilage and inferior cornu of the thyroid cartilage, as mentioned earlier. These are synovial joints that permit the cricoid and thyroid to rotate and glide relative to each other. As seen in Figure 5–13, rotation at the cricothyroid joint permits the thyroid cartilage to rock down in front, and the joint also permits the thyroid to glide forward and backward slightly relative to the cricoid. This joint will provide the major adjustment for change in vocal pitch.

The **cricoarytenoid joint** is the articulation formed between the cricoid and arytenoid cartilages. As you will recall, the base of the arytenoid cartilage is concave, mating with the smooth convex superior surface of the cricoid cartilage. These synovial joints permit rocking, gliding, and perhaps rotation. The arytenoid facet of the cricoid is a convex, oblong surface, and the axis of motion is around a line projecting back along the superior surface of the arytenoid and converging above at a point above the arytenoid (see Figure 5–14). This rocking action folds the two vocal processes toward each other, permitting the vocal folds to **approximate** (make contact). The arytenoids are capable also of gliding on the long axis of the facet, facilitating changes in vocal fold length. The arytenoids also may rotate upon a vertical axis drawn through the apex of the arytenoid, but this motion appears to be limited to extremes of abduction (Fink & Demarest, 1978). The combination of these gestures provides the mechanism for vocal fold approximation and abduction.

Your understanding of the movement of these cartilages in relation to each other will provide a valuable backdrop to understanding laryngeal physiology presented in Chapter 6.

To summarize:

■ The laryngeal cartilages have a number of important landmarks to which muscles are attached.
■ The **cricoid** cartilage is shaped like a signet ring, higher in back.
■ The **arytenoid** cartilages ride on the superior surface of the cricoid, with the cricoarytenoid joint permitting rotation, rocking, and gliding.
■ The **muscular** and **vocal processes** provide attachment for the **thyromuscularis** and **thyrovocalis** muscles.
■ The **corniculate** cartilages attach to the upper margin of the arytenoids.
■ The **thyroid** cartilage has two prominent laminae, superior and inferior horns, and a prominent thyroid notch.

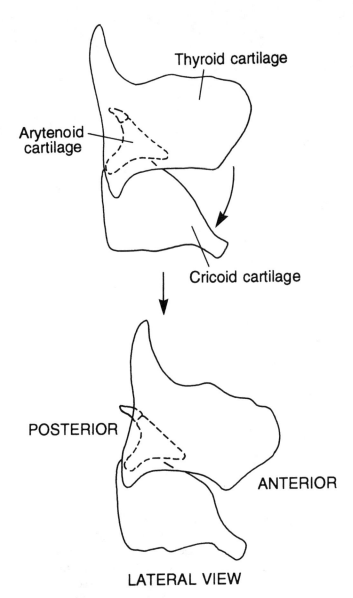

FIGURE 5-13. Movement of the cricoid and thyroid cartilages about the cricothyroid joint. When the cricoid and thyroid move toward each other in front the arytenoid cartilage moves farther away from the thyroid cartilage, tensing the vocal folds.

■ The **hyoid bone** attaches to the superior cornu of thyroid, while the **cricoid** cartilage attaches to the inferior horn via the cricothyroid joint.
■ The **epiglottis** attaches to the tongue and thyroid cartilage, dropping down to cover the larynx during swallowing.
■ The **cuneiform** cartilages are embedded within the aryepiglottic folds.

FIGURE 5-14. The articular facet for the arytenoid cartilage permits rocking, gliding, and rotation. **a.** The shape of the articular facet for the arytenoid cartilage promotes inward rocking of the arytenoid cartilage and vocal folds, as shown by the arrows. **b.** The long axis of the facet permits limited anterior-posterior gliding. **c.** The arytenoids may also rotate as shown. (Based on data of Broad, 1973; Fink, 1978; Netter, 1989; Zemlin, 1989.)

LARYNGEAL MUSCULATURE

As summarized in Table 5–1, muscles of the larynx may be conveniently divided into muscles that have both origin and insertion on laryngeal cartilages (**intrinsic laryngeal muscles**) and those with one attachment on a laryngeal cartilage and the other attachment on a nonlaryngeal structure (**extrinsic laryngeal muscles**). The extrinsic muscles make major adjustments of the larynx, such as elevating or depressing it, while the intrinsic musculature makes fine adjustments of the vocal mechanism itself. Extrinsic muscles tend to work in concert with articulatory gestures of the tongue, and many are important in swallowing. Intrinsic muscles assume responsibility for opening, closing, tensing, and relaxing the vocal folds. We will begin with a dis-

Table 5–1. Muscles associated with laryngeal function.

Intrinsic Muscles of Larynx

Adductors
Lateral cricoarytenoid
Transverse arytenoid
Oblique arytenoid

Abductor
Posterior cricoarytenoid

Tensors
Thyrovocalis (medial thyroarytenoid)
Cricothyroid, pars recta and pars oblique

Relaxers
Thyromuscularis (lateral thyroarytenoid)

Extrinsic Muscles of Larynx

Hyoid and Laryngeal Elevators
Stylohyoid
Mylohyoid
Geniohyoid
Genioglossus
Hyoglossus
Inferior pharyngeal constrictor

Hyoid and Laryngeal Depressors
Sternothyroid
Sternohyoid
Omohyoid
Thyrohyoid

cussion of the intrinsic muscles. The summary information of Appendix D may be helpful to your studies.

Intrinsic Laryngeal Muscles

Adductors

■ Lateral Cricoarytenoid
■ Transverse Arytenoid
■ Oblique Arytenoid

Lateral Cricoarytenoid Muscle. This extremely important muscle is one of the more difficult laryngeal muscles to visualize. The **lateral cricoarytenoid muscle** attaches to the cricoid and the muscular process of the arytenoid, causing the muscular process to move forward and medially (see Figure 5–15). The origin of the lateral cricoarytenoid muscle is the superior-lateral surface of the cricoid cartilage. The muscle courses up and back to insert into the muscular process of the arytenoid cartilage. As you can see from this figure, the course of the muscle dictates that the muscular process will be drawn forward, and that motion will rock the arytenoid inward and downward. This inward-and-downward rocking is the major adjustment associated with adduction of the vocal folds. In addition, this movement may lengthen the vocal folds (Hirano, Kiyokawa, & Kurita, 1988).

Innervation. Innervation of all intrinsic muscles of the larynx is by means of the X Vagus nerve. The Vagus is a large, wandering nerve with multiple responsibilities for sensation and motor function in the thorax, neck, and abdomen. The Vagus arises from the nucleus ambiguus of the medulla oblongata and divides into two major branches, the recurrent (inferior) laryngeal nerve (RLN) and the superior laryngeal nerve (SLN). The RLN is so named because of its course. The left RLN "re-courses" beneath the aorta, after which it ascends to innervate the larynx. The right RLN courses under the subclavian artery before ascending to the larynx. (This close association to the vascular supply results in voice problems arising from vascular disease, because **aneurysm** or enlargement of the aorta or subclavian artery may compress the left RLN and cause vocal dysfunction).

aneurysm: Gr.,
anyeurysma, *widening*

Transverse Arytenoid Muscle. The **transverse arytenoid muscle** also may be called the **transverse interarytenoid** muscle. This unpaired muscle is a band of fibers spanning the posterior surface of both arytenoid cartilages. As you can see from Figure 5–16, it is a band of fibers running from the lateral margin of the posterior surface of one arytenoid to the other, corresponding surface of arytenoid. Its function is to pull the two arytenoids closer together, and, by association, to approximate the vocal folds. It provides additional support for tight occlusion or closing of the vocal folds, and is an important element of

LATERAL VIEW

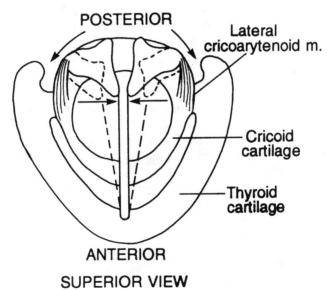

SUPERIOR VIEW

FIGURE 5–15. Contraction of the lateral cricoarytenoid muscle pulls the muscular process forward, adducting the vocal folds.

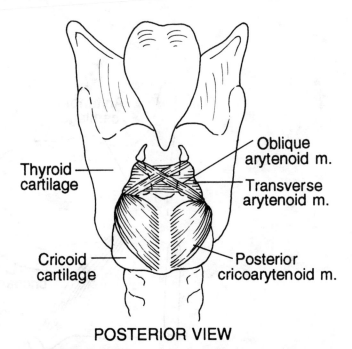

POSTERIOR VIEW

FIGURE 5–16. Schematic of posterior cricoarytenoid muscle and transverse and oblique arytenoid muscles. Contraction of the transverse and oblique arytenoid muscles will pull the arytenoids closer together, thereby supporting adduction. Contraction of the posterior cricoarytenoid muscle pulls the muscular process back, abducting the vocal folds.

medial compression. **Medial compression** refers to the degree of force that may be applied by the vocal folds at their point of contact. Increased medial compression is a function of increased force of adduction, and this is a vital element in vocal intensity change as you shall see.

> *Innervation.* Motor innervation of the arytenoid muscles is by means of the inferior branch of the recurrent laryngeal nerve arising from the X vagus.

Oblique Arytenoid Muscles. The **oblique arytenoid muscles** also are known as the oblique interarytenoid muscle. The oblique arytenoid muscles are immediately superficial to the transverse arytenoid muscles, and perform a similar function. The paired oblique arytenoid muscles take their origins at the posterior base of the muscular processes to course obliquely up to the apex of the opposite arytenoid. This course results in a characteristic "X" arrangement of the muscles, as well as in the ability of these muscles to pull the apex medially. The result of this action would be to promote adduction, enforce medial compression, and to rock the arytenoid (and vocal folds) down and in. Working in concert with the aryepiglottic muscle, the oblique arytenoid muscle will aid in pulling the epiglottis to cover the opening to the larynx as it also serves tight adduction.

> *Innervation.* Innervation of the oblique arytenoid muscles is the same as for the transverse arytenoid muscles.

Abductor

■ Posterior Cricoarytenoid Muscle

Posterior Cricoarytenoid Muscle. The **posterior cricoarytenoid muscle** is the sole abductor of the vocal folds. It is a small but prominent muscle of the posterior larynx. As you can see from Figure 5–16, the posterior cricoarytenoid muscle originates on the posterior cricoid lamina. Fibers project up and out to insert into the posterior aspect of the muscular process of the arytenoid cartilage. By virtue of their attachments to the muscular processes, the posterior cricoarytenoid muscles are direct antagonists to the lateral cricoarytenoids (see Figures 5–16 and 5–17).

Contraction of this muscle pulls the muscular process posteriorly, rocking the arytenoid cartilage out on its axis, and abducting the vocal folds. This muscle will be quite active during physical exertion, broadly abducting the vocal folds to permit greater air movement into and out of the lungs.

> *Innervation.* The posterior cricoarytenoid is innervated by the recurrent laryngeal nerve, a branch of the X vagus.

Glottal Tensors

■ Cricothyroid Muscle
■ Thyrovocalis Muscle

Cricothyroid Muscle. The primary tensor of the vocal folds achieves its function by rocking the thyroid cartilage forward relative to the cricoid cartilage. The **cricothyroid muscle** is composed of two heads, the pars recta and pars oblique, as seen in Figure 5–18.

The **pars recta** is the medial-most component of the cricothyroid muscle, originating on the anterior surface of the cricoid cartilage immediately beneath the arch. The pars recta courses up and out, to insert into the lower surface of the thyroid lamina. The **pars oblique** arises from the cricoid cartilage lateral to the pars recta, coursing obliquely up to insert into point of juncture between the thyroid laminae and inferior horns.

pars recta: *L., part + straight*

Vocal Hyperfunction

We have emphasized the notion that the larynx is a *small* structure, but we should add that even small muscles are capable of being misused. **Vocal hyperfunction** refers to using excessive adductory force, often resulting in **laryngitis**, which is inflammation of the vocal folds. Excessively forceful contraction of the lateral cricoarytenoid and the arytenoid muscles is undoubtedly the primary contributor to this problem, although it is also likely that laryngeal tension arising from contraction of the thyroarytenoid (thyromuscularis and thyrovocalis) and cricothyroid (with support by posterior cricoarytenoid) are contributors to this extraordinary force. In case you did not notice, that list included virtually all of the significant intrinsic laryngeal musculature, which should emphasize the notion that vocal hyperfunction is the result of general laryngeal tension. Vocal hyperfunction can result in laryngitis, vocal nodules, contact ulcers, and vocal fatigue, and is usually behavioral in nature.

Treatment typically requires a significant behavioral change in the client, but this is not without a cost. The voice is an extremely personal entity and is very tightly woven to an individual's self-concept. Approaching a client to change his or her voice is a delicate and challenging task for a clinician.

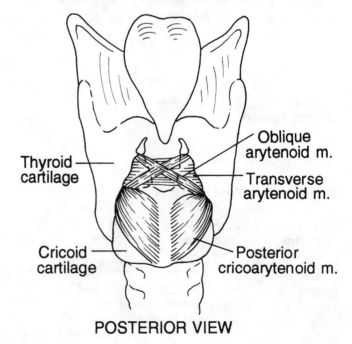

POSTERIOR VIEW

FIGURE 5-17. Action of the posterior cricoarytenoid muscle.

Cricothyroid m.
Pars recta
Pars oblique

LATERAL VIEW

FIGURE 5-18. Cricothyroid muscle, pars recta and pars oblique.

The angle of incidence of these two segments speaks to their relative functions. Although both will tense the vocal folds, individually these muscles will have differing effects on the motion of the thyroid. Let us look at both of them.

By virtue of its more directly superior course, contraction of the pars recta will have the effect of rocking the thyroid cartilage downward, rotating upon the cricothyroid joint. Due to the flexibility of the loosely joined tracheal cartilages below, the cricoid will rise to meet the thyroid as well. This is a good time to remind you that the points of attachment of the vocal folds are the inner margin of the thyroid cartilage and arytenoid cartilages, and that the arytenoid cartilages are well-attached to the posterior cricoid cartilage. The effect of rocking the thyroid cartilage forward is that the vocal folds, slung between the posterior cricoid and anterior thyroid, will be stretched. That is, rocking the thyroid and cricoid closer together in front makes the posterior cricoid more distant from the thyroid.

The cricothyroid joint also permits the thyroid to slide forward and backward. The forward sliding motion is a function of the pars oblique, and the result will be to tense the vocal folds as well. Together, the pars recta and oblique are responsible for the major laryngeal adjustment associated with pitch change.

Innervation. The cricothyroid is innervated by the external branch of the superior laryngeal nerve of the X vagus. This branch courses lateral to the inferior pharyngeal constrictor to terminate on the cricothyroid muscle.

Thyrovocalis Muscle. The **thyrovocalis muscle** is actually the medial muscle of the vocal folds. Many anatomists define a singular muscle coursing from the posterior surface of the thyroid cartilage to the arytenoid cartilages, labeling it as the thyroarytenoid. There is ample *functional* evidence to support differentiating the thyroarytenoid into two separate muscles, the thyromuscularis and the thyrovocalis, although anatomical support for dividing it into two muscles is questionable. While the thyromuscularis will be discussed as a glottal relaxer, the contraction of the thyrovocalis distinctly tenses the vocal folds, especially when contracted in concert with the cricothyroid.

The thyrovocalis (abbreviated as vocalis) originates from the inner surface of thyroid cartilage near the thyroid notch. The muscle courses back to insert into the lateral surface of the arytenoid vocal process. Contraction of this muscle will draw the thyroid and cricoid cartilages farther apart in front, making this muscle a functional antagonist of the cricothyroid muscle (which draws the anterior cricoid and anterior thyroid closer together). This antagonistic function has earned the thyrovocalis classification as a glottal tensor, because contraction of the thyrovocalis (balanced by contraction of the cricothyroid muscle) would tense the vocal folds.

Innervation. The thyrovocalis is innervated by the recurrent laryngeal nerve, a branch of the X vagus.

Relaxers

■ Thyromuscularis
■ Superior Thyroarytenoid Muscle

Thyromuscularis Muscle. The paired **thyromuscularis muscles** (or simply, muscularis) are considered to be the muscle masses immediately lateral to the each thyrovocalis, and which, with the thyrovocalis, make up the thyroarytenoid muscle. The **thyromuscularis** or **external (lateral) thyroarytenoid** originates on the inner surface of the thyroid cartilage, near the notch and lateral to the origin of the thyrovocalis. It runs back to insert into the arytenoid cartilage at the muscular process and base.

There is question about whether this muscle is truly differentiated from the vocalis, because anatomical evidence does not support this categorization. Nonetheless, functional differences are clearly seen. As you can see from Figure 5–19, the forces exerted on the arytenoid from pulling differentially on the vocal or muscular process would produce

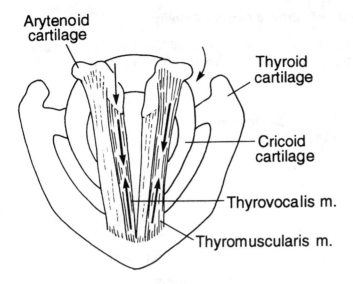

Arytenoid cartilage

Thyroid cartilage

Cricoid cartilage

Thyrovocalis m.

Thyromuscularis m.

SUPERIOR VIEW

FIGURE 5-19. The thyromuscularis muscle is the lateral muscular component of the vocal folds, while the thyrovocalis is the medial-most muscle of the vocal folds. Together they are often referred to as thyroarytenoid muscle.

markedly different effects. The lateral thyroarytenoid (thyromuscularis) will have essentially the same effect on the vocal folds as contraction of the lateral cricoarytenoid. The vocal folds will adduct and lengthen (Hirano, Kiyokawa, & Kurita, 1988).

Contraction of the medial fibers of the thyromuscularis may relax the vocal folds as well. By virtue of their attachment on the anterior surface of arytenoid, these fibers pull the arytenoids toward the thyroid cartilage without influencing medial rotation.

Innervation. The thyromuscularis is innervated by the recurrent laryngeal nerve, a branch of the X vagus.

Superior Thyroarytenoid Muscle. The **superior thyroarytenoid** is not present in all individuals, but seems to act as a relaxer when present. It originates on the inner surface of the thyroid cartilage near the angle and courses back to insert into the muscular process of arytenoid. By virtue of its attachment to the thyromuscularis, contraction will relax the vocal folds.

Innervation. The superior thyroarytenoid is innervated by the recurrent laryngeal nerve of X vagus.

Summary of Intrinsic Muscle Activity

Figure 5–20 will help us proceed with this discussion. Intrinsic muscles of the larynx include the thyrovocalis, thyromuscularis, cricothyroid,

FIGURE 5–20. A. Intrinsic muscles of the larynx.

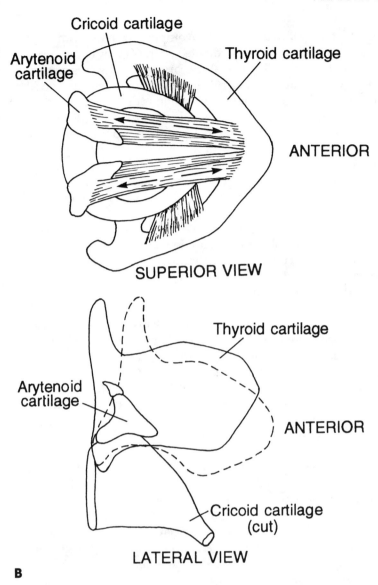

Cricoid cartilage

Arytenoid cartilage

Thyroid cartilage

ANTERIOR

SUPERIOR VIEW

Thyroid cartilage

Arytenoid cartilage

ANTERIOR

Cricoid cartilage (cut)

LATERAL VIEW

B

FIGURE 5-20. B. Action of the cricothyroid in alteration of fundamental frequency of vibrations.

lateral and posterior cricoarytenoid, transverse arytenoid and oblique interarytenoid, and superior thyroarytenoid muscles. The thyrovocalis and thyromuscularis muscles make up the muscular portion of the vocal folds. The cricothyroid pulls the anterior cricoid and anterior thyroid closer together, thereby stretching the vocal folds. The lateral cricoarytenoid adducts the vocal folds by rotating and rocking the arytenoids medially, while the posterior cricoarytenoid muscle abducts the vocal folds. The oblique and transverse arytenoid muscles pull the arytenoids closer together, assisting adduction. The superior thyroarytenoid muscle is variously present, serving to relax the vocal folds.

Movement of the vocal folds into and out of approximation (adduction and abduction) is achieved by coordinated effort of many of the intrinsic muscles of the larynx. The lateral cricoarytenoid muscle is responsible for rocking the arytenoid cartilage on its axis, causing the vocal folds to tip in and slightly down. This action is directly opposed by contraction of the posterior cricoarytenoid muscle, which will rock the arytenoid (and vocal folds) out on that same axis. Contraction of the transverse arytenoid muscle will draw the posterior surfaces of the two arytenoid closer together, but it will be most effective as an adductor if the lateral cricoarytenoid muscle is contracted as well. Contraction of the oblique arytenoid helps the vocal folds dip downward as they are adducted.

The fact that the vocal folds rock in and down is not trivial. The force vector associated with this movement improves the ability of the vocal folds to impede outward flow of air, because more force is directed in an inferior direction than if the arytenoid rotated on a vertical axis.

The muscles of abduction and adduction work in concert to complete their task in one more way. Although you know that the vocal folds must be adducted and abducted, you should start becoming aware that there is a full range of laryngeal adjustments that is possible, from completely abducted to tightly adducted. We use this full range during phonation, and the bulk of the voice clients on the caseload of a public school clinician will arise from inadequate control of this musculature (vocal nodules secondary to laryngeal hyperfunction).

Recalling the physical parameters that can be altered to change pitch will help you realize that either mass or tension is a likely candidate. Increasing the tension on the vocal folds will stretch them and thereby reduce the mass per unit length. Stretching the vocal folds does not *decrease* the mass of the muscle, but does decrease it relative to overall length. Both increased tension and reduced mass per unit length will increase frequency of vibration of the vocal folds, while relaxing the vocal folds will cause the frequency to drop.

Note that when the cricothyroid is contracted, the thyrovocalis will be stretched. If you also contract the thyrovocalis, the vocal folds will become tenser and the pitch increased.

Extrinsic Laryngeal Muscles

The extrinsic musculature consists of muscles with one attachment to a laryngeal cartilage. These include the sternothyroid, thyrohyoid, and thyropharyngeus muscles. A number of muscles attached to the hyoid also move the larynx, and these are described as infrahyoid muscles, which run from the hyoid to a structure below, and **suprahyoid muscles**, which attach to a structure above the hyoid. Infrahyoid muscles consist of the sternohyoid and omohyoid muscles, while the suprahyoid muscles are digastricus, stylohyoid, mylohyoid, geniohyoid, genioglossus, and hyoglossus muscles. They are often called the strap muscles.

A more meaningful categorization is based on function relative to the larynx. Muscles that elevate the hyoid and larynx are termed **laryngeal elevators** (digastricus, stylohyoid, mylohyoid, geniohyoid muscles, genioglossus, hyoglossus, and thyropharyngeus muscles) and those that depress the larynx and hyoid are **laryngeal depressors** (sternohyoid, omohyoid, thyrohyoid, and sternothyroid muscles).

Hyoid and Laryngeal Elevators

- **Digastricus Anterior and Posterior**
- **Stylohyoid Muscle**
- **Mylohyoid Muscle**
- **Geniohyoid Muscle**
- **Genioglossus Muscle**
- **Hyoglossus Muscle**
- **Thyropharyngeus Muscle**

Digastricus. As seen in Figure 5–21, the **digastricus muscle** is actually composed of two separate bellies. The anterior and posterior bellies of the digastricus muscle converge at the hyoid bone, and their

digastricus: *L., two + belly*
symphysis: *Gr., growing together*

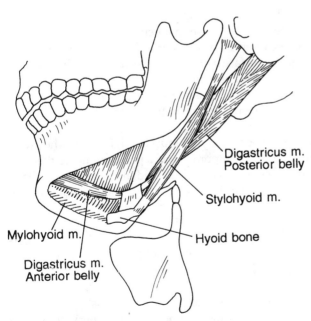

FIGURE 5–21. Schematic of digastricus, stylohyoid, and mylohyoid muscles. (After data and view of Netter, 1989.)

paired contraction will elevate the hyoid. **Digastricus anterior** originates on the inner surface of the mandible at the digastricus fossa, near the point of fusion of the two halves of the mandible, the symphysis. The muscle courses medially and down to the level of the hyoid, where it joins with the posterior digastricus by means of an **intermediate tendon**. The **posterior digastricus** originates on the mastoid process of the temporal bone, behind and beneath the ear. The intermediate tendon passes through and separates the fibers of another muscle, the stylohyoid, as it inserts into the hyoid at the juncture of the hyoid corpus and greater cornu.

The structure and attachment of the digastricus bellies will define their function. Contraction of the anterior component will result in the hyoid being drawn up and forward, whereas contraction of the posterior belly will cause the hyoid to be drawn up and back. Simultaneous contraction results in hyoid elevation without anterior or posterior migration. You will see a great deal of activity in the posterior belly during chewing and swallowing.

At this point, it is wise to point out that muscles attached to the mandible, such as the digastricus, also may be **depressors** of the mandible. That is, the digastricus could help to pull the mandible down if the musculature *below* the hyoid were to fix it in place. You will want to retain this notion for our discussion of the role of hyoid musculature in oral motor development and control.

> *Innervation.* The anterior belly is innervated by the mandibular branch of V trigeminal nerve via the mylohyoid branch of the inferior alveolar nerve. This branch courses along the inner surface of the mandible in the mylohyoid groove, and exits to innervate the mylohyoid (to be discussed) and the anterior digastricus. The posterior belly is supplied by the digastric branch of the VII facial nerve.

trigeminal: L., tres, *three;* gemina, *twin*

Stylohyoid Muscle. The **stylohyoid muscle** originates on the prominent styloid process of the temporal bone, a point medial to the mastoid process. The course of this muscle is medially down, such that it crosses the path of the posterior digastricus (which actually passes through the stylohyoid) and inserts into the corpus of hyoid.

Contraction of the stylohyoid elevates and retracts the hyoid bone. As with the digastricus, the stylohyoid also could facilitate tongue movement by anchoring the hyoid in conjunction with infrahyoid muscles.

> *Innervation.* The stylohyoid and posterior digastricus are closely allied in development, function, and innervation. Both the stylohyoid and posterior belly of digastricus are innervated by the motor branch of the VII facial nerves.

Mylohyoid Muscle. As with digastricus anterior, the **mylohyoid muscle** originates on the underside of the mandible and courses to the corpus hyoid. Unlike digastricus, the mylohyoid is fanlike, originating along the lateral aspects of the inner mandible on a prominence known as the mylohyoid line. The anterior fibers converge at the median fibrous raphe (ridge), a structure that runs from the **symphysis mente** (the juncture of the fused paired bones of the mandible) to the hyoid. The posterior fibers course directly to the hyoid. Taken together, the fibers of mylohyoid form the floor of the oral cavity. The relationship between digastricus and mylohyoid may be seen in Figure 5–22. As may be derived from examination of fiber course, the mylohyoid elevates the hyoid and projects it forward, or alternately depresses the mandible, in much the manner of the digastricus anterior. Unlike the digastricus, the mylohyoid muscle is responsible for elevation of the floor of the mouth during the first stage of deglutition.

> *Innervation.* The mylohyoid is allied with the anterior belly of the digastricus, through proximity, development, and innervation. As with anterior digastricus, mylohyoid is innervated by the alveolar nerve, arising from the V trigeminal nerve, mandibular branch. As stated for digastricus anterior, this nerve courses within the mylohyoid groove of the inner surface of mandible, branches, and innervates the mylohyoid.

Geniohyoid Muscle. The **geniohyoid muscle** is superior to the mylohyoid, originating at the mental spines projecting in a course parallel to the anterior belly of digastricus from the inner mandibular surface. Fibers of this narrow muscle course back and down to insert into the hyoid bone at the corpus. When contracted, the geniohyoid elevates the hyoid and draws it forward. It may depress the mandible also if the hyoid is fixed.

> *Innervation.* The geniohyoid is innervated by the XII hypoglossal nerve. Although most of the hypoglossal originates in the hypoglossal nucleus of the medulla oblongata of the brainstem, those fibers innervating the geniohyoid arise from the first cervical spinal nerve.

hypoglossal: L., glossa, tongue; under + tongue

Hyoglossus Muscle. The **hyoglossus** and genioglossus provide another example of the interrelatedness of musculature. These muscles also are lingual (tongue) depressors, because they have attachments on both of these structures. Speech-language pathologists concerned about oral motor control are painfully aware of these relationships, and studying them will benefit you as well. The hyoglossus is a laterally placed muscle. It arises from the entire superior surface of the greater cornu of hyoid, courses up to insert into the side of the tongue. The point of insertion in the tongue is near that of the sty-

hyoglossus: hyo, hyoid + glossus, tongue

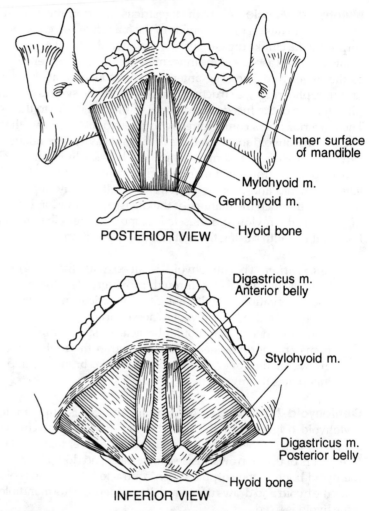

Inner surface
of mandible

Mylohyoid m.

Geniohyoid m.

Hyoid bone

POSTERIOR VIEW

Digastricus m.
Anterior belly

Stylohyoid m.

Digastricus m.
Posterior belly

Hyoid bone

INFERIOR VIEW

FIGURE 5–22. Schematic of the relationship among geniohyoid, mylohyoid, digastricus, and stylohyoid muscles.

*See the Clinical Note in
Chapter 3 for a discus-
sion of Trunk Stability
and Upper Body
Mobility.*

loglossus, a muscle we will discuss in the chapter covering the articulators. The muscle takes on a quadrilateral appearance and is a lingual
depressor or hyoid elevator.

Innervation. The hyoglossus muscle is innervated by the
motor branch of the XII hypoglossal.

Genioglossus Muscle. Although the **genioglossus muscle** is more
appropriately considered a muscle of the tongue, it definitely is a
hyoid elevator. The genioglossus originates on the inner surface of the
mandible at the symphysis and courses up, back, and down to insert
into the tongue and anterior surface of the hyoid corpus. We will discuss the lingual function of this muscle in Chapter 7, but the attachment at the hyoid guarantees that this muscle will elevate the hyoid.

Innervation. The genioglossus muscle is innervated by the motor branch of the XII hypoglossal.

Thyropharyngeus Muscle of Inferior Constrictor. The **thyropharyngeus** and **cricopharyngeus muscles** comprise the **inferior pharyngeal constrictor**, to be discussed in detail later. The cricopharyngeus is the sphincter muscle at the orifice of the esophagus, while the thyropharyngeus is involved in propelling food through the pharynx. Its attachment to the cricoid and thyroid provides an opportunity for laryngeal elevation.

The thyropharyngeus arises from the posterior pharyngeal raphe, coursing down fanlike and laterally to the thyroid lamina and inferior cornu. Contraction of this muscle promotes elevation of the larynx while constricting the pharynx.

> *Innervation*. The inferior constrictors are innervated by branches from the X vagi, and the recurrent laryngeal nerves off the vagi.

Hyoid and Laryngeal Depressors

- **Sternohyoid Muscle**
- **Omohyoid Muscle**
- **Sternothyroid Muscle**
- **Thyrohyoid Muscle**

Laryngeal depressors will depress and stabilize the larynx via attachment to the hyoid, but also stabilize the tongue by serving as antagonists to the laryngeal elevators. The interconnectedness of the laryngeal and tongue musculature may be at first imposing, but take heart. Mastery of the components will greatly enhance your clinical competency, because oral motor control is founded in these interactions. We will discuss this in detail in Chapter 6.

Sternohyoid Muscle. As the name implies, the **sternohyoid** runs from sternum to hyoid. It originates from the posterior-superior region of the manubrium sterni, as well as from the medial end of the clavicle. It courses superiorly to insert into the inferior margin of the hyoid corpus.

Contraction of the sternohyoid will depress the hyoid or, if suprahyoid muscles are in contraction, will fix the hyoid and larynx. The lowering function is clearly evident following the pharyngeal stage in swallowing.

> *Innervation*. The sternohyoid is innervated by the ansa cervicalis (*ansa* = loop; i.e., cervical loop), arising from C1 through C3 spinal nerves.

Laryngeal Stability

Laryngeal stability is the key to laryngeal control, and this stability is gained through development of the infra- and suprahyoid musculature. You can think of the larynx as a box connected to a flexible tube on one end (trachea) and loosely bound above. This "box" has liberal movement in the vertical dimension and some horizontal movement as well, but there must be a great deal of control in contraction of all of this musculature for this arrangement to work.

The larynx is intimately linked, via the hyoid bone, to the tongue, so that movement of the tongue is translated to the larynx. During development, an infant begins to gain control of neck musculature as early as 4 weeks, as seen in the ability to elevate the neck in prone. This ability to extend the previously flexed neck heralds the beginning of oral motor control, because the ability to balance neck extension with flexion permits the child to control the gross movement of the head. During this stage, the larynx is quite elevated, so much so that you can easily see the superior tip of the epiglottis behind the tongue of a 2-year old. In the early stages, the elevated larynx facilitates the anterior tongue protrusion required in infancy for nursing.

As the child develops, the larynx descends, starting a process of muscular differentiation between the tongue and the larynx. In the "nursing" position of the tongue, laryngeal stability is not as important, but the ability to move semi-hard and hard food around in the oral cavity is quite important. Now the child will develop the ability to move the tongue and larynx independently, permitting a much wider set of oral gestures. With this differentiation comes the control needed for accurate speech production. For information on head and neck control in children with motor dysfunction, you may wish to examine Jones-Owens (1991), and certainly you will want to read the work of Bly (1994) for insight into the development of muscle control.

Omohyoid Muscle. As you can see in Figure 5–23, the **omohyoid** is a muscle with two bellies. The superior belly terminates on the side of the hyoid corpus, while the inferior belly has its origin on the upper border of the scapula. The bellies are joined at an intermediate tendon. As you can see from this figure, the omohyoid passes deep to the sternocleidomastoid that, along with the deep cervical fascia, restrain the muscle to retain that characteristic "dogleg" angle. When contracted, the omohyoid will depress the hyoid bone and larynx.

See Chapters 3 and 8 for discussion of spinal nerves.

Innervation. The superior belly is innervated by the superior ramus of the ansa cervicalis arising from C1 spinal nerve,

FIGURE 5-23. Schematic of the relationship among omohy-oid, sternocleidomastoid, and sternohyoid muscles.

whereas the inferior belly is innervated by the main ansa cervicalis, arising from C2 and C3 spinal nerves.

Sternothyroid Muscle. As shown in Figure 5–24, contraction of the **sternothyroid muscle** will depress the thyroid cartilage. It originates at the manubrium sterni and first costal cartilage, coursing up and out to insert into the oblique line of the thyroid cartilage. It is active during swallowing, drawing the larynx downward following elevation for the pharyngeal stage of deglutition.

Innervation. The sternothyroid is innervated by fibers from the spinal nerves C1 and C2 that pass in the hypoglossal nerve.

Thyrohyoid Muscle. This muscle is easily seen as the superior counterpart to the sternothyroid (Figure 5–24). Coursing from the oblique line of the thyroid cartilage to the inferior margin of the greater cornu of hyoid bone, the **thyrohyoid** muscle will either depress the hyoid or raise the larynx.

Innervation. The thyrohyoid is innervated by the fibers from spinal nerve C1 that course in the hypoglossal nerves.

Hyoid bone

Thyrohyoid m.

Thyroid cartilage

Oblique line

Sternothyroid m.

Manubrium sterni

FIGURE 5–24. The sternothyroid and thyrohyoid muscles.

In summary:

- ■ The **extrinsic muscles** of the larynx include **infrahyoid** and **suprahyoid** muscles.
- ■ The **digastricus** anterior and posterior elevate the hyoid, whereas the **stylohyoid** retracts it.
- ■ The **mylohyoid** and **hyoglossus** elevate the hyoid, and the **geniohyoid** elevates the hyoid and draws it forward.
- ■ The **thyropharyngeus** and **cricopharyngeus** muscles elevate the larynx, and the **sternohyoid**, **sternothyroid**, **thyrohyoid**, and **omohyoid** muscles depress the larynx.

Interaction of Musculature

The larynx is virtually suspended from a broad sling of muscles that must work in concert to achieve the complex motions required for speech and nonspeech function. Movement of the larynx and its cartilages requires both gross and fine adjustments. It appears that the gross movements associated with laryngeal elevation and depression provide the background for the fine adjustments of phonatory control. The supra- and infrahyoid muscles raise and lower the larynx, changing the

Vocal Fold Paralysis

Paralysis refers to loss of voluntary motor function, whereas **paresis** refers to weakness. Either can arise from damage to either **upper motor neurons**, which are neurons that arise from the brain and end in the spinal column or brainstem, or damage to **lower motor neurons**, which are neurons which leave the spinal column or brainstem to innervate the muscles involved.

Vocal fold paralysis may take several forms, dependent on the nerve damage. If only one side of the recurrent laryngeal nerve (lower motor neuron) is damaged, the result will be unilateral vocal fold paralysis. Bilateral vocal fold paralysis would result from bilateral lower motor neuron damage.

If the result of damage is **adductor paralysis**, the muscles of adduction are paralyzed and the vocal folds will remain in the abducted position. If the damage results in **abductor paralysis**, the individual will not be able to abduct the vocal folds, and respiration will be compromised (you may want to read the note on "laryngeal stridor" in Chapter 6 to get a notion of what happens). If the superior laryngeal nerve is involved, the individual will suffer loss of the ability to alter vocal pitch, because the cricothyroid is innervated by this branch of the vagus.

In unilateral paralysis, one vocal fold is still capable of motion. Phonation can still occur, but production will be markedly breathy. Bilateral adductor paralysis will result in virtually complete loss of phonation.

There are several causes of vocal fold paralysis, but among the leaders are damage to the nerve during thyroid surgery and blunt trauma, often from the steering wheel of an automobile. **Cerebrovascular accidents** (CVA: hemorrhage or other condition causing loss of blood supply to the brain) may damage upper or lower motor neurons, resulting in paralysis, and a host of neurodegenerative diseases will weaken or paralyze the vocal folds. You should also be aware that paralysis may occur as a result of **aneurysm** of the aortic arch. An aneurysm is a focal "ballooning" of an blood vessel caused by a weakness in the wall. When the aneurysm balloons out it compresses the recurrent laryngeal nerve, causing paresis or paralysis. A **phonatory sign** (objective evidence of phonatory deficit) is not to be taken lightly.

vocal tract length, but the intrinsic laryngeal muscles are responsible for the fine adjustments associated with phonation control.

To say that the musculature works as a unit is clearly an understatement. The simple gesture of laryngeal elevation must be countered with the controlled antagonistic tone of the laryngeal depressors. To elevate the tongue will tend to elevate the larynx and increase the tension of the cricothyroid, and this must be countered through intrinsic muscle adjustment to keep the articulatory system from driving the phonatory mechanism. It is time to move to Chapter 6 to see how these components work together.

CHAPTER SUMMARY

Phonation is the product of vibrating vocal folds within the **larynx.** The **vocal folds** vibrate as air flows past them, capitalizing upon the **Bernoulli phenomenon** and **tissue elasticity** to maintain phonation. The interaction of **subglottal pressure, tissue elasticity**, and **constriction** within the airflow caused by the vocal folds produces sustained phonation as long as **pressure**, flow, and **vocal fold approximation** are maintained.

The **larynx** is comprised of the **cricoid, thyroid**, and **epiglottis** cartilages, as well as the paired **arytenoid, corniculate**, and **cuneiform** cartilages. The thyroid and cricoid cartilages articulate by means of the **cricothyroid joint** that lets the two cartilages come closer together in front. The **arytenoid** and **cricoid** cartilages also articulate with a joint that permits a wide range of arytenoid motion. The **epiglottis** is attached to the **thyroid** cartilage and base of the **tongue.** The **corniculate cartilages** rest on the upper surface of the **arytenoids**, while the **cuneiform** cartilages reside within the **aryepiglottic folds.**

The **cavity** of the **larynx** is a constricted tube with a smooth surface. Sheets and cords of **ligaments** connect the cartilages, while smooth **mucous membrane** covers the medial-most surface of the larynx. The **valleculae** are found between the tongue and the epiglottis, within folds arising from the **lateral** and **median glossoepiglottic ligaments.** The **fibroelastic membrane** is composed of the upper **quadrangular membranes** and **aryepiglottic folds**, the lower **conus elasticus**, and the **vocal ligament**, which is actually the upward free extension of the conus elasticus.

The **vocal folds** are made up of five layers of tissue, the deepest being the muscle of the vocal folds. The **aditus** is the entryway of the larynx, marking the entry to the **vestibule.** The **ventricular** and **vocal folds** are separated by the laryngeal ventricle. The **glottis** is the variable space between the vocal folds.

Intrinsic muscles of the larynx include the **thyrovocalis, thyromuscularis, cricothyroid, lateral** and **posterior cricoarytenoid, transverse arytenoid** and **oblique interarytenoid**, and **superior thyroarytenoid** muscles. **Extrinsic muscles** of the larynx include **infrahyoid** and **suprahyoid** muscles. The **digastricus anterior** and **posterior** elevate the hyoid, while the **stylohyoid** retracts it. The **mylohyoid** and **hyo-**

glossus elevate the hyoid, and the **geniohyoid** elevates the hyoid and draws it forward. The **thyropharyngeus** and **cricopharyngeus** muscles elevate the larynx, and the **sternohyoid**, **sternothyroid**, and **omohyoid** muscles depress the larynx.

Movement of the vocal folds into and out of approximation requires coordinated effort the intrinsic muscles of the larynx. The **lateral cricoarytenoid** muscle rocks the arytenoid cartilage on its axis, tipping the vocal folds in and slightly down. The **posterior cricoarytenoid** muscle rocks the arytenoid out. The **transverse arytenoid** muscle draws the posterior surfaces of the arytenoids closer together. The **oblique arytenoid** assists the vocal folds to dip downward when they are adducted. Vocal fundamental frequency is increased by increasing tension, a function of the **thyrovocalis** and **cricothyroid**.

END NOTE: MECHANICS OF VIBRATION

You are already familiar with the notion that things are capable of vibrating, because you have undoubtedly set a ruler into vibration on your desktop, or plucked a guitar string. When a physical body is set into vibration, it tends to continue vibrating (that is, oscillating), and that vibration tends to continue at the same rate.

Let us examine why a body tends to oscillate. If you have a guitar, pluck one of the strings. As you listen to the twang of the string, you will notice that it continues vibrating for quite a while before finally quieting down. The tone produced remains about the same pitch throughout the audible portion of its vibration.

The actual process of vibration is determined by a lawful interplay among the elastic restoring forces of a material, the stiffness of the material, and inertia, a quality of its mass. **Elasticity** is that property of a material that causes it to return to its original shape after being displaced. **Stiffness** refers to the *strength* of the forces held within a given material that restore it to its original shape on being distended. **Inertia** is the property of mass that dictates that a body in motion tends to stay in motion. If we discuss the vibration of the guitar string in detail, the interaction of these elements may become clearer. Look at Figure 5–25 as we discuss this.

In the first panel of Figure 5–25, the guitar string is at its resting point. At this point, all forces are balanced. Next, the string is being displaced by someone's finger. This is a displacing force that is distending the string. In the next panel, the string has been released and is moving toward its starting point. This is a direct result of the restoring forces of the elastic material. The elastic qualities of the material from which the string is made and the stiffness of that material determine the efficiency with which the string returns. (If you were to try this with a highly inelastic material, such as a bar of lead or a slab of roast beef, would it return?)

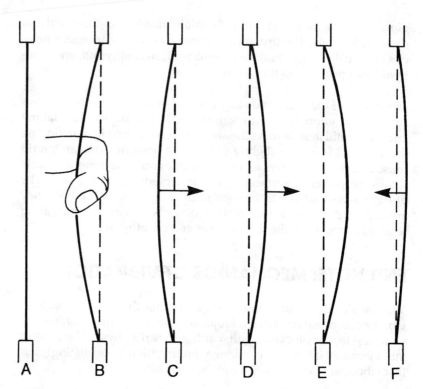

FIGURE 5–25. A guitar string illustrates oscillation. **a.** The string is at rest. **b.** A finger forces the string into displacement. **c.** The string is released and its elastic elements cause it to return toward the rest position. **d.** The string overshoots the rest position because of its inertia. **e.** The string reaches the extreme point of its excursion past the rest position. **f.** Elastic forces within the string cause the string to return toward the rest position.

In Panel D, when the string reaches the midpoint it is moving too fast to stop and sails on by that midpoint even though it is the point of equilibrium. Just as when you push someone in a swing, the swing does not simply return to the point of rest and stop, but rather overshoots that point. The reason the string travels past the point of rest is that it has mass. It takes energy to move mass and it takes energy to stop it once it has started moving. The string will not only return to its original resting position due to elastic restoring forces, but will fly past that position due to the inertia associated with moving the mass of the object. In Panel E, the string eventually stops moving because it is now being distended in the opposite direction. The energy you expended in the first distension has now been translated into an opposite distortion as a result of inertia. In the final panel, the string may now begin its return trip toward the starting point, but it will once again overshoot that point because of inertia.

If you had set a pencil into vibration instead of a string and we had moved a sheet of paper in front of it as it vibrated, it might have drawn a picture something like shown in Figure 5–26, which depicts the periodic motion of a vibrating body. This picture is a graphic representation of the vibration of that object. The drawing represents a waveform, which is the representation of displacement of a body over time, and displays what the pencil or string was doing as it vibrated.

This waveform is **periodic**. When we say that vibration is periodic, we mean that it repeats itself in a predictable fashion. If it took the ruler 1/100 of a second to move from its the first point of distension back to that point again, it will take 1/100 of a second to repeat that cycle if it is vibrating periodically.

Moving from one point in the vibratory pattern to the same point again defines one **cycle** of vibration, and the time it takes to pass through one cycle of vibration is referred to as the **period**. In our example, the period of vibration was 1/100 second, or 0.01 seconds. **Frequency** refers to how often something occurs, as in the frequency with which you shop for groceries (e.g., two times per month). The frequency of vibration is how often a cycle of vibration repeats itself, which, in our example, is 100 times per second. Frequency and period are the inverse of each other, and that relationship may be stated as $f = 1/T$ or $T = 1/f$. That is, frequency (f) equals 1 divided by period (T for "Time"). For our example, frequency = 1 / 0.01 seconds. If you will take a moment with your calculator, you will find that this calculation gives a result of 100.

Because frequency refers to the repetition rate of vibration, we speak of it in terms of number of **cycles per second**. The pencil vibrated with a frequency of 100 cycles per second, but shorthand notation for cycles

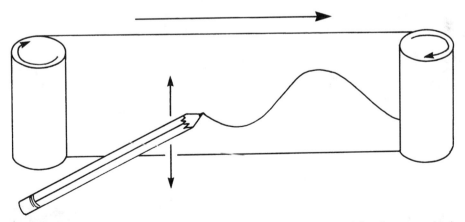

FIGURE 5–26. Periodic motion of a vibrating body graphically recorded.

per second is **Hertz (Hz)**, after Heinrich Hertz. When we set the pencil into vibration, it vibrated with a period of .01 seconds and a frequency of 100 Hz.

We said that frequency of vibration in a body was governed by the elasticity, stiffness, and mass. If you had added a large weight to the guitar string, it would have vibrated slower. As mass increases, frequency of vibration decreases.

If you were to make the string stiffer, it would vibrate more rapidly. Increased stiffness would drive the string to return to its point of equilibrium at a faster rate, increasing the frequency of vibration.

Study Questions

1. Please identify the indicated structures on the figure below.

   a. _____ cartilage

   b. _____ cartilage

   c. _____ cartilage

   d. _____ cartilage

   e. _____ cartilage

   f. _____ bone

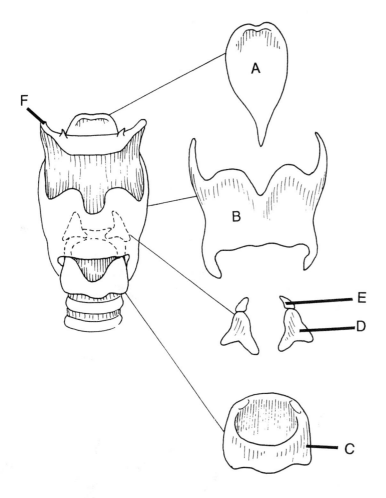

2. Please identify the indicated landmarks on the figure below.

a. _____

b. _____

c. _____

d. _____

e. _____

f. _____

3. Please identify the indicated landmarks on the figure below.

    a. _____ process

    b. _____ process

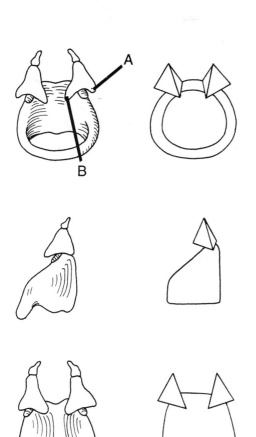

4. Please identify the muscles indicated below.

a. _____

b. _____

c. _____

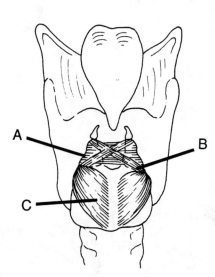

5. Please identify the muscles indicated below.

a. _____

b. _____

c. _____

d. _____

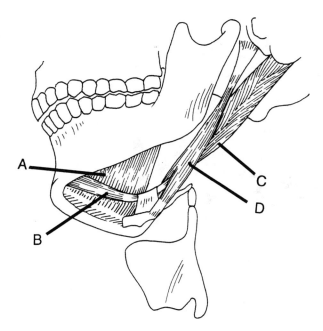

6. Please identify the muscles indicated below.

a. _____

b. _____

c. _____

d. _____

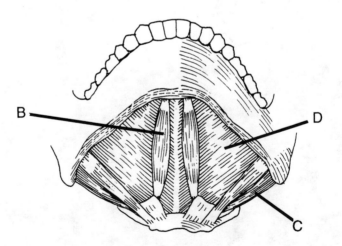

7. This is a view of the laryngeal opening from above. Please identify the structures indicated

   a. _____

   b. _____

   c. _____

   d. _____

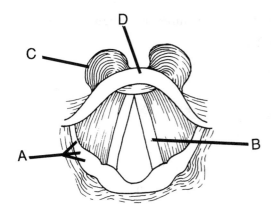

8. Please identify the two muscles indicated below.

   a. _____

   b. _____

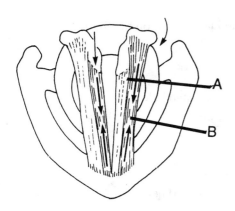

9. The _____ muscle is the primary muscle responsible for change of vocal fundamental frequency.

10. The space between the vocal folds is termed the _____ _____.

11. The _____ effect states that, given a constant volume flow of air or fluid, at a point of constriction there will be a decrease in air pressure perpendicular to the flow and an increase in velocity of the flow.

Study Question Answers

1. Please identify the indicated structures on the figure below.
   a. EPIGLOTTIS cartilage
   b. THYROID cartilage
   c. CRICOID cartilage
   d. ARYTENOID cartilage
   e. CORNICULATE cartilage
   f. HYOID bone

2. Please identify the indicated landmarks on the figure below.
   a. GREATER CORNU
   b. LESSER CORNU
   c. OBLIQUE LINE
   d. THYROID NOTCH
   e. ANGLE OF THYROID
   f. LAMINA

3. Please identify the indicated landmarks on the figure below.
   a. MUSCULAR process
   b. VOCAL process

4. Please identify the muscles indicated below.
   a. TRANSVERSE ARYTENOID
   b. OBLIQUE ARYTENOID
   c. POSTERIOR CRICOARYTENOID

5. Please identify the muscles indicated below.
   a. MYLOHYOID
   b. DIGASTRICUS ANTERIOR

   c. <u>DIGASTRICUS POSTERIOR</u>

   d. <u>STYLOHYOID</u>

6. Please identify the muscles indicated below.

   a. <u>GENIOHYOID</u>

   b. <u>DIGASTRICUS ANTERIOR</u>

   c. <u>DIGASTRICUS POSTERIOR</u>

   d. <u>MYLOHYOID</u>

7. This is a view of the laryngeal opening from above. Please identify the structures indicated

   a. <u>ARYEPIGLOTTIC FOLD</u>

   b. <u>TRUE VOCAL FOLDS</u>

   c. <u>VALLECULAE</u>

   d. <u>EPIGLOTTIS</u>

8. Please identify the two muscles indicated below.

   a. <u>THYROVOCALIS</u>

   b. <u>THYROMUSCULARIS</u>

9. The <u>CRICOTHYROID</u> muscle is the primary muscle responsible for change of vocal fundamental frequency.

10. The space between the vocal folds is termed the <u>GLOTTIS</u>.

11. The <u>BERNOULLI</u> effect states that, given a constant volume flow of air or fluid, at a point of constriction there will be a decrease in air pressure perpendicular to the flow and an increase in velocity of the flow.

REFERENCES

Adair, R. K. (1995). The physics of baseball. *Physics Today, 48*(5), 26–31.

Aronson, E. A. (1985). *Clinical voice disorders.* New York: Thieme.

Baer, T., Sasaki, C., & Harris, K. (1985). *Laryngeal function in phonation and respiration.* Boston, MA: College-Hill Press.

Bateman, H. E. (1977). *A clinical approach to speech anatomy and physiology.* Springfield, IL: Charles C. Thomas.

Bless, D. M., & Abbs, J. H. (1983). *Vocal fold physiology.* San Diego, CA: College-Hill Press.

Bly, L. (1994). *Motor skills acquisition in the first year.* Tucson, AZ: Therapy Skill Builders.

Boone, D. R. (1977). *The voice and voice therapy.* Englewood Cliffs, NJ: Prentice-Hall.

Broad, D. J. (1973). *Phonation*. In F. D. Minifie, T. J. Hixon, & F. Williams, (Eds.), *Normal aspects of speech, hearing, and language*. Englewood Cliffs, NJ: Prentice-Hall.

Chusid, J. G. (1979). *Correlative neuroanatomy and functional neurology (17th ed.)*. Los Altos, CA: Lange Medical Publications.

Daniloff, R. G. (1989) *Speech science*. San Diego, CA: College-Hill Press.

Durrant, J. D., & Lovrinic, J. H. (1984). *Bases of hearing science*. Baltimore, MD: Williams & Wilkins.

Fink, B. R., & Demarest, R. J. (1978). *Laryngeal biomechanics*. Cambridge, MA: Harvard University Press.

Fink, B. R. (1975). *The human larynx*. New York: Raven Press.

Frable, M. A. (1961). Computation of motion of the cricoarytenoid joint. *Archives of Otolaryngology, 73*, 551–556.

Fujimura, O. (1988). *Vocal fold physiology. Vol. 2. Vocal physiology*. New York: Raven Press.

Fukida, H., Kawaida, M., Tatehara, T., Ling, E., Kita, K., Ohki, K., Kawasaki, Y. & Saito, S. (1988). A new concept of lubricating mechanisms of the larynx. In Fujimura, O. (Ed.), *Vocal physiology: Voice production, mechanisms and functions* (pp. 83–92). New York: Raven Press.

Gosling, J. A., Harris, P. F., Humpherson, J. R., Whitmore, I., & Willan, P. L. T. (1985). *Atlas of human anatomy*. Philadelphia, PA: J. B. Lippincott.

Grobler, N. J. (1977). *Textbook of clinical anatomy* (Vol. 1). Amsterdam: Elsevier Scientific.

Hirano, M. (1974). Morphological structure of the vocal cord as a vibrator and its variations. *Folia Phoniatrica, 26*, 89–94.

Hirano, M., Kirchner, J. A., & Bless, D. M. (1987). *Neurolaryngology*. Boston, MA: College-Hill Press.

Hirano, M., Kiyokawa, K., & Kurita, S. (1988). Laryngeal muscles and glottic shaping. In O. Fujimura, (Ed.), *Vocal physiology: Voice production, mechanisms and functions* (pp. 49–65). New York: Raven Press.

Jones-Owens, J. L. (1991). Prespeech assessment and treatment strategies. In M. B. Langley, & L. J. Lombardino, (Eds.), *Neurodevelopmental strategies for managing communication disorders in children with severe motor dysfunction*. Austin, TX: Pro-Ed.

Kaplan, H. M. (1971). *Anatomy and physiology of speech*. New York: McGraw-Hill.

Kirchner, J. A., & Suzuki, M. (1968). Laryngeal reflexes and voice production. In M. Krauss, (Ed.) Sound Production in Man. *Annals of the New York Academy of Sciences, 155*, 98–109.

Kuehn, D. P., Lemme, M. L., & Baumgartner, J. M. (1989). *Neural bases of speech, hearing, and language*. Boston, MA: Little, Brown.

Langley, M. B., & Lombardino, L. J. (1991). *Neurodevelopmental strategies for managing communication disorders in children with severe motor dysfunction*. Austin, TX: Pro-Ed.

Lieberman, P. (1968). *Intonation, perception, and language*. Research Monograph No. 38. Cambridge, MA: The M.I.T. Press.

Lieberman, P. (1977). *Speech physiology and acoustic phonetics: An introduction*. New York: Macmillan.

Logemann, J. (1983). *Evaluation and treatment of swallowing disorders*. Boston, MA: College-Hill Press.

McMinn, R. M. H., Hutchings, R. T., & Logan, B. M. (1994). *Color atlas of head and neck anatomy*. London: Mosby-Wolfe.

Netter, F. H. (1983). *The CIBA collection of medical illustrations. Vol. 1. Nervous System. Part I. Anatomy and physiology.* West Caldwell, NJ: CIBA Pharmaceutical Company.

Netter, F. H. (1983). *The CIBA collection of medical illustrations. Vol. 1. Nervous system. Part II. Neurologic and neuromuscular disorders.* West Caldwell, NJ: CIBA Pharmaceutical Company.

Netter, F. H. (1989). *Atlas of human anatomy.* West Caldwell, NJ: CIBA Pharmaceutical Company.

Proctor, D. F. (1968). The physiologic basis of voice training. In M. Krauss, (Ed.), Sound Production in Man. *Annals of the New York Academy of Sciences, 155,* 208–228.

Rohen, J. W., & Yokochi, C. (1993). *Color atlas of anatomy.* New York: Igaku-Shoin.

Sonninen, A. (1968). The external frame function in the control of pitch in the human voice. In M. Krauss, (Ed.), Sound Production in Man. *Annals of the New York Academy of Sciences, 155,* 68–89.

Titze, I. R. (1994). *Principles of voice production.* Englewood Cliffs, NJ: Prentice-Hall.

Van den Berg, J. (1968). Sound production in isolated human larynges. In M. Krauss, (Ed.) Sound Production in Man. *Annals of the New York Academy of Sciences, 155,* 18–27.

Verdolini, K., Titze, I. R., & Fennell, A. (1994). Dependence of phonatory effort on hydration level. *Journal of speech & hearing research, 37,* 1001–1007.

Whillis, J. (1946). Movements of the tongue in swallowing. *Journal of anatomy, 80,* 115–116.

Williams, P. & Warrick, R. (1980). *Gray's anatomy* (36th Brit. ed.). Philadelphia, PA: W. B. Saunders.

Zemlin, W. R. (1988). *Speech & hearing science. Anatomy and physiology.* Englewood Cliffs, NJ: Prentice-Hall.

CHAPTER

6

Physiology of Phonation

Discussion of the function of the larynx and vocal folds revolves around the movable components and the results of that movement. We will concentrate on the nonspeech functions initially, which will help as we talk about speech and vocal function. We use these nonspeech functions in our treatment of voice disorders, and this discussion may serve you well.

NONSPEECH LARYNGEAL FUNCTION

As we noted in Chapter 5, the protective function of the larynx is its most important role, because failure to prohibit entry of foreign objects into the lungs is life-threatening. This function is fulfilled through the cough and other associated reflexive gestures.

Coughing is a response by the tissue of the respiratory passageway to an irritant or foreign object, mediated by the visceral afferent (sensory) portion of the X vagus innervating the bronchial mucosa. Coughing is a violent and broadly predictable behavior, which includes deep inhalation through widely abducted vocal folds, followed by tensing and tight adduction of the vocal folds and elevation of the larynx. The axis of rotation of the arytenoids guarantees that, as they are moved for adduction, they also are directed somewhat downward, providing more force in opposition to expiration. Significant positive subglottal pressure for the cough comes from tissue recoil and muscles of expiration. The high pressure of forced expiration blows the vocal folds apart.

The aerodynamic benefit of this is that the person coughing generates a maximal flow of air through the passageway to expel the irritating object. The negative side of the cough is the force required for its production. Chronic irritation of the respiratory system leads to vocal abuse in the form of repeated coughing.

The "near cousin" of the cough is **throat clearing**. It is not as violent as the full cough, but is nonetheless stressful. If you will spend a quiet moment clearing your throat and feeling its effects, you will sense increased respiratory effort that is countered by tightening of the laryngeal musculature. You build pressure in the subglottal region and clamp the vocal folds shut to restrain the pressure. Although this clamping serves a purpose in that it permits you to clear your respiratory passageway of mucus, it also places the delicate tissues of the vocal folds under a great deal of strain, and the result can be catastrophic to a trained voice.

There is a positive clinical side to this gesture, as well. If a client cannot approximate the vocal folds because of muscular weakness, the clinician has a means of achieving this closure in the cough. If you can get a client to cough voluntarily, you can very likely get the client to phonate. Both of these gestures involve the muscles of adduction: lateral cricoarytenoid, arytenoids, and lateral thyromuscularis. The medial compression generated in the cough is quite large, rivaled only by that required for abdominal fixation.

Abdominal fixation is the process of capturing air within the thorax to provide the muscles with a structure on which to push or pull. The laryngeal gesture of this effort closure is one form of the Valsalva maneuver. The preparatory gesture for thorax/abdomen fixation is similar to that for the cough: Take in a large inspiratory charge, followed by tight adduction of the vocal folds. The effect is for the thorax to become a relatively rigid frame, so that the forces applied for lifting are translated to the legs. If the thorax is not fixed, those forces will act on the thorax instead, causing the rib cage to be depressed.

You may have wondered why you tend to grunt when lifting heavy objects or pushing your car. All of the components are there for phonation. You are using force that would cause expiration, and your vocal folds are adducted. With sufficient effort, some air escapes through the adducted vocal folds, and you hear the grunt.

So far we have dealt primarily with laryngeal functions focused only on tight adduction of the vocal folds, but abduction has its place as well. Abduction dilates the larynx, an important function for physical exertion. You will recall from Chapter 4 that physical requirements for oxygen increase significantly during work and exertion. During normal quiet respiration the vocal folds are abducted to provide a width of about 8 mm in the adult. During forced respiration the need for air cause you to **dilate** or open the respiratory tract as widely as possible, doubling that width (see Figure 6–1).

Abdominal fixation plays an important role in child birth, defecation, and vomiting. Review the Clinical Notes of Chapter 3 to refresh your memory.

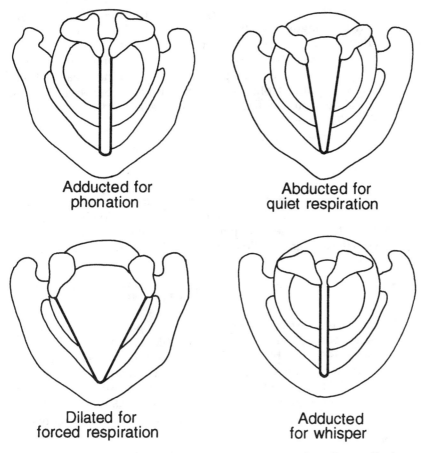

Adducted for
phonation

Abducted for
quiet respiration

Dilated for
forced respiration

Adducted
for whisper

FIGURE 6–1. Laryngeal postures for various functions. During adduction for phonation the vocal folds are approximated. For quiet respiration the folds are moderately abducted, but for forced respiration they are widely separated. Adduction for whisper involves bringing the folds close together but retaining an open space between the arytenoid cartilages.

Reflexes are involuntary, although respiratory reflexes can come under some voluntary control (e.g., you can hold your breath or stifle a yawn). We eventually *must* breathe, which requires reflexively abducting the vocal folds. In cases of drowning and near-drowning, the victim may attempt to maintain adducted vocal folds, but must eventually attempt to breathe despite all logic that militates against it. In addition, individuals rapidly immersed in cold water will reflexively gasp for air, and the ability to inhibit this reflex is significantly reduced by alcohol consumption (a fact that explains one of the risks of combining drinking and boating).

A bolus is a mass of chewed food formed into a ball in preparation for swallowing.

We will discuss the **swallowing reflex** more fully in Chapter 8, but it needs to be mentioned here. During normal deglutition, a bolus of food will trigger a swallowing reflex as it passes into the region behind the tongue and above the larynx. When the reflex is triggered, the larynx elevates, and the epiglottis (attached to the root of the tongue) drops down to cover the aditus. The aryepiglottic folds tense by action of the aryepiglottic muscle, and the vocal folds are adducted. Try this: Hold your finger lightly on your thyroid notch and swallow. You may feel your larynx elevate and tense up as you swallow. That finger on the thyroid, by the way, is one component of the swallowing evaluation.

In summary:

■ We use the larynx and associated structures for many **nonspeech functions,** including coughing, throat-clearing, and abdominal fixation.
■ These functions serve important biological needs, and provide us with the background for useful clinical intervention techniques.

LARYNGEAL FUNCTION FOR SPEECH

Phonation is an extremely important component of the speech signal. To accomplish phonation we must achieve three basic laryngeal adjustments. To *start* phonation, we must adduct the vocal folds, moving them into the air stream, referred to as **vocal attack**. We then hold the vocal folds in a fixed position in the airstream as the aerodynamics of phonation control the actual vibration associated with **sustained phonation**. Finally, we abduct the vocal folds to **terminate** phonation.

Attack

When we are *not* phonating the vocal folds are sufficiently abducted to prohibit air turbulence in the airway to start audible vibration of the vocal folds. To initiate voicing, we bring the vocal folds close enough together that the forces of turbulence can cause vocal fold vibration. **Attack** is the process of bringing vocal folds together to *begin* phonation, and this requires muscular action. Vocal attack occurs quite frequently in running speech. If you were to say the sentence "Anatomy is not for the faint of heart" you would have brought the vocal folds together and drawn them apart at least six times in 2 seconds to accommodate voiced and voiceless phonemes.

There are three basic types of attack. When we initiate phonation using **simultaneous vocal attack,** we coordinate adduction and onset of respiration so that they occur simultaneously. The vocal folds reach the critical degree of adduction at the same time that the respiratory flow is adequate to support phonation. Chances are you are using simultaneous attack when you say the word "zany," because to start the flow of air before voicing would add the unvoiced /s/ to the beginning of the word, although adducting the vocal folds before producing the first sound would add a glottal stop to production.

Breathy vocal attack involves starting significant airflow before adducting the vocal folds. This occurs frequently during running speech, because we keep air flowing throughout production of long strings of words. Say the following sentence while attending to the airflow over your tongue and past your lips: "Harry is my friend." If you did this, you felt the constant airflow that says that some of the adductions involved had to be produced with air already flowing.

The third type of attack is **glottal attack.** In this attack, adduction of the vocal folds occurs prior to the airflow, much like a cough. Try this. Bring your vocal folds together (be gentle!) as if to cough, but instead of opening your vocal folds as you push air through the folds, keep them adducted and say /a/. That was a glottal attack. You might have felt a little tension or irritation from doing this exercise, a reminder of the delicacy of the vocal mechanism. We use glottal attack when a word begins with a stressed vowel. Say the following sentence and pay close attention to your vocal folds during production of the first phoneme of the underlined words: "*Okay, I* want the car." If you noticed a build-up of tension and pressure for those words, you were experiencing glottal attack.

All three of these attacks are quite functional in speech and are not at all pathological. Problems occur when an attack is misused. If a glottal attack becomes a **hard glottal attack**, the speaker may damage the delicate vocal mechanism tissues. If the speaker inadequately adducts the vocal folds, air may escape between them to produce a **breathy phonation**, although much more common will be breathy voice caused by obstruction of adduction by a physical tissue change.

Termination

We bring the vocal folds together to begin phonation, and **termination** of phonation requires that we abduct them. We pull the vocal folds out

Ventricular Phonation

The false or ventricular vocal folds are technically unable to vibrate for voice, but in some instances clients may use them for this purpose. Boone (1971) cites instances in which clients use ventricular phonation as an adaptive response to severe vocal fold dysfunction, such as growths on the folds. Apparently the client forces the lateral superior walls closely together during the adductory gesture, permitting the folds to make contact and vibrate.

The ventricular folds are thick, and the phonation heard is deep and often raspy. The false folds may **hypertrophy** (increase in size), facilitating ventricular phonation.

of the airstream far enough to reduce the turbulence using muscular action. When the turbulence is sufficiently reduced, the vocal folds stop vibrating. As with attack, we terminate phonation many times during running speech to accommodate voiced and voiceless speech sounds.

Both adduction and abduction occur very rapidly. Muscles controlling these functions can complete contraction within about 9 msec (9/1000 seconds). In running speech, you may see periods of vibration of the vocal folds as brief as three cycles of vibration (approximately 25 msec) for unstressed vowels, which would bring total adduction, phonation, and abduction time to only 53/1000 of a second!

Adduction is a constant in all types of attack. The arytenoid cartilages are capable of moving in three dimensions, including **rotating, rocking,** and **gliding**. It appears that the primary arytenoid gesture for adduction is inward rocking. When the arytenoids are pulled medially on the convex arytenoid facet of the cricoid, the result is that the arytenoids will rock down, with apices approaching each other. (You may wish to review Figure 5–14 in Chapter 5.) Some rotatory movement will occur during movement of the arytenoid, but it appears to be greatest at the extremes of lateral movement (i.e., nearly abducted; Fink, 1975). These motions are the product of the lateral cricoarytenoid muscle and the lateral portion of the thyromuscularis, facilitated by the oblique and transverse arytenoids. The arytenoid cartilages are also capable of limited gliding in the anterior-posterior dimension that could alter total vocal fold length. Adduction does not seem to affect the overall length of the glottis, although it will tend to lengthen the membranous portion. The combined forces of the cricothyroid and posterior cricoarytenoid cause the entire glottis to lengthen (Hirano, Kiyokawa, & Kurita, 1988).

Vocal Fold Nodules

Vocal fold nodules are aggregates of tissue arising from abuse. This condition makes up a large share of the voice disorder cases seen by school clinicians. Common forms of vocal abuse are yelling, screaming, cheerleading, or "barking" commands (such as a drill sergeant). The result of this abuse is a sequence of events that can lead to permanent change in the vocal fold tissue. You are probably familiar with **laryngitis**, which is hoarseness, often with loss of voice (**aphonia**). The laryngeal effect is swelling (**edema**) of the delicate vocal fold tissue, so that it is difficult to make the folds vibrate. In fact, they are often bowed so badly that expiratory flow will pass between them, even if you can produce phonation, and we refer to this as a **breathy voice**. Laryngitis may easily be caused by **vocal hyperfunction**, which is over-adduction of the vocal folds. This is a form of **vocal abuse**, and you may have experienced it after a particularly thrilling football game.

The soreness is a message from your body to stop doing what made the vocal folds sore in the first place. Continued abuse results in a protective layer of epithelium which is callous-like and is not a very effective oscillator. If the vocal hyperfunction continues, the hardened tissue will increase in size until a nodule may be found on one (**unilateral**) or both (**bilateral**) vocal folds. The site of abuse is usually at the juncture of the anterior and middle thirds of the vocal folds, because this is the point of greatest impact during phonation. Although untreated vocal nodules may eventually have to be removed surgically, voice therapy to reverse the vocal behavior driving the phenomenon is always appropriate. If the vocal hyperfunction is not eliminated, the vocal nodules will return after surgery, and surgery may be avoided if therapy is sought in a timely manner.

Sustained Phonation

Sustained phonation is the purpose of adduction and abduction for speech. Let us examine this closely.

Vocal attack requires muscular action, as does termination of phonation. In contrast, sustaining phonation simply requires *maintenance* of a laryngeal posture through **tonic** (sustained tensing) contraction of musculature. This is a very important point. The vibration of the vocal folds is achieved by placing and holding the vocal folds in the airstream in a manner that permits their physical qualities to interact with the airflow, thereby causing vibration. The vocal folds are *held* in place during sustained phonation, and vibration of the vocal folds is *not* the product of repeated adduction and abduction of the vocal folds.

Phonation actually begins a few milliseconds prior to the vocal fold approximation. As the vocal folds are brought together during attack, they begin vibrating as the turbulence increases, and this vibration is sustained as long as the folds are approximated and there is sufficient subglottal air pressure. By the way, vocal folds need not be touching to vibrate, as you can demonstrate for yourself. Begin the word "hairy" by stretching out the /h/ sound, and then let that breathiness carry forward into the vowel. The vocal folds very likely are not touching or are making only very light contact if you hear a breathy quality.

Vocal Register

Asking clients to practice adding /h/ to the beginning of words is a useful tool for reducing vocal hyperfunction.

The **mode of vibration** of the vocal folds during sustained phonation refers to the pattern of activity that the vocal folds undergo during a cycle of vibration. Moving from one point in the vibratory pattern to the same point again defines one **cycle** of vibration, and within one cycle the vocal folds undergo some very significant changes. There are actually a number of modes or **vocal registers** that have been differentiated perceptually. Narrowly defined for purposes of phonatory discussion, **register** refers to differences in mode of vibration of the vocal folds.

Trained singers will refer to combinations of thorax/oral/nasal cavity configurations, laryngeal gestures, and muscular "concentrations" to define registers which are perceptually differentiable but about which there are few acoustical or physiological data: See Titze (1994) for a lively discussion of register.

The three registers most commonly referred to are modal register, glottal fry or pulse register, and falsetto. We will be also interested in the variant breathy and pressed phonatory modes, as well as whispered speech.

Modal Register

The first register, known as the **modal register** or modal phonation refers to the pattern of phonation used in daily conversation. This pattern is the most important one for the speech-language pathologist, and it is the most efficient.

The "mode" is that which occurs most often in a distribution.

Figure 6–2 shows the vocal folds from the sides and from above, which will let us talk about the vertical and anterior-posterior modes of phonation. In the **vertical mode** of phonation, the vocal folds *open* from inferior to superior (bottom to top), and also *close* from inferior to superior. You might suspect that they would open and close like a door swinging on a hinge, but that is not the case. The folds are an undulating wave of tissue, and it is more appropriate to think of air as "bubbling" through the adducted folds than of them opening and closing as if hinged.

You can see from the first panel of Figure 6–2 that the vocal folds are approximated at the beginning of a cycle of vibration. In the second

Sustained and Maximum Phonation

Physical systems, such as those encompassing the mechanisms of speech, are rarely employed at maximum output and stress. For instance, we generally don't breathe in maximally or speak using our entire vital capacity, although we are capable of doing this. When clinicians wish to examine whether there is a deficit in a system, one useful technique is to ask the client to perform a test of maximal output for a given parameter. In respiration, such tests would be examination of vital capacity, inspiratory reserve, and expiratory reserve.

This useful concept may be extended to voicing. If you ask a client to sustain a vowel for as long as he or she can, you are testing not only how well the vocal folds function but the vital capacity *and* checking action ability of the person under examination. If the respiratory system is intact, on average an adult female in the 17- to 41-year-old range will be able to sustain the /a/ vowel for approximately 15 seconds, and the male will be able to sustain that vowel for 23 seconds. This function changes with age, increasing through the second decade of life. Generally you may expect the phonation time of children to increase from about 10 seconds at 6 years, but you may be interested in looking at the norms by age as summarized by Kent, Kent, and Rosenbek (1987). By the way, did you wonder why males are able to phonate a little longer? If you blamed it on larger vital capacity, you were right.

Another phonation-related task involves maximum duration of the sustained sibilants, /s/ and /z/. Boone (1977) states that individuals are able to sustain these phonemes for approximately the same durations, but that the addition of physical change to the vocal folds (such as vocal nodules) will cause a significant reduction in the duration of the voiced /z/. Males again produce longer fricatives, and the duration increases with age. Clinicians calculate the ratio of s:z duration to aid their decisions. If the two durations are the same, the value will be 1.0, whereas as the /z/ duration drops, the ratio will increase. Although the ratio undergoes continual examination for its clinical utility, many studies have substantiated the use of this clinical tool.

panel, air pressure from beneath is forcing the folds apart in the inferior aspect. (This makes sense, because that is where the pressure is located.) In the third panel, the bubble of air has moved upward so that the superior portion of the folds is now open, and in Panel E you can see that they are closing again. Note that they begin closing at the bottom: They open at the bottom first, and they start closing first at the bottom as well. In the final panel the cycle is complete.

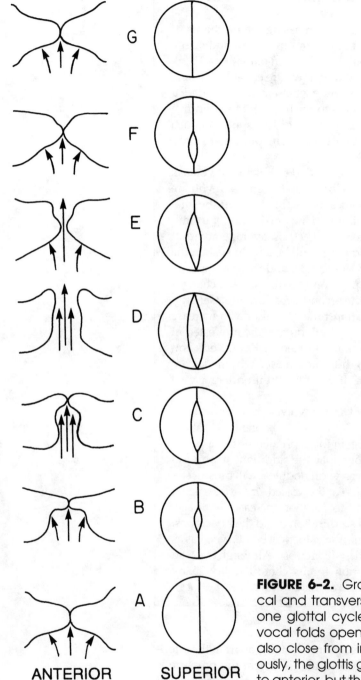

G

F

E

D

C

B

A

ANTERIOR VIEW

SUPERIOR VIEW

FIGURE 6–2. Graphic representation of vertical and transverse phase relationships during one glottal cycle. Notice that generally the vocal folds open from inferior to superior and also close from inferior to superior. Simultaneously, the glottis grows generally from posterior to anterior, but the vocal folds close from anterior to posterior.

Titze (1994) has demonstrated that this phase difference in the mucosal wave from inferior to superior is a result of the mass and elasticity of the vocal folds, and that these conditions support continued **oscillation** by the vocal folds (i.e., the tissue continues to vibrate after the energy has been removed). You are able to change the tension and mass per unit length to arrive at a given, relatively constant laryngeal tone.

The vocal folds have one *primary* frequency of vibration, called the **vocal fundamental frequency**, but they produce an extremely rich set of harmonics as well, which are whole-number multiples of the fundamental. These harmonics provide important acoustical information for identification of voiced phonemes. If the vocal folds were simple tuning forks without these harmonics, we would not be able to tell one vowel from another. The complex vibrational mode of the vocal folds is extremely important.

The second mode of vibration of the vocal folds is in the **anterior-posterior** dimension. Whereas the vertical phase difference appears to be consistent in modal vibration, the anterior-posterior mode is less stereotypical. Zemlin (1988) reports that the vocal folds tend to open from posterior to anterior, but that closure at the end of a cycle is made by contact of the medial edge of the vocal fold, but with the posterior closing last.

Because the vocal folds offer resistance to air flow, the **minimum driving pressure** of the vocal folds in modal phonation is approximately 3–5 cm H_2O subglottal pressure. If pressure is lower than this, the folds will not be blown apart. This is clinically important, because a client who cannot generate 3–5 cm H_2O and sustain it for 5 seconds will not be able to use the vocal folds for speech. (See the Clinical Note on measurement of subglottal pressure and Figure 6–3.)

Glottal Fry

The second register is known as **glottal fry**, but is known also as **pulse register** and **Strohbass** ("straw bass"). What "fry," "pulse," and "straw bass" all allude to is the crackly, "popcorn" quality of this voice. Perceptually, this voice is extremely low in pitch and sounds rough, almost like eggs frying in a pan. Some voice scientists jokingly refer to it as the "I'm sick" voice, as it is the weak, low-pitched voice you might use to explain the reason you cannot come to work today.

Glottal fry is the product of a complex glottal configuration, and it occurs in frequencies ranging as low as 30 Hz, up to 80 or 90 Hz. This mode of vibration requires low subglottal pressure to sustain it (on the order of 2 cm H_2O), and tension of the vocalis is significantly reduced relative to modal vibration, so that the vibrating margin is flaccid and thick. The lateral portion of the vocal folds is tensed, so that there is strong medial compression with short, thick vocal folds and low sub-

FIGURE 6-3. A useful clinical tool described by Hixon, Hawley, and Wilson (1982). This portable manometer gives the client feedback concerning respiratory ability and provides the clinician with a measure of function.

glottal pressure. If either vocalis tension or subglottal pressure is increased, the popcorn-like perception of this mode of vibration is lost.

In glottal fry, the vocal folds take on a secondary, syncopated mode of vibration, such that there is a secondary beat for every cycle of the fundamental frequency. In addition to this syncopation, the vocal folds spend up to 90% of the cycle in approximation. Oscillographic waveforms of modal vibration and glottal fry are shown in Figure 6–4, and the presence of the extra beat may be clearly seen. This should re-emphasize the notion that the vocal folds are not simply vibrating at a slower rate than in modal phonation, but are vibrating *differently*.

In music, **syncopation** *is the change in accent arising from stressing of a weak beat. In the case of glottal fry this definition is stretched to accommodate the notion of including a weak beat in the rhythm. Glottal fry appears to include both weak and strong beats.*

Falsetto

The third and highest register of phonation, the **falsetto**, also is characterized by a vibratory pattern that varies from modal production. In falsetto, the vocal folds lengthen and become extremely thin and

Clinical Measurement of Subglottal Air Pressure

Hixon, Hawley, and Wilson (1982) have provided us with an excellent and simple tool to assess adequacy of subglottal pressure for speech. In their article, the authors recommend marking a cup of water in cm gradations (see Figure 6–3). Place a small pin-hole in a flexible soda straw, and put a paper clip over the straw so that it may be held onto the edge of the glass. Fill the glass up to the top centimeter mark.

As you push the straw deeper into the water, it becomes increasingly more difficult to blow bubbles in the water through the straw. At the point where the straw is three centimeters below the water line you must generate 3 cm H_2O subglottal pressure to make bubbles.

When assessing a client for adequacy of subglottal pressure, you can have the individual begin blowing as you push the straw into the water. The point at which bubbles no longer flow is the limit of the individual's pressure ability. This is an excellent therapy tool, as well, because it provides a practice device with visual feedback of progress toward improved respiratory support for speech.

FIGURE 6–4. Oscillographic comparison of glottal fry *(top)* and modal phonation for the vowel /a/ *(bottom)*.

"reedlike." When set into vibration, they tend to vibrate along the tensed, bowed margins, in contrast to the complex pattern seen in other modes of phonation. The vocal folds make contact only briefly, as compared with modal phonation, and the degree of movement (amplitude of excursion) is reduced. The posterior portion of the vocal folds tends to be damped, so that the length of the vibrating surface is decreased to a narrow opening. Contrast this to elevated pitch in modal phonation, which involves *lengthening* the vocal folds.

The perception of falsetto is one of an extremely "thin," high-pitched vocal production. The difference between falsetto and modal vibration is not simply one of the frequency of vibration (in the 300 to 600 Hz range). Although it is true that falsetto is the highest register, the modal and falsetto registers overlap.

Whistle Register. There is actually a register above falsetto, known as the **whistle register**, but it is not apparently a mode of vibration as much as it is the product of turbulence on the edge of the vocal fold. It occurs at frequencies as high as 2500 Hz, typically in females, and sounds very much like a whistle.

The shift from modal register to glottal fry or falsetto is clearly audible in the untrained voice. If you perform an up-glide of a sung note, reaching up to your highest production, you will hear an audible "break" in voice as you enter that register. Trained singers learn to smooth that transition so that it is inaudible.

Pressed and Breathy Phonation

There are two variations on modal phonation that we should mention. **Pressed** phonation is one in which medial compression is greatly increased. The product of pressed phonation is an increase in the strident or harsh quality, as well as an increase in abuse to the voice. Greater medial compression *is* translated as stronger, louder phonation, perhaps commanding greater attention. This forceful adduction often results in damage to the vocal fold tissue.

Breathy voice may be the product of the other end of this tension spectrum. If the vocal folds are inadequately approximated so that the vibrating margins permit excessive airflow between them when in the closed phase, you will hear air escape as a **breathy** phonation. Breathiness is inefficient and causes air wastage, but is not a condition that will damage the phonatory mechanism.

There is potential danger in the breathy voice, however. The underlying factor keeping the vocal folds from approximating also could be any of a number of organic conditions, so that even when the speaker pushes the vocal folds tightly together, air escapes. In this case, breathy voice may signal the presence of vocal nodules, or even benign or

Puberphonia

During normal development, children undergo a great deal of change during **puberty**, the time in a child's life when he or she becomes capable of reproduction. This occurs between 13 and 15 years for boys and between 9 and 16 years for girls and is characterized by rapid muscle development and height and weight gain. The thyroid cartilage and thyroarytenoid are not left out of development. They grow rapidly during this time, although the larynges of boys will grow considerably more than those of girls.

The result of this spurt of laryngeal growth is that the child (typically a boy) will have periods of voice change (**mutation**) in which his voice "breaks" down in pitch as he is speaking. This is, of course, a normal result of the changing tissue and the young man's attempt to control it for phonation, but it is nonetheless disturbing. **Puberphonia** refers to the maintenance of the childhood pitch despite having passed through the developmental stage of puberty. It surely represents an attempt to hold *something* constant during the roller-coaster ride of puberty, but the result is a significant mismatch between the large body of the developing teenaged boy and the high-pitched voice of the prepubescent child. Typically, the young man is speaking in falsetto but is aware of the "lower" voice. Therapy performed over the summer to help the individual alter habitual pitch, in absence of peer pressures associated with the classroom regimen, is quite effective.

malignant growths such as polyps or laryngeal cancer. In addition, if an individual attempts to overcome the breathy quality caused by nodules or other obstructing pathology, the vocal hyperfunction will be abuse.

Whispering

Whispering is not really a phonatory mode, because no voicing occurs. This does *not* mean that there are no laryngeal adjustments, but rather that they do not produce vibration in the vocal folds. Prove this to yourself. Exhale forcefully and attend to your larynx, and then on the next forceful exhalation *whisper* the word "Ha!" You probably felt the tension in your larynx increase during whispering. In respiration the vocal folds are abducted, but when whispering they must be partially adducted and tensed to develop turbulence in the airstream, and that turbulence is the noise you use to make speech. The arytenoid cartilages are rotated slightly in but are separated posteriorly, so that there is an enlarged space in the cartilaginous larynx. It is *not* voiced, but it is strenuous and can cause vocal fatigue. Whispering is not economical, as you can prove to yourself by sustaining production of an /a/ in

Electroglottography

The electroglottograph (EGG) is a useful and nonintrusive instrument for examination of vocal function. A pair of surface electrodes are placed on the thyroid lamina, typically held in place by an elastic band. An extremely small and imperceptible current is introduced through one electrode, and the impedance (resistance to current flow) is measured at the other electrode. When the vocal folds are approximated during phonation, there is less resistance to flow. The less contact the vocal folds make, the greater is the impedance.

This nice arrangement permits researchers to examine at least some aspects of vocal fold function with ease. As you can see from the EGG trace of Figure 6–7, there are marked differences in the duration of vocal fold contact for quiet (a) versus loud (b) speech. For further reading, you may want to review Childers, Hicks, Moore, Eskenazi, and Lalwani (1990).

modal phonation and again in whispered production. You should see quite a difference in maximum duration.

In Chapter 5 we discussed the notion of frequency of vibration. As mentioned earlier in this chapter, the primary frequency of vibration of the vocal folds is called the fundamental frequency. This is the number of cycles the vocal folds go through per second, and it is audible. The movement of the vocal folds in air produces an audible disturbance in the medium of air known as **sound**. That sound is transmitted through the air as a wave, with molecules being compressed by movement of the vocal folds.

In Chapter 5 we also discussed the notion of periodicity. The interplay of the elasticity and mass of the vocal folds leads them to vibrate in a periodic fashion. However, we have not yet mentioned a final element of phonation, intensity. **Intensity** refers to the relative power or pressure of an acoustic signal, measured in decibels (abbreviated **dB**). In phonation, we may refer to the intensity of voice as **vocal intensity**. Intensity is a direct function of the amount of pressure exerted by the *sound wave* (as opposed to air pressure, as generated by the respiratory system). As molecules vibrate from movement of the vocal folds the movement of molecules exerts an extremely small but measurable force over an area, and that is defined as pressure. The larger is the excursion of the vibrating body, the greater will be the intensity of the signal produced because air will be displaced with greater force. The next two sections deal with frequency and intensity of vocal fold vibration.

To summarize:

- We must adduct the vocal folds to **initiate phonation,** and this may take several forms, including **breathy, simultaneous,** and **glottal attacks.**
- Conversational speech will naturally encompass all of these, although overuse of glottal attack in inappropriate contexts may be problematic.
- **Termination** of **phonation** requires abduction of the vocal folds, a process which must occur with the transition of voiced to voiceless speech sounds.
- **Sustained phonation** may take several forms, dependent upon the laryngeal configuration.
- **Modal phonation** will, by definition, characterize most speech.
- **Falsetto** occupies the upper range of laryngeal function, while **glottal fry** is found in the lower range.
- Vocal fold vibration varies for each of these phonatory modes, and the differences are governed by **laryngeal tension, medial compression,** and **subglottal pressure**.
- **Breathy phonation** occurs when there is inadequate medial compression to approximate the vocal folds, while **whispering** arises from tensing the vocal fold margins while holding the folds in a partially adducted position.

Frequency, Pitch, and Pitch Change

Pitch is the psychological correlate of frequency and is closely related to frequency: As frequency increases, pitch increases, and as frequency decreases, so does pitch. It is an important element in speech perception. Therefore, we should closely examine the mechanism of pitch change.

The vocal folds are made up of masses and elastic elements that tend to promote oscillation or repeated vibration at the same frequency. Because of these qualities the vocal folds will tend to vibrate at the same frequency when mass and elastic elements remain constant. However, the frequency of vibration will change when these characteristics are altered.

There are several important terms with which we should become familiar. Unfortunately, most of these terms refer to perceived *pitch* when they really should refer to physical *frequency*! Let us take a look at optimal and habitual pitch, average fundamental frequency, and range of fundamental frequency.

Optimal Pitch

The term **optimal pitch** is used to refer to the pitch (actually, the *frequency*) of vocal fold vibration that is optimal or most appropriate for

*An **octave** is a doubling of frequency, so that the octave beginning at 120 Hz will end at 240 Hz, the octave beginning at 203 Hz will end at 406 Hz and so forth.*

an individual. This frequency of vibration will be the most efficient for a given pair of vocal folds, and is a function of the mass and elasticity of the vocal folds. Some voice scientists and clinicians estimate optimal pitch directly from the individual's range of phonation, because it is considered to be approximately 1/4 octave above the lowest frequency of vibration of an individual. Others will estimate it from a cough or throat-clearing, because frequency of the vibrating vocal folds during throat-clearing will approximate conditions associated with conversational frequency, but without psychological conditions associated with use of phonation for communication.

Optimal pitch varies as a function of gender and age. You can expect an adult female to have a fundamental frequency of approximately 230 Hz, whereas the optimal fundamental frequency for adult males will be much lower, around 120 Hz. The reason for this difference has everything to do with tissue mass and length of vocal folds. During puberty, males undergo a significant growth of muscle and cartilage, resulting in greater muscle mass in males than in females. The laryngeal product of this growth is the prominent Adam's apple you can see in boys, as well as a significant drop in fundamental frequency arising from the increased mass of the folds (see Figure 6–5) . Children will have fundamental frequency in the range of 250 Hz, but that rapidly changes in both boys and girls during puberty. Take a look at the clinical note on puberphonia to see the case where fundamental frequency *does not* change with puberty.

Habitual Pitch

We use the term **habitual pitch** to refer to the frequency of vibration of vocal folds that is habitually used during speech. In the ideal condition this would be the same as optimal pitch. For some individuals there are compelling reasons to alter their everyday pitch in speech beyond the range expected for their age, size, or gender. Although the choice to use an abnormally higher or lower fundamental frequency is often not a conscious decision, it will have an effect on phonatory efficiency and effort. When the vocal folds are forced into the extremes of their range of ability, greater effort is required to sustain phonation, and this will result in vocal and physical fatigue. Many different techniques are used to estimate this from a speech sample, including asking the individual to sustain a vowel or sustaining a vowel in a spoken word.

Average Fundamental Frequency

The **average fundamental frequency** of vibration of the vocal folds during phonation may reflect the frequency of vibration of *sustained phonation*, or some other condition, such as conversational speech. This actually reflects habitual pitch over a longer averaging period, and use of conversational speech or reading passages probably more accurate-

Habitual Use of Low Pitch

Habitual use of vocal pitch below optimum can result in **contact ulcers**, open sores on the delicate vocal fold epithelium. These lesions are most often found on the medial margins of the vocal processes and arise from repeated, forceful compression of the arytenoids at that point. Contact ulcers are frequently found in "driven" individuals under a great deal of stress who speak at a frequency habitually below optimum using hard glottal contact. They have also been associated with esophageal reflux, the regurgitation of small quantities of acidic esophageal contents into the pharynx.

Contact ulcers result in vocal fatigue but rarely aphonia. Treatment may include voice therapy to alter habitual pitch and vocal hyperfunction or means to alleviate the reflux.

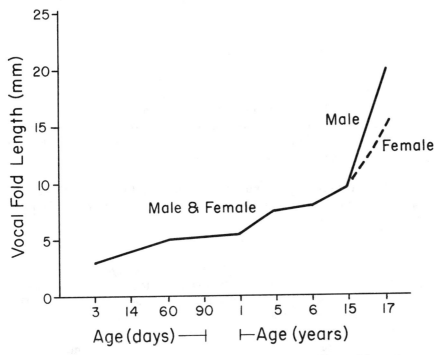

FIGURE 6-5. Changes in vocal fold length for males and females as a function of age. Note that males and females have essentially the same length of vocal folds until puberty, at which time both genders undergo marked physical development. (Data of Kaplan, 1971)

ly reflects an individual's true average rate of vocal fold vibration than a single vowel sample.

Pitch Range

Pitch range refers to the range of fundamental frequency for an individual and is calculated as the difference between the highest and lowest frequencies. The vocal mechanism is quite flexible and is capable of approximately two octaves of change in fundamental frequency from the lowest possible frequency to the highest. An individual with a low fundamental frequency of 90 Hz will be able to reach a high of about 360 Hz (Octave 1 = 90 Hz to 180 Hz; Octave 2 = 180 to 360 Hz). This range is often reduced by laryngeal pathology, for example, vocal nodules. It can be expanded through voice training as well. Let us examine how we make changes in vocal fundamental frequency, hence in perceived pitch.

Pitch Changing Mechanism

Pitch increase comes from stretching and tensing the vocal folds using the cricothyroid and thyrovocalis muscles. Here is the mechanism of this change.

Tension, Length, and Mass

The changeable elements of the vocal folds are tension, length, and mass. We cannot actually change the mass of the vocal folds, but we can change the mass per unit length by spreading the muscle, mucosa, and ligament out over more distance. We also can change the tension of the vocal folds by stretching them tighter or relaxing them. Both of these changes arise from elongation.

The **natural frequency** *of vibration refers to the frequency at which a body vibrates given the mass, tension, and elastic properties of the body.)*

When the cricothyroid muscle is contracted, the thyroid tilts down, lengthening the vocal folds and increasing the fundamental frequency. *When the tension on the vocal folds is increased the natural frequency of vibration will increase.*

The thyrovocalis is a tenser of the vocal folds as well, because contraction of this muscle will pull both cricoid and thyroid closer together, an action opposed by the simultaneously contracted cricothyroid. This tensing process must be opposed by contraction of the posterior cricoarytenoid, although it is not classified as a tenser of the vocal folds.

See Chapter 9 for a discussion of the muscle spindle.

The posterior cricoarytenoid is invested with **muscle spindles**, bodies responsible for monitoring and maintaining tonic muscle length. As the length of this muscle changes, its length may be reflexively controlled to compensate for the stretching force on the vocal folds.

These tensers tend to operate together, but for slightly different function. It is currently believed that the cricothyroid contracts to approximate the degree of tension required for a given frequency of vibration. The thyrovocalis appears to fine tune this adjustment. That is, the cricothyroid makes the gross adjustment, and the thyrovocalis causes the fine movement.

We still have not dealt with mass changes. *As the mass of a vibrating body decreases, frequency of vibration will increase.* The mass of the vocal folds is constant, because to actually increase or decrease mass would require growth of tissue or atrophy, and neither of these processes occurs quickly. Instead, the mass is rearranged by lengthening. When the vocal folds are stretched by contraction of the tensers, the mass of the folds will be distributed over a greater distance, thus reducing mass per unit length.

The effect of the lengthening and tensing gesture is to make vocal folds longer and thinner in appearance. Interestingly, there is evidence that the vocal folds do not lengthen continuously as fundamental frequency increases, but rather that, at some point near or in the falsetto range, the vocal folds again begin to shorten as frequency increases (Nishizawa, Sawashima, & Yonemoto, 1988). Others have found that increased medial compression may effectively shorten the vibrating surface, increasing frequency (van den Berg & Tan, 1959).

Lowering fundamental frequency requires the opposite manipulation. *As mass per unit length increases and tension decreases, fundamental frequency will decrease.* We **relax** the vocal folds by shortening them, moving the cricoid and thyroid closer together in front. This process is achieved by contraction of the thyromuscularis. When it contracts, the vocal folds are relaxed and shortened so that they become more massive and less tense. It appears that there is help from some of the suprahyoid musculature that indirectly pulls up on the thyroid cartilage, shortening the vocal folds by distancing the thyroid from the cricoid.

Subglottal Pressure and Pitch. There also are changes in subglottal pressure that must be reckoned with. *Increasing pitch requires increasing the tension of the system, thereby increasing the glottal resistance to airflow.* If airflow is to remain constant through the glottis, pressure must increase. It appears, however, that the increases in subglottal pressure are a *response* to the increased tension required for frequency change rather than a *cause*. Subglottal pressure does increase, but of itself has little effect on frequency change. It is a delicate balancing act that we perform.

To summarize:

■ **Pitch** is the psychological correlate of frequency of vibration, although the term has come into common usage when referring to phenomena associated with the physical vibration of the vocal folds.

■ **Optimal pitch** refers to the frequency of vibration that is most efficient for a given pair of vocal folds, and **habitual pitch** is the frequency of vibration habitually used by an individual.

■ The **pitch range** of an individual will span approximately two octaves, although it will be reduced by pathology and may be increased through vocal training.

■ Changes in **vocal fundamental frequency** are governed by the tension of the vocal folds and their mass per unit length.

■ Increasing the length of the vocal folds will increase vocal fold tension as well as decrease the mass per unit area.

■ This will increase the fundamental frequency.

■ The **respiratory system** will respond to increased vocal fold tension with **increased subglottal pressure,** so that pitch and subglottal pressure tend to covary.

■ Increased subglottal pressure is a response to increased vocal fold tension.

Intensity and Intensity Change

Just as pitch is the psychological correlate of frequency, **loudness** is the psychological correlate of intensity. **Intensity** (or its correlate, sound pressure level) is the physical measure of power (or pressure) ratios, but loudness is how we perceive power or pressure differences. As with pitch, there is a close relationship between loudness and intensity.

To increase vocal intensity of vibrating vocal folds, one must somehow increase the vigor with which the vocal folds open and close. In sustained phonation, the vocal folds move only as a result of the air pressure beneath them and the flow between them. Subglottal pressure and flow provide the energy for this vocal engine, so to increase the intensity or strength of the phonatory product we will have to increase the energy that drives it. *We increase subglottal pressure to increase vocal intensity*. To prove this to yourself, do the following. You need to feel what you do to produce loud speech. You may be in a quiet setting right now and you really may not want to yell, but that is fine. Pay attention to your lungs and larynx as you *prepare to yell as loudly as you can* to someone across the room. Without even yelling, you should have been able to feel your lungs take in a large charge of air, and you also should have felt your vocal folds tighten up. These are the two gestures of significance for increasing vocal intensity: increased subglottal pressure and medial compression.

Subglottal pressure and increased medial compression vary together, but the causal relationship is better established for vocal intensity than the tension-pressure relationship for pitch. For intensity to increase, the energy source also must increase, so subglottal pressure must rise. To explain the effect that medial compression has on vocal intensity requires a return to discussion of a cycle of vocal fold vibration.

We can break a cycle of vibration into stages, such as an **opening stage**, in which the vocal folds are opening up, a **closing stage**, in which the vocal folds are returning to the point of approximation, and a **closed stage**, in which there is no air escaping between the vocal folds (see Figures 6–6 and 6–7). In modal phonation at conversational intensities,

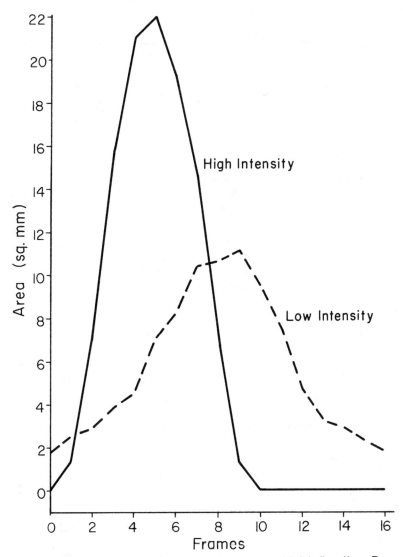

FIGURE 6–6. Effect of vocal intensity on vocal fold vibration. During low-intensity speech the opening and closing phases occupy most of the vibratory cycle, as revealed in the area of the glottis. During high intensity speech the opening phase is greatly compressed, as is the closing phase, while the time spent in closed phase is greatly increased. (Data from Fletcher, 1950)

FIGURE 6-7. Effect of vocal intensity, as shown through electroglottographic trace. The electroglottograph measures impedance across the vocal folds, and the peak represents the closed phase of the glottal cycle. **a.** Conversational level sustained vowel. **b.** High level sustained vowel.

it has been found that the vocal folds spend about 50% of their time in the opening phase, 37% of the time in the closing phase, and 13% of the cycle completely closed. When the vocal folds are tightly adducted for increased vocal intensity, they tend to return to the closed position more quickly and to stay closed for a longer period of time. The opening phase reduces to approximately 33%, while the closed phase increases to over 30%, depending on the intensity increase.

The concept you should retain is this: To increase vocal intensity, the vocal folds are tightly compressed, it takes more force to blow them open, they close more rapidly, and they tend to stay closed because they are tightly compressed. This is the *cause* side of the equation. The *effect* portion is that, because so much energy is required to hold the folds in compression, the release of the folds from this condition is going to be markedly stronger. Each time the folds open they do so with vigor, producing an explosive compression of the air medium. The harder that eruption of the vocal folds is, the greater is the amplitude of the cycle of vibration. Remembering that as the amplitude of the signal increases so does the intensity, you will recognize the increase in intensity between the two panels of Figure 6–8.

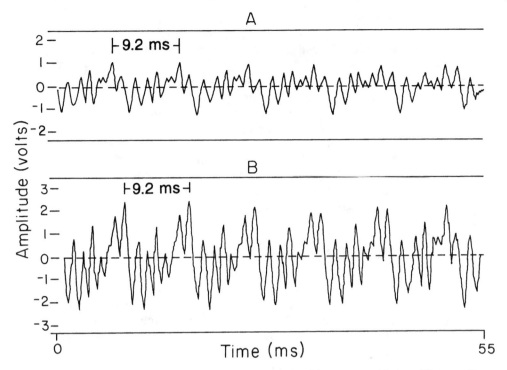

FIGURE 6-8. Oscillogram of sustained vowel at two vocal intensities. **a.** Sustained vowel at conversational level. **b.** Sustained vowel at increased vocal intensity. Although the vocal intensity increases the period for each cycle, vibration remains constant at 9.2 msec.

The two waveforms in Figure 6–8 are different in intensity, but not in frequency. The time between the cycles is exactly the same, so the frequency must be the same. From this comes a very important point: *Intensity and frequency are controlled independently, and you can increase intensity without increasing frequency.* Here is the paradox. Increases in intensity and fundamental frequency depend upon the same basic mechanism (tension/compression and subglottal pressure), so it is difficult to increase intensity without increasing pitch, but trained or well-controlled speakers can do this. The tendency is for frequency and intensity to increase together, which is a natural gesture that you can demonstrate to yourself. Find a place where you can shout, and then say a word before shouting it. Your pitch will most certainly go up, unless you try very hard to avoid it.

The relationship between subglottal pressure and the actual sound pressure level output of the vocal folds depends on the speaker. However, it appears that for every doubling of subglottal pressure there is an increase of between 8 and 12 decibels in vocal intensity.

In summary:

- ■ **Vocal intensity** refers to the increase in sound pressure of the speech signal.
- ■ To increase vocal intensity of phonation the speaker must increase **medial compression** through the muscles of adduction.
- ■ This increased adductory force requires greater **subglottal pressure** to produce phonation and forces the vocal folds to remain in the closed portion of the phonatory cycle for a longer period of time.
- ■ The increased **laryngeal tension** required for increasing intensity also will increase the vocal fundamental, although the trained voice is quite capable of controlling fundamental frequency and vocal intensity independently.

CLINICAL CONSIDERATIONS

The phonatory mechanism is extraordinarily sensitive to the physical well-being of the speaker. When individuals are ill their voices often get weaker and, in the case of upper respiratory problems, "rough." Diseases that weaken individuals also tend to compromise phonatory effort, so that the voice weakens in intensity, and pitch range is reduced. Increasing muscle tension for pitch and intensity variation requires work, and illness tends to reduce the ability to exert such forces. A number of neuromuscular diseases have been shown to affect phonation, and many measures of phonatory stability and ability have gained clinical acceptance.

Frequency perturbation is a measure of cycle-by-cycle variability in phonation. Perturbation, or **vocal jitter**, provides an exquisite index of muscle tone and stability but requires instrumentation for measurement. The client is asked to sustain a vowel as steadily as possible while it is being recorded by computer. Following this, the computer program measures each cycle of vibration and calculates how closely each cycle corresponds to the next in duration. The computer measures the duration of the first cycle (e.g., 10.2 msec), and subtracts that of the next cycle (e.g., 10.4 msec) and stores that number. It performs this for all succeeding cycles of vibration and calculates the average of the (unsigned) differences as compared with the average period of vibration. The resulting **percent of perturbation** (or percent jitter) is an indication of how perfectly this imperfect system is oscillating. The broad rule of thumb is that variation in excess of 1–2% will be perceived as hoarse. This is a good measure of client change over time and a less effective means of comparing clients.

This measure has been shown to be sensitive to a number of characteristics. Individuals who are more physically fit will have lower perturbation values than those who are not. Individuals with **neuromotor dysfunction** (neurological conditions that affect motor function) will have higher perturbation than healthy individuals. Increased mass (such as vocal folds) will increase perturbation, while therapy to reduce the mass will show a decrease in the jitter.

More prosaic measures do not require this degree of instrumentation, but nonetheless provide insight into phonatory function. The process of assessment often requires us to stress the system under examination so that its weakness can be seen with relation to normal abilities. (Kent, Kent, and Rosenbek [1987] provide an excellent overview of methods of stressing the phonatory system.) As mentioned earlier, **maximum phonation time** refers to the duration of phonation an individual is capable of sustaining. Sustained phonation provides an index of phonatory-plus-respiratory efficiency. You can examine the respiratory system by itself to determine the ability of your client to sustain expiration in absence of voicing and have some confidence that length and steadiness of a sustained vowel is an indicator of laryngeal function.

Another time-honored measures is diadochokinetic rate. Oral **diado-chokinesis** refers to the alternation of articulators (you may hear it referred to as alternating motor rate as well). Specifically, it is the number of productions of a single or multiple syllables an individual produces per second. This is an excellent tool for assessing the articulators (the topic of Chapters 7 and 8), but also helps assessment of the coordination of the phonatory and articulatory systems.

Pathological conditions often have an impact on vocal range and vocal intensity, as well. For instance, the presence of vocal nodules may reduce an individual's vocal range from two octaves to one half octave or less, and the breathy component will have a real impact on vocal intensity. Similarly, physical weakness may limit the ability of a client to exert effort for either pitch or vocal intensity change.

The exquisitely sensitive vocal mechanism is an excellent window on the health and well-being of a client, as you will find in your advanced studies of voice.

LINGUISTIC ASPECTS OF PITCH AND INTENSITY

Pitch and intensity play significant roles in the suprasegmental aspects of communication. **Suprasegmental** elements are the parameters of speech that are above the segment (phonetic) level. This term generally refers to elements of **prosody**, the system of stress used to vary meaning in speech. The prosodic elements include pitch, intonation, loudness, stress, duration, and rhythm; and these elements convey not only a great deal of information concerning emotion and intent, but also provide information that can disambiguate meaning. Even though it is not the purpose of an anatomy text to delve into these suprasegmental elements, pitch and intensity play such a heavy role that we should at least glance at them.

Intonation refers to the changes in pitch in speech, whereas **stress** refers to syllable or word emphasis relative to an entire utterance. For example, say the following sentence out loud: "That's a cat." You end it with a falling *intonation* and put more *stress* on "that's" than on "a" or "cat." To a large extent, these elements both arise out of variation in vocal intensity and fundamental frequency. Intonation may be considered the melodic envelope that contains the sentence and may serve to mark sentence type. Generally, statements tend to have falling intonation at the end; questions tend to have rising intonation. Figure 6–9 shows traces of the fundamental frequency for the productions of "Bev bombed Bob." and "Bev bombed Bob?" If you say these two sentence you can hear for yourself the changes that are so strong in the second sentence. Hirano, Ohala, and Vennard (1969) used this sentence contrast to show that the lateral cricoarytenoid, thyrovocalis, and cricothyroid were all quite active in making these rapid laryngeal adjustments.

Stress helps punctuate speech, providing emphasis to syllables or words through both intensity and frequency changes. To increase stress, we increase fundamental frequency and intensity through increasing subglottal pressure, medial compression, and glottal tension. As you will remember from our earlier discussion, both frequen-

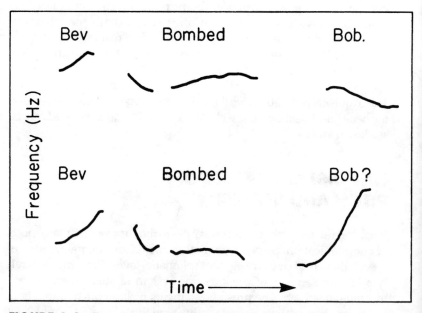

FIGURE 6–9. Fundamental frequency fluctuation for declarative statement and question form. Note the difference in falling and rising intonation between these two sentence forms.

cy and intensity involve adjustments of these variables. We capitalize on the fact that both intensity and fundamental frequency vary together, so that stressed syllables or words will show changes in both. If you look at the pitch and intensity traces of Figure 6–10, you can see how they vary together.

The musculature involved in stress is not unlike that in intonation, although we must add in the increase in subglottal pressure. The changes in fundamental frequency will be on the order of 50 Hz (Netsell, 1973), governed by the lateral cricoarytenoid, thyrovocalis, and cricothyroid. The changes in subglottal pressure will be small but rapid, or pulsatile (Hixon, 1973). Because they require bursts of increased expiratory force, they are going to be driven by expiratory muscles.

Although stress and intonation are not *essential* for communication, they *are* essential for naturalness. Clearly you can speak in a **monopitch** (unvarying vocal pitch) or **monoloud** voice (unvarying vocal loudness), but the effect is so distracting that it certainly interferes with communication. You may find individuals with neurological impairments who show both of these characteristics. Treatment directed toward increased muscular effort at points requiring stress will greatly enhance the naturalness of speech, because increasing vocal effort at these points will inevitably increase both fundamental frequency and vocal intensity.

THEORIES OF PHONATION

The history of theories of vocal fold vibration is long and colorful, leading certainly from Helmholtz of the 1800s to the present. Although it

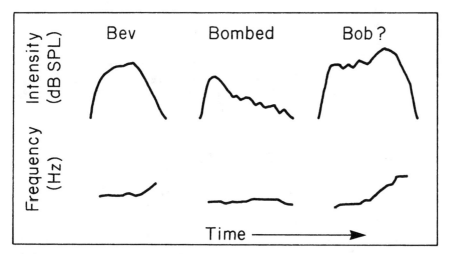

FIGURE 6-10. Fundamental frequency and intensity changes during production of a question form.

has long been known that the vocal folds are the source of voicing, only recently did we develop an understanding of the mechanism of phonation, and refinements continue. Certainly, the underlying principles embodied in the discussion of Chapter 5 are broadly accepted, although it has not always been so.

As discussed earlier, the myoelastic-aerodynamic theory of phonation states that vibration of the vocal folds depends on the elements embodied in the name of the theory. The myoelastic element is the elastic component of muscle (*myo* = muscle) and associated soft tissues of the larynx, and the aerodynamic component is that of the airflow and pressure through this constricted tube. Van den Berg (1958) recognized that the combination of tissue elasticity, which causes the vocal folds to return to their original position after being distended, and the Bernoulli effect, which helped promote this return by dropping the pressure at the constriction, could account for the sustained vibration shown in even a cadaverous specimen provided with an artificial source of expiratory charge.

Recently work by Titze (1994) has sought to explain how complex acoustic output can come from a simple oscillator such as the vocal folds. We have long recognized that the vocal folds are not simple oscillators, but rather undulate in the modes discussed earlier. Titze recognized that this complex vibration arises from the loosely bound masses associated with the membranous **cover** of the vocal folds (the epithelium and superficial layer of the lamina propria) and the **body** of the vocal folds (the intermediate and deep layers of lamina propria and thyrovocalis muscle). The loosely bound elastic tissue supports oscillation, and viewing the soft tissue as an infinite (or at least uncountable) number of masses reveals that a very large number of modes of vibration is possible. This discussion in no way gives justice to the elegance of this theory, and we recommend that you take time for the exceptionally readable work of Titze.

The phonatory mechanism is an important component of the speaking mechanism, providing the voiced source for speech. It is time for us to see what happens to the voice source after it leaves the larynx. See Chapter 7 for a continuation of this story.

CHAPTER SUMMARY

Phonation is the product of vocal fold vibration. The **larynx** is an important structure for a number of **nonspeech** functions, including **coughing, throat-clearing,** and **abdominal fixation.** The degree of muscle control during phonation is greatly increased, however, because the successful use of voice requires careful attention to vocal fold **tension** and **length.**

Laryngeal Stridor

Laryngeal stridor refers to a harsh sound produced during respiration. The sound is associated with some obstruction in the respiratory passageway and is always a sign of dysfunction. Stridor may arise from a growth in the larynx or trachea causing turbulence during respiration, or it may arise from the vocal folds. If the vocal folds are paralyzed in the adducted position (**abductor paralysis**), they will not only obstruct the airway but also will vibrate as the air of inspiration passes by them. In this case, the harsh sound will be referred to as **inhalatory stridor**. You may want to imitate this in yourself so that you will come to recognize this sign of obstruction. Phonate while breathing out, and then, without abducting your vocal folds, force your inspiration through the closed vocal folds. You will notice not only a harsh sound but also the extreme difficulty of inhaling through an obstruction.

Adduction takes several forms, including **breathy, simultaneous,** and **glottal attacks,** and **termination** of phonation requires **abduction** of the vocal folds. **Sustained phonation** depends on the laryngeal configuration. The **modal pattern** of phonation is most efficient, capitalizing on the optimal combination of muscular tension and respiratory support for the vocal folds. **Falsetto** requires increased vocal fold tension, and **glottal fry** demands a unique glottal and respiratory configuration. Each of these modes of vocal fold vibration is different, and the variations are governed by laryngeal **tension, medial compression,** and **subglottal pressure**. **Breathy phonation** occurs when there is inadequate medial compression to approximate the vocal folds, and **whispering** results from tensing the vocal fold margins while holding the folds partially adducted.

Pitch is the psychological correlated of **frequency** of vibration, and **loudness** is the correlate of **intensity,** although both pitch and intensity have been used to represent physical phenomena. **Optimal pitch** is the most efficient frequency of vibration for a given pair of vocal folds, and **habitual pitch** is the frequency of vibration used by an individual habitually. The **pitch range** of an individual will span approximately two octaves but can be reduced by pathology or increased through vocal training.

Vocal fundamental frequency changes are governed by vocal fold tension and mass per unit length. To increase fundamental frequency, we increase the **length** of the vocal folds which will increase the **ten-**

sion of the vocal folds and decrease the **mass per unit length.** To compensate for increased tension, subglottal pressure will increase.

Medial compression is increased to produce an increase in vocal **intensity** of phonation, and this is performed largely through the muscles of adduction. Increased **adductory force** requires greater subglottal pressure to produce phonation, and this forces the vocal folds to remain in the closed portion of the phonatory cycle for a longer period of time. The **increased laryngeal tension** will increase the vocal fundamental as well, although the fundamental frequency and vocal intensity may be controlled independently.

Study Questions

1. _____ is the process of capturing air within the thorax to provide the muscles with a structure upon which to push or pull.

2. In _____ attack, the vocal folds are adducted prior to initiation of expiratory flow.

3. In _____ attack, the vocal folds are adducted after the initiation of expiratory flow.

4. In _____ attack, the vocal folds are adducted simultaneous with initiation of expiratory flow.

5. During modal phonation, the vocal folds will open from _____ (inferior/superior) to _____ (inferior/superior). The folds will close from _____ (inferior/superior) to _____ (inferior/superior).

6. The minimum subglottal driving pressure for speech is _____ cm H_2O.

7. In the mode of vibration known as _____, the vocal folds vibrate at a much lower rate than in modal phonation, and the folds exhibit a syncopated vibratory pattern.

8. In the mode of vibration known as _____, the vocal folds lengthen and become extremely thin and "reed-like."

9. Presence of vocal nodules or other space-occupying laryngeal pathology may result in _____ phonation.

10. To increase vocal intensity, one must _____ (increase/decrease) subglottal pressure and _____ (increase/decrease) medial compression.

11. To increase vocal fundamental frequency, one must _____ vocal fold tension by _____ (lengthening/shortening) the vocal folds.

12. _____ refers to the pitch of phonation that is optimal or most appropriate for an individual.

13. _____ refers to the vocal pitch that is habitually used during speech.

14. As vocal intensity increases, the closed phase of the vibratory cycle _____ (increases/decreases).

Study Question Answers

1. ABDOMINAL FIXATION is the process of capturing air within the thorax to provide the muscles with a structure upon which to push or pull.

2. In GLOTTAL attack, the vocal folds are adducted prior to initiation of expiratory flow.

3. In BREATHY attack, the vocal folds are adducted after the initiation of expiratory flow.

4. In SIMULTANEOUS attack, the vocal folds are adducted simultaneous with initiation of expiratory flow.

5. During modal phonation, the vocal folds will open from INFERIOR to SUPERIOR. The folds will close from INFERIOR to SUPERIOR.

6. The minimum subglottal driving pressure for speech is 3–5 cm H_2O.

7. In the mode of vibration known as GLOTTAL FRY the vocal folds vibrate at a much lower rate than in modal phonation, and the folds exhibit a syncopated vibratory pattern.

8. In the mode of vibration known as FALSETTO the vocal folds lengthen and become extremely thin and "reed-like."

9. Presence of vocal nodules or other space-occupying laryngeal pathology may result in BREATHY phonation.

10. To increase vocal intensity, one must INCREASE subglottal pressure and INCREASE medial compression.

11. To increase vocal fundamental frequency, one must INCREASE vocal fold tension by LENGTHENING (lengthening/shortening) the vocal folds.

12. OPTIMAL PITCH refers to the pitch of phonation that is optimal or most appropriate for an individual.

13. HABITUAL PITCH refers to the vocal pitch that is habitually used during speech.

14. As vocal intensity increases, the closed phase of the vibratory cycle <u>INCREASES</u>.

REFERENCES

Adair, R. K. (1995). The physics of baseball. *Physics Today, 48*(5), 26–31.

Aronson, A. E. (1985). *Clinical voice disorders.* New York: Thieme.

Baer, T., Sasaki, C., & Harris, K. (1985). *Laryngeal function in phonation and respiration.* Boston, MA: College-Hill Press.

Bateman, H. E., & Mason, R. M. (1984). *Applied anatomy and physiology of the speech and hearing mechanism.* Springfield, IL: Charles C. Thomas.

Bless, D. M., & Abbs, J. H. (1983). *Vocal fold physiology.* San Diego, CA: College-Hill Press.

Boone, D. R. (1977). *The voice and voice therapy.* Englewood Cliffs, NJ. Prentice-Hall.

Broad, D. J. (1973). Phonation. In F. D. Minifie, T. J. Hixon, & F. Williams, (Eds.) *Normal aspects of speech, hearing, and language* (pp. 127–168). Englewood Cliffs, NJ: Prentice-Hall.

Childers, D. G., Hicks, D. M., Moore, G. P., Eskenazi, L., & Lalwani A. L. (1990). Electroglottography and vocal fold physiology. *Journal of Speech and Hearing Research, 33,* 245–254.

Chusid, J. G. (1979). *Correlative neuroanatomy and functional neurology* (17th ed.). Los Altos, CA: Lange Medical Publications.

Daniloff, R. G. *Speech science.* San Diego, CA: College-Hill Press.

Doyle, P. C., Grantmyre, A., & Myers, C. (1989). Clinical modification of the tracheostoma breathing valve for voice restoration. *Journal of Speech and Hearing Disorders, 54,* 189–192.

Eckel, F., & Boone, D. (1981). The s/z ratio as an indicator of laryngeal pathology. *Journal of Speech & Hearing Disorders, 46,* 147–149.

Fink, B. R., (1975). *The human larynx.* New York: Raven Press.

Fink, B. R. & Demarest, R. J. (1978). *Laryngeal biomechanics.* Cambridge, MA: Harvard University Press.

Fletcher, W. W. (1950). *A study of internal laryngeal activity in relation to vocal intensity.* Doctoral dissertation, Northwestern University, Evanston, IL.

Fujimura, O. (1988). *Vocal fold physiology. Vol. 2: Vocal physiology.* New York: Raven Press.

Fukida, H., Kawaida, M., Tatehara, T., Ling, E., Kita, K., Ohki, K., Kawasaki, Y., & Saito, S. (1988). A new concept of lubricating mechanisms of the larynx. In O. Fujimura, (Ed.), *Vocal physiology: Voice production, mechanisms and functions* (pp. 83–92). New York: Raven Press.

Gosling, J. A., Harris, P. F., Humpherson, J. R., Whitmore, I., & Willan, P. L. T. (1985). *Atlas of human anatomy.* Philadelphia, PA: J. B. Lippincott.

Grobler, N. J. (1977). *Textbook of clinical anatomy,* Vol. 1. Amsterdam: Elsevier Scientific.

Hirano, M. (1974). Morphological structure of the vocal cord as a vibrator and its variations. *Folia Phoniatrica, 26,* 89–94.

Hirano, M., Kiyokawa, K., & Kurita, S. (1988). Laryngeal muscles and glottic shaping. In Fujimua, O. (Ed.), *Vocal physiology: Voice production, mechanisms and functions* (pp. 49–65). New York: Raven Press.

Hirano, M., Ohala, J., & Vennard, W. (1969). The function of laryngeal muscles in regulation of fundamental frequency and intensity of phonation. *Journal of Speech and Hearing Research, 12,* 616–628.

Hixon, T. J. (1973). Respiratory function in speech. In F. D. Minifie, T. J. Hixon, and F. Williams, (Eds.), *Normal aspects of speech, hearing, and language.* (pp. 73–126) Englewood Cliffs, NJ: Prentice-Hall.

Hixon, T. J. (1982). Speech breathing kinematics and mechanism inferences therefrom. In S. Grillner, A. Persson, B. Lindblom & J. Lubker, (Eds.), *Speech motor control* (pp. 75–94). New York: Pergamon Press.

Hixon, T. J., Hawley, J. L., & Wilson, K. J. (1982). An around-the-house device for the clinical determination of respiratory driving pressure: A note on making simple even simpler. *Journal of Speech and Hearing Disorders, 47,* 413–415.

Hollien, H., & Moore, G. P. (1968). Stroboscopic laminography of the larynx during phonation. *Acta Otolaryngologica, 65,* 209–215.

Hufnagle, J., & Hufnagle, K. K. (1988). S/Z ratio in dysphonic children with and without vocal cord nodules. *Language, Speech, and Hearing Services in Schools, 19,* 418–422.

Husson, R. (1953). Sur la physiologie vocale. *Annals of Otolaryngology, 69,* 124–137.

Isshiki, N. (1964). Regulatory mechanisms of voice intensity variation. *Journal of Speech and Hearing Research, 7,* 17–29.

Kaplan, H. M. (1971). *Anatomy and physiology of speech.* New York: McGraw-Hill.

Kent, R. D., Kent, J. F., & Rosenbek, J. C. (1987). Maximum performance tests of speech production. *Journal of Speech and Hearing Disorders, 52,* 367–387.

Kirchner, J. A., & Suzuki, M. (1968). Laryngeal reflexes and voice production. In M. Krauss (Ed.) Sound Production in Man. *Annals of the New York Academy of Sciences, 155,* 98–109.

Kuehn, D. P., Lemme, M. L., & Baumgartner, J. M. (1989). *Neural bases of speech, hearing, and language.* Boston, MA: Little, Brown.

Langley, M. B., & Lombardino, L. J. (1991). *Neurodevelopmental strategies for managing communication disorders in children with severe motor dysfunction.* Austin, TX: Pro-Ed.

Lieberman, P. (1968a). *Intonation, perception, and language.* Research monograph no. 38. Cambridge, MA: The M.I.T. Press.

Lieberman, P. (1968b). Vocal cord motion in man. *Annals of the New York Academy of Sciences, 155,* 28–38.

Lieberman, P. (1977). *Speech science and acoustic phonetics: An introduction.* New York: Macmillan.

Logemann, J. (1983). *Evaluation and treatment of swallowing disorders.* Boston, MA: College-Hill Press.

Netsell, R. (1973). Speech physiology. In F. D. Minifie, T. J. Hixon, & F. Williams, (Eds.), *Normal aspects of speech, hearing and language* (pp. 211–134). Englewood Cliffs, NJ: Prentice-Hall.

Netsell, R. & Hixon, T. J. (1978). A noninvasive method for clinically estimating subglottal air pressure. *Journal of Speech and Hearing Disorders, 43,* 326–330.

Nishizawa, N., Sawashima, M., & Yonemoto, K (1988). Vocal fold length in vocal pitch change. In O. Fujimua, (Ed.), *Vocal physiology: Voice production, mechanisms and functions* (pp. 49–65). New York: Raven Press.

Proctor, D. F. (1968). The physiologic basis of voice training. In M. Krauss, (Ed.), Sound Production in Man. *Annals of the New York Academy of Sciences, 155,* 208–228.

Ptacek, P. H., & Sander, E. K. (1963). Maximum duration of phonation. *Journal of Speech and Hearing Disorders, 28*(2), 171–182.

Ramig, L. A., & Ringel, R. L. (1983). Effects of physiological aging on selected acoustic characteristics of voice. *Journal of Speech and Hearing Research, 26,* 22–30.

Rastatter, M. P., & Hyman, M. (1982). Maximum phoneme duration of /s/ and /z/ by children with vocal nodules. *Language, Speech, and Hearing Services in Schools, 13,* 197–199.

Sapienza, C. M., & Stathopoulos, E. T. (1994). Respiratory and laryngeal measures of children and women with bilateral vocal fold nodules. *Journal of Speech, and Hearing Research, 37,* 1229–1243.

Sonninen, A. (1968). The external frame function in the control of pitch in the human voice. In M. Krauss, (Ed.), Sound Production in Man. *Annals of the New York Academy of Sciences, 155,* 68–89.

Sorensen, D. N., & Parker, P. A. (1992). The voiced/voiceless phonation time in children with and without laryngeal pathology. *Language, Speech and Hearing Services in Schools, 23,* 163–168.

Tait, N. A., Michel, J. F., & Carpenter, M. A. (1980). Maximum duration of sustained /s/ and /z/ in children. *Journal of Speech and Hearing Disorders, 15,* 239–246.

Timcke, R., Von Leden, H., & Moore, G. P. (1958). Laryngeal vibrations: Measurements of the glottic wave I: The normal vibratory cycle. *Archives of Otolaryngology, 68,* 1–19.

Titze, I. R. (1994). *Principles of voice production.* Englewood Cliffs, NJ: Prentice-Hall.

Titze, I. R. (1988). The physics of small amplitude oscillation of the vocal folds. *Journal of the Acoustical Society of America, 83*(4), 1536–1552.

Van den Berg, J. W., (1958). Myoelastic-aerodynamic theory of voice production. *Journal of Speech and Hearing Research, 1,* 227–244.

Van den Berg, J. W. & Tan, T. S. (1959). Results of experiments with human larynxes. *Practica Oto-rhino-laryngologica, 21,* 425–450.

Van den Berg, J. (1968). Sound production in isolated human larynges. In M. Krauss, (Ed.) Sound production in man. *Annals of the New York Academy of Sciences, 155,* 18–27.

Verdolini, K., Titze, I. R. , & Fennell, A. (1994). Dependence of phonatory effort on hydration level. *Journal of Speech and Hearing Research, 37,* 1001–1007.

Whillis, J. (1946). Movements of the tongue in swallowing. *Journal of Anatomy, 80,* 115–116.

Zemlin, W. R. (1988). *Speech and hearing science. anatomy and physiology.* Englewood Cliffs, NJ: Prentice-Hall.

CHAPTER

7

Anatomy of Articulation and Resonation

When the lay person thinks of the process of speaking, it is more than likely that he or she is actually thinking about articulation. You, of course, now know that there is much more to speech than moving the lips, tongue, mandible, and so forth. Nonetheless, the articulatory system is an extremely important element in our communication system.

Articulation is the process of joining two elements together, and the **articulatory system** is the system of mobile and immobile articulators brought into contact for the purpose of shaping the sounds of speech. As you will remember from Chapters 5 and 6, laryngeal vibration produces the sound required for voicing in speech. We are capable of rapidly starting and stopping phonation, depending on whether we want voiced or voiceless production. This chapter focuses on what happens after that sound reaches the oral cavity. In this cavity, the undifferentiated buzz produced by the vocal folds is shaped into the sounds we call phonemes. Let us present an overview of how the oral cavity is capable of such a creation.

SOURCE-FILTER THEORY OF VOWEL PRODUCTION

A widely accepted description of how the oral cavity is capable of creating speech sounds is the **source-filter theory** of vowel production. In general terms, the theory states that a voicing source is generated by the vocal folds and routed through the vocal tract where it is shaped into the sounds of speech. Changes in the shape and configuration of the tongue, mandible, soft palate, and other articulators govern the resonance characteristics of the vocal tract, and the resonances of the tract determine the sound of a given vowel. Here is how that works.

The **vocal tract**, consisting of the mouth (oral cavity), the region behind the mouth (pharynx), and the nasal cavity, may be thought of as a series of linked tubes (see Figure 7–1). From your experience you know that if you blow carefully across the top of a soda bottle you will hear a tone. If you decrease the volume of the air in the bottle by adding fluid to it, the frequency of vibration of the tone increases. Likewise, if you blow across the top of a bottle with larger volume, the tone decreases in frequency. As the volume of the air in the bottle increases, the frequency of the tone decreases. As the volume decreases, the frequency increases. You are experimenting with the **resonant frequency** of a cavity, which is the frequency of sound to which the cavity most effectively responds. You might think of the bottle as a filter that lets only one frequency of sound through and rejects the other frequencies, much as a coffee filter lets the liquid through but traps the grounds. The airstream blowing across the top of the bottle is actually producing a very broad-spectrum

FIGURE 7-1. Visualization of the oral, nasal, and pharyngeal cavities as a series of linked tubes. This linkage provides the variable resonating cavity that produces speech.

signal, but the bottle selects the frequency components that are at its resonant frequency. The resonant frequency of a cavity is largely governed by its volume and length. Now, if you were somehow able to blow across two bottles (one low resonant frequency, one high-frequency), the two tones would combine.

When you move your tongue around in your mouth, you are changing the shape of your oral cavity, making it smaller or larger, lengthening or shortening it. It is as if you had a series of bottles that you could manipulate in your mouth, changing their shape at will. When you change the shape of the oral cavity, you are changing the resonant frequencies, and therefore you are changing the sound that comes out of the mouth.

This, then, is the source-filter theory view of speech production. The vocal folds produce a quasi-periodic tone (see Chapters 5 and 6), and that tone is passed through the filter of your vocal tract. The vocal tract filter is manipulable, so that you are able to change its shape and therefore change the sound.

The resonant frequencies govern our perception of vowels. To prove that it is *not* your vocal folds that govern the nature of a vowel, whisper the words *he* and *who*. Could you tell the difference? The vocal folds were not vibrating, but you excited the oral cavity filter through the turbulence of your whispered production, and the vowels were quite intelligible.

The source-filter theory can be easily expanded to other phonemes as well. The source of the sound may vary. With vowels, the source will always be phonation in normal speech. With consonants, other sources will include the turbulence of frication or combinations of voicing and turbulence. In all cases, you produce a noise source and pass it through the filter of the oral cavity that has been configured to meet your acoustic needs. One example will prove this to you.

Look at Figure 7–2, and notice the difference between production of the /s/ and /ʃ/ phonemes. Sustain an /s/ and realize that when you produce it, your tongue is high, forward, and tense. You pass a compact stream of air over the surface of the tongue, and then between the tongue tip and the upper front teeth. Now produce the /ʃ/ and recognize that the tongue is farther back in your mouth, much as in the figure. The source in both cases is the turbulence associated with the airstream escaping from its course between your tongue and an immobile structure of your mouth (front teeth or roof of your mouth). The turbulence excites the cavity in front of the constriction and you have a recognizable sound. Which of the two phonemes has the larger cavity distal to the constriction? The /ʃ/ has a larger resonant cavity than the /s/, so its resonant frequency will be lower, following our discussion of bottles. Now make the /s/ again, but without stopping, slide

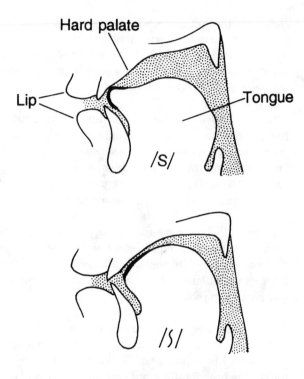

SAGITTAL VIEW

FIGURE 7-2. Comparison of the articulatory posture used for production of /s/ and /ʃ/. (After data and view of Carpenter, 1978.)

your tongue back in your mouth until you reach the /ʃ/ position. As you do this you will hear the noise drop in frequency because the cavity is increasing in size. The source-filter theory dictates this change.

To summarize:

■ The source-filter theory states that speech is the product of sending an acoustic source, such as the sound produced by the vibrating vocal folds, through the filter of the vocal tract that shapes the output.
■ The ever-changing speech signal is the product of moving articulators.
■ Sources may be voicing, as in the case of vowels, or the product of turbulence, as in fricatives. Articulators may be moveable (such as the tongue, lips, pharynx, mandible, and velum) or immobile (such as the teeth, hard palate, and alveolar ridge).

Let us now examine the structures of the articulatory system. As with the phonatory system, we must examine the support structure (the skull and bones of the face) and the muscles that move the articulators. Before we begin, we will define the articulators used in speech production.

THE ARTICULATORS

As noted, articulators may be either mobile or immobile. In speech we will often move one articulator to make contact with another, thus positioning a mobile articulator in relation to an immobile articulator.

The largest mobile articulator is the *tongue*, with the lower jaw (*mandible*) a close second (see Figure 7–3). The *velum* or *soft palate* is another mobile articulator, used to differentiate nasal sounds such as /m/ or /n/ from non-nasal sounds. The *lips* are moved to produce different speech sounds, and the *cheeks* play a role in changes of resonance of the cavity. The region behind the oral cavity (the *fauces* and the *pharynx*) may be moved through muscular action, and the *larynx* and *hyoid bone* both change to accommodate different articulatory postures.

There are three immobile articulators. The *alveolar ridge* of the upper jaw (*maxillae*) and the *hard palate* are both significant articulatory surfaces. The *teeth* are used in production of a variety of speech sounds.

The process of articulation for speech is quite automatic. To get a feel for changes in speech that occur when you alter the function of an articulator, try this. Place a small stack of tongue depressors between your molars on one side of your mouth and bite lightly (this is a *bite block*). Now say "You wish to know all about my grandfather." Now say the same sentence after placing your tongue between your front teeth, and biting lightly. Finally, say the sentence while pulling your cheeks out with your fingers. There are two important points to this demonstration. First, your speech changed when you altered the articulatory and resonatory characteristics of the tract. You restrained articulators and had to work harder to make yourself understood. Second, you were able to overcome these difficulties. Despite having a bite block or clamped tongue tip you were able to make yourself understood. In fact, you automatically adjusted your articulation to match the new physical constraints. As a student in speech-language pathology you should be quite heartened by the extraordinary flexibility of motor planning exhibited in this demonstration, because you can use this to your advantage in treatment.

Of these mobile and immobile articulators, the tongue, mandible, teeth, hard palate, and velum are the major players, although all surfaces and cavities within the articulatory/resonatory system are contributors to the production of speech.

You may wish to refer to Figures 7–4 through 7–9 as we begin our discussion of the bones of the facial and cranial skeleton. In addition, Table 7–1 may help you to organize this body of material.

Nasal
cavity

Oral
cavity

Mandible Tongue

b

b. Photograph of articulators seen through sagittal section.

Velum

Hard palate

Nasal cavity

Tongue

Alveolar ridge

Lips
Teeth

Mandible

Oral Cavity

SAGITTAL VIEW

a

FIGURE 7–3. a. Relationships among the articulators.

b. Photograph of anterior skull.

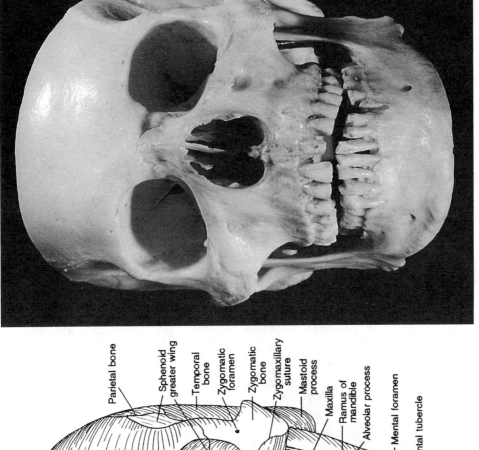

FIGURE 7-4. a. Anterior view of the skull.

Frontal bone

Parietal bone

Sphenoid greater wing

Temporal bone

Zygomatic foramen

Zygomatic bone

Zygomaxillary suture

Mastoid process

Maxilla

Ramus of mandible

Alveolar process

Mental foramen

Mental tubercle

Symphysis mente

Mandible

Nasal bone

Ethmoid perpendicular plate

Zygomatic frontal process

Maxilla frontal process

Infraorbital foramen

Middle nasal concha

Inferor nasal concha

Anterior nasal spine

Vomer

ANTERIOR VIEW

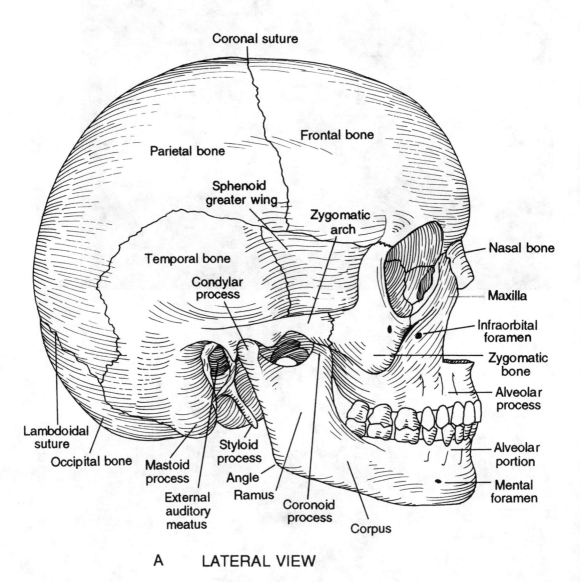

Coronal suture

Frontal bone

Parietal bone

Sphenoid
greater wing

Zygomatic
arch

Nasal bone

Temporal bone

Condylar
process

Maxilla

Infraorbital
foramen

Zygomatic
bone

Alveolar
process

Lambdoidal
suture

Occipital bone

Mastoid
process

Styloid
process

Angle

Ramus

External
auditory
meatus

Coronoid
process

Corpus

Alveolar
portion

Mental
foramen

A   LATERAL VIEW

FIGURE 7–5. a. Lateral view of the skull.

b. Medial surface of the skull. **c.** Photo of lateral skull.

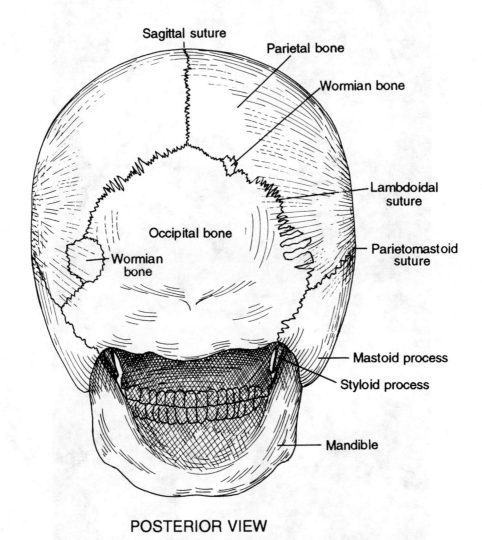

POSTERIOR VIEW

FIGURE 7-6. Posterior view of skull.

b

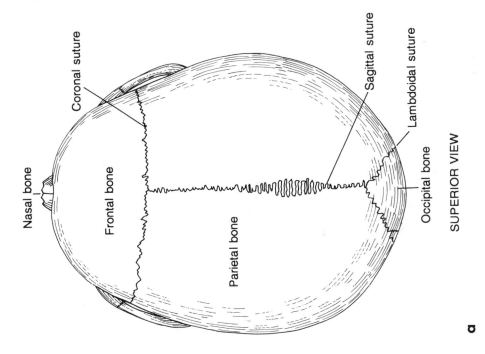

Nasal bone

Coronal suture

Frontal bone

Parietal bone

Sagittal suture

Lambdoidal suture

Occipital bone

SUPERIOR VIEW

a

FIGURE 7-7. a. Superior view of skull. **b.** Superior view photo of skull.

267

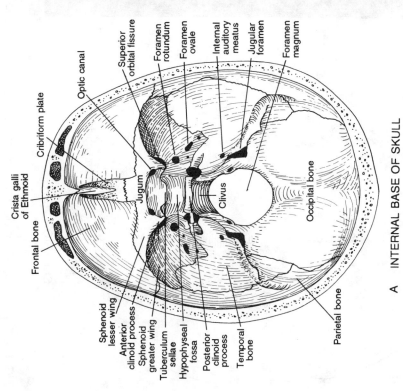

Crista galli
of Ethmoid

Frontal bone

Sphenoid
lesser wing

Anterior
clinoid process

Sphenoid
greater wing

Tuberculum
sellae

Hypophyseal
fossa

Posterior
clinoid process

Temporal
bone

Parietal bone

Cribriform plate

Optic canal

Superior
orbital fissure

Foramen
rotundum

Foramen
ovale

Internal
auditory
meatus

Jugular
foramen

Foramen
magnum

Jugum

Clivus

Occipital bone

A   INTERNAL BASE OF SKULL

FIGURE 7–8. a. Internal view of base of skull. **b.** Photo of internal skull.

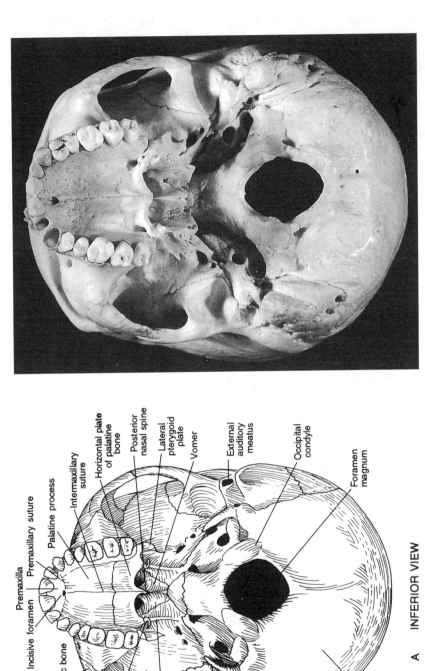

Premaxilla
Premaxillary suture
Incisive foramen
Palatine process
Intermaxillary suture
Horizontal plate of palatine bone
Posterior nasal spine
Lateral pterygoid plate
Vomer
External auditory meatus
Occipital condyle
Foramen magnum
Zygomatic bone
Frontal bone
Hamulus
Sphenoid greater wing
Medial pterygoid plate
Zygomatic process
Styloid process
Mastoid process
Parietal bone
Occipital bone

A   INFERIOR VIEW

FIGURE 7-9. **a.** Inferior view of skull. **b.** Photo of inferior view of skull.

Table 7–1. Bones of the face and cranial skeleton.

Bones of the Face	Bones of the Cranial Skeleton
Mandible	Ethmoid bone
Maxillae	Sphenoid bone
Nasal bone	Frontal bone
Palatine bone and nasal conchae	Parietal bone
Vomer	Occipital bone
Zygomatic bone	Temporal bone
Lacrimal bone	
Hyoid bone	

BONES OF THE FACE AND CRANIAL SKELETON

Bones of the Face

- **Mandible**
- **Maxillae**
- **Nasal Bone**
- **Palatine Bone and Nasal Conchae**
- **Vomer**
- **Zygomatic Bone**
- **Lacrimal Bone**
- **Hyoid Bone**

There are numerous bones of the face with which you should become familiar. As with the respiratory and phonatory systems, learning the landmarks will serve you well as you identify the course and function of the muscles of articulation.

Mandible

The mandible is the massive unpaired bone making up the lower jaw of the face. It begins as a paired bone but fuses at the midline by the child's first birthday. As you can see from Figure 7–10, there are several landmarks of interest on both outer and inner surfaces. The point of fusion of the two halves of the mandible is the **symphysis mente** or **mental symphysis**, marking the midline **mental protuberance** and separating the paired **mental tubercles**. Lateral to the tubercles on either side is the **mental foramen**, the hole through which the mental nerve of V trigeminal passes in life. The lateral mass of bone is the **corpus** or body, and the point at which the mandible angles upward is the **angle**. The rhomboidal plate rising up from the mandible is the **ramus**. The **condylar** and **coronoid** processes are important landmarks and are separated by the **mandibular notch**. The prominent **head** of the

mental: L., mentum, chin

foramen: L., a passage, opening, orifice

fovea: L., a pit

symphysis: Gr., growing together

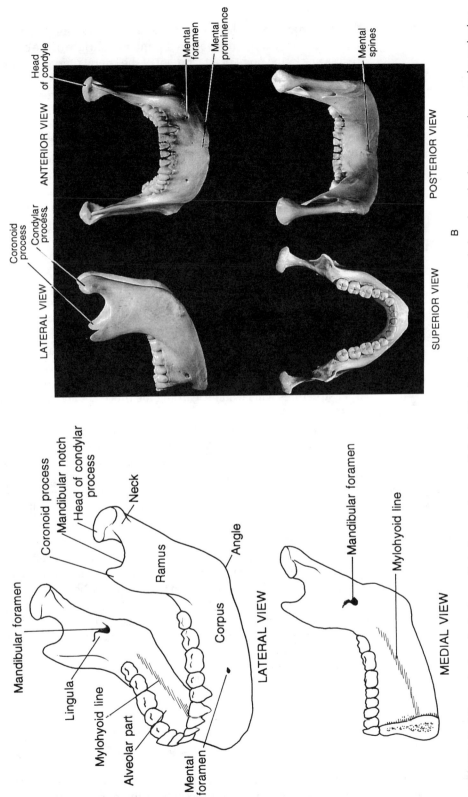

FIGURE 7-10. a. Lateral and medial views of mandible. **b.** Photo of mandible from lateral, anterior, superior, and posterior aspects.

271

protuberance: Gr., pro, before + tuber, bulge

tubercles: L., tuberculum, little swelling

ramus: L., branch

condylar process articulates with the skull, permitting rotation of the mandible. The **pterygoid fovea** on the anterior surface of the condylar process marks the point of attachment of the lateral pterygoid muscle, to be discussed. In the healthy mandible, teeth will be found within small **dental alveoli** (sacs) on the upper surface of the **alveolar arch** of the mandible.

On the inner surface of the mandible are prominent midline **superior** and **inferior mental spines** and the laterally placed **mylohyoid line**, landmarks which will figure prominently as we attach muscles to this structure. The **mandibular foramen** is the conduit for the inferior alveolar nerve of V trigeminal providing sensory innervation for the teeth and gums.

Maxillae

maxilla is the singular of maxillae

The paired maxillae (singular, **maxilla**) are the bones making up the upper jaw. These bones deserve careful study for they make up most of the roof of the mouth (**hard palate**), nose, and upper dental ridge and are involved in clefting of the lip and hard palate. As you study the landmarks of this complex bone, it might help you to realize that the various processes are logically named. That is, the *frontal* process of maxilla articulates with the *frontal* bone. Thus, learning the names of the larger structures will facilitate learning the processes and attachments.

In Figure 7–11 you can see the significant landmarks of the maxillae. As you can see, the **frontal process** is the superior-most point of this bone. You can palpate this process on yourself by placing your finger on your nose at the nasal side of your eye. You could run your finger down the **infra-orbital margin** from there to the lower midpoint of your eye. Supporting your eye is the **orbital process**, the lower portion of the orbital surface. Just below your finger is the **infraorbital foramen**, the conduit for the infraorbital nerve arising from the maxillary nerve of the V trigeminal, providing sensory innervation of the lower eyelid, upper lip, and nasal alae. Lateral to your finger is the **zygomatic process** of the maxilla bone, which articulates with the zygomatic bone.

At the midline you can see the **anterior nasal spine** and **nasal crest**, and lateral to this is the **nasal notch**. The lower tooth-bearing ridge, the **alveolar process**, contains alveoli that hold teeth in the intact adult maxilla. The region between the **canine eminence** and the **incisive fossa** will become important as we discuss cleft lip.

canine: L., caninus, related to dog

fossa: L., furrow or depression

A medial view requires disarticulation of left and right maxillae. This view reveals the **maxillary sinus**, the **palatine process**, and the important inner margin of the alveolar process.

sinus: L., curve or hollow

Figure 7–12 shows an inferior view of the maxillae. As you can see from this, the two palatine processes of the maxilla articulate at the

Mandibular Hypoplasia and Micrognathia

Congenital mandibular hypoplasia is a condition in which there is inadequate development of the mandible. Although some specific genetic syndromes have this as a trait (e.g., Pierre Robin syndrome), **micrognathia** (small jaw) may occur without known mediating condition. The misalignment of the mandibular and maxillary arches may be corrected through surgery to extend the mandible. It is hypothesized that, during development, micrognathia may lead to cleft palate: The mandible may not develop adequately to accommodate the tongue, which in turn blocks the extension of the palatine processes of the maxillae.

intermaxillary suture (also known as the **median palatine suture**). This suture marks the point of a cleft of the hard palate. The palatine process makes up three fourths of the hard palate, with the other one-fourth being the horizontal plate of the palatine bone, to be discussed.

suture: L., sutura, seam; the fibrous union of skull bones

The **incisive foramen** in the anterior aspect of the hard palate serves as a conduit for nasopalatine nerve serving the nasal mucosa. Trace the **premaxillary suture** forward from the incisive foramen to the alveolar process and you have identified the borders of the **premaxilla**. The premaxilla is difficult to see on the adult skull, but is nonetheless an important topic of discussion. Note that the premaxillary suture neatly separates the lateral incisors from the cuspids. A cleft of the lip will occur at this location and may include lip, alveolar bone, and the region of the premaxillary suture. Cleft lip may be either unilateral or bilateral, but in virtually all cases it will occur at this suture (there is very rarely a midline cleft lip).

Nasal Bones

The nasal bones are small, making up the superior nasal surface. As you can see from Figure 7–4 the nasal bones articulate with the frontal bones superiorly, the maxillae laterally, and perpendicular plate of the ethmoid bone and the nasal septal cartilage, all to be discussed.

Palatine Bones and Nasal Conchae

You will recall that the posterior one fourth of the hard palate is made up of the horizontal plate of the palatine bone. Let us now examine this small but complex bone (see Figure 7–13).

When viewed from the front, you can see that the articulated palatine bones echo the nasal cavity defined by the maxillae. The **posterior**

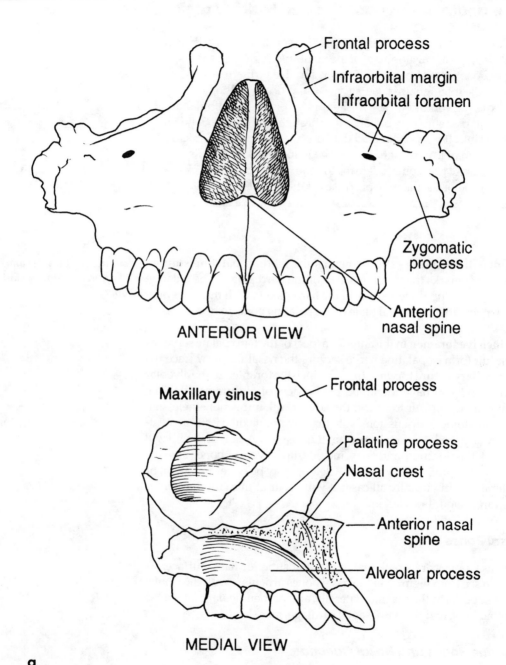

Frontal process

Infraorbital margin

Infraorbital foramen

Zygomatic
process

Anterior
nasal spine

ANTERIOR VIEW

Maxillary sinus

Frontal process

Palatine process

Nasal crest

Anterior nasal
spine

Alveolar process

MEDIAL VIEW

a

FIGURE 7–11. **a.** Anterior and medial views of maxilla.

Nasal bone

Zygomatic bone

Alveolar process

ANTERIOR VIEW

b

FIGURE 7-11. b. Anterior view of maxillae showing relationship with nasal and zygomatic bones.

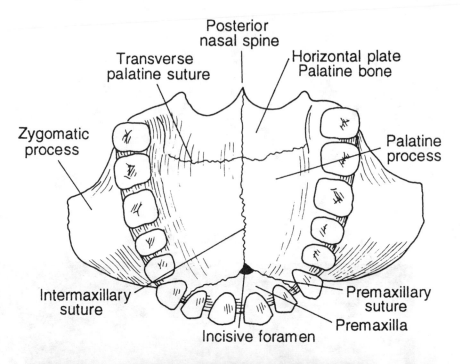

Posterior
nasal spine

Transverse
palatine suture

Horizontal plate
Palatine bone

Zygomatic
process

Palatine
process

Intermaxillary
suture

Premaxillary
suture

Premaxilla

Incisive foramen

INFERIOR VIEW

FIGURE 7-12. Schematic and photograph of inferior view of hard palate.

Cleft Lip and Cleft Palate

Cleft lip and cleft palate arise from sequelae during early development. Cleft lip may be either unilateral or bilateral, occurring along the premaxillary suture. Cleft lip will almost never be midline, but may involve soft tissue alone, or include a cleft of the maxilla up to the incisive foramen. Cleft palate may involve both hard and soft palates.

Cleft lip appears to result from a failure of embryonic facial and labial tissue to fuse during development. It looks as though tissues migrate and develop normally, but for some reason either fail to fuse or the fusion of the migrating medial nasal, maxillary, and lateral nasal processes breaks down. Cleft palate apparently arises from some mechanical intervention in development. Prior to the seventh embryonic week the palatine processes of the maxillae have been resting alongside the tongue so that the tongue separates the processes. As the oral cavity and mandible grow, the tongue drops away from the processes, and the processes can extend, make midline contact, and fuse. If something blocks the movement of the tongue (such as micrognathia), the palatine processes will not move in time to make contact. The head grows rapidly, and the plates will have missed their chance to become an intact palate.

nasal spine and **nasal crest** provide midline correlates to the anterior nasal spine and nasal crest of the maxillae, while the **horizontal plate** parallels the palatine process of the maxilla. When viewed from the side you can note the **perpendicular plate** that will make up the posterior wall of the nasal cavity. The **orbital process** makes up a small portion of the orbit cavity.

The **inferior nasal conchae (inferior turbinates)** are small, scroll-like bones placed on the lateral surface of the nasal cavity. These small but significant bones articulate with the maxilla, palatine, and ethmoid bones. The **middle** and **superior nasal conchae**, processes of the ethmoid bone (to be discussed), are superiorly placed correlates of the inferior conchae, all of which have important function in mammals. The mucosal lining covering the nasal conchae is the thickest of the nose and is richly endowed with vascular supply. Air passing over the nasal conchae will be warmed and humidified before reaching the delicate tissues of the lower respiratory system. The shape of the conchae greatly increases the surface area available, promoting rapid heat exchange.

turbinate: L., **turbo,** *whirl*

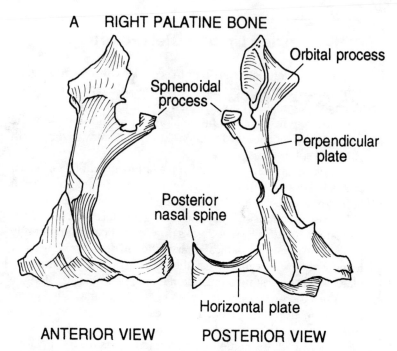

A RIGHT PALATINE BONE

FIGURE 7–13. a. Anterior and posterior views of palatine bones.

Vomer

septum: L., partition

rostrum: L., beak or beak-like

ala: L., wing

The vomer is an unpaired, midline bone making up the inferior and posterior **nasal septum**, the dividing plate between the two nasal cavities (see Figure 7–14). The vomer has the appearance of a knife blade or a plowshare, with its point aimed toward the front. It articulates with the sphenoid rostrum and perpendicular plate of the ethmoid bone in the posterior-superior, and with the maxillae and palatine bones on the inferior margin. The posterior **ala** of the vomer marks the midline terminus of the nasal cavities. As you examine Figure 7–14, attend to the fact that the bony nasal septum is made up of two elements: the vomer, and the perpendicular plate of the ethmoid bone. With the addition of a the midline **septal cartilage**, the nasal septum is complete.

Zygomatic Bone

The zygomatic bone makes up the prominent structure we identify as cheekbones. As you can see from Figure 7–15, the zygomatic bone articulates with the maxillae, frontal bone, and temporal bone (you cannot see the articulation with the sphenoid bone) and makes up the lateral orbit. Fortunately the landmarks of the zygomatic bone make intuitive sense.

B

ANTERIOR VIEW

Perpendicular plate

Orbital process

Posterior nasal spine

Horizontal plate

INFERIOR VIEW

FIGURE 7-13. b. Articulated palatine bones from front and beneath. Note that the left perpendicular plate is incomplete.

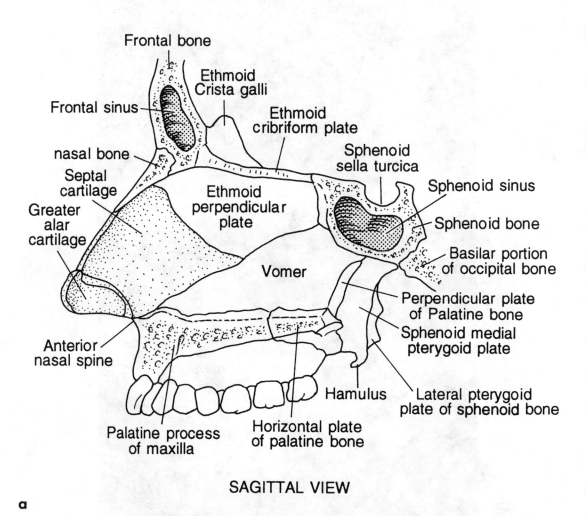

SAGITTAL VIEW

a

FIGURE 7-14. a. Medial view of nasal septum. Notice that the septum is composed of the perpendicular plate of ethmoid, the vomer, and the septal cartilage.

b

FIGURE 7-14. b. Photo of septum.

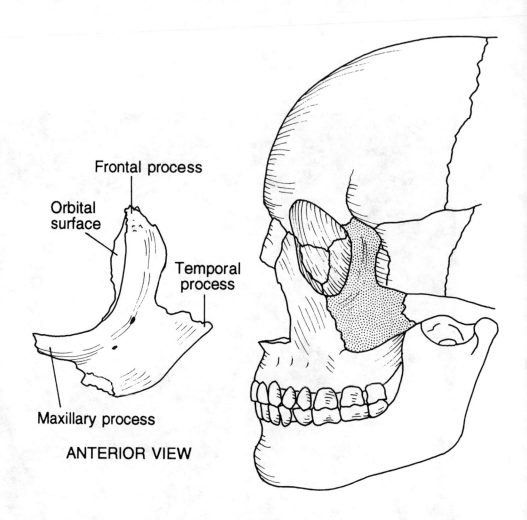

FIGURE 7–15. Anterior view of zygomatic bone.

orbital: L., orbita, orbit

At the base of the **orbital margin** is the **maxillary process**, the point of articulation of the zygomatic bone and maxilla. The **temporal process** seen in the lateral aspect projects back, forming half of the **zygomatic arch**. (The zygomatic arch consists of the temporal process of the zygomatic bone and the zygomatic process of the temporal bone.) The **frontal process** forms the articulation with the frontal and sphenoid bones.

Lacrimal Bones

lacrimal: L., lacrima, tear

These small bones are almost completely hidden in the intact skull. They articulate with the maxillae, frontal bone, nasal bone, and inferior conchae. They constitute a small portion of the lateral nasal wall and form a small portion of the medial orbit as well.

Hyoid Bone

The hyoid bone was discussed in the previous chapter, but rightfully belongs in this chapter as well. Its presence in this listing should re-mind you of the interconnectedness of the phonatory and articulatory systems.

Bones of the Cranial Skeleton

■ **Ethmoid Bone**
■ **Sphenoid Bone**
■ **Frontal Bone**
■ **Parietal Bone**
■ **Occipital Bone**
■ **Temporal Bone**

The bones of the cranium include those involved in creation of the cranial cavity.

Ethmoid Bone

The ethmoid bone is a complex, delicate structure with a presence in the cranial, nasal, and orbital spaces. If the cranium and facial skeleton were an apple, the ethmoid would be the core. You may want to refer to Figure 7–16 for this discussion.

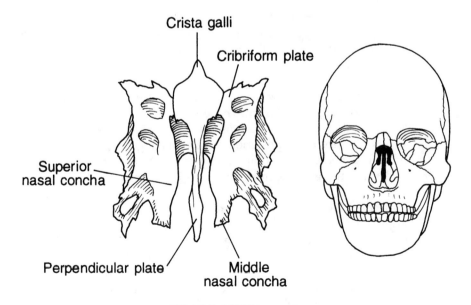

Crista galli

Cribriform plate

Superior nasal concha

Perpendicular plate

Middle nasal concha

ANTERIOR VIEW

FIGURE 7–16. Anterior view of ethmoid bone.

cribriform: L., **cribum,** *sieve* + **forma,** *form*

ethmoid: Gr., **ethmos,** *sieve* + **eidos,** *like*

crista: L., crest

conchae: Gr., **konche,** *shell*

When viewed from the front, the superior surface is dominated by the **crista galli**, which protrudes into the cranial space. Projecting down is the **perpendicular plate**, making up the superior nasal septum, and lateral to this plate are the **middle** and **superior nasal conchae**. On both sides of the perpendicular plate and perpendicular to it are the **cribriform plates**. The cribriform plates separate the nasal and cranial cavities, and provide the conduit for the olfactory nerves as they enter the cranial space. The lateral **orbital plates** articulate with the frontal bone, lacrimal bone, and maxilla to form the medial orbit.

Sphenoid Bone

sphenoid: Gr., **spheno,** *wedge* + **eidos,** *like*

The sphenoid bone exceeds the ethmoid bone in complexity. A glance at Figure 7–17 will show that the sphenoid is a significant contributor to the cranial structure. The sphenoid consists of a corpus and three pairs of processes, the greater wings of sphenoid, lesser wings of sphenoid, and pterygoid processes. The sphenoid also contains numerous foramina through which nerves and blood vessels pass.

sella turcica: L., Turkish saddle

tuberculum: L., little swelling

clivus: L., slope

When viewed from above, you can see that the medially placed **corpus** is dominated by the **hypophyseal fossa** (also known as the **sella turcica** or **pituitary fossa**), the indentation holding the pituitary gland (hypophysis) in life. This gland projects down from the hypothalamus and is placed at the point where the optic nerve decussates, the chiasma. The anterior portion of the fossa is the **tuberculum sellae** and the posterior aspect is the **dorsum sellae**. The **anterior clinoid processes** project from the lesser wing of sphenoid, lateral to the tuberculum sellae: The optic nerve passes under these processes, having passed through the optic foramen anteriorly. The **clivus** forms the union with the foramen magnum of the occipital bone. Within the corpus are the air-filled **sphenoid sinuses**.

The **lesser** and **greater wings** of the sphenoid are striking landmarks, likened to the wings of a bat. The lesser wings arise from the corpus and clinoid process, and partially cover the optic canal. The greater wings arise form the posterior corpus, making up a portion of the orbit. The greater wing comprises a portion of the anterolateral skull, and articulates with the frontal and temporal bones.

chiasma: Gr., **khiasma,** *cross; an X-shaped crossing*

jugum: L., a yoke

Projecting downward from the greater wing and corpus are the **lateral** and **medial pterygoid plates**. The **fossa** between the medial and lateral plates will be the point of attachment for one of the muscles of mastication (medial pterygoid muscle), and the tensor veli palatini will attach to the **scaphoid fossa**. A hamulus projects from each medial lamina, and the tendon of the tensor veli palatini passes around this on its course to the velum, as will be discussed.

The openings of the superior sphenoid are particularly significant. For example, the **optic canal** carries the II optic nerve, and the **foramen**

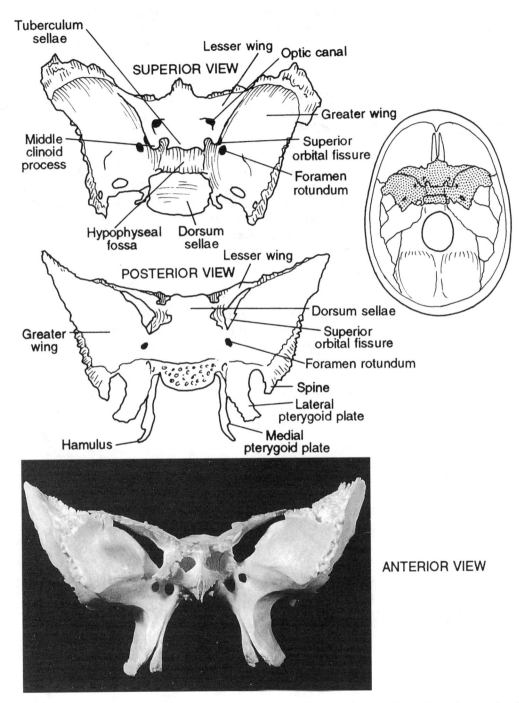

FIGURE 7-17. Schematics of superior and posterior sphenoid, and photograph of anterior view of sphenoid.

ovale provides the conduit for the mandibular nerve of V trigeminal. The maxillary nerve arising from the V trigeminal passes through the **foramen rotundum**, and the **superior orbital fissure** conveys the III oculomotor, IV trochlear, several branches of the ophthalmic nerve of V trigeminal, and VI abducens nerves. The **body** of the sphenoid includes the anteriorly placed **jugum** and the **chiasmatic groove**, which accommodates the optic chiasm.

Frontal Bone

The unpaired frontal bone shown in Figure 7–18 makes up the bony forehead, anterior cranial case, and supraorbital region. Near the middle of the intact skull, the coronal suture marks the point of articulation of the frontal and parietal bones. The frontal bone articulates with the zygomatic bones via the **zygomatic processes** and with the nasal bones by means of the **nasal portion**. From beneath, the **orbital portion** provides the superior surface of the eye socket.

Parietal Bones

lambdoidal: Gr., "L"-like

squamosal: L., scale

wormian: after Olaus Worm, anatomist

The paired parietal bones overlay the parietal lobes of the cerebrum and form the middle portion of the braincase (see Figure 7–19). These bones are united at the midline by the sagittal suture, running from the frontal bone in front to the occipital bone in back, separated by the **lambdoidal suture**. Small, irregular **wormian bones** may be formed by the bifurcations of the lambdoidal suture. The lateral margin of the parietal bone is marked by the **squamosal suture**, forming the union between parietal and temporal bones.

Supraorbital margin   Zygomatic process

ANTERIOR VIEW

FIGURE 7-18. Anterior view of frontal bone.

A   LATERAL VIEW

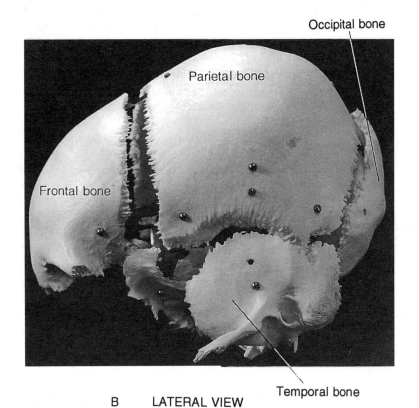

B   LATERAL VIEW

FIGURE 7–19. **a.** Lateral view of parietal bone. **b.** Photo of disarticulated parietal, frontal, temporal, and occipital bones.

Occipital Bone

The unpaired occipital bone is deceptively simple in appearance (see Figure 7–20). It overlies the occipital lobe of the brain and makes up the posterior brain case. It articulates with the temporal, parietal, and sphenoid bones. The **external occipital protuberance** is a midline prominence visible from behind. The **cerebral** and **cerebellar fossa** of the inner superior surface mark the locations of the occipital lobe and cerebellum, respectively in the intact braincase.

The most significant landmarks are those visible from beneath. From this vantage point, you can see that the occipital bone forms the base of the skull, wrapping beneath the brain. The **foramen magnum** provides the conduit for the spinal cord and beginning of the medulla oblongata, and the **condyles** mark the resting point for the first cervical vertebra. The **basilar part** articulates with the corpus of sphenoid.

Temporal Bone

The temporal bone is an important structure for students of speech pathology and audiology. On gross examination of the lateral skull, you can see that the temporal bone is separated from the parietal bone by the **squamosal suture** (also known as the parietomastoid suture) and from the occipital bone by the **occipitomastoid suture** (see Figure 7–21).

The temporal bone seen from the side is extremely dense and is remarkably rich in important landmarks. This complex bone is divided into four segments, the squamous, tympanic, mastoid, and petrous portions.

tegmen tympani: L., drum covering

tympanic antrum: L., drum cavity

meatus: L., opening

gingival: L., gingiva, gum

The **squamous portion, which** abuts the squamosal suture, is fan-shaped and thin. The lower margin includes the roof of the **external auditory meatus**, the conduit for sound energy to the middle ear. The anteriorly directed **zygomatic process** also arises from the squamous portion, articulating with the temporal process of the zygomatic bone to form the **zygomatic arch**. Beneath the base of the zygomatic process is the **mandibular fossa** of the temporal bone with which the condyloid process of the mandible articulates.

Behind it is the **mastoid portion**, which makes up the posterior part of the temporal bone. Air cells in the mastoid portion communicate with the **tympanic antrum**. Above the antrum is the **tegmen tympani**, a thin plate of bone, and medial to it is the lateral semicircular canal. The **mastoid process,** a structure you can easily palpate by feeling behind your ear, arises from this portion. The **tympanic portion** includes the anterior and inferior walls of the external auditory meatus. The prominent **styloid process** protrudes beneath the external auditory meatus and medial to the mastoid process. The **petrous portion** includes the cochlea and semicircular canals in life.

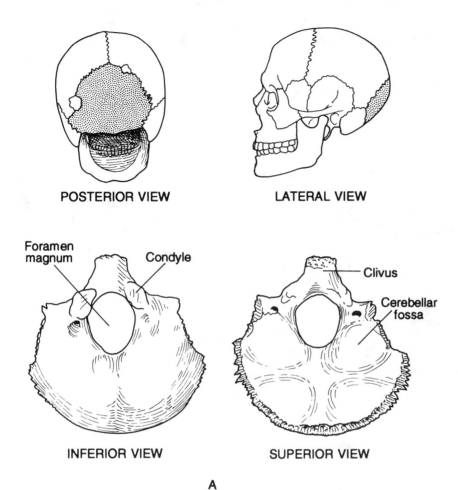

POSTERIOR VIEW

LATERAL VIEW

Foramen
magnum

Condyle

Clivus

Cerebellar
fossa

INFERIOR VIEW

SUPERIOR VIEW

A

FIGURE 7-20. a. Occipital bone seen from inferior and superior aspects. **b.** Photo of occipital bone, inferior view.

LATERAL VIEW

FIGURE 7–21. Schematic and photo of lateral view of temporal bone.

The **temporal fossa** is a region including a portion of the temporal, parietal, and occipital bones. The temporal portion is the large region near the parietal and occipital bones. A band including the squamosal suture on the parietal bone and the superior portion of the occipitotemporal suture are included in the temporal fossa as well, with the entire region marking the point of origin of the fan-shaped temporalis muscle, to be discussed. The medial surface of the temporal bone reveals the **internal auditory meatus** through which the VIII cranial nerve will pass on its way to the brainstem.

To summarize, the bones of the **face** and **skull** work together in a complex fashion to produce the structures of **articulation.**

■ The **mandible** provides the lower **dental arch, alveolar region,** and the resting location for the tongue.
■ The **maxillae** provide the **hard palate,** point of attachment for the **soft palate, alveolar ridge,** upper **dental arch,** and dominant structures of the **nasal cavities.**
■ The midline **vomer** articulates with the perpendicular plate of **ethmoid** and the **cartilaginous septum** to form the **nasal septum.**
■ The **zygomatic bone** articulates with the **frontal bone** and **maxillae** to form the cheek bone. The small **nasal bones** provide the upper margin of the nasal cavity.
■ The **ethmoid bone** serves as the core of the skull and face, with the prominent **crista galli** protruding into the **cranium** and the **perpendicular plate** dividing the nasal cavities.
■ The **frontal, parietal, temporal,** and **occipital** bones of the skull overlie the lobes of the brain of the same names.
■ The **sphenoid bone** has a marked presence within the brain case, with the prominent **greater** and **lesser wings** of sphenoid being found lateral to the **corpus.** The **hypophyseal fossa** houses the pituitary gland. The **clivus** joins the **occipital** bone near the **foramen magnum.**

DENTITION

The teeth are vital components of the speech mechanism. Housed within the alveoli of the maxillae and mandible, teeth provide the mechanism for mastication, as well as articulatory surfaces for several speech sounds.

Before we discuss the specific teeth, let us begin with an orientation to the dental arch itself. The upper and lower dental arches contain equal numbers of teeth of four types: incisors, cuspids, bicuspids, and molars. It is convenient to think of half-arches, knowing that left and right sides will have equal distribution of teeth (Figure 7–22).

Generally, teeth in the upper arch are larger than those in the lower arch, and the upper arch typically overlaps the lower arch in front. Each tooth has a **root**, hidden beneath the protective **gingival** or gum line (see Figure 7–23). The **crown** is the visible one third of the tooth, and the juncture of the crown and root is termed the **neck**. The surface of the crown is composed of the dental **enamel**, an extremely hard sur-

gingival: L., gingiva, gum

dentin: L., dens, tooth

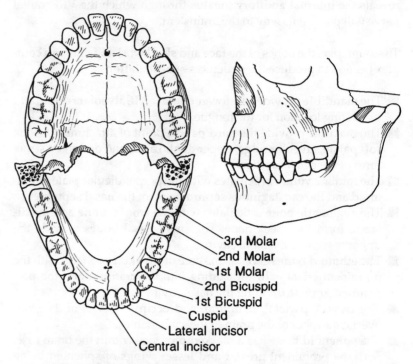

MAXILLARY DENTAL ARCH

3rd Molar
2nd Molar
1st Molar
2nd Bicuspid
1st Bicuspid
Cuspid
Lateral incisor
Central incisor

MANDIBULAR DENTAL ARCH

FIGURE 7–22. Permanent dental arches.

face that overlies the **dentin**, or ivory, of the tooth. At the heart of the tooth is the **pulp**, in which the nerve supplying the tooth resides. The tooth is held in its socket by **cementum**, which is a thin layer of bone. As teeth shift from pressures (such as the forces accompanying tongue thrust), the cementum will develop to ensure that the tooth remains firmly in its socket.

Five surfaces are important to remember when discussing teeth. To understand the terminology you need to alter your thinking about the dental arch a bit. Examine Figure 7–24 and you will see that the center of the dental arch is considered to be the point between the two central incisors, in front. Follow the arch around toward the molars in back and you have traced a path distal to those incisors. That is, *medial* refers to movement along the arch toward the midline between the central incisors, whereas *lateral* refers to movement along the arch away from that midpoint. From this you can see that the **medial surface** (or **mesial**) of any tooth is the surface "looking" along the arch toward the midpoint between the central incisors. The **distal surface** is the surface of any tooth that is farthest from that midline point. Every tooth has a medial and a distal surface.

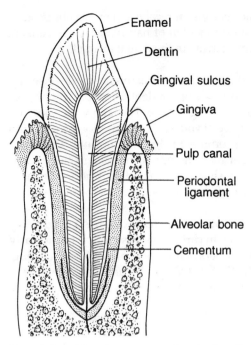

FIGURE 7–23. Components of a tooth.

FIGURE 7–24. Surface referents of teeth and the dental arch.

The **buccal surface** of a tooth is that which could come in contact with the buccal wall (cheek), and the **lingual surface** is the surface facing the tongue. The **occlusal surface** is the contact surface between teeth of the upper and lower arches. Not surprisingly, the thickest enamel

*buccal: L., **bucca**, cheek*

overlays the occlusal surface because it receives the most abrasion. A habit of chewing ice can undo this plan of nature, however, causing premature **attrition** or wearing away of the dental enamel.

incisor: L., cutter

cingulum: L., girdle

Incisors clearly are designed for cutting, as their name implies (see Figure 7–25). The **central incisors** of the upper dental arch present a large, spade-like surface with a thin cutting surface. The **lateral incisors** present a smaller but similar surface. If you feel your superior incisors with your tongue you will feel a prominent ridge or **cingulum**. The lower incisors are markedly smaller than the upper incisors, resting within the upper arch, and you must slightly open and protrude your mandible to make contact between the occlusal surfaces of the incisors.

cuspid: L., cuspis, point

The **cuspid** (also **canine; eye tooth**) is well named. It has a single cusp or point that is used for tearing. In carnivores this tooth is particularly well suited for separating the fibers of muscle to promote meat eating. Lateral to the cuspids are the **first** and **second bicuspids** or **premolars**. These teeth have two cusps on the occlusal surface, and are absent in the deciduous dental arch.

UPPER ARCH

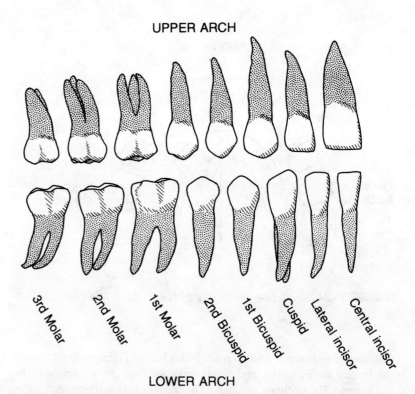

3rd Molar 2nd Molar 1st Molar 2nd Bicuspid 1st Bicuspid Cuspid Lateral incisor Central incisor

LOWER ARCH

FIGURE 7–25. Types of teeth.

Molars are large teeth with great occlusal surfaces designed to grind material, and their placement in the posterior arch capitalizes on the significant force available in the muscles of mastication. This mix of cutting teeth (incisors, cuspids, bicuspids) and grinding teeth (molars) is just right for omnivorous humans: We will eat virtually anything!

molar: L., molaris, grinding

There are three molars in each half of the adult dental arch. The medial-most **first molar** is the largest of the group, with the **second** and **third molars** descending in size. The first molar will have four cusps, the second molar may have three or four, and the third molar will have three. The third molar is sometimes known as the **wisdom tooth**, often erupting well into adulthood. The third molar is very likely a safeguard against losing teeth. In days before dental hygiene it was not uncommon to lose many teeth to **caries**. A late-emerging set of molars, useful for grinding grain and pulverizing fibers, would be just the item to extend the life of our ancestors. Now those wisdom teeth seem less "wise," as they tend to crowd the other teeth and often develop with an orientation that makes them not only useless, but a threat to the healthy teeth.

The roots of the teeth reflect the forces applied to the teeth. The incisors and cuspids have a single long root, with the cuspid, which has a great deal of force on it from tearing, having the longest root. The bicuspids have variously one or two roots, and the molars will have two or three roots to help anchor them against the massive forces of grinding.

Dental Development

Dental development clearly parallels that of the individual. Infants develop **deciduous** or **shedding teeth** (also known as milk teeth) that give way to the **permanent teeth** that must last a lifetime. Deciduous teeth actually begin development quite early in prenatal development, but start **erupting** through the bone (**intraosseous eruption**) and the gum (**clinical eruption**) between 6 and 9 months of age. Tooth buds form when the developing mandible and maxillae are only 1 mm long, but by birth the buds have spread out to match the jaw that is 40 times longer. These teeth are not only much smaller than the adult teeth, matching the size of the arch, but are fewer in number. Generally, central incisors emerge first (lower, then upper), followed by lateral incisors (upper, then lower). The first molars emerge at approximately the same time as the cuspids (between 15 and 20 months), and the second molars will have erupted by the second birthday. You will notice that there is no third molar, and the first and second bicuspids are conspicuously absent. These teeth are reserved for the adult arch. Each deciduous arch has 10 teeth, whereas the adult arch has 16 (see Figure 7–26).

deciduous: L., deciduus, falling off

FIGURE 7-26. Age of eruption of teeth in the permanent and deciduous arches.

Your first-grade school photograph will remind you of the period during which shedding begins. That gap-toothed grin of the 6-year-old child comes from shedding of the deciduous arch, beginning with the incisors (6 through 9 years), followed by first molars and cuspids (9 to 12 years), and finally second molars (beginning around 10 years of age).

Shedding is not a passive process. If you have occasion to view a tooth shed by a child you will see very little of the root. The deciduous tooth is suspended in the socket by means of a **periodontal ligament** that serves as a pressure sensor. As the permanent tooth migrates toward the surface its proximity stimulates conversion of the deciduous periodontal ligament into osteoclasts that promote resorption of the root and enamel. Thus, by the time the permanent tooth is ready to erupt, the deciduous tooth has lost its anchor in the alveolus and comes out easily.

periodontal: Gr., peri, around + odous, tooth

The permanent teeth that replace deciduous teeth are called **successional** teeth. The third molar and bicuspids erupt in addition to the original constellation, and thus are referred to as **superadded**.

Dental Anomalies

There are numerous developmental dental anomalies. Children may be born with **supernumerary** teeth (teeth in addition to the normal number), or teeth may be smaller than appropriate for the dental arch (**microdontia**). Teeth may **fuse** together at the root or crown. In addition to this, enamel may be extremely thin or even missing from the surface of the tooth (**amelogenesis imperfecta**), or the enamel may be stained from use of the antibiotic tetracycline or fluoride.

Dental Occlusion

The primary purpose of dentition is mastication, and this fact makes the orientation of teeth of the utmost importance. **Occlusion** is the process of bringing the upper and lower teeth into contact, and proper occlusion is essential for successful mastication. Clearly, if the upper molars do not make contact with the lower molars, no grinding will occur. We will discuss orientation of the upper and lower dental arches, as well as orientation that the individual teeth can take within the arches. These terms of orientation will serve you well as you prepare for your clinical work, because they are central to the oral-peripheral examination of teeth.

To discuss this orientation, first examine your own dental arch relationship. Lightly tap your molars, and then bite down lightly and leave them occluded. This sets the orientation of the arches. With your teeth making contact in this manner, open your lips so that you can see the front teeth while looking in a mirror. If you have a **Class I occlusal relationship** between your upper and lower teeth, the first molar of the mandibular arch is one-half tooth advanced of the maxillary molar. Your upper incisors project beyond the lower incisors vertically by a few millimeters (termed **overjet**), and the upper incisors naturally hide the lower incisors (termed **overbite**) so that only a little of the lower teeth will show. This Class I occlusion (also known as **neutroclusion**) (see Figure 7–27) is considered the normal relationship between the molars of the dental arches.

In **Class II malocclusion**, the first mandibular molars are retracted at least one tooth from the first maxillary molars. This is sometimes the product of **relative micrognathia**, a condition in which the mandible is small in relation to the maxillae.

A **Class III malocclusion** is identified if the first mandibular molar is advanced farther than one tooth beyond the first maxillary molar. Thus, in Class II malocclusion the mandible is retracted, whereas in

CLASS I
OCCLUSION

CLASS II
MALOCCLUSION

CLASS III
MALOCCLUSION

FIGURE 7–27. Types of malocclusion.

Class III the mandible is protruded. There is a **Class I malocclusion**, as well. This is defined as an occlusion in which there is normal orientation of the molars, but an abnormal orientation of the incisors.

micrognathia: Gr., micro, small + gnathos, jaw

Individual teeth may be misaligned as well. If a tooth is rotated or twisted on its long axis, it has undergone **torsiversion**. If it tilts toward the lips, it is referred to as **labioverted**, whereas tilting toward the tongue is **linguaverted** (see Figure 7–28). A tooth that tilts away from the midline along the arch is said to be **distoverted**, whereas one tilting toward that midline between the two central incisors is **mesioverted.** When a tooth does not erupt sufficiently to make occlusal contact with its pair in the opposite arch it is said to be **infraverted**, whereas the tooth that erupts too far is said to be **supraverted**. In some cases the front teeth may not demonstrate the proper occlusion because teeth in the posterior arch prohibit anterior contact, which is termed **persistent open bite.** If supraversion prohibits the posterior teeth from occlusion it is called **persistent closed bite**.

In summary:

■ The **teeth** are housed within the **alveoli** of the **maxillae** and **mandible,** and consist of **incisors, cuspids, bicuspids,** and **molars.**
■ Each tooth has a **root** and **crown,** with the surface of the crown composed of **enamel** overlying **dentin.**
■ Each tooth has a **medial, lateral, lingual, buccal** (or labial), and **occlusal** surface, and the occlusal surface reflects the function of the teeth in the omnivorous human dental arch.

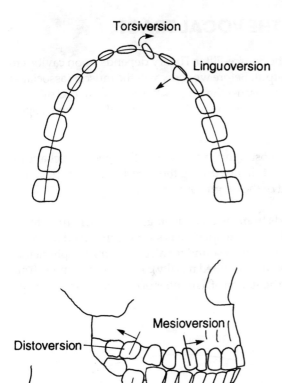

FIGURE 7-28. Graphic representation of torsiversion, linguaversion, infraversion, distoversion, and mesioversion.

■ **Clinical eruption** of the **deciduous** arch begins between 6 and 9 months of age, while the **permanent arch** emerges between 6 and 9 years.

■ **Class I occlusion** refers to normal orientation of mandible and maxillae, while **Class II malocclusion** refers to a relatively retracted mandible. **Class III malocclusion** refers to a relatively protruded **mandible**.

■ Individual teeth may have aberrant orientation within the alveolus, including **torsiversion, labioversion, linguaversion, distoversion** and **mesioversion**.

■ Inadequately erupted or hypererupted teeth are referred to as **infraverted** and **supraverted**.

CAVITIES OF THE VOCAL TRACT

We mentioned that the Source-Filter Theory depends upon cavities to shape the acoustic output. Before we show you the muscles associated with articulation, let us discuss the cavities that will be shaped by moving those muscles. These are the oral, buccal, nasal, and pharyngeal cavities (see Figure 7–29).

The **oral cavity** is the most significant cavity of the speech mechanism, as it undergoes the most change during the speech act. Its shape can be altered by movement of the tongue or mandible.

The oral cavity extends from the oral opening, or mouth, in front to the faucial pillars in back. The oral opening is strongly involved in articulation, being the point of exit of sound for all orally emitted phonemes (i.e., all sounds except those emitted nasally). The lips of the mouth are quite important for articulation of a number of consonants and vowels (see Figure 7–30).

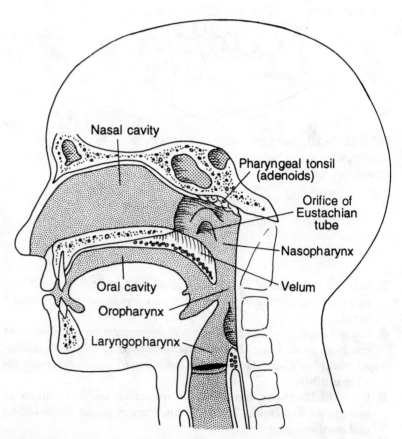

FIGURE 7–29. Oral, nasal, and pharyngeal cavities.

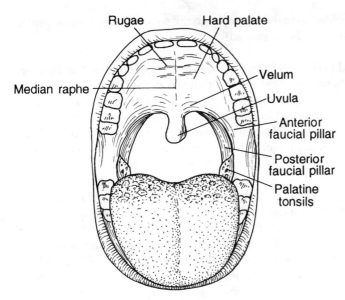

FIGURE 7–30. Anterior view of oral cavity.

This is a good opportunity to take a guided tour of your own mouth. Palpate the roof of your mouth (you can use your tongue to feel this if you wish). The hard roof of your mouth is the **hard palate**. The prominent ridges running laterally are the **rugae**, potentially useful structures in formation of the bolus of food during deglutition and serving as a landmark in articulation. The **median raphe** divides the hard palate into equal halves.

As you run your tongue or finger back along the roof of your mouth, you can feel the point at which the hard palate suddenly becomes soft. This is the juncture of the hard and soft palate, and the soft portion is the **soft palate** or **velum**, with the **uvula** marking the terminus of the velum. The velum is the movable muscle mass separating the oral and nasal cavities (or more technically, the oropharynx and nasopharynx, as you shall see). The velum is attached in front to the palatine bone and is thus a muscular extension of the hard palate.

On either side of the soft palate and continuous with it are two prominent bands of tissue on either side. These are the **anterior** and **posterior faucial pillars,** and they mark the posterior margin of the oral cavity. The teeth and alveolar ridge of the maxillae make up the lateral margins of the oral cavity. The tongue occupies most of the lower mouth.

Between the anterior and posterior faucial pillars you may see the **palatine tonsils**. These masses of lymphoid tissue are situated between the pillars on either side, and even invade the lateral undersurface of the

raphe: Gr., crease

rugae: L., folds or creases

velum: L., veil

fauces: L., throat

soft palate. Medial to these tonsils, on the surface of the tongue, are the lingual tonsils (to be discussed).

The **buccal cavity** lies lateral to the oral cavity, composed of the space between the posterior teeth and the cheeks of the face. It is bounded by the cheeks laterally, the lips in front, and the teeth medially. The posterior margin is at the third molar. This space plays a role in oral resonance when the mandible is depressed to expose it, is involved in high-pressure consonant production, and is the source of the distortion heard in the misarticulation known as the lateral /s/.

The **pharyngeal cavity**, or **pharynx**, is broken into three logically named regions. You can envision the pharynx as a tube approximately 12 cm in length, extending from the vocal folds below to the region behind the nasal cavities, above. This tube is lined with muscle capable of constricting the size of the tube to facilitate deglutition, and this musculature plays an important role in effecting closure of the **velopharyngeal port**, the opening between the oropharynx and nasopharynx.

The **oropharynx** is the portion of the pharynx immediately posterior to the fauces, bounded above by the velum. The lower boundary of the oropharynx is the hyoid bone, which marks the upper boundary of the laryngopharynx. The **laryngopharynx** (or **hypopharynx**) is bounded anteriorly by the epiglottis and inferiorly by the esophagus.

The third pharyngeal space is the **nasopharynx**, the space above the soft palate, bounded posteriorly by the pharyngeal protuberance of the occipital bone and by the nasal choanae in front. The lateral nasopharyngeal wall contains the **orifice** of the **Eustachian tube** (also known as the **auditory tube**; see Figure 7–29).

Although minute, the Eustachian tube serves an extremely important function in that it provides a means of aerating the middle ear cavity. Recognize that the nasopharynx is on level with the ears, so that the tube connecting the nasopharynx with the middle ear space must course slightly up, back, and out to reach that cavity. The Eustachian tube is actively opened through contraction of the tensor veli palatini muscle, as discussed later in this chapter. The bulge of tissue partially encircling the orifice of the Eustachian tube is the **torus tubarius**, and the ridge of tissue coursing down from the orifice is the **salpingopharyngeal fold**, actually the salpingopharyngeus muscle covered with mucous membrane.

salpingopharyngeus: Gr.,
salpinx, *tube + pharynx*

Also within the nasopharynx is the **pharyngeal tonsil** (also known as **adenoids**). This mass of lymphoid tissue typically is found to arise from the base of the posterior nasopharynx. By virtue of its proximity to the velopharyngeal port, the tissue of the pharyngeal tonsil may provide support for velar function. Removal of the adenoids from children with short or hypotrophied soft palates may result in persistent hypernasality.

The final cavities of concern to articulation are the nasal cavities (see Figure 7–31). The nasal cavities are produced by the paired maxillae, palatine, and nasal bones, and are divided by the nasal septum, made up of the singular vomer bone, perpendicular plate of ethmoid, and the cartilaginous septum (as discussed in the previous section). The nasal cavities and turbinates are covered with mucous membrane endowed with beating and secreting epithelia, as well as a rich vascular supply. Air entering the nasal cavities is quickly warmed and humidified to protect the lungs, and fine nasal hairs help prevent particulate matter from entering the lower respiratory passageway. Beating epithelia propel encapsulated pollutants toward the nasopharynx, from whence they slowly work their way toward the esophagus, to be swallowed (a much better fate than to be deposited in the lungs).

The **nares** or nostrils mark the anterior boundaries of the nasal cavities, while the **nasal choanae** are the posterior portals connecting the nasopharynx and nasal cavities. The floor of the nasal cavity is the hard palate of the oral cavity, specifically the palatine processes of maxillae and horizontal plates of the palatine bones.

choanae: Gr., funnel

To summarize, the **cavities** of the articulatory system can be likened to a series of linked tubes.

■ The most posterior of the tubes is the vertically directed **pharynx,** made up of the **laryngopharynx, oropharynx,** and **nasopharynx.**
■ The horizontally coursing tube representing the nasal cavities arises from the nasopharynx, with the nasal and nasopharyngeal regions entirely separated from the oral cavity by elevation of the **soft palate.**
■ The large tube representing the **oral cavity** is flanked by the small **buccal cavities.**
■ The shape and size of the oral cavity is altered through movement of the tongue and mandible, and the nasal cavity may be coupled with the oral/pharyngeal cavities by means of the **velum.**
■ The shape of the pharyngeal cavity is altered primarily by use of the **pharyngeal constrictor muscles** and by elevation or depression of the larynx.

Let us examine the muscles involved in the articulatory system. The summary table in Appendix E may assist you in your study of these muscles.

MUSCLES OF THE FACE AND MOUTH

The articulatory system is dominated by three significant structures, the lips, the tongue, and the velum. Movement of the lips for speech is

Eustachian Tube Development

The eustachian tube is the communicative port between the nasopharynx and middle ear cavity. It is opened during deglutition and yawning and provides a means of aeration of the middle ear cavity. In the adult, the eustachian courses down at an angle of about 45°. In the infant, the tube is more horizontal, with the shift in angle of descent brought about by head growth. It is felt that this horizontal course in the infant contributes to middle ear disease, with the assumption being that liquids and bacteria have a low-resistance path to the middle ear from the nasopharynx of an infant being bottle-fed in the supine position.

FIGURE 7-31. Nasal cavity and nasopharynx.

a product of the muscles of the face, while the tongue capitalizes upon its own musculature and that of the mandible and hyoid for its movement. The muscles of the velum elevate that structure to completely separate the oral and nasal regions. Table 7–2 may assist you in organizing the muscles of the face and mouth.

Muscles of the Face

■ **Orbicularis Oris**
■ **Risorius**
■ **Buccinator**
■ **Levator Labii Superioris Muscle**
■ **Zygomatic Minor Muscle**
■ **Levator Labii Superioris Alaeque Nasi Muscle**
■ **Levator Anguli Oris Muscle**
■ **Zygomatic Major Muscle**
■ **Depressor Labii Inferioris Muscle**
■ **Depressor Anguli Oris Muscle**
■ **Mentalis**
■ **Platysma**

Orbicularis Oris. The lips form the focus of the facial muscles, as their movement largely determines their function in both facial expression and speech (see Figure 7–32). The lips are comprised of muscle and mucous membrane that is richly invested with vascular supply, a trait made apparent by the translucent superficial epithelia. Although the lips serve a significant articulatory function, their social, cultural, and aesthetic value as a central feature of the face is quite important. In cases where symmetry and morphology of the lips are compromised, as in clefting of the lip, the plastic surgeon will perform precise examination and measurement of the structure prior to performing exacting procedures to restore aesthetic balance.

To the plastic surgeon, the fine points of the **cupid's bow** are extremely important. The symmetry of this region is judged by the grace of its curve and its relationship to the **columella** and **philtrum**.

columella: L., small column

The **orbicularis oris** has been characterized as both a single muscle encircling the mouth opening (see Figure 7–33) and paired upper and lower muscles (**orbicularis oris superior** and **orbicularis oris inferior**). As we shall see in Chapter 8, there is ample evidence for *functional* differentiation of upper and lower orbicularis oris. The upper and lower orbicularis oris act much like a drawstring to pull the lips closer together and effect a labial seal.

> *Innervation.* The orbicularis oris is innervated by the mandibular marginal and lower buccal branches of the VII facial nerve.

Table 7-2. Muscles of articulation.

Muscles of the Face
Orbicularis Oris
Risorius
Buccinator
Levator labii superioris muscle
Zygomatic minor muscle
Levator labii superioris alaeque nasi muscle
Levator anguli oris muscle
Zygomatic major muscle
Depressor labii inferioris muscle
Depressor anguli oris muscle
Mentalis
Platysma

Intrinsic Tongue Muscles
Superior longitudinal muscle of tongue
Inferior longitudinal muscle of tongue
Transverse muscle of tongue
Vertical muscle of tongue

Extrinsic Tongue Muscles
Genioglossus muscle
Hyoglossus muscle
Styloglossus muscle
Chondroglossus muscle
Palatoglossus muscle

Mandibular Elevators and Depressors
Masseter
Temporalis muscle
Medial pterygoid muscle
Lateral pterygoid muscle
Digastricus muscle
Mylohyoid muscle
Geniohyoid
Platysma

Muscles of the Velum
Levator veli palatini muscle
Musculus uvulae
Tensor veli palatini muscle
Palatoglossus muscle
Palatopharyngeus muscle

Pharyngeal Musculature
Superior pharyngeal constrictor
Middle pharyngeal constrictor
Inferior pharyngeal constrictor
Cricopharyngeal muscle
Thyropharyngeus muscle
Salpingopharyngeus
Stylopharyngeus muscle

FIGURE 7–32. Landmarks of the lips.

The orbicularis oris serves as the point of insertion for many other muscles and interacts with the muscles of the face to produce the wide variety of facial gestures of which we are capable. The muscles inserting into the orbicularis oris have different effects, based on their course and point of insertion into the lips. The risorius and buccinator muscles insert into the corners of the mouth and retract the lips. The depressor labii inferioris depresses the lower lip, and the levator labii superioris, zygomatic minor, and levator labii superioris alaeque nasi muscles elevate the upper lip. The zygomatic major muscle elevates and retracts the lips, whereas the depressor anguli oris depresses the corner of the mouth. The levator anguli oris pulls the corner of the mouth up and medially.

Risorius Muscle. It is evident from the course of the buccinator and risorius that they retract the corners of the mouth (see Figure 7–33). The buccinator is the dominant muscle of the cheeks. The **risorius muscle** is the most superficial of the pair, originating from the posterior region of the face along the fascia of the masseter muscle. The risorius is considerably smaller than the buccinator, coursing forward to insert into the corners of the mouth. The function of the risorius muscles are to retract the lips at the corners, facilitating smiling and grinning.

risorius: L., laughing

> *Innervation.* Innervation of the risorius is by means of the buccal branch of the VII facial nerve.

Buccinator Muscle. The **buccinator muscle** ("bugler's muscle") lies deep to the risorius, following a parallel course. It originates on the pterygomandibular ligament, a tendinous slip running from the hamulus of the internal pterygoid plate of the sphenoid to the posterior mylohyoid line of the inner mandible. Fibers of the buccinator also arise from the posterior alveolar portion of the mandible and maxillae, while the posterior fibers appear to be continuous with those of the superior pharyngeal constrictor. The buccinator courses forward to insert into the upper and lower orbicularis oris.

FIGURE 7–33. Muscles of the face.

The buccinator, like the risorius, is primarily involved in mastication. The buccinator is used to move food onto the grinding surfaces of the molars, and contraction of this muscle tends to constrict the oropharynx.

> *Innervation.* The risorius and buccinator are innervated by the buccal branch of the VII facial nerve.

Levator Labii Superioris, Zygomatic Minor, and Levator Labii Superioris Alaeque Nasi. The levator labii superioris, zygomatic minor, and levator labii superioris alaeque nasi share a common insertion into the mid-lateral region of the upper lip, such that some anatomists refer to them as heads of the same muscle. The three hold the major responsibility for elevation of the upper lip.

The medial-most **levator labii superiorier alaeque nasi** courses nearly vertically along the lateral margin of the nose, arising from the frontal process of maxilla. The intermediate **levator labii superioris** originates from the infraorbital margin of the maxilla, coursing down and in to the upper lip. The **zygomatic minor** begins its downward course from the facial surface of the zygomatic bone.

zygomatic: Gr., zygoma, cheekbone

Together, these three muscles are the dominant forces in lip elevation. Working in conjunction, these muscles readily dilate the oral opening, and fibers from the levator labii superioris alaeque nasi that insert into the wing of the nostril will flare the nasal opening.

> *Innervation*. The levator labii superioris, zygomatic minor, and levator labii superioris alaeque nasi are innervated by the buccal branches of the VII facial nerve.

Levator Anguli Oris. The **levator anguli oris** arises from the canine fossa of the maxilla, coursing to insert into the upper and lower lips. This muscle is obscured by the levator labii superioris. The levator anguli oris draws the corner of the mouth up and medial-ward.

> *Innervation*. The levator anguli oris is innervated by the superior buccal branches of the VII facial nerve.

Zygomatic Major. The **zygomatic major muscle** (zygomaticus) arises lateral to the zygomatic minor on the zygomatic bone. It takes a more oblique course than the minor, inserting into the corner of the orbicularis oris. The zygomatic major elevates and retracts the angle of the mouth, as in the gesture of smiling.

> *Innervation*. The zygomatic major muscle is innervated by the buccal branches of the VII facial nerve.

Depressor Labii Inferioris. The **depressor labii inferioris** is the counterpart to the levator triad listed previously. It originates from the mandible at the oblique line, coursing up and in to insert into the lower lip. Contraction of the depressor labii inferioris dilates the orifice of the mouth by pulling the lips down and out.

> *Innervation*. The depressor labii inferioris is innervated by the mandibular marginal branches of the VII facial nerve.

Depressor Anguli Oris. The **depressor anguli oris** (triangularis) originates along the lateral margins of the mandible on the oblique line. Its fanlike fibers converge on the orbicularis oris and upper lip at the corner. Contraction of the depressor anguli oris will depress the corners of the mouth and, by virtue of attachment to upper lip, help compress the upper lip against the lower lip.

Innervation. The depressor anguli oris is innervated by the mandibular marginal branch of the VII facial nerve.

Mentalis Muscle. The **mentalis muscle** arises from the region of the incisive fossa of the mandible, inserting into the skin of the chin below. Contraction of the mentalis elevates and wrinkles the chin and pulls the lower lip out.

Innervation. The mentalis receives its innervation via the mandibular marginal branch of the facial nerve.

Platysma. The **platysma** is more typically considered a muscle of the neck, but it is discussed here because of its function as a mandibular depressor. The platysma arises from the fascia overlying the pectoralis major and deltoid, coursing up to insert into the corner of the mouth, the region below the symphysis mente, and the lower margin of the mandible, fanning as well to insert into the skin near the masseter. The platysma is highly variable, but appears to assist in depression of the mandible. Its proximity to the external jugular vein has led to speculation that it promotes venous drainage.

platysma: Gr., plate

Innervation. The platysma is innervated by the cervical branch of the VII facial nerve.

In summary, the muscles of **facial expression** are important for articulation involving the lips.

■ Numerous muscles insert into the **orbicularis oris** inferior and superior muscles, providing a flexible system for lip **protrusion, closure, retraction, elevation,** and **depression.**

■ The **risorius** and **buccinator** muscles assist in retraction of the lips, as well as support entrapment of air within the oral cavity.

■ Contraction of the **levator labii superioris, zygomatic minor,** and **levator labii superioris alaeque nasi** elevate the upper lip, and contraction of the **depressor labii inferioris** depresses the lower lip.

■ Contraction of the **zygomatic major** muscle elevates and retracts the corner of the mouth, while the **depressor labii inferioris** pulls the lips down and out.

■ The **depressor anguli oris** muscle depresses the corner of the mouth, the **mentalis** muscle pulls the lower lip out, and the **platysma** depresses the mandible.

Muscles of the Mouth

Musculature of the mouth is dominated by intrinsic and extrinsic muscles of the tongue, as well as those responsible for elevation of the soft palate. Movement of the tongue is an interesting engineering feat, as you shall see.

The Tongue

The tongue is a massive structure occupying the floor of the mouth. If you take a moment to examine Figure 7–34 you can get some notion of the magnitude of this organ. When a child uses the tongue as an expressive instrument, she or he protrudes only a small portion of it, leaving the bulk of the tongue within the mouth. We divide the muscles of the tongue into intrinsic and extrinsic musculature, a division that proves to be both anatomical and functional. The extrinsic muscles tend to move the tongue into the general region desired, while the intrinsic muscles tend to provide the fine, graded control of the articulatory gesture. The tongue is involved primarily in mastication and deglutition, being responsible for movement of food within the oral cavity to position it for chewing and to propel it backward for swallowing.

The tongue is divided longitudinally by the **median fibrous septum**, a dividing wall between right and left halves that serves as the point of origin for the transverse muscle of the tongue. The septum originates on the body of the hyoid bone via the hyoglossal membrane, forming

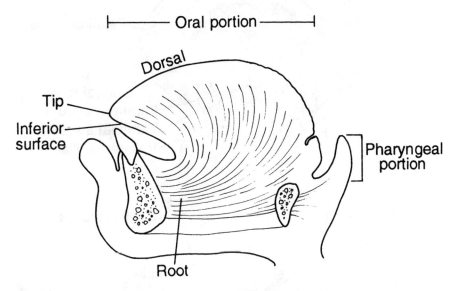

FIGURE 7–34. Demarkation of regions of the tongue.

the tongue attachment with the hyoid. The septum courses the length of the tongue.

It is useful to divide the tongue into regions as we discuss its characteristics (see Figure 7–34). The superior surface is referred to as the **dorsum**, and the anterior-most portion is the **tip** or **apex**. The **base** of the tongue is the portion of the tongue that resides in the oropharynx. The portion of the tongue surface within the oral cavity is referred to as the **oral** or **palatine surface**, making up about two thirds of the surface of the tongue. The other third of the tongue surface lies within the oropharynx and is referred to as the **pharyngeal surface**.

The mucous membrane covering the tongue dorsum has numerous landmarks (see Figure 7–35). The prominent **median sulcus** divides the tongue into left and right sides. The posterior of the tongue is invested with **lingual papillae**, small, irregular prominences on the surface of the tongue. The **terminal sulcus** marks the posterior palatine surface, and the center of this groove is the **foramen cecum**, a deep recess in the tongue.

papillae: L., nipple

cecum: L., caecum, blindness

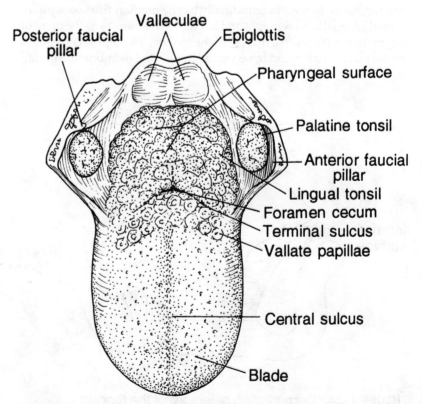

FIGURE 7–35. Landmarks of the tongue.

Beneath the membranous lining of the pharyngeal surface of the tongue are **lingual tonsils,** groups of lymphoid tissue. Taken in conjunction with the pharyngeal and palatine tonsils, the lingual tonsils form the final portion of the ring of lymph tissue in the oral and pharyngeal cavities. Tonsils tend to atrophy over time. Although the pharyngeal and palatine tonsils may be quite prominent during childhood, they are markedly diminished in size by puberty.

The tongue is invested with taste buds to convey the gustatory sense. The tip of the tongue has receptors sensitive to both sweet and sour tastes, and the sides of the tongue are sensitive only to sour tastes. Bitter tastes are sensed near the terminal sulcus.

If you examine the inferior surface of your tongue in a mirror, you will see three important landmarks (see Figure 7–36). Notice the rich vascular supply on that under-surface: Medications administered under the tongue will be very quickly absorbed into the blood stream. You will see a prominent band of tissue running from the inner mandibular mucosa to the underside of the tongue. The **lingual frenulum** (or **lingual frenum**) joins the inferior tongue and the mandible, perhaps stabilizing the tongue during movement. Notice also the transverse band of tissue on either side of the tongue (the **sublingual fold**). At this point are the ducts for the sublingual salivary glands. Lateral to the lingual frenulum are the ducts for the submandibular salivary glands that are hidden under the mucosa on the inner surface of the mandible.

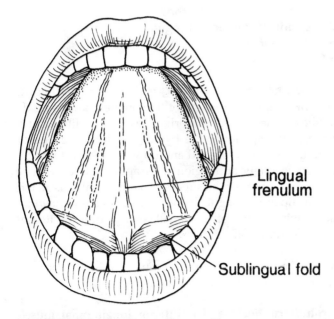

Lingual frenulum

Sublingual fold

FIGURE 7–36. Inferior surface of tongue.

Tongue Tie

The **lingual frenulum** is a band of tissue connecting the tongue to the floor of the mouth. It appears to assist in stabilizing the tongue during movement, but occasionally may be too short for proper lingual function. This condition, colloquially referred to as **tongue tie**, will result in difficulty elevating the tongue for phonemes requiring palatal or alveolar contact. The tongue may appear heart-shaped when protruded, resulting from the excessive tension on the midline by the short frenulum. A surgical procedure to correct the condition may be useful, although the surgery is not minor in nature.

Intrinsic Tongue Muscles

The intrinsic muscles of the tongue include two pairs of muscles running longitudinally, as well as muscles coursing transversely and vertically. At the outset we should note that the intrinsic muscles of the tongue interact in a complex fashion to produce the rapid, delicate articulations for speech and nonspeech activities. As we discuss each muscle, we will provide you with the basic function, but will deal more fully with the integration of these muscles in Chapter 8. Examination of Figure 7–37 will assist you in our discussion of these very important lingual muscles.

- **Superior Longitudinal Muscle of Tongue**
- **Inferior Longitudinal Muscle of Tongue**
- **Transverse Muscle of Tongue**
- **Vertical Muscle of Tongue**

Superior Longitudinal Muscle of Tongue. The **superior longitudinal muscle** courses along the length of the tongue, comprising the upper layer of the tongue. This muscle originates from the fibrous submucous layer near the epiglottis, the hyoid, and from the median fibrous septum. Its fibers fan forward and outward to insert into the lateral margins of the tongue and region of the apex. By virtue of their course and insertions, fibers of the superior longitudinal muscle will tend to elevate the tip of the tongue. If one superior longitudinal muscle is contracted without the other, it will tend to pull the tongue toward the side of contraction.

> *Innervation.* Innervation of all intrinsic muscles of the tongue is by means of the XII hypoglossal nerve.

Inferior Longitudinal Muscle. The **inferior longitudinal muscle** originates at the root of the tongue and corpus hyoid, with fibers cours-

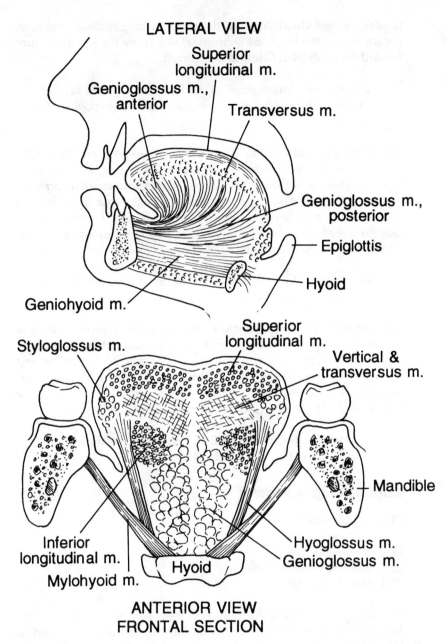

LATERAL VIEW

Superior
longitudinal m.

Genioglossus m.,
anterior

Transversus m.

Genioglossus m.,
posterior

Epiglottis

Hyoid

Geniohyoid m.

Styloglossus m.

Superior
longitudinal m.

Vertical &
transversus m.

Mandible

Inferior
longitudinal m.

Mylohyoid m.

Hyoid

Hyoglossus m.

Genioglossus m.

ANTERIOR VIEW
FRONTAL SECTION

FIGURE 7-37. Intrinsic muscles of the tongue. (From data of Netter, 1989.)

ing to the apex of the tongue. This muscle occupies the lower sides of the tongue, but is absent in the medial tongue base, which is occupied by the extrinsic genioglossus muscle, to be described in a later section. The inferior longitudinal muscle will pull the tip of the tongue downward and assist in retraction of the tongue if co-contracted with the superior longitudinal. As with the superior longitudinal, unilateral contraction of the inferior longitudinal will cause the tongue to turn toward the contracted side and downward.

>   *Innervation.* Innervation of all intrinsic muscles of the tongue is by means of the contralateral XII hypoglossal nerve.

Transverse Muscle of the Tongue. The **transverse muscles of the tongue** provide a mechanism for narrowing the tongue. Fibers of these muscles originate at the median fibrous septum and course laterally to insert into the side of the tongue in the submucous tissue. Some fibers of the transverse muscle continue as the palatopharyngeus muscle, to be described in a later section. The transverse muscle of the tongue pulls the edges of the tongue toward midline, effectively narrowing the tongue.

>   *Innervation* Innervation of all intrinsic muscles of the tongue is by means of the XII hypoglossal nerve.

Vertical Muscles of the Tongue. The **vertical muscles of the tongue** run at right angles to the transverse muscles and flatten the tongue. Fibers of the vertical muscle course from the base of the tongue and insert into the membranous cover. The fibers of the transverse and vertical muscles interweave. Contraction of the vertical muscles of the tongue will pull the tongue down into the floor of the mouth.

>   *Innervation.* Innervation of all intrinsic muscles of the tongue is by means of the XII hypoglossal nerve.

Extrinsic Tongue Muscles

- **Genioglossus Muscle**
- **Hyoglossus Muscle**
- **Styloglossus Muscle**
- **Chondroglossus Muscle**
- **Palatoglossus Muscle**

The intrinsic muscles of the tongue are responsible for precise articulatory performance and the extrinsic muscles of the tongue tend to move the tongue as a unit. It appears that they set the general posture for articulation, with the intrinsic muscles performing the refined perfection of that gesture.

Genioglossus Muscle. The **genioglossus** is the prime mover of the tongue, making up most of its deeper bulk. As you can see from Figure 7–38, the genioglossus arises from the inner mandibular surface at the symphysis and fans to insert into the tip and dorsum of the tongue, as well as to the corpus of the hyoid bone.

FIGURE 7-38. Genioglossus and related muscles.

The genioglossus muscle occupies a medial position in the tongue, with the inferior longitudinal muscle, hyoglossus, and styloglossus being lateral to it. Fibers of the genioglossus insert into the entire surface of the tongue, but are sparse to absent in the tip. Contraction of the anterior fibers of the genioglossus muscle results in retraction of the tongue, whereas contraction of the posterior fibers will draw the tongue forward to aid protrusion of the apex. If both anterior and posterior portions are contracted, the middle portion of the tongue will be drawn down into the floor of the mouth, functionally cupping the tongue along its length. Needless to say, we will return to the interaction of the genioglossus and intrinsic muscles when we discuss deglutition.

> *Innervation.* The genioglossus is innervated by the XII hypoglossal nerve.

Hyoglossus Muscle. As the name implies, the **hyoglossus** arises from the length of the greater cornu and lateral body of the hyoid bone, coursing upward to insert into the sides of the tongue between the styloglossus (to be discussed) and the inferior longitudinal muscles. The hyoglossus pulls the sides of the tongue down, in direct antagonism to the palatoglossus (to be discussed).

> *Innervation.* The hyoglossus is innervated by the XII hypoglossal nerve.

Styloglossus. If you will examine Figure 7–38 again, you will see that the **styloglossus** originates from the anterolateral margin of styloid process of the temporal bone, coursing forward and down to insert into the inferior sides of the tongue. It divides into two portions, with one interdigitating with the inferior longitudinal muscle, and the other with the fibers of the hyoglossus. As you can guess from examination of the course and insertion of this muscle, contraction of the paired styloglossi will draw the tongue back and up.

> *Innervation.* The styloglossus is innervated by the XII hypoglossal nerve.

chondroglossus: Gr. chondros, cartilage + glossus, tongue

Chondroglossus. The **chondroglossus** muscle is often considered to be part of the hyoglossus muscle. As with the hyoglossus, the chondroglossus arises from the hyoid (lesser cornu), coursing up to interdigitate with the intrinsic muscles of the tongue medial to the point of insertion of the hyoglossus. The chondroglossus is a depressor of the tongue.

> *Innervation.* The chondroglossus is innervated by the XII hypoglossal nerve.

Palatoglossus. The **palatoglossus** may be functionally defined as a muscle of the tongue or of the velum, although it is more closely allied with palatal architecture and origin. It will be described in a later section, but you should realize that it serves the dual purpose of depressing the soft palate or elevating the back of the tongue.

To summarize:

■ The **tongue** is a massive structure occupying the floor of the mouth. It is divided by a **median fibrous septum** that provides the origination for the transverse intrinsic muscle of the tongue.

■ The tongue is divided into **dorsum, apex** (tip), and **base.**

■ Fine movements are produced by contraction of the intrinsic musculature (**transverse, vertical, inferior longitudinal** and **superior longitudinal** muscles of the tongue).

■ Larger adjustments of lingual movement are completed through use of **extrinsic muscles.** The **genioglossus** retracts, protrudes, or depresses the tongue. The **hyoglossus** and **chondroglossus** depress the tongue, while the **styloglossus** and **palatoglossus** elevate the posterior tongue.

Muscles of Mastication: Mandibular Elevators and Depressors

The process of chewing food, or **mastication**, requires movement of the mandible so that the molars can make a solid, grinding contact. The muscles of mastication are among the strongest of the body, and the coordinated contraction of these muscles is required for proper food preparation. The muscles of mastication include the mandibular elevators (masseter, temporalis, medial pterygoid), muscles of protrusion (lateral pterygoid), and depressors (digastricus, mylohyoid, geniohyoid, platysma).

mastication: L., masticare, chewing

■ **Masseter**
■ **Temporalis Muscle**
■ **Medial Pterygoid Muscle**
■ **Lateral Pterygoid Muscle**
■ **Digastricus Muscle**
■ **Mylohyoid Muscle**
■ **Geniohyoid**
■ **Platysma**

Masseter. As you may see from Figure 7–39, the **masseter** is the most superficial of the muscles of mastication. This massive quadrilateral muscle originates on the lateral, inferior, and medial surfaces of the zygomatic arch, coursing down to insert primarily into the ramus of the mandible, but with some of the deeper fibers terminating on the coronoid process. The course and attachments of the masseter make it ideally suited for placing maximum force on the molars. Contraction of this muscle will elevate the mandible, and when the teeth are clenched, the prominent muscular belly is clearly visible.

> *Innervation.* The masseter is innervated by the anterior trunk of the mandibular nerve arising from the V trigeminal.

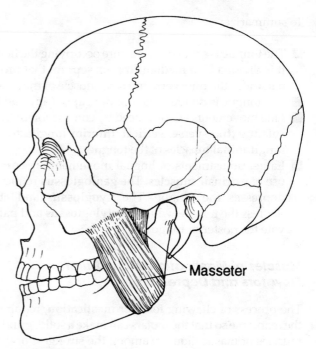

FIGURE 7–39. Graphic representation of masseter.

Temporalis Muscle. The **temporalis muscle** is deep to the masseter, arising from a region of the temporal and parietal bones known as the **temporal fossa.** As you can see in Figure 7–40, it arises from a broad region of the lateral skull, converging as it courses down and forward. The terminal tendon of the temporalis passes through the zygomatic arch and inserts in the coronoid process and ramus. The temporalis elevates the mandible and draws it back if protruded. It appears to be capable for more rapid contraction than the masseter.

> *Innervation.* The temporalis is innervated by the temporal branches arising from the mandibular nerve of V trigeminal.

Medial Pterygoid Muscle. The **medial pterygoid muscle** (also known as the **internal pterygoid muscle**) originates from the medial pterygoid plate and fossa lateral to it (see Figure 7–41). Fibers from the muscle course down and back to insert into the mandibular ramus. The medial pterygoid muscle elevates the mandible, acting in conjunction with the masseter.

> *Innervation* The medial pterygoid muscle is innervated by the mandibular division of the V trigeminal nerve.

Lateral Pterygoid Muscle. The **lateral** (or external) **pterygoid muscle** arises from the sphenoid bone. One head of the lateral pterygoid

Tongue Thrust

As with other motor functions, swallowing develops from imma-ture to mature forms. The immature swallow capitalizes on the needs of the moment: An infant needs to compress his or her mother's nipple to stimulate release of milk, so the tongue moves forward naturally during this process. As the infant develops teeth, anterior movement of the tongue is blocked even as the need for it diminishes. The child begins eating semisolid and solid food, and chewing becomes more important than sucking. The mature swallow propels a bolus back toward the oropharynx, a maneuver requiring posterior direction of the tongue.

If the child fails to develop the mature swallow, he or she has a condition known as **tongue thrust**. The anterior direction of the tongue will cause labioversion of the incisors. This child may have flaccid oral musculature, weak masseter action during swallow, and a disorganized approach to generation of the bolus. Consid-ering we swallow between 400 and 600 times per day, the imma-ture swallow is difficult (but far from impossible) to re-organize into a mature swallow. Many speech-language pathologists spe-cialize in **oral myofunctional therapy** directed toward remedia-tion of such problems.

FIGURE 7–40. Graphic representation of temporalis.

FIGURE 7-41. Lateral and medial pterygoid muscles.

arises from the lateral pterygoid plate (hence the name of the muscle); another head attaches to the greater wing of sphenoid. Fibers course back to insert into the pterygoid fovea of the mandible, the lower inner margin of the condyloid process of the mandible (see Figure 7–41). Contraction of the lateral pterygoid muscle will protrude the mandible, and it works in contrast with the mandibular elevators for grinding action at the molars.

> *Innervation.* The lateral pterygoid muscle is innervated by the mandibular branch of the V trigeminal nerve.

pterygoid: Gr., pterygodes, wing

digastric: L., two + belly

Digastricus. The dual-bellied digastricus was described in Chapter 5, so it is only briefly discussed here. **Digastricus anterior** originates on the inner surface of the mandible at the digastricus fossa, near the symphysis, while the **digastricus posterior** originates on the mastoid process of the temporal bone. The anterior fibers course medially and down to the hyoid, where they join with the posterior digastricus by means of an intermediate tendon that inserts into the hyoid at the juncture of the hyoid corpus and greater cornu. If the hyoid bone is fixed by infrahyoid musculature, contraction of the anterior component will result in depression of the mandible.

> *Innervation.* The anterior belly is innervated by the mandibular branch of V trigeminal nerve via the mylohyoid

branch of the inferior alveolar nerve. The posterior belly is supplied by the digastric branch of the VII facial nerve.

Mylohyoid Muscle. This muscle was described in Chapter 5. The **mylohyoid** originates on the underside of the mandible and courses to the corpus hyoid. This fanlike muscle courses from the **mylohyoid line** of the mandible to the median fibrous raphe and inferiorly to the hyoid, forming the floor of the mouth. With the hyoid fixed in position, the mylohyoid will depress the mandible.

> *Innervation.* The mylohyoid is innervated by the alveolar nerve, arising from the V trigeminal nerve, mandibular branch.

Geniohyoid Muscle. Also described in Chapter 5, the **geniohyoid muscle** originates at the mental spines of the mandible, and projects parallel to the anterior digastricus from the inner mandibular surface to insert into the corpus hyoid. Contraction of the geniohyoid depresses the mandible if the hyoid is fixed.

> *Innervation.* Innervation of the geniohyoid is by means of the XII hypoglossal nerve.

Platysma. The platysma was discussed under Muscles of the Face.

To summarize, the muscles of **mastication** include mandibular **elevators** and **depressors,** as well as muscles to **protrude** the mandible.

■ Mandibular elevators include the **masseter, temporalis,** and **medial pterygoid** muscles, while the **lateral pterygoid** protrudes the mandible.

■ Depression of the mandible is performed by the **mylohyoid, geniohyoid,** and **platysma** muscles. The grinding action of the molars requires coordinated and synchronized contraction of the muscles of mastication.

Muscles of the Velum

Only three speech sounds in English require that the soft palate be depressed (/m/, /ŋ/ and /n/). During most speaking time the soft palate is actively elevated. We will discuss the general configuration of the soft palate and then discuss how we go about elevating and depressing this important structure.

The **soft palate** or **velum** is actually a combination of muscle, aponeurosis, nerves, and blood supply covered by mucous membrane lining. The **palatal aponeurosis** makes up the mid-front portion of the soft palate, being an extension of an aponeurosis arising from the tensor veli palatini, to be described. The palatal aponeurosis divides around the musculus uvulae, but serves as the point of insertion for other muscles of the soft palate. The mucous membrane lining is invested with lymph and mucous glands, and the oral side of the lining also has taste buds.

- ■ Levator Veli Palatini Muscle
- ■ Musculus Uvulae
- ■ Tensor Veli Palatini Muscle
- ■ Palatoglossus Muscle
- ■ Palatopharyngeus Muscle

Muscles of the soft palate include elevators (levator veli palatini, musculus uvulae), a tensor (tensor veli palatini), and depressors (palatoglossus and palatopharyngeus). Although the superior constrictor muscle is a pharyngeal muscle, it should be noted that it is an important muscle for function of the soft palate. We will discuss the muscles of the pharynx following discussion of the muscles of the soft palate. Figure 7–42 will assist you in the following discussion.

Levator Veli Palatini Muscle. The **levator veli palatini** (or **levator palati**) is the palatal elevator, making up the bulk of the soft palate (see Figure 7–43). This muscle arises from the apex of the petrous portion of the temporal bone, as well as from the medial wall of the Eustachian tube cartilage. The levator veli palatini courses down and forward to insert into the palatal aponeurosis of the soft palate, lateral to the musculus uvulae. The levator veli palatini is the primary elevator of the soft palate. Contraction elevates and retracts the posterior velum.

levator: L. lifter

> *Innervation.* The levator veli palatini is innervated by the pharyngeal plexus, arising from the XI accessory and X vagus nerves.

Musculus Uvulae. Casual examination of the inner workings of your own mouth reveal the structure of the **musculus uvulae**. The **uvula** makes up the medial and posterior portions of the soft palate, and the musculus uvulae is the muscle embodied within this structure. This paired muscle arises from the posterior nasal spines of the palatine bones and from the palatal aponeurosis. Fibers run the length of the soft palate on either side of the midline, inserting into the mucous membrane cover of the velum. Contraction of the uvula shortens the soft palate, effectively bunching it up.

uvulae: L., little grape

> *Innervation.* The musculus uvulae is innervated by the pharyngeal plexus, arising from the XI accessory and X vagus nerves.

Tensor Veli Palatini Muscle. The **tensor veli palatini** (tensor veli palati) is the tensor of the soft palate, as well as the dilator of the Eustachian tube. This muscle arises from the sphenoid bone (scaphoid

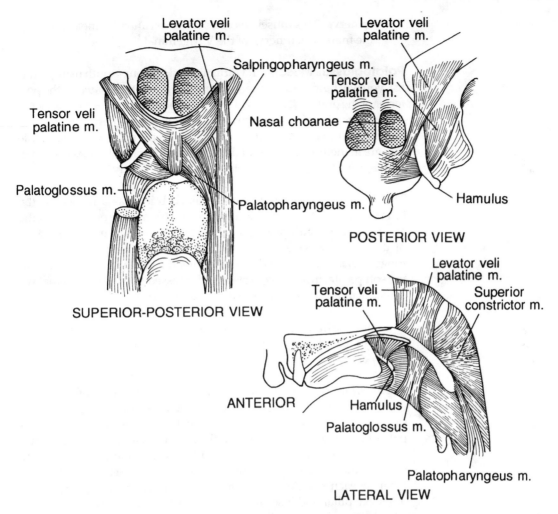

FIGURE 7–42. Muscles of the soft palate from superior-posterior *(left)*, posterior *(right)*, and the side *(lower figure)*. (From data of Schprintzen & Bardach, 1995; Langley, Telford, & Christensen, 1969; and Williams & Warrick, 1980.)

fossa between lateral and medial pterygoid plates, and sphenoid spine) as well as from the lateral Eustachian tube wall. The fibers converge to course down to terminate in a tendon. The tendon, in turn, passes around the pterygoid hamulus and then is directed medially. This tendon expands to become the palatal aponeurosis in conjunction with the tendon of the opposite side. Contraction of the tensor veli palatini tenses the soft palate and flattens it. It also assists in dilating or opening the Eustachian tube, thereby permitting **aeration** (exchange of air) of the middle ear cavity.

Innervation. The tensor veli palatini muscle is the only muscle of the soft palate not innervated by the XI accessory nerve. This muscle receives its innervation by means of the mandibular nerve of the V trigeminal.

Palatoglossus Muscle. If you again look in your mouth using a mirror, you will be able to see the structure of the **palatoglossus**. At the posterior of the oral cavity you will see two prominent arches that mark the entry to the pharynx. The arch closest to you is the anterior **faucial pillar**, and the muscle of which it is comprised is the palatoglossus. (While you are in there, take a look at the posterior faucial pillar, just behind it. That is the palatopharyngeus, to be discussed shortly.)

The palatoglossus muscle was discussed briefly as a muscle of the tongue, because it serves a dual purpose. This muscle originates at the anterolateral palatal aponeurosis, coursing down to insert into the sides of the posterior tongue. This muscle will either help to elevate the tongue, as mentioned earlier, or depress the soft palate. The fact that the soft palate, in its relaxed state, is depressed does not mean that we do not actively depress it, especially during speech.

> *Innervation.* The palatoglossus is innervated by the pharyngeal plexus, arising from the XI accessory and X vagus nerves.

Palatopharyngeus Muscle. Although classically considered a pharyngeal muscle, the **palatopharyngeus** is included in this discussion because of its role in velar function. Anterior fibers of the palatopharyngeus originate from the anterior hard palate, and posterior fibers arise from the midline of the soft palate posterior to the fibers of the levator veli palatine, attached to the palatal aponeurosis. Fibers of each muscle course laterally and down, forming the posterior faucial pillar and inserting into the posterior thyroid cartilage. This muscle has wide variability, mingling with fibers of the stylopharyngeus and salpingopharyngeus muscles prior to its ultimate insertion into the posterior margin of the thyroid cartilage. This muscle will assist in narrowing the pharyngeal cavity, as well as lower the soft palate. It may also help to elevate the larynx.

> *Innervation.* The palatopharyngeus is innervated by the pharyngeal plexus, arising from the XI accessory and pharyngeal branch of the X vagus nerve.

Pharyngeal Musculature

- ■ Superior Pharyngeal Constrictor
- ■ Middle Pharyngeal Constrictor
- ■ Inferior Pharyngeal Constrictor
- ■ Cricopharyngeal Muscle
- ■ Thyropharyngeus Muscle
- ■ Salpingopharyngeus
- ■ Stylopharyngeus Muscle

Muscles of the pharynx are closely allied with the tongue, muscles of the face, and laryngeal musculature. It will help if you imagine the pharynx as a vertical tube. This tube is made of muscles wrapping more-or-less horizontally from the front to a midline point in the back, as well as by muscles and connective tissue running from skull structures. Thus, the pharynx is composed of a complex of muscles that, when contracted, will constrict the pharynx to assist in deglutition.

Pharyngeal Constrictor Muscles. The superior, middle, and inferior **constrictor muscles** are the means by which the pharyngeal space is reduced in diameter. Of these, the superior constrictor is an important muscle of velopharyngeal function (see Figure 7–43).

Superior Pharyngeal Constrictor. Conceptually, the **superior pharyngeal constrictor** forms a tube beginning at the pterygomandibular raphe (the point of attachment of the buccinator). It projects back from this structure on both sides to the **median pharyngeal raphe**, the mid-

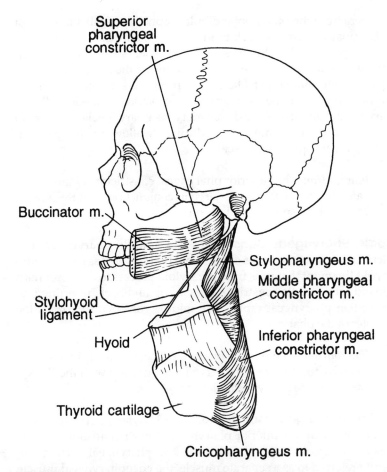

FIGURE 7–43. Pharyngeal constrictor muscles.

line tendinous component of the pharyngeal aponeurosis. This aponeurosis arises from the pharyngeal tubercle of the occipital bone (immediately anterior to the foramen magnum) and forms the superior sleeve of the pharyngeal wall by attaching to the temporal bone (petrous portion), medial pterygoid plate, and Eustachian tube. The median pharyngeal raphe is the midline portion of this structure, descending along the back wall of the pharynx, and providing the points of insertion for pharyngeal muscles. The superior constrictor muscle forms the sides and back wall of the nasopharynx and part of the back wall of the oropharynx, a function requiring a variety of points of attachment.

The median pterygoid plate gives rise to the upper-most fibers of the muscle, and these fibers are the "landing pad" for the soft palate, known as **Passavant's pad**. When present, this pad of muscle at the posterior pharyngeal wall appears as a ridge at the point of articulation of the soft palate with the wall. Clearly, the addition of tissue at this point can only assist effecting a seal with the soft palate, and in fact, this pad appears to develop most markedly in individuals with palatal insufficiency, perhaps from compensatory activity.

The fibers from the pterygomandibular raphe are parallel to those of the buccinator, coursing back to insert into the median raphe of the posterior pharynx. Beneath these fibers, another portion of the superior constrictor arises from the mylohyoid line on the inner mandibular surface, while some other fibers arise from the sides of the tongue. Contraction of the superior pharyngeal constrictor muscle pulls the pharyngeal wall forward and constricts the pharyngeal diameter, an especially prominent movement during swallowing. It assists in effecting the velopharyngeal seal.

> *Innervation*. The superior pharyngeal constrictor is innervated by the XI accessory nerve in conjunction with the X vagus, via the pharyngeal plexus.

Middle Pharyngeal Constrictor. The **middle pharyngeal constrictor** arises from the horns of the hyoid bone, as well as from the **stylohyoid ligament** that runs from the styloid process to the lesser horn of hyoid. The middle constrictor courses up and back, inserting into the median pharyngeal raphe. The middle constrictor narrows the diameter of the pharynx.

> *Innervation*. The middle pharyngeal constrictor is innervated by the XI accessory nerve in conjunction with the X vagus, via the pharyngeal plexus.

Inferior Pharyngeal Constrictor. The **inferior pharyngeal constrictor** makes up the inferior pharynx. The portion arising from the sides of the cricoid cartilage forms the cricopharyngeal portion, frequently referred to as a separate muscle, the **cricopharyngeal muscle**

(or **cricopharyngeus**). This portion, which courses back to form the muscular orifice of the esophagus, is an important muscle for swallowing and is the structure set into vibration during esophageal speech. The upper thyropharyngeal portion (or **thyropharyngeus muscle**) arises from the oblique line of the thyroid lamina, coursing up and back to insert into the median pharyngeal raphe. Contraction of the inferior constrictor reduces the diameter of the lower pharynx.

> *Innervation*. The inferior pharyngeal constrictor is innervated by the XI accessory nerve in conjunction with the X vagus, via the pharyngeal plexus.

Salpingopharyngeus. The **salpingopharyngeus muscle** arises from the lower margin of the Eustachian tube, descending the lateral pharynx to join the palatopharyngeus muscle (see Figure 7–44). The **salpingopharyngeal fold** is a crease in the lateral nasopharynx formed by the mucosa covering this muscle. The salpingopharyngeus assists in elevation of the lateral pharyngeal wall.

> *Innervation*. The salpingopharyngeus is innervated by the X vagus and XI spinal accessory nerve via the pharyngeal plexus.

Stylopharyngeus Muscle. As the name implies, the **stylopharyngeus** arises from the styloid process of the temporal bone, coursing

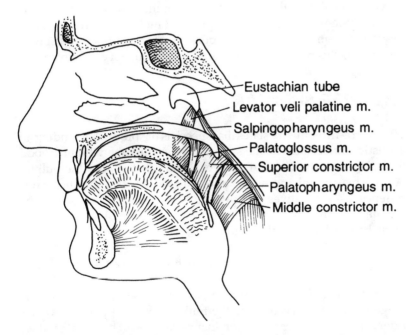

FIGURE 7–44. Salpingopharyngeus muscle.

down between the superior and middle pharyngeal constrictors. Some fibers insert into the constrictors, others insert into the posterior thyroid cartilage in concert with the palatopharyngeus muscle. The stylopharyngeus elevates and opens the pharynx, particularly during deglutition.

> *Innervation.* The stylopharyngeus muscle is innervated by the muscular branch of the IX glossopharyngeal nerve.

To summarize, the **soft palate** is a structure attached to the posterior hard palate and comprised of muscle and aponeurosis.

■ The **levator veli palatini** muscle elevates the soft palate, the **musculus uvulae** bunches the soft palate, and the **tensor veli palatini** tenses and shortens the palate.
■ The soft palate is depressed by means of the **palatoglossus** and **palatopharyngeus.**
■ The **superior pharyngeal constrictor** assists in gaining velopharyngeal closure, while peristaltic movement of food is facilitated by the **middle** and **inferior pharyngeal constrictors.**
■ The **cricopharyngeal muscle,** a component of the inferior constrictor, forms the muscular orifice of the **esophagus.**
■ Fibers of the **salpingopharyngeus** intermingle with those of the superior constrictor, providing assistance in elevation of the pharyngeal wall.
■ The **stylopharyngeus** assists in elevation of the larynx.

As you can tell from the preceding chapter, the structures of the articulatory system are extremely complex and mobile. We are capable of myriad movements that are incorporated into nonspeech and speech function. Let us move on to Chapter 8 and articulatory physiology.

CHAPTER SUMMARY

The **source-filter theory** states that speech is the product of sending an **acoustic source**, such as the sound produced by the vibrating vocal folds, through the **filter of the vocal tract** that shapes the output. Sources may be **voicing**, as in the case of vowels, or the product of **turbulence**, as in fricatives. Articulators may be **movable** (such as the tongue, lips, pharynx, mandible, and velum) or **immobile** (such as the teeth, hard palate, and alveolar ridge).

Facial bones and those of the skull work together in a complex fashion to produce the structures of articulation. The **mandible** provides the lower dental arch, alveolar regions, and the resting location for the tongue. The **maxillae** provide the bulk of the hard palate, alveolar ridge, upper dental arch, and dominant structures of the nasal cavities, and the **palatine bones** provide the rest of the hard palate and the point of attachment for the velum. The midline **vomer** articulates with the perpendicular plate of **ethmoid** and the cartilaginous septum to form the **nasal septum**. The **zygomatic bone** articulates with the **frontal bone** and **maxillae** to form the cheek bone. The small **nasal bones** form the upper margin of the nasal cavity. The **ethmoid bone** serves as the core of the skull and face, with the prominent crista galli protruding into the **cranium** and the **perpendicular plate** dividing the nasal cavities. The **frontal, parietal, temporal**, and **occipital** bones of the skull overlie the lobes of the brain of the same name. The **sphenoid bone** has a marked presence within the brain case, with the prominent greater and lesser wings of sphenoid located lateral to the corpus. The **hypophyseal fossa** houses the pituitary gland. The clivus joins the occipital bone near the foramen magnum.

Incisors, cuspids, bicuspids, and **molars** are housed within the alveoli of the maxillae and mandible. **Teeth** have roots and crowns, and the exposed surface of is covered with enamel. Each tooth has a **medial, lateral, lingual, buccal** (or labial), and **occlusal** surface. **Clinical eruption** of the deciduous arch begins between 6 and 9 months, and eruption of the permanent arch begins at 6 years. **Class I occlusion** refers to normal orientation of mandible and maxillae. **Class II malocclusion** refers to a relatively retracted mandible, and **Class III malocclusion** refers to a relatively protruded mandible. Individual teeth may have aberrant orientations within the alveolus, including **torsiversion, labio-version, linguaversion, distoversion** and **mesioversion**. Inadequately erupted or hypererupted teeth are referred to as **infraverted** and **supraverted**.

The cavities of the articulatory and resonatory system can be envisioned as a series of linked tubes. The vertically directed **pharynx** is comprised of the **laryngopharynx, oropharynx**, and **nasopharynx**. The nasal cavities arise from the nasopharynx, with the nasal and nasopharyngeal regions entirely separated from the oral cavity by the **soft palate** of velum. The oral cavity is flanked by the small **buccal cavities**. The shape and size of the oral cavity is altered through movement of the **tongue** and **mandible**, and the nasal cavity may be coupled with the oral and pharyngeal cavities by means of the soft palate. The shape of the pharyngeal cavity is altered by the **pharyngeal constrictor muscles**, but is secondarily changed by elevation or depression of the **larynx**.

Facial muscles are important for articulations involving the lips. Numerous muscles insert into the **orbicularis oris** inferior and superior muscles, permitting lip protrusion, closure, retraction, elevation, and depression. The **risorius** and **buccinator** muscles retract the lips and support entrapment of air within the oral cavity. The **levator labii superioris, zygomatic minor, levator labii superioris alaeque nasi**, and **levator anguli oris** elevate the upper lip, and the **depressor labii inferioris** depresses the lower lip. The **zygomatic major** muscle elevates and retracts the corner of the mouth. The **depressor labii inferi-oris** pulls the lips down and out. The **depressor anguli oris** muscle will depress the corner of the mouth, and the mentalis muscle pulls the lower lip out. The **platysma** will depress the mandible.

The **tongue** occupies the floor of the mouth, being divided into **dor-sum**, **apex** (tip), and **base**. Fine movements are the product of the **intrinsic musculature (transverse, vertical, inferior longitudinal** and **superior longitudinal** muscles of the tongue). Larger adjustments of lingual movement requires extrinsic muscles. The **genioglossus** retracts, protrudes, or depresses the tongue, and the **hyoglossus** and **chon-droglossus** depress the tongue. The **styloglossus** and **palatoglossus** elevate the posterior tongue.

Muscles of **mastication** include mandibular elevators and depressors, as well as muscles to protrude the mandible. The **masseter, tempo-ralis,** and **medial pterygoid** muscles elevate the mandible, and the **lat-eral pterygoids** protrude it. **Mandibular depression** is achieved by the **mylohyoid, geniohyoid,** and **platysma** muscles.

The **velum** or **soft palate** is attached to the posterior hard palate. The **levator veli palatini** muscle elevates the soft palate and the **musculus uvulae** bunches it. The **tensor veli palatini** tenses and shortens the palate. The velum is depressed by the **palatoglossus** and **palatopha-ryngeus**. The **superior pharyngeal constrictor** assists in gaining velopharyngeal closure, while peristaltic movement of food is facili-tated by the **middle** and **inferior pharyngeal constrictors**. The **cricopharyngeus** forms the muscular orifice of the esophagus. The **salpingopharyngeus** elevates the pharyngeal wall, and the **stylopha-ryngeus** assists in elevation of the larynx.

Study Questions

1. The _____ theory of vowel production states that the voicing source routed through the vocal tract where is shaped into the sounds of speech by the articulators.

2. On the figure below please identify the bones and landmarks indicated.

   a. _____ (bone)

   b. _____ (bone)

   c. _____ bone

   d. _____ bone

   e. _____ bone

   f. _____ process

   g. _____ process

   h. _____

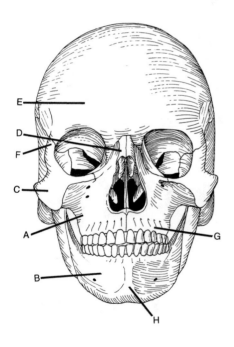

3. On the figure below please identify the bones and landmarks indicated.

a. _____ (bone)

b. _____ bone

c. _____ bone

d. _____

e. _____

f. _____

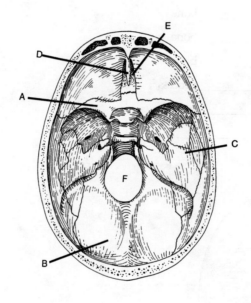

4. On the figure below please identify the bones and landmarks indicated.

a. _____ bone

b. _____ bone

c. _____ (bone)

d. _____ (bone)

e. _____ bone

f. _____ bone

g. _____ bone

h. _____ bone

i. _____

j. _____

k. _____ process

l. _____ process

m. _____ process

n. _____

o. _____ process

p. _____ process

q. _____

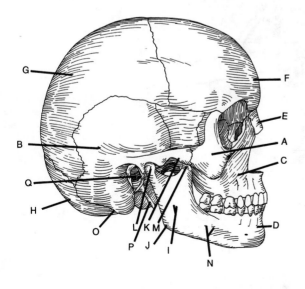

5. On the figure below identify the structures indicated.

a. _____ process

b. _____ (bone)

c. _____ bone

d. _____

e. _____ foramen

f. _____ suture

g. _____ process

h. _____ plate

i. _____ plate

j. _____ process

k. _____

l. _____

6. On the figure below please identify the muscles indicated.

a. _____

b. _____

c. _____

d. _____

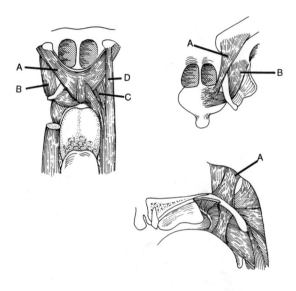

7. On the figure below please identify the muscles indicated.

a. _____

b. _____

c. _____

d. _____

e. _____

f. _____

g. _____

h. _____

i. _____

j. _____

k. _____

l. _____

8. On the figure below please identify the muscles indicated.

a. _____

b. _____

c. _____

d. _____

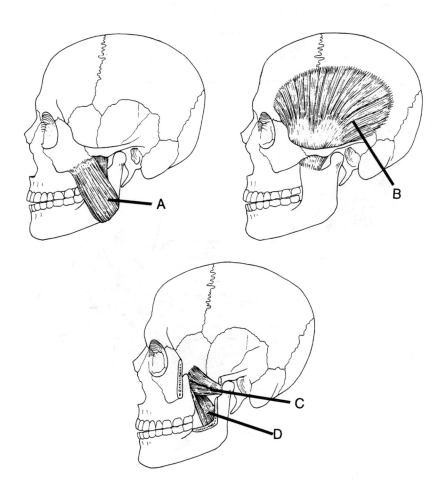

9. On the figure below please identify the muscles indicated.

a. _____

b. _____

c. _____

d. _____

e. _____

f. _____

g. _____

h. _____

10. On the figure below please structures the muscles indicate.

a. _____ (bone)

b. _____ process

c. _____ plate

d. _____ plate

e. _____

f. _____ bone

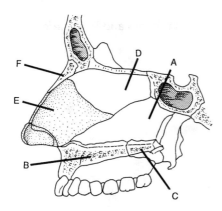

Study Question Answers

1. The <u>SOURCE-FILTER</u> theory of vowel production states that the voicing source routed through the vocal tract where is shaped into the sounds of speech by the articulators.

2. On the figure below please identify the bones and landmarks indicated.

a. <u>MAXILLA</u> (bone)

b. <u>MANDIBLE</u> (bone)

c. <u>ZYGOMATIC</u> bone

d. <u>NASAL</u> bone

e. <u>FRONTAL</u> bone

f. <u>FRONTAL</u> process

g. <u>ALVEOLAR</u> process

    h. <u>SYMPHYSIS MENTE</u>

3. On the figure below please identify the bones and landmarks indicated.

    a. <u>SPHENOID</u> bone

    b. <u>OCCIPITAL</u> bone

    c. <u>TEMPORAL</u> bone

    d. <u>CRISTA GALLI</u>

    e. <u>CRIBRIFORM PLATE</u>

    f. <u>FORAMEN MAGNUM</u>

4. On the figure below please identify the bones and landmarks indicated.

    a. <u>ZYGOMATIC</u> bone

    b. <u>TEMPORAL</u> bone

    c. <u>MAXILLAE</u> (bone)

    d. <u>MANDIBLE</u> (bone)

    e. <u>NASAL</u> bone

    f. <u>FRONTAL</u> bone

    g. <u>PARIETAL</u> bone

    h. <u>OCCIPITAL</u> bone

    i. <u>RAMUS</u>

    j. <u>ANGLE</u>

    k. <u>ZYGOMATIC</u> process

    l. <u>CONDYLAR</u> process

    m. <u>CORONOID</u> process

    n. <u>CORPUS</u>

    o. <u>MASTOID</u> process

    p. <u>STYLOID</u> process

    q. <u>EXTERNAL AUDITORY MEATUS</u>

5. On the figure below identify the structures indicated.

    a. <u>PALATINE</u> process

    b. <u>MAXILLAE</u> (bone)

    c. <u>PALATINE</u> bone

    d. <u>PREMAXILLA</u>

e. INCISIVE foramen

f. INTERMAXILLARY suture

g. STYLOID process

h. MEDIAL PTERYGOID plate

i. LATERAL PTERYGOID plate

j. MASTOID process

k. FORAMEN MAGNUM

l. PTERYGOID HAMULUS

6. On the figure below please identify the muscles indicated.

a. LEVATOR VELI PALATINE

b. TENSOR VELI PALATINE

c. PALATOGLOSSUS

d. PALATOPHARYNGEUS

7. On the figure below please identify the muscles indicated.

a. BUCCINATOR

b. ORBICULARIS ORIS SUPERIORIS

c. ORBICULARIS ORIS INFERIORIS

d. DEPRESSOR ANGULI ORIS

e. DEPRESSOR LABII INFERIORIS

f. ZYGOMATIC MAJOR

g. ZYGOMATIC MINOR

h. LEVATOR LABII SUPERIORIS ALAEQUE NASI

i. LEVATOR ANGULI ORIS

j. LEVATOR LABII SUPERIORIS

k RISORIUS

l PLATYSMA

8. On the figure below please identify the muscles indicated.

a. MASSETER

b. TEMPORALIS

c. LATERAL PTERYGOID

d. MEDIAL PTERYGOID

9. On the figure below please identify the muscles indicated.

a. GENIOGLOSSUS

    b. <u>HYOGLOSSUS</u>

    c. <u>DIGASTRICUS POSTERIOR</u>

    d. <u>STYLOGLOSSUS</u>

    e. <u>STYLOHYOID</u>

    f. <u>PALATOGLOSSUS</u>

    g. <u>INFERIOR LONGITUDINAL</u>

    h. <u>SUPERIOR LONGITUDINAL</u>

10. On the figure below please structures the muscles indicate.

    a. <u>VOMER</u> (bone)

    b. <u>PALATINE</u> process

    c. <u>HORIZONTAL</u> plate

    d. <u>PERPENDICULAR</u> plate

    e. <u>CARTILAGINOUS SEPTUM</u>

    f. <u>NASAL</u> bone

REFERENCES

Baken, R. J. (1987). *Clinical measurement of speech and voice*. Austin, TX: Pro-Ed.

Basmajian, J. V. (1975). *Grant's method of anatomy*. Baltimore: Williams & Wilkins.

Bateman, H. E. (1977). *A clinical approach to speech anatomy and physiology*. Springfield, IL: Charles C. Thomas.

Bateman, H. E., & Mason, R. M. (1984). *Applied anatomy and physiology of the speech and hearing mechanism*. Springfield, IL: Charles C. Thomas.

Beck, E. W. (1982). *Mosby's atlas of functional human anatomy*. St. Louis, MO: C. V. Mosby.

Chusid, J. G. (1979). *Correlative neuroanatomy and functional neurology* (17th ed.). Los Altos, CA: Lange Medical Publications.

Ettema, S. L., & Kuehn, D. P. (1994). A quantitative histologic study of the normal human adult soft palate. *Journal of Speech and Hearing Research, 37*, 303–313.

Gelb, H. (1977). *Clinical management of head, neck and TMJ pain and dysfunction*. Philadelphia, PA: W. B. Saunders.

Gosling, J. A., Harris, P. F., Humpherson, J. R., Whitmore, I., & Willan, P. L. T. (1985). *Atlas of human anatomy*. Philadelphia, PA: J. B. Lippincott .

Grobler, N. J. (1977). *Textbook of clinical anatomy* (Vol. 1). Amsterdam: Elsevier Scientific.

Hauser, G., Daponte, A., & Roberts, M. J. (1989). Palatal rugae. *Journal of Anatomy, 124*, 237–249.

Kahane, J. C., & Folkins, J. F. (1984). *Atlas of speech and hearing anatomy*. Columbus, OH: Charles E. Merrill.

Kapetansky, D. I. (1987). *Cleft lip, nose, and palate reconstruction*. Philadelphia, PA: J. B. Lippincott.

Kaplan, H. (1960). *Anatomy and physiology of speech.* New York: McGraw-Hill.

Kuehn, D. P., Lemme, M. L., & Baumgartner, J. M. (1989). *Neural bases of speech, hearing, and language.* Boston, MA: Little, Brown.

Langley, L. L., Telford, I. R., & Christensen, J. B. (1969). *Dynamic anatomy and physiology.* New York: McGraw-Hill.

Lieberman, P. (1977). *Speech physiology and acoustic phonetics: An introduction.* New York: Macmillan.

McMinn, R. M. H., Hutchings, R. T., & Logan, B. M. (1994). *Color atlas of head and neck anatomy.* London: Mosby-Wolfe.

Minifie, F. (1973). Speech acoustics. In F. D. Minifie, T. J. Hixon, & F. Williams, (Eds.) *Normal aspects of speech, hearing, and language* (pp. 11–72). Englewood Cliffs, NJ: Prentice-Hall.

Moore, K. L. (1988). *The developing human.* Philadelphia, PA: W. B. Saunders.

Netter, F. H. (1983). *The CIBA collection of medical illustrations. Vol. 1. Nervous system. Part I. Anatomy and physiology* West Caldwell, NJ: CIBA Pharmaceutical Company.

Netter, F. H. (1989). *Atlas of human anatomy.* West Caldwell, NJ: CIBA Pharmaceutical Company.

Pickett, J. M. (1980). *The sounds of speech communication.* Baltimore, MD: University Park Press.

Rohen, J. W., & Yokochi, C. (1993). *Color atlas of anatomy.* New York: Igaku-Shoin.

Sawashima, M., & Cooper, F. S. (1977). *Dynamic aspects of speech production.* Tokyo: University of Tokyo Press.

Shprintzen, R. J., & Bardach, J. (1995). *Cleft palate speech management.* St. Louis, MO: C. V. Mosby.

Shriberg, L. D., & Kent, R. D. (1982). *Clinical phonetics.* New York: John Wiley & Sons.

Small, A. M. (1973). Acoustics. In F. D. Minifie, T. J. Hixon, & F. Williams, (Eds.), *Normal aspects of speech, hearing, and language.* Englewood Cliffs, NJ: Prentice-Hall.

Snell, R. S. (1978). *Gross anatomy dissector.* Boston, MA: Little, Brown.

Williams, P. & Warrick, R. (1980). *Gray's anatomy* (36th British ed.). Philadelphia, PA: W. B. Saunders.

Zemlin, W. R. (1988). *Speech and hearing science. Anatomy and physiology.* Englewood Cliffs, NJ: Prentice-Hall.

CHAPTER

8

Physiology of Articulation

Clearly, the function of the articulatory system is of paramount importance in speech production. Although a review of acoustic phonetics is beyond the scope of an anatomy text, the Source-Filter Theory of speech production discussed in Chapter 7 nonetheless provides the framework for our discussion. Intrinsic to that explanation of speech production is the notion that the movement of articulators shapes the resonant cavities of the vocal tract, and altered resonances give the acoustic output we call speech.

BIOLOGICAL FUNCTION

In preparation for our discussion of the physiology of speech production, we will first discuss the **biological functions** from which the speech functions arise: mastication and deglutition. **Mastication** refers to the processes involved in food preparation, including moving unchewed food onto the grinding surface of the teeth, chewing it, and mixing it with saliva in preparation for swallowing. **Deglutition** refers to swallowing. These two biological processes require integration of lingual, velar, pharyngeal, and facial muscle movement (Chapter 7) with laryngeal adjustments (Chapters 5 and 6). Consider this. During the mature mastication and deglutition process, all muscles inserting into the orbicularis oris may be called into action to open, close, purse, and retract the lips as food is received. All intrinsic and extrinsic muscles of the tongue will be invoked to move the food into position for chewing and preparation of the **bolus** (a soft mass of food) for swallowing. The velar elevators and tensors seal off the nasal cavity to prevent regurgitation, and the pharyngeal constrictors must contract in a highly predictable fashion to move the bolus down the pharynx and into the esophagus. With the addition of laryngeal elevation, we have just invoked over 55 pairs of muscles whose timing and innervation pattern must be integrated through accurate activation of cranial and spinal nerves. All this for a midnight snack!

As you ponder the biological processes associated with deglutition, please do not lose sight of the relationship between feeding and speech. We have long recognized that feeding skills are both preparatory and supportive of the speech act, and inadequate development of feeding reflects directly on speech development.

Mastication and Deglutition

Mastication and deglutition consist of a sequence of four extremely well orchestrated events or stages. These stages are the oral preparatory stage, oral stage of swallow, pharyngeal stage, and esophageal stage. We have voluntary control over the first two stages.

Oral Preparatory Stage

In this stage, food is prepared for swallowing. To complete this task a number of processes must occur at virtually the same time (see Table 8–1). We should emphasize that, although this is a voluntary process, it can be performed automatically.

First, we introduce food into the mouth and keep it there by tightly occluding the oral seal (lips). This lip seal demands that we breathe through the nose, so the tongue bunches up in back and the soft palate is pulled down to keep the food in the oral cavity, processes neatly performed with the aid of the palatoglossus muscle.

The food must be ground up so that it can easily pass through the esophagus for digestion, and this is performed by the coordinated activity of the muscles of mastication and the lingual muscles. The tongue is in charge of keeping the food in the oral cavity, and it does this by effecting a seal along the alveolar ridge. As it holds the food in place it compresses it against the hard palate, partially crushing it in preparation for the teeth. The tongue then begins moving the food onto the grinding surfaces of the teeth, pulling the food back into the

Table 8-1. Muscles of the oral preparation stage required to effect oral seal, maintain buccal compression, tongue movements to move food in onto grinding surface, and grinding action.

Muscle	Function	Innervation (Cranial Nerve)
Facial Muscles		
Orbicularis oris	Maintain oral seal	VII
Mentalis	Elevates lower lip	VII
Buccinator	Flatten cheeks	VII
Risorius	Flatten cheeks	VII
Mandibular Muscles		
Masseter	Elevate mandible	V
Temporalis	Elevate mandible, retracts, protrudes	V
Medial pterygoid	Elevate mandible, lateral movement, grind	V
Lateral pterygoid	Protrudes, grind	V
Tongue Muscles		
Mylohyoid	Elevates floor of mouth	V
Geniohyoid	Elevate hyoid, depress mandible	XII
Digastric	Elevates hyoid, depresses mandible	V, XII
Superior longitudinal	Elevate tip, deviate tip	XII
Inferior longitudinal	Depress tip, deviate tip	XII
Vertical	Cupping and grooving of tongue	XII
Genioglossus	Tongue body movement, cupping of tongue	XII
Styloglossus	Elevates posterior tongue	XII
Palatoglossus	Elevates posterior tongue	IX, X, XI
Soft Palate Muscles		
Palatoglossus	Depress velum	IX, X, XI
Palatopharyngeus	Depress velum	X, XI

oral cavity to be mixed with saliva, and then moving it back to the teeth for more of a work-up. The salivary glands (parotid, submandibular, and sublingual glands) secrete saliva into the oral cavity to help form the mass of food into a bolus for swallowing. The muscles of the buccal wall (risorius and buccinator) contract to keep the food from entering the **lateral sulcus** (between the gums and cheek wall).

This is quite a feat of coordination. To prove this to yourself, take a bite of a cracker and attend to the process. If you count the number of times you chew on the cracker, you will realize that you grind it between 15 and 30 times *before* you swallow any of it. As you introduce the cracker into your mouth, your tongue probably pushes it up against the anterior hard palate to begin breaking it down. Your tongue then performs the dance of mastication, flicking in between the molars as your mandible lowers, then quickly moving out of the way before they close forcefully to continue grinding. Your tongue organizes the ground food onto its dorsum, mixes the food with saliva, and moves it back out to the teeth if the bolus does not meet your specification for "ready to swallow."

If you still question the grace of this process, try to remember the last time you bit your tongue, lip, or cheek. A snack of 10 crackers will invoke at least 600 oscillations of the mastication musculature, and a full meal clearly requires thousands of grinding gestures. Despite this, you can scarcely remember the last painful time your tongue and mandible failed the coordination test!

Oral Stage

When the bolus of food is finally ready to swallow, the **oral stage** of swallowing begins (Table 8–2). When this point is reached, several processes must occur sequentially. The tongue was humped up in the back during mastication, but now it will drop down and pull posteriorly. Mastication will stop, and the anterior tongue will elevate to the hard palate and squeeze the bolus back toward the faucial pillars. It is contact with the fauces that triggers the reflexes of the pharyngeal stage.

Pharyngeal Stage

When the bolus contacts the anterior faucial pillars, the **pharyngeal stage** begins with a complex sequence of reflexively controlled events (Table 8–3). The soft palate, which was depressed, will now elevate to close off the oropharynx from the nasopharynx.

Respiration ceases reflexively at this point. Both oral and nasal outlets are closed so air cannot escape or enter for respiration. More importantly, food is ready to enter the pharynx, and the airway must be protected. To accomplish the protective function the vocal folds tightly adduct, followed by constriction of the false vocal folds and epiglottis via the aryepiglottic muscles.

Deficits of the Oral Preparation Stage

Numerous problems arise when neuromuscular control of mastication is compromised. Loss of sensation and awareness, coupled with weak buccal musculature, can lead to pocketing of food in the lateral or anterior sulci. Weak muscles of mastication can cause inadequately chewed food, and weak lingual muscles will result in poor mixture of saliva with the food, inadequate bolus production, and difficulty compressing the bolus onto the hard palate. If the muscles of the soft palate are compromised, the velum may not be fully depressed and the tongue may not be elevated in the back, permitting food to escape into the pharynx prior to initiation of the pharyngeal reflexes. This is life-threatening, because food entering the pharynx in absence of reflexive response may well reach the open airway. **Aspiration pneumonia** (pneumonia secondary to aspirated matter) is a constant concern for individuals with **dysphagia** (a disorder of swallowing).

With the airway sealed, the larynx moves up and forward as a unit. The hyoid bone is a palpable indication of laryngeal elevation, because we can feel it elevate and move forward in this stage. The larynx elevates and moves forward, and the epiglottis drops down to cover the laryngeal aditus, assisted by the aryepiglottic muscles.

Simultaneously, the cricopharyngeus muscle relaxes. This muscle is the sphincteric muscle of the superior esophagus. When you are not swallowing it needs to maintain a constant pressure on the opening to the esophagus to keep food and gastric juices from escaping into the laryngopharynx (**esophageal reflux**), and it is therefore tonically contracted until the swallow is initiated. Relaxing this muscle gives the bolus a place to go.

Food is propelled down the pharynx toward the esophagus by means of contraction of the pharyngeal constrictors. As food is forced into the oropharynx, the posterior faucial pillars move medially, effectively channeling the bolus downward.

After about 1 second of pharyngeal transit, the bolus reaches the laryngopharynx where it passes over the epiglottis. The bolus is divided into two roughly equal masses, passing to either side of the larynx, through the pyriform sinuses, to recombine at the esophageal entrance.

Esophageal Phase

The **esophageal phase** is out of voluntary control, as soon as the bolus reaches the orifice of the esophagus. The bolus is transported through

Table 8–2. Muscles of the oral stage required to propel the bolus into the oropharynx.

Muscle	Function	Innervation (Cranial Nerve)
Mandibular Muscles		
Masseter	Elevate mandible	V
Temporalis	Elevate mandible	V
Internal Pterygoid	Elevate mandible	V
Tongue Muscles		
Mylohyoid	Elevates tongue and floor of mouth	V
Superior longitudinal	Elevate tip	XII
Vertical	Cupping and grooving of tongue	XII
Genioglossus	Tongue body movement, cupping of tongue	XII
Styloglossus	Elevates posterior tongue	XII
Palatoglossus	Elevates posterior tongue	IX, X, XI

Deficits of the Oral Stage

Deficits of the oral stage center around sensory and motor dysfunction. Weakened movements cause reduced posterior transit time of the bolus toward the pharynx. With greater motor involvement, food may remain on the tongue or hard palate following transit.

In patients with oral-phase involvement, there is a tendency for the epiglottis to fail to invert over the laryngeal opening and to have limited elevation of the hyoid. Perlman, Grahack, and Booth (1992) found that individuals with such a deficit showed increased pooling of food or liquid within the valleculae.

Difficulty initiating a reflexive swallow may be the result of sensory deficit. Application of a cold stimulus to the anterior faucial pillars, coupled with instructions to attempt to swallow, is a time-honored method to assist these individuals initiate a swallow, although ongoing clinical research is needed to determine its efficacy (Rosenbek, Robbins, Fishback, & Levine, 1991).

Table 8–3. Muscles of the pharyngeal stage required to propel the bolus toward the esophagus, elevate larynx, and to close the airway.

Muscle	Function	Innervation (Cranial Nerve)
Tongue Muscles		
Mylohyoid	Elevates hyoid and tongue	V
Geniohyoid	Elevate hyoid and larynx, depress mandible	C-1
Digastricus	Elevates hyoid and larynx	V, XII
Genioglossus	Retract tongue	XII
Styloglossus	Elevates posterior tongue	XII
Palatoglossus	Narrows fauces, elevates posterior tongue	IX, X, XI
Stylohyoid	Elevate hyoid and larynx	VII
Hyoglossus	Elevate hyoid	XII
Thyrohyoid	Elevates hyoid	XII
Superior longitudinal	Elevates tongue	XII
Inferior longitudinal	Depresses tongue	XII
Transverse	Flattens tongue	XII
Vertical	Narrows tongue	XII
Soft Palate Muscles		
Levator veli palatini	Elevate soft palate	X, XI
Tensor veli palatini	Tense soft palate	V
Musculus uvulae	Shorten soft palate	X, XI
Pharyngeal Muscles		
Palatopharyngeus	Constrict oropharynx to channel bolus	X, XI
Salpingopharyngeus	Elevates pharynx	XI
Stylopharyngeus	Raises larynx	IX
Cricopharyngeus	Relaxes esophageal orifice	X, XI
Middle constrictor	Narrow pharynx	X, XI
Inferior constrictor	Narrow pharynx	X, XI
Laryngeal Muscles		
Lateral cricoarytenoid	Adducts vocal folds	X
Transverse arytenoid	Adducts vocal folds	X
Oblique arytenoid	Adducts vocal folds	X
Aryepiglottic	Retracts epiglottis, constricts aditus	X
Thyroepiglottic	Retracts epiglottis	X

Deficits of the Pharyngeal Stage

Sensory and motor deficit can be dangerous at this stage of swallowing. Slowed velar elevation may result in **nasal regurgitation** (loss of food or liquid through the nose), while reduced sensation at the fauces, posterior tongue, pharyngeal wall, and soft palate may result in elevated threshold for trigger of the swallowing reflex. Reduced function of the pharyngeal constrictors may result in slowed pharyngeal transit time of the bolus, in which case the individual may prematurely re-initiate respiration. Weakened pharyngeal function may result in residue left in the valleculae. Failure of the hyoid and thyroid to elevate may result in loss of airway protection, so that food will fall into the larynx to be aspirated on reinflation of the lungs.

the esophagus to the inferior esophageal sphincter by means of peristaltic contraction and gravity, arriving at the stomach for the process of digestion after 10 to 20 seconds of transit time. When the bolus enters the esophagus for transit to the stomach, the cricopharyngeus will again contract, the larynx and soft palate will be depressed, and respiration will begin again. In the normal swallow, respiration is suspended for only about a second. Re-initiation of respiration increases pressure in the laryngopharynx, and food at the laryngeal entryway will be blown clear and propelled to the esophagus.

Pressures of Deglutition

You can think of the swallowing process as a series of manipulations of a bolus by muscles, but you also can think of swallowing in terms of manipulation of oral, pharyngeal, and esophageal pressures that in turn move the bolus. When entering the oral stage of the swallow, the soft palate tightly clamps off the pharynx and the tongue begins squeezing the bolus posteriorly. The positive pressure created by the oral movements of the tongue propel the bolus toward the oropharynx. The tongue proceeds to make contact with the posterior oropharynx, transferring the bolus into the pharynx with an additional pressure gradient. The pharyngeal walls compress the bolus, increasing pressure to prompt it toward the esophagus. Elevation of the larynx creates a relatively lower pressure at the esophageal entry way, and relaxation of the cricopharyngeus further increases the superior-inferior pressure gradient. The laryngeal entry way is tightly clamped to restrict confounding pressures of deglutition with those of respiration, so that the bolus is naturally drawn to the area of lower pressure, the esophageal entrance. The cricopharyngeus contracts most forcefully during inspiration, thereby prohibiting inflation of the esophagus.

Mouth Breathing

Chronic mouth breathing is more than an unpleasant habit, because it is at the root of facial malformation and hearing loss. Mouth breathing is attributed to hypertrophy of the tonsilar ring, prohibiting adequate nasal respiration. In children with this condition, the adenoids are frequently enlarged, blocking the nasal choanae and also the orifice of the eustachian tube. Inadequate ventilation of the middle ear cavity may result in **otitis media** (inflammation of the middle ear cavity). Chronic otitis media is often associated with fluid in the middle ear (**serous otitis media**), a condition resulting in conductive hearing impairment.

The hypertrophy also makes mouth breathing mandatory. During normal nasal respiration, the tongue maintains fairly constant contact with the upper alveolar ridge and hard palate; but with the mouth open constantly for respiration, the tongue will exert little pressure there. Without that pressure, the dental arch will narrow and the palate will bulge upward to an extreme **vault** as the facial bones develop. With narrow dental arches, the permanent teeth will not have adequate space so that they become crowded and prone to **caries** (decay of bone or tooth). The narrowed maxillae will cause the upper lip to pull up, exposing the upper front teeth. The nasal cavity will become narrow, increasing the probability of later nasal obstruction. The look of **"adenoid facies"** includes an open mouth, narrow mandible, and dental crowding. When coupled with a persistent conductive hearing loss, mouth breathing presents a sizable (yet generally preventable) deficit to the developing child.

In summary, there are four stages of **mastication** and **deglutition.**

■ In the **oral preparation** stage, food is introduced into the oral cavity, moved onto the molars for chewing, and mixed with saliva to form a concise bolus between the tongue and hard palate.

■ In the **oral stage,** the bolus is moved back by pressure of movement of the tongue on the hard palate.

■ The **pharyngeal** stage begins when the bolus reaches the faucial pillars. The soft palate and larynx elevate, and the bolus is propelled through the pharynx to the esophageal sphincter which has relaxed to receive the material. The epiglottis has dropped to partially cover the laryngeal opening, while the intrinsic musculature of the larynx has effected a tight seal to protect the airway. Food passes over the epiglottis and through pyriform sinuses to the esophagus.

■ The final, **esophageal stage** involves peristaltic movement of the bolus through the esophagus.

Speech Function

Speech production requires execution of an extremely well-organized and integrated sequence of neuromotor events. Say the word "tube" and pay attention to the sequence of articulations. Ignoring respiratory preparation for the moment, your tongue must elevate to the alveolar ridge simultaneously with elevation and tensing of the velum. Air pressure builds behind your tongue, and then your tongue actively drops to release the pressure and produce the /t/. Even as it releases, your tongue must quickly draw back to produce the /u/, assisted by the rounding of your lips. Your lips must then clamp together to permit build-up of air pressure for the final /b/. This all happens in under 3/10 of a second, and quite easily for most of us.

As you can see, thinking about the interaction of articulators and the articulatory plan can get complex in a hurry. Let us begin with function of the individual movable articulators.

Lips

The lips are deceptively simple articulators. As discussed in Chapter 7, the orbicularis is primarily responsible for ensuring a labial seal, but numerous facial muscles insert into it. Those muscles are capable of exerting a distinct force on the lips, often in combination with other muscles. Contraction of these muscles becomes an exercise in physics and force vectors: The direction of lip movement is the result of adding the directional forces of these muscles.

The lips are deceptive in another sense, as well. At first glance, one might assume that the upper and lower lips have very similar qualities. In reality, however, the lower lip achieves a greater velocity and force than the upper lip, and it seems to do most of the work in lip closure. The extra force is a function of the mentalis muscle, for which there is no parallel in the upper lip, and the doubled velocity is necessitated by the variable movement and placement of the mandible. The lower lip is attached to a movable articulator (the mandible), and it must quickly adapt to being closer or farther from the maxillary upper lip. That is, for sound to be accurately perceived as the chosen phoneme the lips must make contact within closely timed tolerances. The lower lip is capable of rapidly altering its rate of closure to accommodate a variety of jaw positions, unflinchingly.

The notion of variable mandible position reinforces another fine point of labial function. The lips (as with the other articulators) are amazingly resistant to interference. We can easily adjust to perturbations of our articulators, or even to gross malformation. As an example, you could ask a friend to recite a poem with her eyes closed. At an unpredictable point you could briefly pull down on her lip, and she would quickly adjust to the distorted articulatory position and continue talking with the new configuration (within limits, of course).

Similarly, you are able to adapt to other restrictions on supportive articulators. Try this. Repeat the syllable "puh" as rapidly as you can, counting the number of syllables you can produce in 5 seconds. Notice that your mandible was helping, and it moved when you closed your lips. Now bite lightly on a pencil using your incisors and do the same task. Your rate of repetition was probably very similar, despite the fact that your mandible was no longer able to help your lips close.

We are amazingly resistant to interference with the articulatory mechanism. This resistance, by the way, is evidence that the plan for an articulatory gesture is not "micro-managed" by central cortical control, but rather that the details of motor execution are left to be worked out by some type of "coordinative structures," as will be discussed. If the neural command, for instance, said simply to elevate the lower lip 1.3 cm, either of the distortions mentioned previously would have resulted in a faulty articulation.

This does not mean that we do not use the proprioceptive information provided by sensors in our facial muscles to help us note muscle tone and position. Although we do not have spindles in facial muscles to assist in this process, we do have other sensors (such as those for pressure and touch) that provide feedback on the condition of facial muscles. Reflexive contraction of the orbicularis oris occurs with increased intraoral pressure, such as that produced during production of a bilabial stop plosive. The oral mucosa and lips have sensors for light mechanical stimulation as would occur during lingua-dental articulation. Although there is little evidence of stretch receptors of the lips, a stretch reflex can be elicited through retraction of the angles of the mouth.

Evidence that you *do* use this type of information to control muscles may be found in remembering your last trip to the dentist. If the dentist's anesthetic deadened your lip, you may remember accidently biting it while chewing or talking. Your unconscious perception of its position generally keeps that from happening. Mechanical stimulation of the lips affects other articulators as well. When the lower lip is stimulated, reflexive excitation in both the masseter and genioglossus can be recorded. The *degree* to which this information is *required* for speech accuracy is still a lively topic of debate.

Mandible

The mandible is something of an "unsung hero" among articulators. It quietly and unceremoniously goes about its business, assisting the lips, changing its position for tongue movement, and tightly closing when necessary. It *does* move, however, and you can remind yourself of that by placing one finger of your right hand on your upper lip, and another finger on your chin. Close your eyes and count to 20 quickly, paying attention to the degree of movement you feel. You probably felt very little movement, but the mandible *did* move. Now clamp your mandible and count to 20. Were you still intelligible? (Yes.) Now do the opposite: Let your mouth hang absolutely slack-jaw open, and count to 20.

If you really relaxed your jaw and refused to elevate it for your speech, you probably noticed that you were largely unintelligible. The mandible is an extremely important articulator in its supportive role of carrying the lips, tongue, and teeth to their targets in the maxilla (lips, teeth, alveolar ridge, hard palate), but its adjustments are rather minute in normal speech. For this reason, paralysis of the muscles of mastication can be devastating to speech intelligibility.

The muscles of mandibular elevation (temporalis, masseter, medial pterygoid) are endowed with muscle spindles, although those of mandibular depression (digastricus, mylohyoid, geniohyoid, lateral pterygoid) are not. You can easily see the effects of muscle spindles on yourself. Relax your jaw while looking into a mirror. Now apply a firm rubbing pressure to the masseter in a downward-pulling direction. You will see your mandible elevate slightly as you trigger the mandibular reflex. There are also sensors of joint position within the temporomandibular joint that permit extremely accurate positioning of the jaw (within 1 mm). If these sensors are anesthetized, the speaker's accuracy diminishes markedly.

The mandible is, of course, quite important for mastication, and the function of the muscles of mastication is distinctly different for speech than for chewing. It appears that there is a central pattern generator within the brainstem that produces the rhythmic muscular contraction needed for chewing. The mandible must elevate, grind laterally, and depress, requiring coordinated activation of the elevators and depressors in a synergistic, rhythmic fashion.

For speech, on the other hand, the mandibular elevators and depressors stay in dynamic balance, so that slight modification in muscle activation (and inhibition of antagonists) permits a quick adjustment of the mandible (Moore, 1993). Indeed, depression of the mandible seems to be not only a function of the classically defined mandibular depressors (digastricus, mylohyoid, geniohyoid, lateral pterygoid) but also, to a significant extent, of the infrahyoid musculature (Westbury, 1988). The hyoid undergoes a great deal of movement during depression of the mandible.

Tongue

Arguably, the tongue is the most important of the articulators. It is involved in production of the majority of phonemes in English. Let us look at how we achieve the individual movements of the tongue.

As a first approximation, you can think of the tongue as a group of highly organized (intrinsic) muscles being carried on the "shoulders" of the extrinsic muscles. Much as the muscles of the legs and trunk move your upper body to a position where your arms and head can interact with the environment, the extrinsic muscles set the basic posture of the tongue, whereas the intrinsic muscles have a great deal of responsibility for the microstructure of articulation. The two groups of muscles work together closely to achieve the target articulatory gesture. Let us examine each of the basic gestures required for speech (see Table 8–4).

Tongue Tip Elevation. Elevation of the tongue is primarily the responsibility of the superior longitudinal muscle of the tongue. When these fibers are shortened, the tip and lateral margins of the tongue are pulled up.

Tongue Tip Depression. Depression of the tongue is the primary responsibility of the inferior longitudinal muscles. Their course along the lateral margins of the lower tongue make them perfectly suited to pull the tip and sides of the tongue down.

Tongue Tip Deviation, Left and Right. Deviation of the tongue tip to the left requires simultaneous contraction of the left superior and inferior longitudinal muscles. This asymmetrical contraction will have the desired result, which is asymmetrical movement of the tongue tip.

Relaxation of Lateral Margins. The lateral margins of the tongue must be relaxed for the /l/ phoneme even as the tongue is protruded to the anterior alveolar ridge and slightly elevated. This complex gesture is accomplished by slight contraction of the posterior genioglossus (which helps to move the tongue forward) and the superior longitudinal (which elevates the tip). Contraction of the transverse intrinsic muscles of the tongue will pull the sides medially away from the lateral gum ridge, opening the lateral sulcus for resonation.

Tongue Narrowing. The transverse fibers coursing from the median fibrous septum to the lateral margins of the tongue are required for this gesture.

Central Tongue Grooving. The degree of tongue grooving determines the magnitude of muscle involvement in this gesture. Wholesale depression of the medial tongue is accomplished by contraction of

Table 8–4. Muscles of Tongue Movement.

Movement	Muscle
Elevate tongue tip	Superior longitudinal muscles
Depress tongue tip	Inferior longitudinal muscles
Deviate tongue tip	Simultaneous contraction of either left or right superior and inferior longitudinal muscles for left or right deviation
Relax lateral margin	Posterior genioglossus for protrusion; superior longitudinal for tip elevation; transverse intrinsic pulls sides medially
Narrow tongue	Transverse intrinsic
Deep central groove	Genioglossus depresses tongue body; vertical intrinsic depresses central dorsum
Broad central groove	Moderate genioglossus to depress tongue body; vertical intrinsic depresses dorsum; superior longitudinal elevates margins
Protrude tongue	Posterior genioglossus advances body; vertical muscles narrow tongue; superior and inferior longitudinal balance and point tongue
Retract tongue	Anterior genioglossus retracts into oral cavity; superior and inferior longitudinal shorten tongue; styloglossus to retract into pharyngeal cavity
Elevate posterior tongue	Palatoglossus elevates sides; transverse intrinsic bunches tongue
Depress tongue body	Genioglossus contraction depresses medial tongue; hyoglossus and chondroglossus depresses sides if hyoid is fixed by infrahyoid muscles

Unilateral Tongue Weakness

One element of the **oral-peripheral examination** is examination for relative tongue strength. When you ask a client to push forcefully with his or her tongue sideways against a resistance, you are interested in identifying whether the client has adequate strength and symmetrical strength. If there appears to be greater strength in one direction than the other, you will consider activities that will strengthen the musculature. Improving muscle strength will improve tone and muscle control.

the entire genioglossus in conjunction with the vertical fibers. A more moderate groove will involve the genioglossus to a lesser degree, but will still use the vertical muscles. A broadened groove could be accomplished by co-contraction of the superior longitudinal muscle, elevating the sides of the tongue as well.

Tongue Protrusion. Tongue protrusion requires use of the posterior genioglossus, and at least two of the intrinsic muscles. Contraction of the posterior genioglossus will draw the tongue forward, but will not let you point your tongue. To make a proper "statement" with your tongue, however, you will need assistance from vertical and transverse intrinsic muscles, and deviation (up, down, or to the sides) will require the use of superior and inferior longitudinal intrinsics. The genioglossus posterior by itself would leave the tongue hanging down from your opened mouth.

Tongue Retraction. Retraction of the body of the tongue involves both intrinsic and extrinsic muscles. The anterior genioglossus will draw the protruded tongue into the oral cavity, and co-contraction of the superior and inferior longitudinal muscles will shorten the tongue. To retract the tongue into the pharyngeal space, as in the swallowing gesture, the styloglossus must be engaged.

Posterior Tongue Elevation. The palatoglossi insert into the sides of the tongue, and their contraction elevates the sides. Contraction of the transverse muscles in the posterior tongue would assist in bunching the tongue up in that region.

Tongue Body Depression. Contraction of the genioglossus as a unit will depress the medial tongue, while the addition of the hyoglossus and chondroglossus will depress the sides of the tongue, assuming that the hyoid is fixed by the infrahyoid muscles.

Although the tongue is capable of generating a great deal of force through contraction, we typically only use about 20% of its potential

Tongue Deviation on Protrusion

Tongue musculature is paired, and unilateral weakness will produce asymmetry on protrusion. When the tongue is protruded, the bilateral musculature of the genioglossus must contract with equal force. If the left genioglossus is weak, it will not contribute equally to the protrusion, and the right genioglossus will overcome the left's effort. As a result, left genioglossus weakness will result in deviation toward the left side. Put another way, with lower motor neuron damage the tongue "points toward the lesion."

force for speech activities. The tongue is endowed with muscle spindles, golgi tendon organs, and tactile sensors. Muscle spindles have been found in the tongue muscles, and golgi tendon organs have been found in the transverse intrinsic muscles. Passive movement of the tongue (pulling outward) will result in a reflexive retraction of the tongue, and mechanical stimulation of the tongue dorsum will cause excitation of the genioglossus muscle. Stimulation of the tongue dorsum has an effect on other articulators as well, causing excitation of the masseter and lower orbicularis oris.

The tongue is remarkably sensitive to touch, as well. We can differentiate to points on the tongue tip separated by only about 1.5 mm. Another extremely sensitive regions of the mouth is the periodontal ligament of the dental arch, which can sense movement as slight as 10 microns (if you have ever had a strawberry seed wedged between your teeth you will verify this sensitivity). It is likely that this sensitivity is used to monitor production of dental consonants.

Velum

Hypernasality *refers to excessive, linguistically inappropriate nasal resonance arising from failure to adequately close the velopharyngeal port during non-nasal speech sound production. In contrast,* **hyponasality** *refers to the absence of appropriately nasalized speech sounds, such that the velopharyngeal port is inadequately opened for the* /n/, /m/, *and* /ŋ/ *phonemes.*

Early in the history of our field we found it tempting to treat the velum as a binary element: It was either opened or closed. We have since realized that it is unsafe to deal with such a complex structure in so simple a fashion. The velum is capable of a range of motion and rate of movement that, in the normally endowed individual, matches the needs of rapid speech and nonspeech functions.

The velum generally is closed for non-nasal speech, and this is the result of contraction of the levator veli palatini, a direct antagonist to the palatoglossus muscle. In speech, opening and closing of the velar port must occur precisely and rapidly, or the result will be hyper- or hyponasality. Failure to open the port will turn a 70 msec nasal phoneme into a voiced stop consonant, an unacceptable result. The soft palate opens and closes in coordination with the other articulators, thus avoiding the effect of nasal resonance on other phonemes (**assimilation**). In reality, some nasal assimilation is inevitable, acceptable, and in some geographic regions, dialectically appropriate.

Production of high-pressure consonants (such as fricatives and stops) requires greater velopharyngeal effort. To accomplish this seal, additional help is needed from the tensor veli palatini, superior pharyngeal constrictor, and uvular muscles. Even then, the pressures for speech are far less than those for, say, playing a wind instrument. Individuals may have difficulty avoiding nasal air escape when playing in the brass section but will have perfectly normal speech.

The hard and soft palate are richly endowed with receptors that provide feedback concerning pressure, and it appears that these sensors facilitate or inhibit motor lingual activity. Indeed, the tensor veli palatini, palatoglossus, and levator veli palatini muscles have been found to have muscle spindles, and the input from these sensors may be important to initiation of the pharyngeal swallowing reflex (Kuehn, Templeton, & Maynard, 1990; Liss, 1990). In cats, when the soft palate is stimulated electrically, extrinsic tongue movement is inhibited. In contrast, when the hard palate is stimulated (as it would be by food crushed during oral preparation) the extrinsic lingual muscles are excited, producing a rhythmic movement of the tongue. Stretching the faucial pillars by pulling on the tongue or the pillars themselves inhibits the activity of the extrinsic tongue muscles as well. In view of our earlier discussion of the swallowing reflex, it appears that the interaction of the soft palate, fauces, and tongue is a well-organized and integrated system. Palatal, laryngeal, and pharyngeal stimulation activate protrusion of the tongue, whereas stimulation of the anterior oral region appears to stimulate retraction of the tongue.

To summarize, each of the articulators has both speech and nonspeech functions which do not necessarily share the same patterns.

- The **lower lip** is much faster and stronger than the upper lip and responds reflexively to increases of pressure. This added responsiveness makes it quite effective at overcoming incidental **perturbations** while performing its assigned tasks.
- Movement of the **mandible** for speech is slight when compared with movement for chewing. In addition, the mandibular posture for speech is one of **sustained dynamic tension** between antagonists.
- The **tongue** is an extremely versatile organ, with the **extrinsic muscles** providing the major movement of the body, and the **intrinsic muscles** providing the shaping of the tongue. **Muscle spindle** and tactile sensors make the tongue quite sensitive to position and the forces placed upon it by contact with other articulators.
- The **velum** must be maintained in a reasonably elevated position for most speech sounds, although it is capable of a range of movements.

Effects of Neuromuscular Disease on Velopharyngeal Function

A deficit associated with the velopharyngeal port can have significant effects on speech. In neuromuscular disorders, such as amyotrophic lateral sclerosis or multiple sclerosis, muscular weakness arises from damage to the myelin sheath surrounding the axons of motor neurons. When the weakness involves the muscles of the velum, the nasal cavity resonance is added to that of the oral cavity for non-nasal sounds. This "anti-resonance," as it is called, pulls energy out of the speech signal in the 1500 Hz to 2500 Hz range, causing a marked loss of clarity in the speech signal. Speech of the affected individual sounds muffled, monotone, and low in vocal intensity.

It is not uncommon for the speech-language pathologist to be the first person approached by an individual with early signs of neuromuscular disease. The velopharyngeal port requires constant elevation for non-nasal sounds and is an early indicator of progressive muscular weakness. An individual may come to the clinician with the complaint that people say his or her speech sounds muffled. Your oral-peripheral examination will reveal slow velar activity, and your referral to a physician will be most helpful to the client.

Development of Articulatory Ability

The infant is faced with an enormous task during development. She begins life with no knowledge of the universe and with a motor system in which movement is governed by reflexes and out of her control. She will spend the next several years (perhaps the rest of her life!) making sense of the world around her and learning to manipulate her environment. Fortunately she is born with an innate "desire" to acquire information and learn about her environment, and it appears that this drives the often-painful process of development.

The primitive human motor system is actually an extremely complex network of protective reflexes. Reflexes provide the means for an immature infant to respond to the environment in a stereotyped manner, without volition. This is not to argue that infants have no will, but rather to point out that they cannot express it voluntarily. If a breast touches the lips of an infant, the infant will orient to the breast and start sucking reflexively (you can stimulate this reflex with a stroke of your fingers). The infant does not need to think "Gee, I'm hungry. I wonder if there is anything to eat around here?" Rather, nature has "hardwired" the infant to meet its needs.

Use of a Palatal Lift

A **palatal lift prosthesis** is a device, typically anchored to the teeth, which is used to elevate the soft palate to more closely approximate the position of the velum for closure. This prosthesis is useful for individuals with muscular weakness, perhaps as a result of **hypoplasia** (inadequate muscle development) or a **neurogenic** condition (deficit arising from neurological cause). The palatal lift prosthesis has also been useful in working with children with developmental apraxia (Hall, Hardy, & LaVelle, 1990). Although this condition does not cause muscular weakness, velar movement is often slow and poorly coordinated.

This reflexive condition results in what Langley and Lombardino (1991) refer to as "primitive mass patterns of movement." Movements are gross responses to environmental stimuli that help the infant meet its basic needs. Development is a process of gaining cortical control of the motor patterns for volitional purposes, and the development of the articulatory system has its roots in learning to walk.

The most pervasive postnatal experience an infant has is gravity. Always present, gravity provides the ultimate challenge to an infant who wants to experience a universe that is out of reach. Reflexive movement against gravity provides the child with information about the effects of movement. He can see his hands as he moves them and learns that there is a relationship between the sensation and the hands he sees. These are the essential elements of motor development: *reflexive response* to *environmental stimuli*, providing *feedback* to an intact *neuromotor system*. Motor development is a process of refining gross movements, and this refinement will occur **cephalo-caudally** (from head to tail) and **proximo-distally** (from medial structures to distal structures). The infant will develop gross mandibular movements before fine mandibular movements and will have head control before she develops trunk control. She will develop posterior tongue control before anterior tongue control. Four vital elements of basic motor control support later speech development: experience with gravity, flexor-extensor balance, trunk control, and differentiation.

During the reflexive period (roughly birth to 6 months), the infant's vestibular system is being stimulated by handling by the parent. Vestibular stimulation causes changes in muscle tone relative to gravity, setting the stage for the tonic activity of the postural muscles.

The baby begins life in a general state of flexion, and the advent of extension heralds an infant's ability to attend actively to her environment. When the newborn is placed on her stomach, her weight will shift to her face. When she is pulled up from a supine position by her hands, her head will flop back with no control. The 3-month-old has a great deal of extensor balance and can now control her head when pulled from supine. She can now control head rotation to view her environment when sitting, which requires little support. Soon her trunk muscles will be under sufficient control that she can rotate and reach for objects in her environment.

The combination of trunk stability and extensor-flexor balance gives her the tools for standing and walking—and talking. It is no surprise that the infant's speech begins to develop in concert with her locomotor skills. If you remember that the tongue is intimately related to the hyoid and larynx, you will realize that it is unreasonable to expect a child to control the complex, refined movements of the tongue until the trunk and neck muscles are stabilized.

Following stabilization, the infant must develop differential motor control. In the articulatory system the manifestations of this control are evident in the rapidly increasing complexity of his speech production. The simple consonant-vowel (CV) syllable represents the most basic valving of the articulatory system. All the child must do to produce this syllable is begin phonation and open and close the mouth repeatedly. Tongue contact will approximate a velar or alveolar stop, or lip contact will produce a bilabial plosive. In any case, this infant has babbled, much to the delight of its parents!

The simple valving gives way to refined control of the tongue. With mandible stability accomplished, the child can begin the process of differentiating the tongue movements from those of the mandible. Following this, the infant differentiates tongue body and tip movements, as well as lateralization.

This development is hierarchical. The infant must balance muscle tone before being able to sit, and must sit before he can establish independent head and neck control. With control of neck muscles comes the freedom to move the mandible and tongue independently, and with that freedom comes the ability to differentially move the articulators.

Does this mean that a child with deficits of motor development will never develop speech? The answer, fortunately, is "no." The task is doubly difficult, however, and still depends on gaining the voluntary control and differentiation of those muscles. This is where you, the clinician, take your cue.

To summarize, the neonate depends on **reflexive responses** for protection and to meet her needs.

Phonological Development and Motor Control

Certainly the development of a child's phonology is a marvel. It should now be fairly clear that the maturation of the motor speech system governs, in large part, the speech sounds a child is capable of making. The stops (/p,t,k,b,d,g/) are present in the child's repertoire fairly in development, although their mastery will occur later than their emergence. The reason for this is apparently motoric. A child of 2 or 3 years is quite capable of the basic "valving" gesture of opening and closing the mouth (/ba/), raising and lowering the tongue on the alveolar ridge (/da/), or near the velum (/ga/). However, the controlled production of the stops requires the ability to differentiate labial, mandibular, and lingual movements, and thus mastery of the stops may occur as late as 6 years.

As the child develops greater motor control, he gains the ability to make graded movements with the tongue, so that he can sustain one articulator against the other with a constant pressure. The "raspberry" you hear in the preverbal child is very likely the precursor to the fricatives that will develop later. With graded control of lingual pressure comes the ability to make minute adjustments of an articulatory posture, such as those made with the dorsum of the tongue to differentiate /s/ and /ʃ/ through width of the tongue groove and tongue tip elevation.

■ These primitive patterns gradually develop with **voluntary control patterns** to facilitate control of trunk, neck, and limbs.

■ With this control comes the ability to make graded movements of the mandible and, subsequently, differentiated lingual movements.

Coordinated Articulation

Theories of motor control for speech have undergone a great deal of evolution, but are centered generally around the notions of locus of control, the need for consistency for the motor act, and task specification. Speech is arguably the most complex sequential motor task performed by humans. Consider the following hierarchical elements of speech, as implied by MacKay (1982).

Within the initial, **conceptual system**, we must first develop the proposition, or idea to be expressed, and that idea represents the sentence to be spoken. This idea or proposition must be mapped into a syntactical system to establish the language forms acceptable to match the concept, and appropriate words must be selected to match the syntax and to fit the proposition. Thus, if the idea "Tomorrow is Monday" is the chosen proposition, the syntax for that proposition must be selected, and the word chosen to fit the syntax and the proposition.

In the **phonological system**, syllable structure is parsed from the lexical selections. Phonological rules are applied to establish the correct phoneme combinations to meet the needs of the words chosen previously, and the individual features of those phonemes are parsed from the phonological specifications. Thus, at the phonological system level, the syllables associated with the selected words ("Tomorrow is Monday") will be further broken into syllables, selected phonemes, and features for the phonemes. For instance, the /t/ in "tomorrow" will be defined as lingua-alveolar, stop, and voiceless. Notice that, throughout; all of this, there has been no mention of muscles of articulation.

In the **muscle movement system**, muscles are activated to meet the needs of the feature selection process. The /t/ of the phonological system was broken into features, such as "lingua-alveolar," and this is now translated into movement of the muscles of the tongue which will produce that lingua-alveolar gesture (such as the superior longitudinal and genioglossus muscles).

Speaking assumes that we have developed an idea that we wish to express and that we somehow map that idea into muscle movements that change the three-dimensional space of the oral cavity. Those changes result in an acoustical output that is an acceptable representation of our goal.

In the early 20th century researchers recognized that learning sequential acts could be easily explained if one assumed that we linked a series of basic movements, like beads on a string. By this theory, the **associated chain theory**, the production of /t/, required only that the speaker learn all of the motor sequences leading up to elevation of the tongue to the alveolar ridge, and so forth. We could link a series of reflexive movements and entrain them in a sequential activation pattern. Once the motor act was learned, the speaker would forever be prepared to produce a word with /t/ in it. Lashley (1951) argued that the articulatory system is not a set of "sleeping" muscles waiting to be activated, but is rather a set of dynamic structures under continuous activation. In addition, the associative chain theories could not begin to account for variability in speech, much less the overlapping effect of one articulatory pattern on another (**coarticulation**). Future theories would have to account for the fluidity of speech production, the inherent variability of articulation based on context, and the ability of the articulators to achieve their phonetic target despite unpredictable alteration of the context of that production. Two major theoretical frameworks emerged from Lashley's concerns: the central control theory and the dynamic systems perspective.

Central Control Theory

The various forms of central control theory hold that there is a "master control" mechanism that dictates the muscle movements based on the linguistic goal. In the most extreme case, the command system would be oblivious to the state of the articulators at any moment and would administer the muscle commands without regard to articulator conditions of the moment. The beauty of such a model is the direct access that the motor system has to the language processor. Individual phonemes would be represented by a burst of neural excitation, so that the plan for a /t/ would be expertly executed with faithful precision. This provides a very nice solution to a major problem: The articulatory act for any phoneme requires precise activation of an overwhelming number of neurons and muscle fibers, and the activation must be accurate, timely, and result in correct movement. Thus, simply activating a program that your brain knows will produce a /t/ is much simpler than having to "micro-manage" your articulatory system.

Clearly, feedback from sensors within the articulators and related structures, as well as of the auditory signal itself, had to be accounted for. Without feedback we would be unable to arrive at a production that was accurate and acceptable by our communicative partners. Fairbanks (1954) posed the earliest and most stringent of the **feedback theories**, holding that the brain commands the articulators to achieve a target, and a mismatch between the feedback and the ideal results in correction of the output. Modification of articulation is driven by afferent information on an ongoing basis. In this view, the sensory system takes a dominant role in the production of speech.

The downside of these models is that they fail to account for the flexibility of the articulatory system in response to varying environmental conditions. If you pay attention to your tongue as you say the words "beat" and "toot" you will notice that the tongue is in two very different locations as it moves up for the final /t/, yet you are perfectly able to achieve both goals. Central control theories are forced to establish individual articulatory patterns to represent each allophone to accommodate this need, a very weighty proposition. Although the notions of central control remain robust and promising (e.g., MacKay, 1982), clearly there is a need to explain how we are able to articulate with such precision in the face of continuous variability.

Dynamic or Action Theory Models

As theorists worked to explain accurate and variable articulatory ability, the notion of **articulatory goals** evolved. The end-product of mus-

Apraxia

Apraxia refers to a deficit in the programming of musculature for voluntary movement in absence of any muscular weakness or paralysis. There appear to be many types and subtypes of apraxia. **Limb apraxia** is identified as the inability to perform volitional gestures using the limbs. A patient with limb apraxia might reveal deficits in voluntarily using multiple objects to perform a sequence of acts upon request, such as making a sandwich. The act may be fluent, but the object is used inappropriately. The patient's ability to perform the act through imitation would be much less impaired.

A patient with **oral apraxia** might reveal difficulty programming the facial and lingual muscles for nonspeech acts. When this individual is asked to blow out a candle, she may experience a great deal of effortful groping in an attempt to find the right gesture with the lips in coordination with the outward flow of air. Often the oral apractic individual also has a verbal apraxia.

Verbal apraxia refers to a deficit in programming the articulators for speech sound production. The verbally apractic individual will make errors in correct articulation of the sounds of speech, although the errors vary widely from one attempt to another. The individual is aware of the error and will make frequent attempts at production, so that the flow of speech is greatly impeded. This patient will have more difficulty with multisyllabic than monosyllabic words, and semi-automatic speech (such as greetings) may be quite fluent.

By definition, apraxias occur without muscular weakness, although muscular weakness or paralysis may co-occur with the apraxia. Apraxias may arise from lesions to a variety of brain structures. Damage to the premotor region of the cerebral cortex appears to have the greatest probability of producing apraxia, and the specific premotor region involved with speech is known as Broca's area. Damage to the supramarginal gyrus of the parietal lobe also will result in verbal apraxia, with the errors being more pure phonemic errors than those seen with damage in Broca's area, which will contain more distortions.

cle activity (and central control) was viewed as being a major determinant in execution. Saltzman (1986) viewed goal-related movement as composed of an **effector system**, a portion of which is the **terminal device**. The effector system would include the entire group of articulators involved in a given gesture, and the terminal device, or **end-effector**, is that portion of the effector system directly related the articulatory goal (such as the dorsum of the tongue for articulation of the phoneme /i/). By differentiating these components, one can account for the problem of having to coordinate large numbers of muscle fibers in concert. From this point, one can view the articulatory effector system in a dynamic fashion. The components of the effector system are assigned the goal of the articulation, but are free to work within the "degrees of freedom" inherent in the system to accomplish the task. That is, no two acts are ever produced the same way twice, and yet there are definitely commonalities among motor acts. The dynamic models state that the commonality is that the motor act is accurately achieved within the bounds of variability, and the functional units of activation are groups of **coordinative structures**. Coordinative structures are functionally defined muscle groups which, when activated, contribute to achieving the goal at the terminal effector.

Trajectories, or movement paths, can be seen as targets of movement, and the structures involved in achieving a target are grouped as coordinative structures. If the movement is disturbed during execution, the coordinative structures are capable of altering their degree of activation to compensate for this "perturbation" without an altered central command. As an example, if you were to pick up a glass of milk, your target would be accurate movement of the glass rim to your lips. Unknown to you, the glass has a very heavy base. When you lift the glass, you expect it to be lighter than it is, so your muscular effort is less than if you had expected a heavier glass. If you depended on a central program to correct your movement, you might not reach your lips, and you probably would pour the milk down your shirt. As it is, your effector system adapts its activities to match the trajectory (table to lips), you add extra force, and your thirst is quenched. This ability to compensate is essential for speech production.

The **dynamic models** take into account the physical properties of the systems involved in articulation. Muscles and connective tissue have elastic properties that result in recoil, and dynamic models account for these variables in the equation. These models have more quickly accommodated the role of afferent information concerning the state of the musculature. According to Kelso and Ding (1993), there are many solutions to achieving any trajectory, and the relationship of the coordinative structures simply defines the solution from a given point of trajectory initiation to the point of termination.

Models of speech production also must somehow account for the fact that speech occurs at an extraordinarily rapid rate, and that, somehow, the articulatory system is very resistant to perturbation. We can accommodate a wide range of surprises in speech with no trouble at all. Dynamic models account for the dynamic aspects of the physical system required to achieve a specific target within the environment. If the articulatory command specifies an output product rather than a specific movement, the system retains the flexibility to adapt to changes in the environment.

These models attempt to account for many difficulties in articulation theory, not the least of which is **coarticulation** (the overlapping effect of one articulatory gesture on another). During running speech we will begin movement toward an articulatory posture well in advance of when it is needed *if* that activation does not interfere with the articulations preceding it. For example, pay attention to your lips when you say the words "see" and "sue." The /s/ in "see" is made with retracted lips, whereas the /s/ in "sue" is produced with rounded lips, both illustrating preparatory articulation. You will *not* see this effect in the word "booty," however. Try saying that word with your lips retracted for the /I/, and you will hear an unacceptable vowel production.

We are amazingly resilient in our articulatory abilities and our resistance to **perturbation** (sudden, unexpected force applied to an articulator) supports the notion of functional synergies or coordinative structures. A functionally defined group of muscles and associated articulators are assigned a task (such as "close the lips"), but they have many different ways to accomplish the task. A perturbation or bite block reduces the number of ways left to accomplish the task, but as long as there is a solution, the articulators will find it.

To summarize, major theories of motor function approach the task from opposite directions.

■ **Central control theories** postulate that a command for muscle movement originates in response to the linguistic needs.
■ **Task dynamic theories** posit that the movement arises from the response by coordinated structures to an implicit trajectory.
■ **Central control theories** account for the **linguistic dominance** of articulation for speech, while the **dynamic models** account for **variability** and **coarticulatory** effects.
■ Both theories account for feedback in speech.

CHAPTER SUMMARY

Articulators have both speech and nonspeech functions. Biological (nonspeech) functions fulfilled by the articulators include mastication and deglutition. There are four stages of **mastication** and **deglutition.** Food is introduced into the oral cavity, masticated, and formed into a bolus during the **oral preparation stage**. During the **oral stage**, the bolus is moved back on the hard palate, and the **pharyngeal stage** begins when the bolus reaches the fauces. The reflexive swallow includes elevation of the soft palate and larynx, propulsion of the bolus through the pharynx, closure of the laryngeal sphincter, and opening of the esophageal sphincter. The **esophageal stage** involves peristaltic movement of the bolus through the esophagus.

The **lower lip** is much faster and stronger than the **upper lip,** and responds reflexively to increases of pressure. Movement of the **mandible** for speech is slight when compared with movement for chewing. The mandibular posture for speech is one of sustained dynamic tension between antagonists. The **tongue** is versatile, with the extrinsic muscles providing the major movement of the body and the intrinsic muscles providing the shaping of the tongue. The **velum** must be maintained in a reasonably elevated position for most speech sounds, although it is capable of a range of movements.

Development of articulatory function involves gaining control of postural muscles that provide trunk **stability** and **differentiation** of muscle group function. **Reflexive responses** are protective and nurturant, and these primitive patterns gradually develop with **voluntary control** patterns to facilitate control of trunk, neck, and limbs, and finally differentiation for graded oral movement.

Complex speech production requires control of many parameters simultaneously. We use **sensory feedback** to learn articulator function in speech and probably use it for error control as well. **Central control theories** hold that the motor command for an articulation is driven by an articulatory configuration determined through consideration of linguistic elements. The motor command specifies the characteristics of muscle contraction without respect to speaking environment, but the theories cannot account for articulatory variability or the nearly infinite variety of speaking environments. **Dynamic theories** hold that **coordinative structures** interact to accomplish completion of a trajectory, and the theories accommodate the wide variability and flexibility of the articulatory system in speech.

Study Questions

1. _____ refers to the processes involved in food preparation, such as chewing food, moving the food onto the molars, and so forth.

2. _____ refers to swallowing.

3. In the _____ stage of swallowing, food is prepared for swallowing.

4. In the _____ stage of swallowing, mastication ceases, the tongue drops down and pulls posteriorly, and the anterior tongue elevates to the hard palate and squeezes the bolus back toward the faucial pillars.

5. In the _____ stage of swallowing the bolus contacts the anterior faucial pillars, the soft palate elevates, respiration stops, the vocal folds tightly adduct, the larynx elevates and moves forward, and the cricopharyngeus relaxes as food enters the pharynx.

6. During the _____ stage of swallowing, the bolus is transported through the esophagus.

7. Identify the muscle that best fits the statement. (In some cases there is more than one muscle that fills the bill.)

a. _____ Elevates tongue tip

b. _____ Depresses tongue tip

c. _____ Protrudes tongue

d. _____ Retracts tongue

e. _____ Elevates posterior tongue

f. _____ Narrows tongue

g. _____ Flattens tongue

h. _____ Depresses velum

i. _____ Tenses velum

j. _____ Constricts esophageal opening

k. _____ Constricts upper pharynx

l. _____ Elevates velum

8. The _____ (lower lip/upper lip) is faster and stronger than the _____ (lower lip/upper lip).

9. Motor control in the body develops from _____ (head/tail) to _____ (head/tail) and from _____ (proximal/distal) to _____ (proximal/distal).

10. The _____ theory of motor control would require the speaker to learn the sequences of motor acts required for articulation and to link these sequences of motor acts to form an articulatory gesture.

11. _____ is the overlapping effect of one articulatory gesture on another.

12. _____ theory holds that there is a "master control" mechanism that dictates the muscle movements based on the linguistic goal.

13. _____ theories generally see articulation as a process of achieving a goal through interaction of coordinative structures. Coordinative structures are muscle groups which, when activated, contribute to achievement of the goal at the terminal effector.

Study Question Answers

1. <u>MASTICATION</u> refers to the processes involved in food preparation, such as chewing food, moving the food onto the molars, and so forth.

2. <u>DEGLUTITION</u> refers to swallowing.

3. In the <u>ORAL PREPARATORY</u> stage of swallowing, food is prepared for swallowing.

4. In the <u>ORAL</u> stage of swallowing, mastication ceases, the tongue drops down and pulls posteriorly, and the anterior tongue elevates to the hard palate and squeezes the bolus back toward the faucial pillars.

5. In the <u>PHARYNGEAL</u> stage of swallowing, of the bolus contacts the anterior faucial pillars, the soft palate elevates, respiration stops, the vocal folds tightly adduct, the larynx elevates and moves forward, and the cricopharyngeus relaxes as food enters the pharynx.

6. During the <u>ESOPHAGEAL</u> stage of swallowing, the bolus is transported through the esophagus.

7. Identify the muscle that best fits the statement (In some cases there is more than one muscle that fills the bill.)

   a. <u>SUPERIOR LONGITUDINAL INTRINSIC</u> Elevates tongue tip

   b. <u>INFERIOR LONGITUDINAL INTRINSIC</u> Depresses tongue tip

   c. <u>GENIOGLOSSUS, ANTERIOR PORTION</u> Protrudes tongue

   d. <u>GENIOGLOSSUS, POSTERIOR PORTION; STYLOGLOSSUS</u> Retracts tongue

   e. <u>PALATOGLOSSUS</u> Elevates posterior tongue

   f. <u>TRANSVERSE INTRINSIC</u> Narrows tongue

   g. <u>VERTICAL INTRINSIC; GENIOGLOSSUS</u> Flattens tongue

   h. <u>PALATOGLOSSUS; PALATOPHARYNGEUS</u> Depresses velum

   i. <u>TENSOR VELI PALATINI</u> Tenses velum

      j. <u>CRICOPHARYNGEUS</u> Constricts esophageal opening

      k. <u>SUPERIOR PHARYNGEAL CONSTRICTOR</u> Constricts upper pharynx

      l. <u>LEVATOR VELI PALATINI</u> Elevates velum

8. The <u>LOWER</u> is faster and stronger than the <u>UPPER</u>.

9. Motor control in the body develops from <u>HEAD</u> to <u>TAIL</u> and from <u>PROXIMAL</u> to <u>DISTAL</u>.

10. The <u>ASSOCIATED CHAIN</u> theory of motor control would require the speaker to learn the sequences of motor acts required for articulation and to link these sequences of motor acts to form an articulatory gesture.

11. <u>COARTICULATION</u> is the overlapping effect of one articulatory gesture on another.

12. <u>CENTRAL CONTROL THEORY</u> holds that there is a "master control" mechanism that dictates the muscle movements based upon the linguistic goal.

13. <u>TASK DYNAMIC</u> theories generally see articulation as a process of achieving a goal through interaction of coordinative structures. Coordinative structures are muscle groups which, when activated, contribute to achievement of the goal at the terminal effector.

REFERENCES

Abbs, J. H., & Cole, K. J. (1991). Consideration of bulbar and suprabulbar afferent influences upon speech motor coordination and programming. In S. Grillner, B. Lindblom, J. Lubker, & A. Persson (Eds.), *Speech motor control* (pp. 159–186). Oxford: Pergamon Press.

Baken, R. J. (1987). *Clinical measurement of speech and voice.* Austin, TX: Pro-Ed.

Barlow, S. M., & Netsell, R. (1986). Differential fine force control of the upper and lower lips. *Journal of Speech and Hearing Research, 29,* 163–169.

Barlow, S. M., & Rath, E. M. (1985). Maximum voluntary closing forces in the upper and lower lips of humans. *Journal of Speech and Hearing Research, 28,* 373–376.

Bateman, H. E., & Mason, R. M. (1984). *Applied anatomy and physiology of the speech and hearing mechanism.* Springfield, IL: Charles C. Thomas.

Bunton, K., & Weismer, G. (1994). Evaluation of a reiterant force-impulse task in the tongue. *Journal of Speech and Hearing Research, 37,* 1020–1031.

Bly, L. (1983). *The components of normal movement during the first year of life and abnormal motor movement.* Chicago, IL: Neuro-Developmental Treatment Association.

Bly, L. (1994). *Motor skills acquisition in the first year.* Tucson, AZ: Therapy Skill Builders.

DeNil, L. F., & Abbs, J. H (1991). Influence of speaking rate on the upper lip, lower lip, and jaw peak velocity sequencing during bilabial closing movements. *Journal of the Acoustical Society of America, 89*(2), 845–849.

Duffy, J. R. (1995). *Motor speech disorders*. St. Louis, MO: C. V. Mosby.

Fairbanks, G. (1954). A theory of the speech mechanism as a servosystem. *Journal of Speech and Hearing Disorders, 19*, 133–139.

Flege, J. E. (1988). Anticipatory and carry-over nasal coarticulation in the speech of children and adults. *Journal of Speech and Hearing Research, 31*, 525–536.

Folkins, J. W., Linville, R. N., Garrett, J. D., & Brown, C. K. (1988). Interactions in the labial musculature during speech. *Journal of Speech and Hearing Research, 31*, 253–264.

Garcia-Colera, A., & Semjen, A. (1988). Distributed planning of movement sequences. *Journal of Motor Behavior, 20*(3), 341–367.

Goffman, L., & Smith, A. (1994). Motor unit territories in the human perioral musculature. *Journal of Speech and Hearing Research, 37*, 975–984.

Gracco, V. L. (1988). Timing factors in the coordination of speech movements. *Journal of Neuroscience, 8*(12), 4628–4639.

Gracco, V. L. (1994). Some organizational characteristics of speech movement control. *Journal of Speech and Hearing Research, 37*, 4–27.

Gracco, V. L. & Abbs, J. H. (1989). Sensorimotor characteristics of speech motor sequences. *Experimental Brain Research, 75*, 586–598.

Groher, M. E. (1984). *Dysphagia*. Boston, MA: Butterworths.

Hall, P. K., Hardy, J. C., & LaVelle, W. E. (1990). A child with signs of developmental apraxia of speech with whom a palatal lift prosthesis was used to manage palatal dysfunction. *Journal of Speech and Hearing Disorders, 55*, 454–460.

Hellstrand, E. (1981). The neuromuscular system of the tongue. In S. Grillner, B. Lindblom, J. Lubker, & A. Persson (Eds.), *Speech motor control* (pp. 141–157). Oxford: Pergamon Press, 141–157.

Horak, M. (1992). The utility of connectionism for motor learning: A reinterpretation of contextual interference in movement schemas. *Journal of Motor Behavior, 24*(1), 58–66.

Jordan, M. I. (1990). Motor learning and the degrees of freedom problem. In M. Jeannerod (Ed.), *Attention and performance XIII: Motor Representation and control*. Hillsdale, NJ: Lawrence Erlbaum.

Landgren, S., & Olsson, K. A. (1981). Oral mechanoreceptors. In S. Grillner, B. Lindblom, J. Lubker, & A. Persson (Eds.), *Speech motor control* (pp. 129–139). Oxford: Pergamon Press, 129–139.

Kaplan, H. M. (1971). *Anatomy and physiology of speech*. New York: McGraw-Hill.

Katz, W. F., Kripke, C., & Tallal, P. (1991). Anticipatory coarticulation in the speech of adults and young children: acoustic, perceptual, and video data. *Journal of Speech and Hearing Research, 34*, 1222–1249.

Kent, R. D., Kent, J. F., & Rosenbek, J. C. (1987). Maximum performance tests of speech production. *Journal of Speech and Hearing Disorders, 52*, 367–387.

Kelso, J. A., & Ding, M. (1993). Fluctuations, intermittency, and controllable chaos in biological coordination. In Newell, K. M. & Corcos, D. M. (Eds.), *Variability and motor control* (pp. 291–316). Champaign, IL: Human Kinetics.

Kelso, J. A. S., Tuller, B., Vatikiotis-Bateson, E., & Fowler, C. A. (1984). Functionally specific articulatory cooperation following jaw perturbations during speech: Evidence for coordinative structures. *Journal of Experimental Psychology: Perception and Performance, 19*, 812–832.

Kuehn, D. P., Templeton, P. J., & Maynard, J. A. (1990). Muscle spindles in the velopharyngeal musculature of humans. *Journal of Speech and Hearing Research, 33*, 488–493.

Langley, M. B., & Lombardino, L. J. (1991). *Neurodevelopmental strategies for managing communication disorders in children with severe motor dysfunction*. Austin, TX: Pro-Ed.

Lashley, K. S. (1951). The problem of serial order in behavior. In L. A. Jerrers (Ed.), *Cerebral mechanisms in behavior* (pp. 506–528). New York: John Wiley.

Lieberman, P. (1977). *Speech physiology and acoustic phonetics: An introduction*. New York: Macmillan.

Liss, J. M. (1990). Muscle spindles in the human levator veli palatini and palatoglossus muscles. *Journal of Speech and Hearing Research, 33*, 736–746.

Logemann, J. (1983). *Evaluation and treatment of swallowing disorders*. Boston, MA: College-Hill Press.

Love, R. J., Hagerman, E. L., & Taimi, E. G. (1980). Speech performance, dysphagia and oral reflexes in cerebral palsy. *Journal of Speech and Hearing Disorders, 45*, 59–75.

McClean, M. (1973). Forward coarticulation of velar movement at marked junctural boundaries. *Journal of Speech and Hearing Research, 16*, 286–296.

McNeil, M. R., Weismer, G., Adams, S., & Mulligan, M. (1990). Oral structure nonspeech motor control in normal, dysarthric, aphasic, and apraxic speakers: isometric force and static position control. *Journal of Speech and Hearing Research, 33*, 255–268.

Moore, C. A. (1993). Symmetry of mandibular muscle activity as an index of coordinative strategy. *Journal of Speech and Hearing Research, 36*, 1145–1157.

Moore, C. A., Smith, A., & Ringel, R. L. (1988). Task- specific organization of activity in human jaw muscles. *Journal of Speech and Hearing Research, 31*, 670–680.

Netsell, R. (1973). Speech physiology. In Minifie, F. D., Hixon, T. J., & Williams, F. (Eds.), *Normal aspects of speech, hearing and language*. Englewood Cliffs, NJ: Prentice-Hall.

Perlman, A. L., Grayhack, J. P., & Booth, B. M. (1992). The relationship of vallecular residue to oral involvement, reduced hyoid elevation, and epiglottic function. *Journal of Speech and Hearing Research, 35*, 734–741.

Perlman, A. L., Luschei, E. S., & Du Mond, C. E. (1989). Electrical activity from the superior pharyngeal constrictor during reflexive and nonreflexive tasks. *Journal of Speech and Hearing Research, 32*, 749–754.

Rademaker, A. W., Pauloski, B. R., Logemann, J. A., & Shanahan, T. K. (1994). Oropharyngeal swallow efficiency as a representative measure of swallowing function. *Journal of Speech and Hearing Research, 37*, 314–325.

Rosenbaum, D. A., Kenny, S. B., & Derr, M. A. (1983). Hierarchical control of rapid movement sequences. *Journal of Experimental Psychology: Human Perception and Performance, 9*(1), 86–102.

Rosenbek, J. C., Robbins, J., Fishback, B., & Levine, R. L. (1991). Effects of thermal application on dysphagia after stroke. *Journal of Speech and Hearing Research, 34*, 1257–1268.

Saltzman, E. (1986). Task dynamic coordination of the speech articulators: A preliminary model. *Experimental brain research* (pp. 129–144). Berlin-Heidelberg: Springer-Verlag.

Shaffer, L. H. (1976). Intention and performance. *Psychological Review, 33*(5), 375–393.

Schmidt, R. A. (1975). A schema theory of discrete motor skill learning. *Psychological review, 82*, 225–260.

Smith, A., McFarland, D. H., & Weber, C. M. (1986). Interactions between speech and finger movements: An exploration of the dynamic pattern perspective. *Journal of Speech and Hearing Research, 29*, 471–480.

Square-Storer, P., & Roy, E. A. (1989). The apraxias: Commonalities and distinctions. In P. Square-Storer (Ed.), *Acquired apraxia of speech in aphasic adults: Theoretical and clinical issues.* London: Taylor & Francis.

Weber, C. M., & Smith, A. (1987). Reflex responses in human jaw, lip, and tongue muscles elicited by mechanical stimulation. *Journal of Speech and Hearing Research, 30,* 70–79.

Westbury, J. R. (1988). Mandible and hyoid bone movements during speech. *Journal of Speech and Hearing Research, 31,* 405–416.

Wickens, J., Hyland, B., & Anson, G. (1994). Cortical cell assemblies: a possible mechanism for motor programs. *Journal of Motor Behavior, 26*(2), 66–82.

Wohlert, A. B., & Goffman, L. (1994). Human perioral muscle activation patterns. *Journal of Speech and Hearing Research, 37,* 1032–1040.

Zemlin, W. R. (1988). *Speech and hearing science. Anatomy and physiology.* Englewood Cliffs, NJ: Prentice-Hall.

CHAPTER

9

Neuroanatomy

There is nothing in nature so awe inspiring as the nervous system. Despite centuries of study, humans have only gained the slightest understanding of this extraordinarily complex system. There are approximately 100 billion neurons in the nervous system, and each of these neurons may communicate directly with as many as 2,000 other neurons, providing at least one trillion points of communication. As before, we will be concerned with the structure and function of this system.

OVERVIEW

During our discussion of human anatomy associated with speech and language, we have been quite concerned with voluntary musculature and the supporting framework associated with it. Communication *is*, by and large, voluntary. Nonetheless, the term voluntary takes on new meanings when seen in the context of automaticity and background. **Automaticity** refers to development of patterns of responses that no longer require highly specific motor control, but rather are relegated to automated patterns. **Background** activity is the muscular contraction that supports action or movement, providing the form against which voluntary movement is placed. Voluntary activities are generally considered to be conscious activities, but they are, in reality, largely automated responses. To prove this to yourself, try washing the dishes and actually thinking about the act of dishwashing. The movements and responses to this act are so automated that you probably feel you do them "without thinking." In fact, your brain receives over 40,000 signals from body sensors per second (including information about soap suds and water temperature), but you need not respond to all of it, because your brain will monitor and alert you to dangers. You can think about other things while your hands do the dishes.

Speech capitalizes on similar automaticity, as you can see in the ability to easily speak while riding a bike or walking. You no more think of every movement of the extraordinary number of muscles contracting for the simple speech act than you do during dishwashing. This changes when the mechanism changes, however. When your mouth is numb from the dentist's anesthesia, you become very aware of your lack of feedback from that system, and inaccurate speech is the result. When an individual suffers a cerebrovascular accident, the result is often a loss of previously attained automaticity in speech. When a child is born with **developmental apraxia**, a condition which limits the ability of a child to control the articulators voluntarily, achieving automaticity may be a lifelong struggle.

Automatic functions are supported by a background **tonicity**, a partial contraction of musculature to maintain muscle tone. All action occurs within an environment, and the environment of your musculature is the tonic contraction of supporting muscles. As you extend your arm to reach for a coffee cup, the action of the fingers of your hand to grasp the object is supported by the rotation of your shoulder and extension of your arm. Without these background support movements, the act of grasping would not occur. Your body works as a unit to meet your needs.

Voluntary functions are the domain of the **cerebral cortex** or cerebrum, a new structure by evolutionary standards making up the bulk of the human brain. It is the seat of consciousness, and sensory information that does not reach the level of the **cerebrum** does not reach consciousness. The cerebrum also is the source of voluntary movement, although many lower brain centers are involved in execution of commands initiated by the cerebrum (see Figure 9–1).

Movement requires coordination, and that is the responsibility of the **cerebellum**. Information from peripheral sensors is coordinated with the motor plan of the cerebrum to provide the body with the ability to make finely tuned motor gestures. The output from the cerebrum is modified by the **basal ganglia**, a group of nuclei (cell bodies) with functional unity deeply involved in background movement.

a

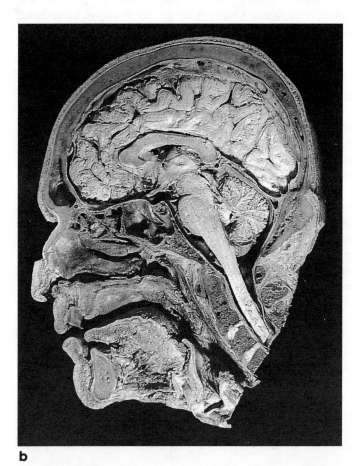

b

FIGURE 9-1. a. Medial view of cerebrum, brainstem, and cerebellum. **b.** Sagittal section showing relationship among cerebrum, cerebellum, and brainstem.

Motor commands are conveyed to the periphery for execution by **nerves** and **tracts**. Sensory pathways transmit information concerning the status of the body back to the brain for evaluation. This information permits the cerebrum and lower centers to act on changing conditions to protect the systems of the body and to adjust to the body's environment.

The brain can only communicate with its environment through sensors and effectors. There are many ways to classify senses and sensation. **Superficial sensation** (temperature, pain, touch) arises from stimulation of the surface of the body. **Deep sensation** includes **proprioception** (muscle and joint position sense), muscle pain, pressure, and vibration (**pallesthesia**). **Combined sensation** integrates both deep and superficial senses to process stimulation. This involves integration of many pieces of sensory information to determine a quality, such as **stereognosis** (the ability to recognize the form of an object through touch).

One also may classify sensation according to type. **Somatic sense** is that sensation related to pain, thermal sensation (temperature sense), and mechanical stimulation. Mechanical stimulation takes the form of light and deep pressure, vibration (which is actually pressure that is perceived to change over time), changes in joints and muscles, particularly stretch. **Kinesthetic sense** or kinesthesia is the sense of the body in motion. **Special senses** are those designed to **transduce** (change one form of energy into another) specific exteroceptive information. For example, in the **visual sense** light from external sources is transduced into electro-chemical energy by the photoreceptors of the retina, whereas in **hearing**, acoustical disturbances in the air are transduced by the hair cells of the cochlea. Other special senses are **olfaction** (sense of smell), **tactile sense** (sense of touch), and **gustation** (sense of taste).

Sensor types vary by the stimulus to which they respond. Sensors communicate with the nervous system by means of dendritic connection with bipolar first order sensory neurons. Axons of these first order neurons **synapse** or make neurochemical connection within the central nervous system. A graded **generator potential** arises from adequate stimulation of the sensor, and adequate stimulation will cause generation of an action potential.

Receptors may be mechanoreceptors, chemoreceptors, photoreceptors, and thermoreceptors. **Mechanoreceptors** respond to physical distortion of tissue. Pressure on the skin, for example, will result in distension of **Pacinian corpuscles**, whereas hair follicles have mechanoreceptors to let you know that something has disturbed your hair. **Muscle spindle** and **Golgi tendon organs** and the **labyrinthine hair receptors** of the inner ear are also mechanoreceptors. In contrast, olfaction and gustation are **chemoreceptors** because they depend on contact with molecules of the target substance. Visual stimulation by light is transduced by highly specialized **photoreceptors**, and temperature sense arises from **thermoreceptors**. Visual and auditory sensors are also termed **teleceptors** because their respective light and sound stimuli arise from a source that does not touch the body (olfactory sense is stimulated directly by molecules of the material being sensed).

Another way to categorize receptors is by the region of the body receiving stimulation. **Interoceptors** monitor events within the body, such as distension of the lungs during inspiration or blood acidity. **Exteroceptors** respond to stimuli outside of body, such as tactile stimulation, audition, and vision. Contact receptors are exteroceptors that respond to stimuli that touch the body (e.g., tactile, pain, deep and light pressure, temperature). **Proprioceptors** are sensors which monitor change in a body's position or the position of its parts, and these include muscle and joint sensors, such as muscle spindles and Golgi tendon organs. Vestibular sense falls into this category, because it provides information about the body's position in space.

Despite our rich communicative ability, we can *only* know our environment by means of the sensory receptors of our skin, muscles, tendons, eyes, ears, and so forth. Without sensation, a perfectly functioning brain would be worthless as a communicating system. Likewise, communication *requires* some sort of muscular activity or glandular secretion. The absence of *all* motor activity would signal the end of communication. Fortunately, the extraordinary number of sensors in the human body permits us to use alternate pathways for receiving communication (e.g., **tactile** or touch communication) or for passing information to another person (e.g., use of eye-blink code). We are rarely completely cut off from communication with others. Let us now examine the components of this system.

DIVISIONS OF THE NERVOUS SYSTEM

The **nervous system** can be viewed and categorized in a number of ways. It is important to develop a framework for discussion of this system, lest the volume of components become overwhelming. In the overview we discussed an informal **functional** view of nervous system organization, assessing the components in terms of their relationship to the systems of communication. Let us examine other systems for categorizing the nervous system.

Central Nervous System/Peripheral Nervous System

The nervous system may be divided anatomically into central and peripheral nervous systems. The **central nervous system** (CNS) includes the brain (cerebrum, cerebellum, subcortical structures, brainstem) and spinal cord. The **peripheral nervous system (PNS)** consists of the 12 pairs of cranial nerves and 31 pairs of spinal nerves, as well as the sensory receptors. All of the CNS components are housed within bone (skull or spinal column), whereas most of the PNS components are outside of bone. We will spend a great deal of time within this organizational structure as we discuss the anatomy of the nervous system.

Autonomic/Somatic Nervous Systems

Another functional view categorizes the brain into autonomic and somatic nervous systems. The **autonomic nervous system (ANS)** governs involuntary activities of the visceral muscles or **viscera**, including glandular secretions, heart function, digestive function, and so forth. You have little control over what happens to that triple cheeseburger once you make the commitment to eat it, although you will admit that occasionally you are *aware* of the digestive process.

The ANS may be further divided into two subsystems. The subsystem that responds to stimulation through energy expenditure is called the **sympathetic system** or **thoracolumbar system**, and the system that counters these responses is known as the **parasympathetic system** or **craniosacral system**. You have felt the result of the sympathetic system when you have had a close call in an automobile or have heard a sudden, loud noise. Sympathetic responses include **vasoconstriction** (constriction of blood vessels), increase in blood pressure, dilation of pupils, cardiac acceleration, and "goosebumps." If you attend for a few more seconds, you will notice the glandular secretion of sweat under your arms. All of these fall into the category of "flight, fight, or fright" responses. Your body has dumped the hormone norepinephrine into your system to provide you with a means of responding to danger.

You may be less aware of the parasympathetic system response. This system is responsible for counteracting the effects of this preparatory act, because the extraordinary muscular activity requires extraordinary energy. Parasympathetic responses include slowing of the heart rate, reduction of blood pressure, and pupillary constriction.

afferent: L., ad ferre, to carry toward

efferent: L., ex ferre, to carry away from

The central nervous system component of the ANS arises from the prefrontal region of the cerebral cortex, as well as from the hypothalamus, thalamus, hippocampus, brainstem, cerebellum, and spinal cord. The viscera are connected to these loci of control by means of **afferent** (ascending, often sensory) and **efferent** (descending, often motor) tracts.

The peripheral nervous system components of the ANS include paired **sympathetic trunk ganglia** running parallel and in close proximity to the spinal column, **plexuses** (networks of nerves) and **ganglia** (groups of cell bodies having functional unity and lying outside the CNS).

The **somatic nervous system** (voluntary component) is of major importance to the discipline of speech pathology. This system involves the aspects of bodily function that are under our conscious and voluntary control, including control of all skeletal or **somatic** muscles. CNS control of muscles arises largely from the precentral region of the cerebral cortex, with neural impulses conveyed through descending motor tracts of the brainstem and spinal cord. Communication with the cranial nerves of the brainstem and with the spinal nerves of the spinal cord permits activation of the periphery of the body.

somatic: Gr., soma, body

The motor component of the somatic system may be subdivided into **pyramidal** and **extrapyramidal** systems, although defining all of the anatomical correlates of this functional division is difficult. The **pyramidal** system arises from pyramidal cells of the motor strip of the cerebral cortex and is largely responsible for initiation of voluntary motor acts. The **extrapyramidal** system also arises from the cerebral cortex (mostly from the premotor region of the frontal lobe), but is responsible for the background tone and movement supporting the primary acts. The extrapyramidal system is referred to as the **indirect system**, projecting to the basal ganglia and reticular formation.

There is one more important way of categorizing structures within the nervous system, and it is developmental in nature. The anatomical and developmental organizations overlap, and both sets of terminology are often used together.

Development Divisions

During the fourth week of embryonic development the brain (**encephalon**) is composed of the **prosencephalon** (forebrain), **mesencephalon** (midbrain), and **rhombencephalon** (hindbrain). As the encephalon develops, further differentiation results in the telencephalon, rhinencephalon, diencephalon, metencephalon, and myelencephalon (see Table 9–1). The **telencephalon** refers to the "extended" or "telescoped" brain, and includes the cerebral hemispheres, the white matter immediately beneath it, the basal ganglia, and the olfactory tract. The **rhinencephalon** refers to structures within the telencephalon. The name arises from the relationship of the structures to olfaction. These are parts of the brain that developed early in our evolution, and include the olfactory bulb, tract, and striae; pyriform area; intermediate olfactory area; paraterminal area; hippocampal formation; and fornix. The **diencephalon** is the next descending level, and includes the thalamus, hypothalamus, pituitary gland (hypophysis), and optic tract. The **mesencephalon** is the midbrain of the brainstem, and the **metencephalon** includes the pons and cerebellum. The **myelencephalon** refers to the medulla oblongata, the lowest level of the encephalon. The term **bulb** or **bulbar** refers technically to the pons and medulla, but nearly always refers to the entire brainstem including the midbrain.

Phylogeny refers to the evolution of a species, whereas ontogeny is the development of an individual organism. The statement that "Ontogeny recapitulates phylogeny" refers to the notion that structures that are phylogenetically oldest tend to emerge earliest in the developing organism, while later evolutionary additions, such as the cerebral cortex, will emerge later in development.

telencephalon: Gr., telos enkephalos, end or distant brain

Table 9-1. Development and elements of the encephalon.

Development of Encephalon	
Prosencephalon	Telencephalon (including rhinencephalon)
	Diencephalon
Mesencephalon	Mesencephalon
Rhombencephalon	Metencephalon
	Myelencephalon

Components of Levels of the Encephalon

Telencephalon
  Cerebral hemispheres
  Basal ganglia
  Olfactory tract
  Rhinencephalon
  Lateral ventricle, part of third ventricle

Diencephalon
  Thalamus
  Hypothalamus
  Pituitary gland (hypophysis)
  Optic tract
  Third ventricle

Mesencephalon
  Midbrain
  Cerebral aqueduct
  Cerebral peduncles
  Corpora quadrigemina

Metencephalon
  Pons
  Cerebellum
  Portion of fourth ventricle

Myelencephalon
  Medulla oblongata
  Portion of fourth ventricle and central canal

rhinencephalon: Gr., rhis enkephalos, *nose brain*

Let us examine the nervous system, from the ground up. The basic units of the nervous system are neurons, from which all larger structures are composed.

ANATOMY OF THE CNS

Structures within the CNS reflect their developmental history, and examination of CNS anatomy is facilitated by working our way through this hierarchy. The smallest organizational unit of the nervous system is the neuron, followed in complexity by the spinal arc reflex, and higher reflexes. Ascending the spinal cord to the brainstem provides the next level of complexity, followed by subcortical structures and the cerebellum, and finally the most complex aggregate of tissue, the cerebral cortex. Let us begin by discussion of the most basic component of the nervous system, the neuron.

Neurons

The nervous system is comprised of the communicating elements, **neurons**, and support tissue, **glia** or **glial cells**. Neurons or nerve cells are the functional building blocks of the nervous system and are unique among tissue types, in that they are *communicating* tissue. Their function is to transmit information.

The general structure of most neurons includes the **soma** or cell body, a **dendrite**, transmitting information toward the soma, and an **axon**, which transmits information away from the soma (see Figure 9–2).

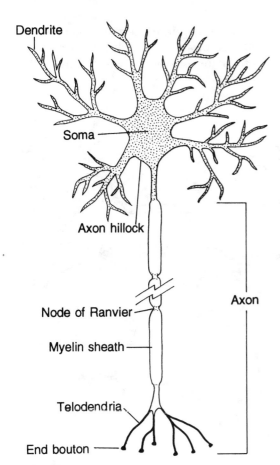

FIGURE 9–2. Schematic of basic elements of a neuron.

Neuronal response to stimulation is the mechanism by which information is transmitted in the nervous system, and this response may be broadly categorized as excitatory or inhibitory. **Excitation** refers to stimulation that causes an increase of activity of the tissue stimulated. That is, if a neuron is receives excitatory stimulation it will increase its activity in response. **Inhibition**, on the other hand, refers to stimulation of a neuron that reduces the neuron's output. That is, when a neuron is inhibited, it will reduce its activity.

There are several important landmarks of the neuron, knowledge of which will reinforce our discussion of physiology in the next chapter (see Figure 9–3). The **axon hillock** is the junction of the axon and soma. Although there are many dendrites for one neuron (often referred to as the "dendritic tree"), the axon projects as a single process. The axon is often covered with a **myelin sheath**, a white fatty wrapping made up of **Schwann cells** (in the PNS) or **oligodendrocytes** (in the CNS) which speeds up neural conduction. The myelin is segmented, with the non-myelinated regions on the axon known as **nodes of Ranvier**. At the distal end of the axon are **telodendria**, long, thin projections with **terminal (end) boutons** (or **buttons**). Within the terminal boutons are **synaptic vesicles** containing neurotransmitter substance or neurotransmitters. **Neurotransmitters** are compounds which activate the

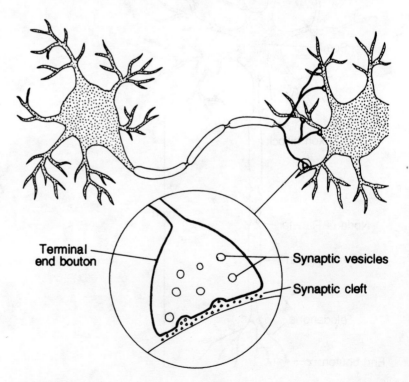

Terminal end bouton

Synaptic vesicles

Synaptic cleft

FIGURE 9–3. Schematic of elements of synapse.

dendrite of following neurons by crossing the juncture between two neurons, the **synapse**. Also within the end boutons are **mitochondria**, organelles responsible for energy generation and protein development. Groups of cell bodies appear gray in color, referred to as **gray matter**, while **white matter** refers to myelin.

When stimulated to do so, the axon discharges neurotransmitter into the **synaptic cleft** (space between two neurons). A neurotransmitter stimulates **receptor sites** of the **postsynaptic** neuron (the neuron following the synapse), causing that neuron to open ion channels which lead to a discharge or "firing" of that neuron. Dendrites are the typical location for synapse on the receiving (post-synaptic) neurons (called **axodendritic synapses**), but synapse also may occur on the soma (so-called **axosomatic synapses**, usually inhibitory), on post-synaptic axons (**axoaxonic synapses**), or simply "in passing" (**en passant**), in which an axon stimulates a neuron secondarily on its way to the synapse with another neuron (see Figure 9–4). Two other less common synapse formations are **somatosomatic synapse**, in which the soma of a neuron synapses with the soma of another neuron, and **dendrodendritic synapse**, in which communication is between two dendrites.

"Synapse" is a noun, but is often used as a verb, indicating the action of communication between two neurons.

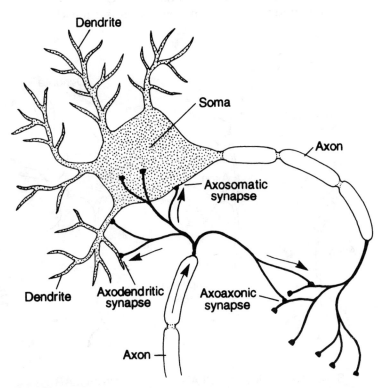

FIGURE 9–4. Types of synapses.

There are several types of neurons distributed throughout the nervous system. **Monopolar (unipolar) neurons** are those with a single, bifurcating process arising from the soma (see Figure 9–5), while **bipolar neurons** are those with two processes. **Multipolar neurons** will have more than two processes. Sensory neurons are monopolar, except those associated with smell (**olfaction**), hearing (**audition**), and vestibular senses, which are bipolar.

Neurons are differentiated by their function as well as form. **Interneurons** make up the largest class of neurons in the brain. These neurons do not exit the CNS but provide communication between other neurons. **Motor neurons** are efferent, typically bipolar neurons which activate muscular or glandular response. These neurons typically have long axons that are myelinated. Motor neurons are further differentiated based on size, **conduction velocity** (how fast they can conduct an impulse), and degree of myelination. Generally speaking, wider diameter and thicker myelin result in more rapid conduction. Fibers are classified in terms of conduction velocity as being A, B, or C class fibers, with A and B fibers being myelinated. The **A fibers** are further broken down, based on conduction velocity, into alpha, beta, gamma, and delta fibers (see Table 9–2). **Alpha motor neurons** have high conduction velocities (between 50 and 120 m/sec) and innervate the majority of skeletal muscle, the **extrafusal muscle fibers**. Slower velocity **gamma motor neurons** innervate **intrafusal muscle fibers**

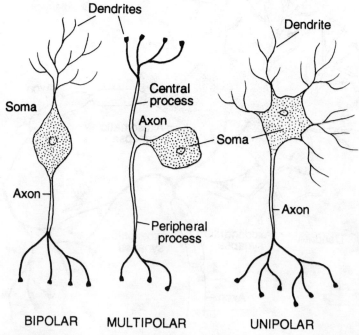

FIGURE 9–5. Bipolar, multipolar, and unipolar neurons.

Table 9-2. Type A sensory and motor fibers (from Gilman & Winans, 1975).

Fiber Class	Velocity (m/sec)	Motor Function	Sensory Function
Alpha	50–120	Extrafusal muscle	
Ia	120		Primary muscle spindle afferents
Ib	120		Golgi tendon organs; pressure receptors
Beta			
II	70		Muscle spindle secondary afferents; touch and pressure
Gamma	40		Intrafusal muscle of spindle
Delta			
III	15		Touch, pressure pain, coolness
IV	2		Pain and warmth

within the **muscle spindle**, the sensory apparatus responsible for maintaining muscle length. Sensory alpha fibers are identified by a Roman numeral and a lower-case letter (type Ia, Ib, II, III, or IV fibers), reflecting a different classification scheme. The **Ia** neurons are the primary afferent fibers from the muscle spindle, while the **Ib** neurons send sensory information generated at the **golgi tendon organs**, sensors that respond to stretching of the tendon. Type **II** afferent fibers are secondary muscle spindle afferents of the beta class, and convey information from touch and pressure receptors. The type **III** afferent fibers are delta class, conducting pain, pressure, touch, coolness, and pressure sensation, and type **IV** fibers convey pain and warmth sense.

Glial cells make up the majority of the brain tissue, providing support and nutrient to the neurons. **Astrocytes** appear to be largely structural, separating neurons from each other and adhering to capillaries. They appear to play a role in supplying nutrients to neurons. **Oligodendrocytes** are glial cells which make up the CNS myelin, and **Schwann cells** are glia comprising myelin of the PNS.

In summary, the **nervous system** is a complex, hierarchical structure made up of **neurons**.

■ Many **motor functions** become automated through practice.

■ **Voluntary movement, sensory awareness,** and **cognitive function** are the domain of the **cerebral cortex,** although we are capable of sensation and response without consciousness.

■ The communication links of the nervous system are **spinal nerves, cranial nerves,** and **tracts** of the **brainstem** and **spinal cord.**

■ The nervous system may be divided functionally as **autonomic** and **somatic nervous systems** serving involuntary and voluntary functions.

■ It may be divided anatomically as **central** and **peripheral nervous systems** as well.

■ **Developmental divisions** separate the brain into **prosencephalon** (which is further divided into telencephalon and diencephalon), the **mesencephalon** or midbrain, and the **rhombencephalon,** which includes the metencephalon and myelencephalon.

■ **Neurons** are widely varied in morphology, but may be broadly categorized as **monopolor, bipolar,** or **multipolar.**

■ Neurons communicate through **synapse** by means of **neurotransmitter** substance, and the response by the postsynaptic neuron may be **excitatory** or **inhibitory.**

■ The size and type of axon is related to conduction of neural impulse.

■ **Glial cells** provide the fatty sheath for **myelinated axons,** as well as support structure for neurons.

Anatomy of the Spinal Cord

The spinal cord is the information lifeline to and from the periphery of the body. Movement of axial skeletal muscles occurs by means of information passed through this structure, and sensory information from the periphery must pass through it as well.

This longitudinal, columnar mass of fibers is composed of white and gray matter, corresponding to tracts and cell bodies, respectively. It is wrapped in **meninges,** thin linings that will be discussed later in the chapter. The cord begins at the foramen magnum (the superior margin of the atlas), and courses about 46 cm through the vertebral canal produced by the spinal column, ending at the **conus medullaris** at the level of the L1 vertebra. The **pia mater,** the deepest of the meningeal linings, continues caudally as the **filum terminale,** which becomes the **coccygeal ligament** after joining the **dural tube,** the outermost meningeal lining. This ligament forms the caudal attachment of the spinal cord, as shown in Figure 9–6.

What you can also see from Figure 9–6 is that there are nerves arising at regular intervals along the cord. The 31 pairs of **spinal nerves** arise from regions related to each vertebra, with the first (spinal nerve C1) arising from the spinal cord on the superior surface of the atlas (C1 vertebra). Thus, there are eight pairs of cervical spinal nerves instead of seven (the number of cervical vertebrae), 12 pairs of thoracic nerves,

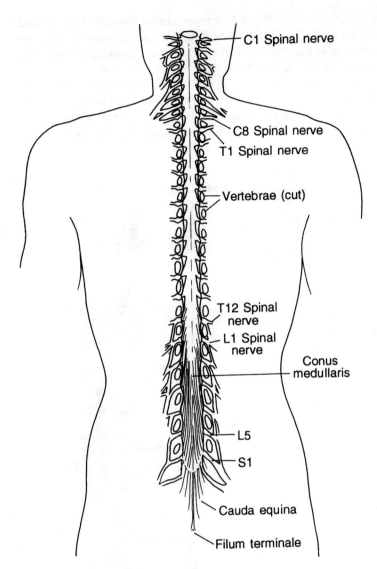

FIGURE 9-6. Spinal cord and emerging spinal nerves.

five pairs of lumbar and sacral nerves, and one pair of coccygeal nerves. The spinal nerves are referred to in the abbreviated manner of vertebrae, with the first thoracic spinal nerve being T1, and so forth.

During embryonic development, the spinal cord is the same length as the spinal column, but (much like the thorax/lung relationship) as the brain and body develop, the spinal cord moves up in the canal so that the adult spinal nerves course downward before exiting the spinal column. When a child is born, the conus medullaris is at the L3 vertebral level, but it will be at the L1 level by adulthood. This changing size relationship is reflected in the relationship between location of **spinal**

cord segment (the functional unit representing the spinal nerve) and vertebra as well. The vertebrae will have a greater number than the cord segment at that vertebral level, as you can see in Figure 9–7. This becomes most marked in the caudal end, where the segment from which the L5 nerve arises corresponds to the L1 vertebra. This relationship gives rise also to a rather graceful descriptive term for the lowermost nerves. The **cauda equina** (horse's tail) is the tail-like region beneath the filum terminale in which no spinal cord segments will be

FIGURE 9–7. Arrangement of spinal nerves relative to vertebral segment. (From data of Carpenter, 1978.)

found. This is, by the way, the region chosen for a lumbar puncture to sample cerebrospinal fluid for medical testing.

Spinal nerves have both sensory (**afferent**) and motor (**efferent**) components. The distribution of sensory function is generally related to segment level, such that upper nerves serve upper body regions, and so forth. A mapping of regions served by spinal nerve afferents reveals a fairly consistent pattern of innervation, with each region served by a nerve being functionally referred to as a **dermatome**. There is overlap of innervation, one of the safeguards of nature against complete loss of sensation. This relationship, shown in Figure 9–8, is not as clearcut for

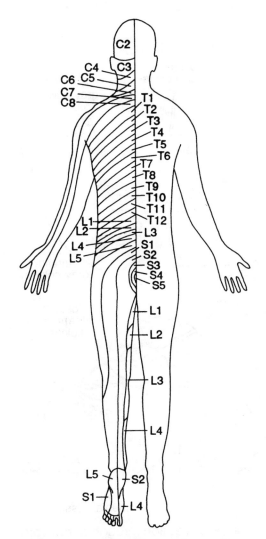

FIGURE 9-8. Dermatomes reflecting sensory innervation by spinal nerves.

motor function, which is mediated by cooperatives of nerves, referred to as plexuses. A **plexus** is a network of nerves which physically communicate with other nerves.

You may think of the spinal cord as a series of ropes lashed together. Each of these ropes is a columnar **tract**, which is a collection of nerve fibers with functional unity (see Figure 9–9). A transverse section of the spinal cord reveals a white periphery encapsulating a gray butterfly "H" shape. The peripheral white segment is made up of the ascending and descending pathways, while the central matter is gray due to the concentration of neuron bodies there.

FIGURE 9–9. Transverse section through spinal cord with landmarks. (After data and view of Carpenter, 1978.)

Several important landmarks of the sectioned spinal cord are shown in Figure 9–9. At the center of the cell mass is the **central canal**, continuous with the fourth ventricle. The anterior surface is marked by the deep longitudinal **anterior median fissure**, and lateral to that, the **anterior lateral sulcus**. In the dorsal aspect is the **posterior median sulcus**, and lateral to this at the cervical and upper thoracic levels is the **posterior intermediate sulcus**.

The cord itself also can be divided into gross regions. The **posterior gray column** (or **horn**) is the mass of nuclei directed posteriorly, while the **anterior gray column** makes up the anterior portion of the gray matter. The white matter is divided into funiculi, which are further divided into fasciculi, as will be discussed.

Sensory information enters via **dorsal root fibers** whose cell bodies lie outside of the spinal cord (Figure 9–10), and motor information leaves the spinal cord through the **ventral root**. These roots combine to form the spinal nerve and then divide into **dorsal** and **ventral rami** to serve the posterior and anterior portions of the body, respectively. A branch of the ventral portion courses anteriorly to communicate with the sympathetic ganglion. From here, efferent neurons join with muscle through a **motor endplate** (the neuromuscular equivalent of a synapse), and afferent fibers communicate with sensors peripheral to

FIGURE 9-10. Transverse section through spinal cord and vertebral segment. Note the dorsal root ganglion and ventral root.

the spinal cord. We now have all the elements in place for the most basic unit of interaction with the environment.

The **segmental spinal reflex arc** is the simplest stimulus-response system of the nervous system (see Figure 9–11). Sensory information concerning the length of the muscle is transmitted via the dorsal root fibers to the spinal cord where it makes synapse with the motor neuron in the ventral cord. That fiber exits the cord to innervate the same or parallel muscle fibers. The purpose of this reflex is to maintain the length of a muscle fiber that is not being actively contracted, typically for maintenance of posture. If, for instance, you are standing and lean forward slightly, the muscles that are stretched by your leaning will be reflexively contracted until they return to their original length. In this way you can maintain tonic posture automatically, without voluntary effort. Let us examine that sequence in detail.

As you can see in the first panel of Figure 9–11, at rest the muscle is not being stretched and the reflex arc is quiescent. In the next panel, the muscle is being stretched and a highly specialized sensor, the muscle spindle, senses that stretching process. This information is passed

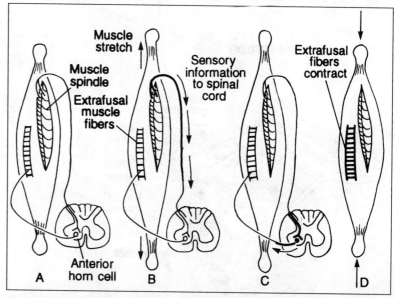

FIGURE 9-11. Schematic of segmental spinal reflex arc. **a.** The muscle is in a stable state. **b.** The muscle has been passively stretched. Information from the muscle spindle concerning muscle length is transmitted to the spinal cord via the dorsal root ganglion. **c.** Synapse with motor neuron causes efferent activation of muscle fiber. **d.** Extrafusal muscle contracts, shortening the muscle to its original length.

along the neuron to the cell body in the **dorsal root ganglion**, and from there to a synapse within the anterior horn cells of the spinal cord. In the third panel, the afferent axon synapses with the efferent dendrite, and the information is transmitted to the soma and axon of the motor neuron. In the final panel, the excitation transmitted via the efferent axon causes the muscle to shorten.

Activation of the muscle contraction occurred through excitation of the efferent fiber whose body resides within the spinal cord. This efferent neuron is known as the **final common pathway** or **lower motor neuron (LMN)**, a very functional unit to remember. **Upper motor neurons (UMNs)** will be the efferent fibers descending from upper brain levels. Damage to LMN will result in muscle weakness or complete paralysis, just as if you cut the power line leading to your radio. Damage to the UMN will cause muscle weakness or paralysis, but will leave reflexes intact. The clinical significance of this will become more clear in the next chapter when we examine function.

These reflexive responses are certainly important, and provide your basic response to the environment. For instance, you reflexively withdraw your hand on touching the hot burner on a stove. However, for you to make *decisions* about the information, it must reach the cerebral cortex, the seat of conscious thought. You might recall that, when you touched the burner on that stove, you retracted your hand well before you felt the heat and pain. This is the hallmark of interaction between the cerebrum and the reflex. Reflexes "put out the brushfire" but neural circuitry also lets the cerebrum know that something has happened so that other action may be taken (such as putting ice on the burn). The time lag between retracting your hand and feeling the burn is an important reminder that reflexes provide nearly instant, automated response well before the cortex could ever respond. On the other hand, the simple reflex is never going to win you the Nobel prize. These neurons will not produce conscious thought or mediate cognitive processes.

There must be a system of pathways for information to reach the higher centers or to come from those centers. Within the central nervous system, such pathways are referred to as **tracts**. Tracts are groups of axons with a functional and anatomical unity (that is, they transmit generally the same information to generally the same locations).

Pathways of the Spinal Cord

The spinal cord is a conduit of information, and the channels are built along the longitudinal axis. The spinal cord is compartmentalized, such that the longitudinal column is actually subdivided into functionally and anatomically similar areas. The gray matter of the spinal cord is divided into nine **laminae** or regions, based on cell type differences. These laminar regions correspond well with the nuclei and regions identified anatomically within the spinal gray.

As you can see from Figure 9–12, a transverse section of the spinal cord is divided into **dorsal, lateral** and **ventral funiculi** (a funiculus is a large column), which are subdivided into **fasciculi** or tracts of white matter. The size and presence of a tract depends on the level of the spinal cord. Tracts which must serve the muscles of the entire body, for instance, will certainly be larger in the upper spinal cord than in the lower cord. Similarly, the gray matter of the cord will be wider in regions serving more muscles, specifically in the cervical (segments C3 to T2) and thoracic segments (segments T9 to T12). Those regions will have more cell bodies to serve the extremities. Tracts of white matter will be widest in the cervical region, because all descending and ascending fibers must pass through those segments. This figure also shows the tracts of white matter at various levels of the spinal cord, and may aid in our discussion of tracts. What will become obvious as we briefly discuss these pathways is that sensory pathways tend to be in the posterior portion of the spinal cord, and motor pathways tend toward the anterior aspect, reflecting the dorsal and ventral orientation of the spinal roots.

Ascending Pathways. The major ascending sensory pathways include the fasciculus gracilis, fasciculus cuneatus, anterior and lateral spinothalamic tracts, and the anterior and posterior spinocerebellar tracts (see Figure 9–12). Neurons are referred to as first order, second

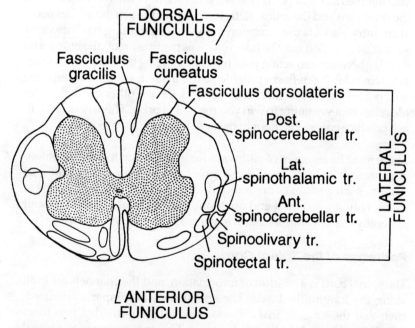

FIGURE 9-12. Transverse section of a spinal cord segment revealing dorsal, lateral, and anterior funiculi and major ascending tracts.

order, and so on to indicate the number of neurons in a chain. Thus, the afferent neuron transmitting information from the sensor will be the first order neuron, the next neuron in the chain following synapse will be the second order neuron, and so forth up to the terminal point in the neural chain.

Posterior Funiculus. The **fasciculus gracilis** and **fasciculus cuneatus** are separated by the posterior intermediate septum of the posterior funiculus. These tracts convey information concerning touch-pressure and **kinesthetic sense** (sense of movement), as well as vibration sense, which is actually a temporal form of touch-pressure. These columns convey information from group Ia muscle spindle sensors and group Golgi tendon organs as well. The Ia spindle fibers convey information about rate of muscle stretch, whereas the Golgi organs appear to respond to stretch of the tendon.

Information concerning sensation in the periphery is conducted by the unipolar first-order neuron of the dorsal root ganglion to the spinal cord. The axons of those neurons ascend on the same side of entry, so that the information is conveyed toward the brain. (The same information remains at the level of entry to form the spinal reflex.) The fasciculus gracilis serves the lower extremities, whereas the fasciculus cuneatus arises from the cervical regions.

The fibers of these tracts ascend **ipsilaterally** (on the same side they entered the cord) until they reach the level of the medulla oblongata of the brainstem to synapse with the **nucleus gracilis** and **nucleus cuneatus**. The axons of the second order neuron arising from those nuclei combine and **decussate** (cross the midline) to ascend **contralaterally** (on the other side) as the **medial lemniscus** to the **thalamus**, which is the major sensory relay of the brain (for this reason, the pathway is also referred to as the **lemniscal pathway**). **Spatiotopic** information (information about the specific region of the body stimulated) is maintained throughout the process.

Damage to these pathways will cause problems in touch discrimination, especially in the hands and feet. Patients may lose **proprioceptive sense** (sense of body position in space), which can greatly impair gait.

Anterior Funiculus. The **anterior spinothalamic tract** conveys information concerning light touch, such as the sense of being stroked by a feather, conveyed from the *spine* to the *thalamus* (see Figure 9–13). Afferent axons of the first-order neuron synapse with anterior spinothalamic tract neurons, the axons of which decussate in the **anterior white commissure** at the level of entry or perhaps two or three segments higher. The second-order tract neurons ascend to the pons of the brainstem, where fibers enter the **medial lemniscus** to terminate at the ventral posterolateral (VPL) nucleus of the thalamus.

CEREBRAL CORTEX
FRONTAL SECTION

Postcentral gyrus

Internal capsule

THALAMUS

MIDBRAIN

Anterior
spinothalamic tract

PONS

Medial lemniscus

MEDULLA

C7

Meissner's
corpuscles

Dorsal root
ganglion

T8

L3

Efferent from
ventral horn

Decussation

FIGURE 9–13. Anterior spinothalamic tract, transmitting information concerning sense of light touch.

Lateral Funiculus. The last time you stubbed your toe, the information concerning that pain travelled through the **lateral spinothalamic tract**. This important tract transmits information concerning pain and thermal sense. Dorsal root fibers synapse with second-order interneurons which subsequently synapse with third-order tract neurons. These decussate in the anterior white commissure to ascend to the VPL of the thalamus and **reticular formation**.

If the spinal cord is cut unilaterally, the result will be *contralateral* loss of pain and thermal sense beginning one segment below the level of the trauma.

Anterior and Posterior Spinocerebellar Tracts. These important tracts convey information concerning muscle tension to the cerebellum. The **posterior spinocerebellar tract** is an uncrossed tract, meaning that information from one side of the body remains on that side during its ascent through the pathway. Afferent information from Golgi tendon organs and muscle spindle stretch receptors enters the spinal cord via the dorsal root ganglion where axons of these neurons synapse with the second-order tract fibers. Branches of these first-order neurons ascend and descend, so that synapse occurs at points above and below the site of entry as well. The second-order neurons arise from the dorsal nucleus of Clarke, located in the posterior gray of the cord.

Upon reaching the medulla oblongata the second-order neurons enter the **inferior cerebellar peduncle**, the lower pathway to the cerebellum. These axons terminate in the rostral and caudal **vermis** of the cerebellum.

None of the information transmitted by this tract reaches consciousness, although the result of damage to the pathway would. Information from muscles concerning length, rate of stretch, degree of muscle and tendon stretch, and some pressure and touch sense would all be impaired, causing deficit in movement and posture.

The **anterior spinocerebellar tract** is a crossed pathway. Information from Ib afferent fibers serving the Golgi apparatus enters the spinal cord via the dorsal root where it synapses with the second order tract neurons. Tract fibers decussate at the same level and ascend through the anterolateral portion of the spinal cord. The tract enters the **superior cerebellar peduncle**, the superior pathway to the cerebellum from the brainstem. Most of the fibers cross to enter the cerebellum on the opposite side of the tract (but the same side as initial stimulation), with the information presumably serving the same function as that of the posterior spinocerebellar tract.

Descending Pathways. Descending motor pathways are the conduits for information commanding muscle contraction that will result in voluntary movement, modification of reflexes, and visceral activation. The most important of these arise from the cerebral cortex, although there are tracts originating in the brainstem as well. The major pathways include the **pyramidal pathways** (the corticospinal and corticobulbar tracts), and the tectospinal, rubrospinal, vestibulospinal, pontine reticulospinal, and the medullary reticulospinal tracts (see Figure 9–14).

rubrospinal: L., ruber spina, red thorn

Corticospinal Tract. As the name implies, this extraordinarily important tract runs from the *cortex* to the *spine*, providing innervation of skeletal muscle (see Figure 9–15). Myelination of the axons of these fibers occurs after birth, and is complete by the second birthday of a child. The corticospinal tract is made up of over one million fibers, with about half of which arise from cells in each frontal lobe of the cerebral cortex (Brodmann areas 4 and 6, areas known as the motor strip and premotor region, to be discussed). The remainder of the neurons supplying the corticospinal tract arise from the region anterior to the motor strip, the premotor region, and from the supplementary motor area on the superior and medial surface of the cerebrum. In addition, some fibers from the parietal sensory cortex (areas 1, 2 and 3) project through the corticospinal tract, generally terminating on the dorsal horn cells of the spinal cord. The fibers from the cortex descend as the

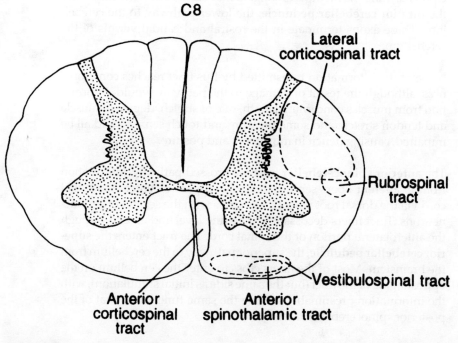

FIGURE 9–14. Major efferent tracts of the spinal cord as seen in transverse segment of cervical spinal cord.

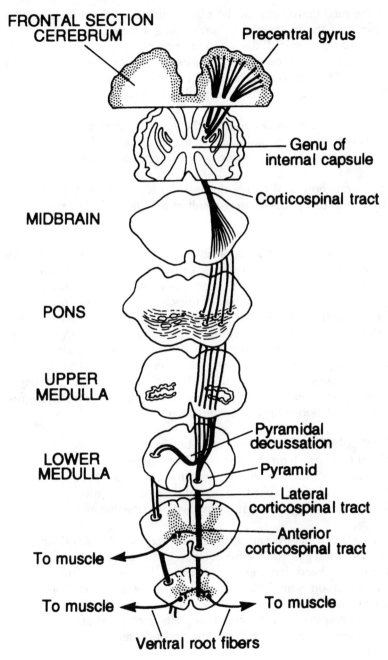

FIGURE 9-15. Corticospinal pathway as traced from cerebral cortex to spinal cord.

Labels in figure:
FRONTAL SECTION CEREBRUM
Precentral gyrus
Genu of internal capsule
Corticospinal tract
MIDBRAIN
PONS
UPPER MEDULLA
LOWER MEDULLA
Pyramidal decussation
Pyramid
Lateral corticospinal tract
Anterior corticospinal tract
To muscle
To muscle
To muscle
Ventral root fibers

corona radiata, through the **internal capsule**, and **crus cerebri** at the level of the midbrain.

At the medulla oblongata the fibers enter the **pyramids**, so-called because of the pyramidal column shape, where they undergo the important **pyramidal decussation**. Seventy-five to 90% of corticospinal tract fibers cross to descend as the lateral corticospinal tract in the lateral funiculus. This tract will become increasingly smaller as it descends through the cord to serve skeletal muscles.

The fibers that do not decussate at the pyramids descend uncrossed as the **anterior corticospinal tract**. On reaching the point of innervation, the axons decussate to synapse with lower motor neurons.

This arrangement of partial decussation is a safeguard. Incomplete damage to this pathway may result in retention of voluntary motor function.

The corticospinal tract is responsible not only for activation of muscles but also for inhibition of reflexes. Corticospinal tract lesions (upper motor neuron lesion) result in muscle weakness, loss of voluntary use of musculature, and initial loss of muscle tone. Reduced muscle tone will return to the antigravity muscles and hyperactive tendon reflexes will be seen. The **Babinski reflex** will be elicitable in many individuals with upper motor neuron lesion. When the sole of a relaxed foot is stroked, a positive Babinski sign would be extension of the great toe and spreading of the outer toes. This reflex is normally present in infants, but diminishes through cortical control arising from progressive myelination of the corticospinal tract.

Corticobulbar Tract. The corticobulbar tract is extraordinarily important for speech production, paralleling the importance of the corticospinal tract for muscles of the trunk and extremities (see Figure 9–16). The corticobulbar tract acts also on sensory information, both facilitating and inhibiting its transmission to the thalamus.

The corticobulbar tract arises from cortical cells in the lateral aspects of the precentral gyrus of the frontal lobe, in the region of the motor strip serving the head, face, neck, and larynx). It arises also from the premotor and **somesthetic** (body sense) regions of the parietal lobe of cortex. Fibers from these areas follow a similar descent pattern as those of the corticospinal tract, passing through the corona radiata, genu (knee) of the internal capsule, and entering the brainstem.

These axons will branch and decussate at various levels of the brainstem, synapsing with nuclei of cranial nerves to provide bilateral innervation to many muscles of the face, neck, pharynx, and larynx. We will discuss the termination points in detail shortly.

Terms of Paralysis

Paralysis refers to temporary or permanent loss of motor function. Paralysis is **spastic** in nature if the lesion causing it is of an upper motor neuron. In this type of paralysis, voluntary control is lost through the lesion, but hyperactive reflexes will remain, producing seemingly paradoxical **hyperreflexia** (brisk and overly active reflex responses) and **hypertonia** (muscle tone greater than appropriate) coupled with muscular weakness. **Flaccid** paralysis arises from lesion to the lower motor neuron, and results in **hypotonia** (reduced muscle tone), **hyporeflexia** (reduced or absent reflex response) with co-occurring muscle weakness.

Paralysis of the lower portion of the body, including legs, is termed **paraplegia**. **Quadriplegia** refers to paralysis of all four limbs, usually arising from damage to the spinal cord above C5 or C6. Spinal cord cut above C3 causes death. If lesions produce paralysis of the same part on both sides of the body, it is referred to as **diplegia**, while **triplegia** involves three limbs. **Monoplegia** refers to paralysis of only one limb or group of muscles. **Hemiplegia** arises from upper motor neuron damage, resulting in loss of function in one side of the body.

Other Descending Pathways

The **tectospinal tract** arises in the superior colliculus ("little hill") of the midbrain, decussates in the dorsal tegmental decussation, and descends to the first four cervical spinal cord segments. Because the superior colliculus is a visual relay, it is assumed that this efferent pathway is associated with reflexive postural control arising from visual stimulation, perhaps orienting to the source of visual stimulation.

The **rubrospinal tract** arises from the red nucleus of the midbrain tegmentum. Fibers of this tract cross in the ventral tegmental decussation of the midbrain, and descend with the **medial longitudinal fasciculus (MLF)** of the spinal cord (see Figure 9–17). Most fibers from this tract serve the cervical region, although they descend the length of the spinal cord. The red nucleus receives input from the cerebral cortex and the cerebellum, and appears to be responsible for maintenance of muscle tone in flexor muscles.

The **vestibulospinal tract** arises from the lateral vestibular nucleus of the pons and medulla and descends ipsilaterally the length of the spinal cord. Fibers of this tract facilitate spinal reflexes and promote muscle tone in extensor musculature.

PRECENTRAL GYRUS OF CEREBRAL CORTEX

- Internal capsule
- Nuclei of III oculomotor
- Substantia nigra
- Trochlear nucleus
- IV trochlear
- Motor nucleus of V
- PONS
- V trigeminal
- PONS
- VII facial
- Dorsal motor nucleus of X
- VI abducens
- MEDULLA
- X vagus
- Nucleus ambiguus
- XII hypoglossal
- XI spinal accessory
- MEDULLA

FIGURE 9–16. Corticobulbar tract as traced from cerebral cortex to cranial nerve nuclei.

The **pontine reticulospinal tract** arises from nuclei in the medial tegmentum of the pons and descends, primarily ipsilaterally, near the MLF in the spinal cord. The **medullary reticulospinal tract** is formed in the medulla oblongata near the inferior olivary complex and

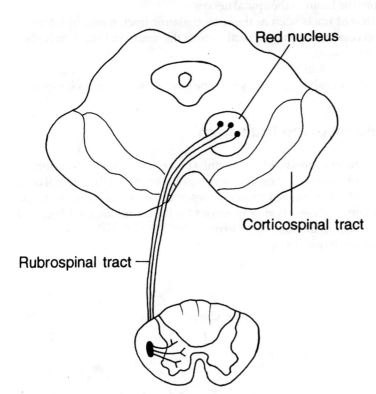

MIDBRAIN

Red nucleus

Corticospinal tract

Rubrospinal tract

FIGURE 9–17. The rubrospinal tract originates at the red nucleus and terminates in the spinal cord.

descends in the lateral funiculus. Activity of these neurons have both facilitating and inhibiting effects on motor neurons and hence on voluntary movement.

In summary, the **spinal cord** is comprised of tracts and nuclei.

■ The 31 pairs of **spinal nerves** arise from spinal segments, serving sensory and voluntary motor function for the limbs and trunk.
■ **Sensory nerves** have their cell bodies within the dorsal root ganglia, whereas **motor neuron** bodies lie within the gray matter of the spinal cord.
■ The **spinal reflex arc** is the simplest motor function, providing an efferent response to a basic change in muscle length.
■ Several landmarks of the transverse cord assist in identifying the **funiculi** and **fasciculi** of the spinal cord.
■ **Upper motor neurons** have their cell bodies rostral to the segment at which the spinal nerve originates, whereas **lower motor neurons** are the final neurons in the efferent chain.

■ **Efferent tracts**, such as the corticospinal tract, transmit information from the brain to the spinal nerves.

■ **Afferent tracts** such as the spinothalamic tract, transmit information concerning the physical state of the limbs and trunk to higher brain centers.

■ The **corticobulbar tract** is of particular interest to speech-language pathologists because of it serves the motor **cranial nerves** for speech.

Anatomy of the Brainstem

The brainstem consists of the medulla oblongata, pons, and midbrain. The brainstem is significantly more highly organized than spinal cord tracts and reflex loops. Cranial nerves and their nuclei arise from the brainstem, and basic bodily functions for life are maintained here. We will work from the superficial to deep structures of the brainstem, and it will help to refer to Figures 9–18 through 9–20 as we do this.

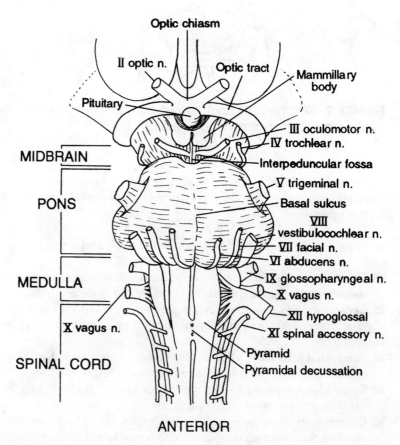

FIGURE 9-18. Anterior view of brainstem.

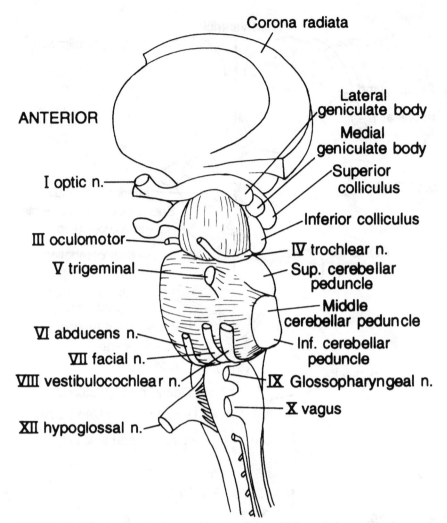

Corona radiata

ANTERIOR

Lateral geniculate body

Medial geniculate body

I optic n.

Superior colliculus

Inferior colliculus

III oculomotor

IV trochlear n.

V trigeminal

Sup. cerebellar peduncle

Middle cerebellar peduncle

VI abducens n.

Inf. cerebellar peduncle

VII facial n.

VIII vestibulocochlear n.

IX Glossopharyngeal n.

X vagus

XII hypoglossal n.

FIGURE 9–19. Lateral view of brainstem. (After data and view of Gilman and Winans, 1982.)

Superficial Brainstem Landmarks

Medulla Oblongata. The **medulla oblongata**, or medulla, is the inferior-most segment of the brainstem, appearing to be an enlargement of the rostral spinal cord, covering about 2.5 cm in length and about 1 cm in diameter. This benign appearance hides the fact that damage to the medulla is imminently life threatening.

Anterior Medulla. There are several important landmarks of the anterior medulla. The **anterior (ventral) median fissure**, continuous with the spinal cord, is interrupted by the **pyramidal decussation**, the point at which fibers of the corticospinal tract cross from one side to the other. Above that decussation are the **pyramids** of the corticospinal tract, the

FIGURE 9–20. Posterior view of brainstem. (After data and view of Gilman and Winans, 1982.)

bulges on either side of the ventral median fissure (see Figure 9–18). The point of decussation marks the lower border of the medulla, while the superior border is the significant expansion of the pons. The lower margin of the medulla is roughly at the level of the foramen magnum.

Lateral Medulla. The sides of the medulla are marked by two prominent sulci. The **ventrolateral sulcus** marks the lateral margin of the pyramid and is the groove from which the XII hypoglossal nerve exits the medulla. The **dorsolateral sulcus** is the groove from which the XI accessory, X vagus, and IX glossopharyngeal nerves exit. You can see from this Figure 9–19 the spinal portion of the XI accessory nerve arising from C2 through C5 spinal segments. The **olive** is the bulge between the ventrolateral and dorsolateral sulci, caused by the **inferior olivary nuclear complex.**

Posterior Medulla. The dorsal medulla presents a little more challenge. In Figure 9–20 the cerebellum has been removed, revealing the fourth ventricle. The inferior-most point on the ventricle is the **obex**, a point that marks the beginning of a region known as the calamus scriptorius, so named because it looks like the point of a calligraphy pen. Lateral to the obex is the **clava** or **gracilis tubercle**, a bulge caused by the **nucleus gracilis**. The column leading to this bulge is the product of the fasciculus gracilis. Lateral and superior to the clava is the **cuneate tubercle**, a prominence marking the nucleus of the fasciculus cuneatus. The **calamus scriptorius** includes the **vagal trigone**, a bulge marking the dorsal vagal nucleus of the X vagus nerve, as well as the **hypoglossal trigone**, a prominence caused by the XII hypoglossal nucleus.

obex: L., band

Calamus scriptorius: L., reed cane (calligraphy) pen

Pons. Superior to the medulla, the **pons** is the "bridge" between medulla and midbrain, as well as to the cerebellum. The significant ventral bulge of the pons is an obvious landmark for this structure. The pons is the site of four cranial nerve nuclei, as well as the origin of the middle and superior cerebellar peduncles, communicating pathways to the cerebellum. At the junction of the medulla and the pons the inferior cerebellar peduncle has expanded in diameter to its maximum and is entering the cerebellum.

Anterior Pons. The anterior pons is marked by a prominent band of transverse fibers, with the **basal sulcus** at midline showing the course of the basilar artery. The VI abducens nerve exits at the inferior border of the pons, from the **inferior pontine sulcus**.

Lateral Pons. In the lateral aspect of the pons, the transverse fibers condense into bundles which make up the middle **cerebellar peduncles (brachia pontis)**, forming the intermediate attachment of the pons to the cerebellum. The space created by the cerebellum, middle cerebellar peduncle, and the medulla is called the **cerebellopontine angle**, so called because of its triangular shape. From this space, the VII facial and VIII vestibulocochlear nerves will emerge. The V trigeminal nerve exits the pons from the middle cerebellar peduncle of the lateral pons.

Posterior Pons. The posterior pons surface is the anterior limit of the fourth ventricle. As can be seen in the Figure 9–18, the **superior cerebellar peduncles (brachia conjunctiva)** form the upper lateral surface of 4th ventricle, and the **superior and inferior medullary veli** and cerebellum provide the superior border. On either side of the median sulcus is a paired **facial colliculus**, the bulge representing the nucleus of the VI abducens nerve and the fibers of the VII that cross the nucleus.

colliculi: L., mound

Midbrain. The superior-most structure of the brainstem is the midbrain.

Anterior Midbrain. As Figure 9–18 reveals, the lower anterior surface of the midbrain is dominated by the prominent paired **crus cere-**

bri. These crura are the **cerebral peduncles**, providing communication between the midbrain and cerebral cortex. Between the peduncles is the **interpeduncular fossa**. The III oculomotor nerve exits from this fossa, at the juncture between the pons and midbrain. The **optic tracts**, an extension of the optic nerve, course around the crus cerebri following the decussation at the **optic chiasm**.

Posterior Midbrain. The posterior midbrain is the tectum, the region dorsal to the cerebral aqueduct, the upper extension of the fourth ventricle. The tectum is dominated by the presence of the four bodies of the **corpora quadrigemina**, the **superior** and **inferior colliculi**. As shown in the figure, the IV trochlear nerve emerges near the inferior colliculus, and courses around the crus cerebri.

corpora quadrigemina: *L., body of four parts*

Deep Structure of Brainstem

An examination of the deep structure of the brainstem requires some patience and a good imagination. The brainstem is organized vertically, being made up of columnar nuclei and tracts which serve the periphery, spinal cord, cerebral, cerebellar, and subcortical structures. Referring to Figure 9–21 may help you with orientation as we discuss the brainstem.

Deep Structures of Medulla Oblongata. The deep structure of the medulla represents an expansion on developments which started in the spinal cord (see Figure 9–22).

Caudal Medulla. At the lowest regions of the medulla, the central canal makes a good reference point. This canal will expand in the upper medulla to become the inferior fourth ventricle. Around this canal is a zone of **central gray matter** containing nuclei, which expands to the **reticular formation**, a nuclear mass spanning the medulla, pons, and midbrain. The **reticular formation** is a composite of brainstem nuclei, forming the "oldest" part of the brainstem and representing our first evolutionary effort at complex processing. This formation begins above the level of the decussation, and forms the central structure of the brainstem. The reticular formation is extremely important for life function, as it contains nuclei associated with respiration and maintenance of blood pressure.

At this lower level you can see the **decussation of the pyramids**. As mentioned earlier, the pyramids are the prominent corticospinal tracts arising from the cerebrum, and producing the paired middle bulges on the medulla. At the decussation, the fibers divide into **lateral** and **anterior corticospinal tracts**: The lateral tract forms after the fibers cross the midline, and the much smaller anterior tract is made up of uncrossed nerve fibers.

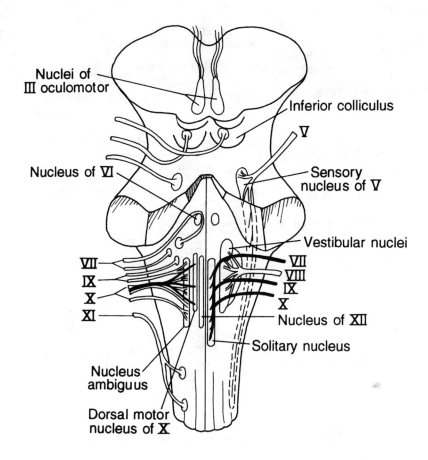

Nuclei of
III oculomotor

Inferior colliculus

V

Nucleus of VI

Sensory
nucleus of V

Vestibular nuclei

VII
IX
X
XI

VII
VIII
IX
X

Nucleus of XII

Solitary nucleus

Nucleus
ambiguus

Dorsal motor
nucleus of X

POSTERIOR VIEW

FIGURE 9-21. Posterior view of brainstem revealing orientation
of major nuclei and cranial nerves supplied by those nuclei.
(After data and view of Carpenter, 1978, and Netter, 1973.)

In the posterior aspect are the prominent fasciculus gracilis and cuneatus, as well as their nuclei. Axons from the **accessory cuneate nucleus** receive fibers from the cuneatus fasciculus, and axons of this nucleus will enter the cerebellum as the **cuneocerebellar tract** via the inferior cerebellar peduncle. In the posterior portion of the medulla are the trigeminal nerve nucleus and the spinal tract of trigeminal.

Upper Medulla. The complexity of the upper medulla reflects the importance of this region. The corticospinal tract has yet to divide into anterior and lateral components. The central canal has now expanded to become the fourth ventricle. Lateral to the hypoglossal and dorsal vagal nuclei is the **nucleus solitarius**. Several cranial nerve nuclei may

FIGURE 9–22. Low, mid, and upper medulla levels in transverse schematic.

be found in the medulla. The inferior-most **hypoglossal nucleus** gives rise to the XII hypoglossal nerve, whereas the IX glossopharyngeal, X vagus, and XI accessory arise from the **nucleus ambiguus**, dorsal vagal nucleus, and solitary tract nucleus. We will discuss these cranial nerves in detail.

You can quickly find the **inferior olivary complex** in the anterolateral aspect of medulla as a structure looking like an intestine doubled over on itself. A number of fibers from this complex will decussate and enter the cerebellum via the inferior cerebellar peduncle. Parts of this structure take on the appearance of a bag with a drawstring (**the principal inferior olivary nucleus**), and axons from the nuclei within the complex decussate at the **median raphe** to ascend to the cerebellum as the major component of the inferior cerebellar peduncle. The lateral medulla is dominated by the inferior cerebellar peduncle, with the trigeminal spinal tract and nucleus medial to it. The nucleus ambiguus may be seen in the anterolateral medulla, marking the anterior boundary of the reticular formation.

Projections from the vestibular portion of the VIII vestibulocochlear nerve reach the **medial** and **inferior vestibular nuclei,** visible in the posterolateral medulla. If you examine the lateral and middle aspects of the medulla, you will see a further testament to the importance of this structure. The lateral and ventral spinothalamic tracts carry pain and touch information from the spine to the thalamus, and the rubrospinal tract carries information in support of extrapyramidal motor activity. A lesion to the medulla would have devastating impact on all motor and sensory function.

Deep Structures of the Pons. The pons is classically divided into the posterior **tegmentum** and the anterior **basilar portion.** Figure 9–23 will assist in examination of the pons.

First, examine the basilar (anterior) portion. In the caudal pons, you can see the corticospinal and corticobulbar tracts. At the level of the lower pons, the tracts are beginning to become organized for their medulla decussation and course through the spine. At levels of the pons above this point you will see that the tracts are less well defined. Surrounding these tracts are the **pontine nuclei** which receive input from the cerebrum. Ventral to the corticospinal tract are the **pontine fibers,** axons of the pontine nuclei which make up the pontocerebellar

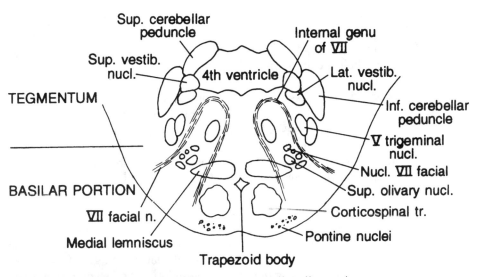

FIGURE 9–23. Schematic of transverse section through pons.

tract and ascend to the cerebellar cortex as the middle cerebellar peduncle. This communication from the cerebrum to pontine nuclei and pontocerebellar tract is an extremely important means of communication between the cerebrum and cerebellum.

The midline medial lemniscus provides an important pathway for somatic sense via the lemniscal pathway. The **lemniscal pathway** coalesces into the medial lemniscus within the medulla, ascending contralaterally through the medial lemniscus.

Most of the ascending fibers of the MLF near the midline of the ventricle floor arise from the vestibular nuclei and project to ocular muscles for regulation of eye movement with relation to head position in space. Visible will be the lateral, superior, and medial vestibular nuclei, with the inferior vestibular nucleus restricted to the medulla. Another center of the auditory system, the **trapezoid body**, is a mass of small nuclei and fibers seen at this level. The trapezoid body is a relay within the auditory pathway. Lateral and posterior to the trapezoid body is the **superior olivary complex**, containing auditory relays associated with localization of sound in space, as well as with the efferent component of the auditory pathway.

The posterior **pontine tegmentum** is actually a continuation of the reticular formation of the medulla. Projections from the reticular formation ascend to the thalamus and hypothalamus. Within the tegmentum are nuclei for cranial nerves V (trigeminal), VI (abducens), VII (facial), and relays of the VIII (vestibulocochlear). The ventral pons is made up largely of fibers of the corticospinal, corticobulbar, and corticopontine tracts. At this level those fibers are less compactly bundled than they will be at the level of the medulla.

The motor nucleus of the VII facial nerve is found in the mediolateral pons near the superior olive. Axons from this nucleus will course around the VI abducens nerve nucleus at the **internal genu** of the facial nerve before exiting the brainstem.

Middle Pons. As we examine the basilar portion of pons in Figure 9–24, you can see corticospinal tract is broken into small bundles, as mentioned previously. Fibers of the **corticopontine tract** course with the corticospinal tract but synapse with the pontine nuclei which surround the corticospinal tract. Axons of these nuclei decussate to make up the middle cerebellar peduncle.

In the dorsolateral aspect, you can see the sensory and motor nuclei of the V trigeminal nerve, as mentioned. This important nerve exits through the middle cerebellar peduncle. Dorsal to these nuclei is the superior cerebellar peduncle, forming the lateral margin of the fourth ventricle. The anterior medullary velum forms the roof of the ventricle.

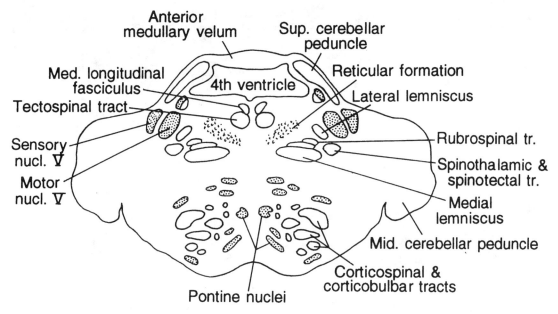

FIGURE 9-24. Schematic of middle pons, transverse section.

Deep Structures of Midbrain. A transverse section of the midbrain (Figure 9–25) may be divided into the posterior **tectum** (also known as the quadrigeminal plate), the medial **tegmentum**, which is a continuation of the pontine tegmentum, and the **crus cerebri**, the prominent anterior structure.

In the caudal portion of the midbrain, the tectum is dominated by the **inferior colliculus**, an important auditory relay. This nucleus receives input from the lateral lemniscus, fibers of which encapsulate it. Within the tegmentum you can see the decussation of the superior cerebellar peduncle within the **tegmental decussation**. Within the crus cerebri are the corticobulbar and corticospinal tracts, as well as **frontopontine** fibers which will terminate in the pons. Between the crus cerebri and tegmentum is the **substantia nigra**, a dark brown mass of cells which manufacture dopamine, a neurotransmitter essential for normal movement. Destruction of this substance results in Parkinson's disease, a debilitating neuromuscular disease.

Surrounding the **cerebral aqueduct**, an extremely narrow tube connecting the fourth ventricle with the third ventricle, is a mass of cells known as the **periaqueductal** or **central gray**. Within the anterior margin of the periaqueductal gray near the MLF can be found the nucleus of the IV trochlear nerve.

In the superior midbrain may be found the **superior colliculus** of the tectum. This nucleus receives input from the cerebral cortex, optic

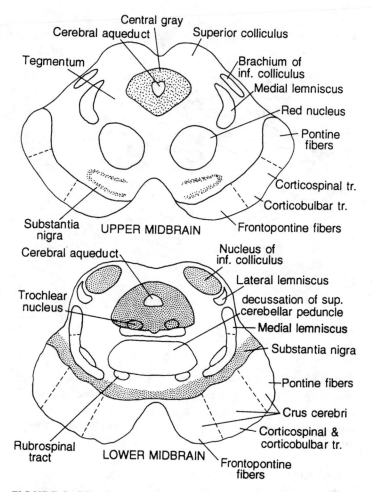

FIGURE 9–25. Schematic of upper and lower midbrain.

tract, inferior colliculus, and the spinal cord and appears to be responsible for eye and head movements relative to visual stimuli, and perhaps (as a result of the inferior colliculus connection) serves as a point of integration of auditory localization and visual orientation.

Within the tegmentum the massive **red nucleus** may be seen, a structure receiving input from the cerebral cortex and cerebellum, and from which the **rubrospinal tract** arises. Input from the red nucleus is from the cerebellum and cerebral cortex, and it is an important element in flexor control. Near the red nucleus is the **Edinger-Westphal nucleus**, controlling accommodation of the eye to light by the iris. Also medially placed is the III oculomotor nerve nucleus. The dorsolaterally placed **medial geniculate body** is actually a nucleus of the thalamus, and is the final subcortical relay of the auditory pathway.

In summary:

■ The **brainstem** is divided into **medulla, pons**, and **midbrain**. It is more highly organized than the spinal cord, mediating higher-level body function such as vestibular responses.

■ The **medulla** contains the important **pyramidal decussation**, the point at which the motor commands originating in one hemisphere of the cerebral cortex cross to serve the opposite side of the body. The **IX, X, XI**, and **XII cranial nerves** emerge at the level of the medulla, and the **inferior cerebellar peduncle** arises there. The **fourth ventricle enlargement** is a prominent brainstem landmark in cross-section. The **pons** contains the **superior** and **middle cerebellar peduncles**, as well as four cranial nerve nuclei, the **V, VI, VII**, and **VIII** nerves.

■ The **midbrain** contains the important **cerebral peduncles** and gives rise to the **III and IV cranial nerves**.

■ The deep structure of the brainstem reflects the level of the brainstem's phylogenetic development.

■ At the **decussation** of the pyramids, the **descending corticospinal tract** has condensed from the less structured form at higher levels to a well-organized tract.

■ The **reticular formation** is a phylogenetically old set of nuclei essential for life function.

■ In the rostral medulla the expansion to accommodate the **fourth ventricle** is apparent, marking a clear divergence from the minute central canal of the spinal cord and lower medulla.

■ The levels of the pons and midbrain set the stage for communication with the higher levels of the brain, including the cerebellum and cerebrum.

■ This communication link permits not only complex motor acts, but consciousness, awareness, and volitional acts.

Cranial Nerves

Working knowledge of the cranial nerves is vital to the speech-language pathologist or audiologist. You may wish to refer to Table 9–3 and Appendixes F and G as we discuss them. Although not all cranial nerves are involved with speech or hearing, knowledge of cranial nerves is of great assistance in assessment.

Cranial nerves are referred to by name, number, or both. By convention, roman numerals are used when discussing cranial nerves, and the number represents inverse height in the brainstem. Cranial nerves I through IV are found at the level of the midbrain, V through VIII are pons' level cranials, and IX through XII are found in the medulla. In examination of the spinal cord, we pointed out that the nuclei of sensory neurons resided in dorsal root ganglia and that their axons

Table 9–3. Cranial nerves.

Terminology

General somatic afferent (GSA):
Pain, temperature, mechanical stimulation of skin, muscle or joints.

Special somatic afferent (SSA):
Special body senses such as vision and hearing.

General visceral afferent (GVA):
Visceral sensation.

Special visceral afferent (SVA):
Special visceral senses of taste and smell.

General visceral efferent (GVE):
Autonomic efferent fibers serving viscera and glands.

General somatic efferent (GSE):
Innervation of skeletal muscle.

Special visceral efferent (SVE):
Innervation of striated muscle of branchial arch origin, including the larynx, pharynx, soft palate, face, and muscles of mastication.

Nerves

I Olfactory Nerve (SVA)
Sense of smell.

II Optic Nerve (SSA)
Visual sensation.

III Oculomotor Nerve (GSE, GVE)

General somatic efferent:
Extrinsic ocular muscles except superior oblique and lateral rectus muscles.

General visceral efferent:
Light and accommodation reflexes associated with pupil constriction and focus.

IV Trochlear Nerve (GSE)
Superior oblique muscle of the eye.

V Trigeminal Nerve (GSA, SVE)

Ophthalmic branch (GSA):
Somatic sense from skin of the upper face, forehead, and scalp, cornea, iris, upper eyelid, conjunctiva, nasal cavity mucous membrane, and lacrimal gland.

Maxillary branch (GSA):
Somatic sense from lower eyelid, sides of the nose, upper jaw, teeth, and lip, buccal and nasal mucosa, maxillary sinuses, and nasopharynx.

Mandibular branch (GSA):
Somatic sense of mandible, lower teeth, gums, and lip, a portion of the skin and mucosal lining of the cheek, somatic sense from anterior two-thirds of the mucous membrane of

the tongue and floor of the mouth, external auditory meatus, auricle, temporomandibular joint, temporal bone, and kinesthetic and proprioceptive sense of muscles of mastication.

Mandibular branch (SVE):
Motor innervation of muscles of mastication, tensor tympani, and tensor veli palatini.

VI Abducens Nerve (GSE)
Motor innervation of lateral rectus ocular muscle.

VII Facial Nerve (SVE, SVA, GVE)

Special visceral efferent:
Motor innervation of upper facial muscles.

General visceral efferent:
Motor innervation of lacrimal, sublingual, and submandibular gland.

Special visceral afferent:
Taste from anterior two thirds of the tongue.

VIII Vestibulocochlear Nerve (SSA)

Special somatic afferent:
Audition and vestibular sense; efferent inhibition of inner and outer hair cell output via crossed and uncrossed olivocochlear bundle.

IX Glossopharyngeal Nerve (GSA, GVA, SVA, GVE, SVE)

Special visceral afferent:
Sense of taste, posterior one third of the tongue and soft palate.

General visceral afferent:
Sense of touch, pain, and temperature from the posterior one third of the tongue, as well as from the faucial pillars, upper pharynx, Eustachian tube to the inferior ganglion.

General somatic afferent:
Pain and temperature sense from skin of ear.

Special visceral efferent:
Motor innervation of the stylopharyngeus and superior constrictor muscles.

General visceral efferent:
Motor innervation of parotid gland for salivation.

X Vagus Nerve (GSA, GVA, SVA, GVE, SVE)

General visceral efferent:
Parasympathetic motor innervation of intestines, pancreas, stomach, esophagus, trachea and bronchial smooth muscle and mucosal glands, kidneys, liver, and the heart.

Special visceral efferent

Recurrent laryngeal nerve:
Inferior pharyngeal constrictor muscle and intrinsic muscles of larynx except cricothyroid muscle.

(continued)

Table 9–3. *(continued)*

Superior laryngeal nerve:
Cricothyroid muscle

Pharyngeal nerve:
In conjunction with XI accessory, palatal muscles except tensor veli palatine. Motor innervation of pharyngeal muscles via IX glossopharyngeal.

General somatic afferent:
Pain, touch, and temperature sense from ear drum, posterior auricle, and external auditory meatus.

General visceral afferent:
Pain sense from mucosa of lower pharynx, larynx, thoracic and abdominal viscera, esophagus, and bronchi.

Special visceral afferent:
Taste from epiglottis and valleculae.

XI Accessory Nerve (SVE)
Motor innervation for sternocleidomastoid and trapezius muscles; accessory to vagus for motor innervation of intrinsic laryngeal, pharyngeal, palatal muscles, except tensor veli palatini and cricothyroid muscles.

XII Hypoglossal (GSE)
Motor innervation of all intrinsic and extrinsic tongue muscles except the palatoglossus.

entered the spinal cord for synapse. This pattern is followed in the brainstem as well, where axons of sensory nuclei will enter the brainstem for synapse and motor nuclei are within the brainstem.

Seven categories of function define cranial nerves, four are afferent and three are efferent. Functions are divided into *general* and *special*, with areas of service being *somatic* and *visceral*. Nerves can be efferent, afferent, or mixed efferent/afferent as well.

General somatic afferent (GSA) are sensory nerves associated with communicating the sensory information from skin, muscles, and joint, including pain, temperature, mechanical stimulation of skin, length and tension of muscle, and movement and position of joints. That is, GSA nerves provide general information about body function, and this information usually reaches consciousness (although the fact that this information reaches the level of consciousness does not necessarily mean that you attend to it). **Special somatic afferent nerves (SSA)**, on the other hand, serve the special body senses such as vision and hearing. **General visceral afferent nerves (GVA)** transmit sensory information from receptors in visceral structures, such as the digestive tract, information which only infrequently reaches conscious levels.

Special visceral afferent nerves (SVA) provide information from the special visceral senses of taste and smell.

Efferent nerves follow parallel form. **General visceral efferent nerves (GVE)** are the autonomic efferent fibers serving viscera and glands. **General somatic efferent nerves (GSE)** provide innervation of skeletal muscle and are quite important for speech production. The "wild card" in this mixture is the **special visceral efferent nerves (SVE)** which are involved with innervation of striated muscle of branchial arch origin, including the larynx, pharynx, soft palate, face, and muscles of mastication.

I Olfactory Nerve (SVA)

The olfactory nerve is not a true cranial nerve because it reaches the brain without passing through the thalamus first. This *special visceral afferent* nerve mediates the sense of smell (olfaction) which developed quite early in our phylogenetic development. The olfactory sensors are embedded in the epithelium of the nasal cavity, including superior conchae and septum.

Dendrites of the bipolar cells which make up this nerve pass superiorly through the cribriform plate of the ethmoid bone to enter one of the paired **olfactory bulbs**, the nuclei of the nerve which reside within the cranium, at the base of the brain (see Figure 9–26). Trauma to the nasal

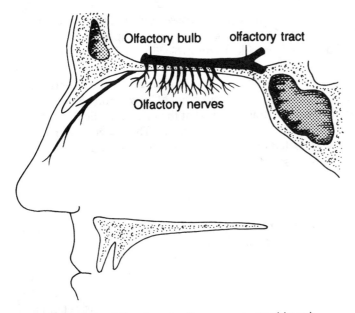

FIGURE 9–26. Olfactory bulb, nerves, and tract.

region can result in loss of cerebrospinal fluid through the nose (**cerebrospinal fluid rhinorrhea**) which alternately becomes a route for **meningeal infection** (infection of the meningeal linings of the brain). The olfactory nerve divides into medial and lateral branches. The lateral branches travel to the olfactory cortex, made up of the pyriform lobe and hippocampal formation.

II Optic Nerve (SSA)

Although not technically related to speech, hearing, or language, the optic nerve provides valuable clinical insight into the extent of damage due to cerebrovascular accident. The optic nerve is the *special somatic afferent* component associated with the visual system. Motor function of the eye is accommodated through other nerves.

The retinal cells receive stimulation from light, and output from the rod and cone cells of the retina (first-order neurons) is relayed to bipolar cells and modified by horizontal interneuron cells (second-order neurons). The output of these cells is transmitted by alterations of membrane potential but in absence of an action potential. Result of this complex process of inhibition and excitation is transmitted to the dendrite of the bipolar ganglion cells of the optic nerve (third-order neurons) whose cell bodies lie in the **lateral geniculate body (LGB)**, a nucleus of the thalamus.

The paired optic nerves converge on the **optic chiasm** where information from the medial half of the retina decussates, whereas information from the lateral half of each retina remains uncrossed (see Figure 9–27). Crossed and uncrossed information passes through the **optic tract** to the LGB. Dendrites of fourth-order neurons synapse and course via the **optic radiation** (geniculostriate projection) to the occipital lobe (Brodmann's area 17, to be discussed), the primary receptive area of the cerebral cortex. Branches from the LGB course to the **superior colliculus** of the midbrain, an apparent point of interaction between visual and auditory information received at the inferior colliculus and the relay involved in orienting to visual stimuli. The image from the retina is neurally projected onto the occipital lobe, inverted from the real world object it represents.

III Oculomotor Nerve (GSE, GVE)

The III oculomotor is comprised of two components. The *general somatic efferent* component serves the extrinsic ocular muscles with the exception of the superior oblique and lateral rectus muscles (see Figure 9–28). This component arises from the oculomotor nucleus of the midbrain. The *general visceral efferent* component arising from the Edinger-Westphal (accessory oculomotor) nucleus provides light and accommodation reflexes associated with pupil constriction and focus. The nuclei reside ventral to the cerebral aqueduct and emerge medial

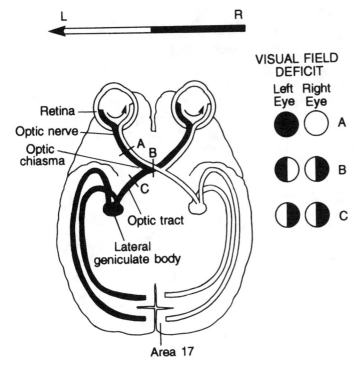

FIGURE 9–27. Representation of visual pathway and effect of site of lesion. A cut in the optic nerve at A would eliminate both left and right visual fields of the left eye. Lesion at B would cause loss of information from the right and left temporal fields (heteronymous bitemporal hemianopia). Lesion at point C on the optic tract will result in loss of information from the right visual field of both eyes (homonymous hemianopia).

to the cerebral peduncle, and passes into the orbit via the superior orbital fissure.

IV Trochlear Nerve (GSE)

The IV trochlear is broadly classed as a *general somatic efferent* nerve which arises from the trochlear nucleus of the midbrain, and innervates the superior oblique muscle of the eye which turns the eye down and out. Fibers of the trochlear nerve course around the cerebral peduncles and enter the orbit.

V Trigeminal Nerve (GSA, SVE)

The V trigeminal nerve is extremely important mixed nerve for speech production, as it provides motor supply to the muscles of mastication and transmits sensory information from the face. As Figure 9–29 indicates, the nerve arises from the motor trigeminal nucleus and sensory

Lesions of the II Optic Nerve and Tract

Function provides a window on site of lesion. In the visual system, the degree of visual **cut** or loss will give clues as to the location of damage to the nerve or tract. Figure 9–27 illustrates the pathway, with reference to a visual image presented to the eyes. The image will reverse as it passes through the lens, so that it is inverted both vertically and horizontally when projected upon the retina.

Information is sensed and transduced such that light reaching the medial portion of the retina (area nearest the nose) crosses at the chiasm, while that on the lateral portion of the retina (near the temples) remains ipsilateral. Thus, light from the left **visual field** strikes the left medial and right lateral retinae, combining in the right hemisphere of the brain. Likewise, information from the right visual field strikes the right medial and left lateral retinae, and courses to the left cerebral hemisphere. In this manner, left visual field enters the right hemisphere, and right visual field enters the left hemisphere.

Difficulties occur when part of the pathway is damaged. Definition of an individual's visual impairment is always with reference to damage to the visual field. If a lesion to the optic tract occurs behind the optic chiasm, the result will loss of vision of the opposite field. Right optic tract damage will result in loss of left visual field, as in point C on the figure. This is referred to as left **homonymous** ("having the same name," or more appropriately, same side) **hemianopia** (blindness in half of the field of vision).

A lesion arising at the chiasm (point B), such as a tumor compressing the nerve, will result in loss of decussating information. In this case, the right eye will lose right visual field and the left eye will lose the left visual field. This is termed **heteronymous** (different side) **bitemporal** (affecting both temporal regions) **hemianopia**. A patient with a chiasm lesion may also lose olfaction, because of the close proximity of the olfactory nerve.

nucleus of the trigeminal within the upper pons, emerging from the pons at the level of the superior margin of the temporal bone. An enlargement in the nerve indicates the trigeminal ganglion containing pseudounipolar cells, and there the nerve divides into three components, the ophthalmic, maxillary, and mandibular nerves.

The **ophthalmic** is the small, superior nerve of the trigeminal, and is entirely sensory. The *general somatic afferent* component of the oph-

Sup. oblique m.
Sup. rectus m.
III oculomotor n.
Edinger-Westphal nucl.
Nuclei of III
Nucl. of IV
Nucl. of VI
IV trochlear n.
VI abducens n.
Inf. oblique m.
Inf. rectus m.
Lat. rectus m.

IV-sup. oblique
III-sup. rectus
III-medial rectus
VI-lateral rectus
III-inf. rectus
III-inf. oblique

LEFT EYE

FIGURE 9-28. Schematic of III oculomotor, IV trochlear, and VI abducens nerve and muscles innervated.

thalmic branch transmits general sensory information from the skin of the upper face, forehead, and scalp, cornea, iris, upper eyelid, conjunctiva, nasal cavity mucous membrane, and lacrimal gland.

The **maxillary nerve** is only sensory, being *general somatic afferent* in nature (see Figure 9–30). It transmits information from the lower eyelid, skin on the sides of the nose, upper jaw, teeth, and lip, mucosal lining of buccal and nasal cavities, maxillary sinuses, and nasopharynx.

The **mandibular branch** is both *general somatic afferent* and *special visceral efferent*. This largest branch of trigeminal exits the skull via the fora-

Lesion to III Oculomotor, IV Trochlear, and VI Abducens

These three nerves provide motor control of the eye, eyelid, and iris. The III oculomotor nerve passes near the circle of Willis and is subject to compression from tumors, aneurysms, or hemorrhage. It serves the muscles responsible for adducting the eye (superior rectus, medial rectus, inferior rectus, and inferior oblique muscles), for elevating the eyelid (levator palpebrae), and for pupil constriction. A LMN lesion of one of the oculomotor nerves will result in ipsilateral paralysis, because decussation occurs before this level. As a result of the unopposed activity of the lateral rectus (which rotates the eye out) oculomotor paralysis will result in abduction (outward deviation, or **divergent strabismus**) of the eye and inability to turn the eye in, **ptosis** (drooping of the eyelid), and **mydriasis** (abnormal dilation of the pupil). Control of the III arises predominantly from area 8 of the frontal lobe, with a projection to the superior colliculus, and, from there to the contralateral pontine reticular formation and nuclei for the III, IV, and VI nerves. As a result of the extreme coordination of movements of the two eyes for **convergence** (bringing the eyes together) and **conjugate movement** (moving the eyes together to look toward the same side), hemispheric damage affecting ocular movements will result in contralateral involvement. That is, right hemisphere damage results in an inability to turn the eyes to the left side, because the right hemisphere controls movements of the eyes to the left. In other words, the patient with UMN lesion will "look at the lesion."

LMN lesion of the IV trochlear nerve affects the superior oblique muscle. When an eye rotates medially, the superior oblique is able to pull the eye down, and paralysis will result of loss of this ability. The VI abducens nerve controls the lateral rectus, which rotates the eye out. A LMN lesion to this nerve results in **internal strabismus** (eye is rotated in). The concomitant inability to fuse the visual images from both eyes is called **diplopia**, or double vision.

men ovale of sphenoid and gives rise to a number of branching nerves. The afferent component conducts general somatic afferent information from a region roughly encompassing the mandible, including the skin, lower teeth, gums, and lip, a portion of the skin and mucosal lining of the cheek, external auditory meatus and auricle, temporomandibular joint, and the region of the temporal bone, as well as kinesthetic and proprioceptive sense of muscles of mastication. The **lingual nerve** conducts somatic sensation from the anterior two thirds of the mucous membrane of the tongue and floor of the mouth.

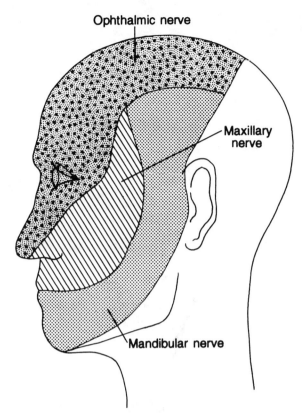

Ophthalmic nerve

Maxillary nerve

Mandibular nerve

FIGURE 9-29. Areas served by the nerves arising from the V trigeminal nerve.

The *special visceral efferent* component arises from the trigeminal motor nucleus of the pons, innervates the muscles of mastication, the tensor tympani, and the tensor veli palatini. Note that taste is *not* mediated by the trigeminal, but the pain from biting the tip of your tongue is.

VI Abducens Nerve (GSE)

As the name implies, the **VI abducens** (or **abducent**) is an abductor, providing *general somatic efferent* innervation to the lateral rectus ocular muscle. It arises from the abducens nucleus of the pons, and emerges from the brainstem at the junction of the pons and medulla. The abducens enters the orbit via the superior orbital fissure to innervate the lateral rectus.

VII Facial Nerve (SVE, SVA, GVE)

The facial nerve is quite important to any discussion of speech musculature. This nerve supplies efferent innervation to the facial muscles of expression and tear glands, as well as sense of taste for a portion of the tongue. It communicates with X vagus, V trigeminal, VIII vestibulocochlear, and the IX glossopharyngeal nerves.

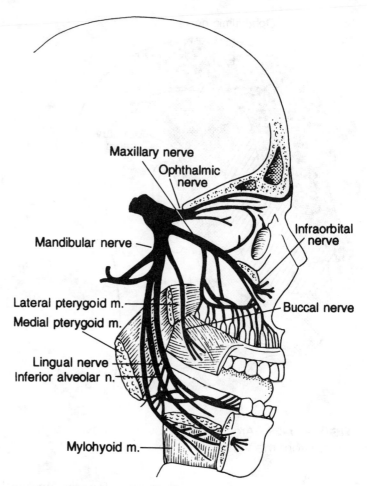

FIGURE 9–30. Ophthalmic, maxillary, and mandibular branches of the V trigeminal nerve.

The *special visceral efferent* component arises from the motor nucleus of the facial nerve within the reticular formation of the inferior pons. As you may see in Figure 9–31, fibers from both hemispheres of the cerebral cortex terminate on this nucleus. The motor nucleus is divided, so that not all muscles are innervated bilaterally. The upper facial muscles receive bilateral cortical input, whereas those of the lower face receive only contralateral innervation. As the figure shows, unilateral cortical damage will produce contralateral deficit in the lower facial muscles but no noticeable deficit of the upper muscles. That is, left hemisphere damage could result in right facial paralysis of the oral muscles, but spare the ability to wrinkle the forehead, close the eye, and so forth.

The nerve exits the pons at the cerebellopontine angle to enter the internal auditory meatus (see Figure 9–32), coursing laterally through the facial canal of the temporal bone. At the **geniculate ganglion** the

Lesions of V Trigeminal Nerve

The V trigeminal nerve has both motor and sensory components, and all have the potential to be affected by lesions. UMN damage to the V trigeminal will result in minimal motor deficit because of strong bilateral innervation by each hemisphere. With UMN lesion you may see increased **jaw jerk reflex** (elicited by pulling down on the passively opened mandible). LMN damage will result in **atrophy** (wasting) and weakness on the affected side. When your patient closes his or her mouth, the jaw will deviate toward the side of the lesion as a result of the action of the intact internal pterygoid muscle. The jaw will hang open with bilateral LMN damage, which has an extreme effect on speech. The tensor veli palatine is also innervated by the trigeminal, and weakness or paralysis may result in hypernasality because of the role of this muscle in maintaining the velopharyngeal sphincter.

Damage to the sensory component of the V cranial will result in loss of tactile sensation for the anterior two thirds of the tongue, loss of the corneal blink reflex elicited by touching the cornea with cotton, and alteration of sensation at orifice eustachian tube, external auditory meatus and tympanic membrane, teeth, and gums. Sensation of the forehead, upper face, and nose region will be lost with ophthalmic branch lesion, and the sensation to the skin region roughly lateral to the zygomatic arch and over the maxilla will be lost with maxillary branch lesion. Damage to the mandibular branch will affect sensation from the side of the face down to the mandible. **Trigeminal neuralgia (Tic doulourex)** may also arise from damage to the V cranial nerve. The result of this is severe and sharp shooting pain along the course of the nerve which may be restricted to areas served by only one of the branches.

nerve turns to continue as a medial prominence in the middle ear cavity. A twig of the facial nerve, the **chorda tympani**, enters the cavity and passes medial to the malleus and tympanic membrane. It ultimately joins the lingual nerve of V trigeminal.

The facial nerve exits at the stylomastoid foramen of the temporal bone, coursing between and innervating the stylohyoid and posterior digastricus muscles. The nerve branches into **cervicofacial** and **temporofacial** divisions. The cervicofacial division further gives off the buccal, lingual, marginal mandibular, and cervical branches, while the temporofacial division gives rise to the temporal and zygomatic branches.

FIGURE 9-31. Effects of upper and lower motor neuron lesion of the VII facial nerve on facial muscle function. (After data and view of Gilman and Winans, 1982.)

Lesions of VII Facial Nerve

Lesions of the facial nerve may significantly affect articulatory function. Because the upper motor neuron supply to the upper face is bilateral, unilateral UMN damage will not result in upper face paralysis. It may, however, paralyze all facial muscles below the eyes. Even then, muscles of facial expression (**mimetic muscles**) may be contracted involuntarily in response to emotional stimuli, because these motor gestures are initiated at regions of the brain which differ from those of speech.

LMN damage will cause upper and lower-face paralysis on the side of the lesion. This may involve the inability to close one's eyelid, and will result in muscle sagging, loss of tone, reduction in wrinkling around the lip, nose, and forehead. When the individual attempts to smile, the affected corners of the mouth will be drawn toward the unaffected side. Your patient may drool due to loss of the ability to impound saliva with the lips, and the cheeks may puff out during expiration due to a flaccid buccinator.

Bell's palsy (palsy means "paralysis") may result from any compression of the VII nerve, or even from cold weather. It results in paralysis of facial musculature which remits in most cases within a few months.

The *general visceral efferent* component of the facial nerve arises from the **salivatory nucleus** of the pons, forming the **nervus intermedius**. Fibers from the nervus intermedius innervate the **lacrimal gland** (for tearing), the **sublingual gland** beneath the tongue, and the **submandibular gland**.

The *special visceral afferent* sense of taste (**gustation**) arising from the anterior two-thirds of the tongue is mediated by the facial nerve. Information is transmitted via the chorda tympani to the nervus intermedius, and ultimately to the **solitary tract nucleus**.

VIII Vestibulocochlear Nerve (SSA)

This nerve, also known as the **auditory nerve**, is extremely important for both the speech-language pathologist and audiologist because it mediates both auditory information and sense of movement in space. The nerve consists of both afferent and efferent components. The *special somatic afferent* portion mediates information concerning hearing and balance, while the efferent component appears to assist in selectively damping output of hair cells.

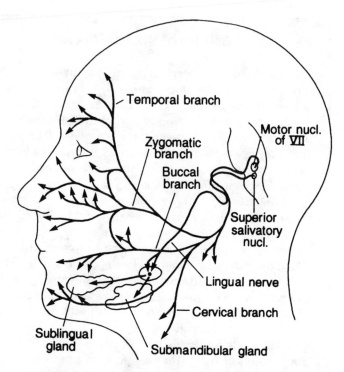

FIGURE 9-32. General course of VII facial nerve.

Acoustic Branch. Information concerning acoustic stimulation at the **cochlea** is transmitted via short dendrites to the spiral ganglion within the modiolus of the bony labyrinth. The spiral ganglion consists of bodies of bipolar cells whose axons project through the internal auditory meatus, where the nerve joins with the vestibular branch of VIII. The nerve enters the medulla oblongata at the junction with the pons to synapse with the **dorsal cochlear nucleus (DCN)** and **ventral cochlear nucleus (VCN)**, lateral to the inferior cerebellar peduncle.

Vestibular Branch. The vestibular branch of the VIII cranial nerve transmits information concerning acceleration and position in space to the bipolar cells of the **vestibular ganglion** within the internal auditory meatus. From within the pons fibers branch to synapse in nuclei of the pons and medulla, as well as directly to the flocculonodular lobe of the cerebellum. Within the pons and medulla the vestibular branch communicates with the superior, medial, lateral, and inferior vestibular nuclei. Vestibular nuclei project to the spinal cord, cerebellum, thalamus, and cerebral cortex.

Efferent Component. Although considered to be a sensory device, the cochlea is served by efferent fibers of the **olivocochlear bundle**. Although only about 1,600 fibers in number (compared with the 30,000 fibers of the afferent VIII), activation of the bundle has a significant attenuating effect on output of the hair cells with which they communicate.

Lesions of VIII Vestibulocochlear Nerve

Clearly, damage to the VIII nerve will result in ipsilateral hearing loss reflecting the degree of trauma. Damage to the VIII nerve may arise from a number of causes, including physical trauma (skull fracture), tumor growth compressing the nerve (benign but life-threatening tumors of the myelin sheath will result in slow-onset unilateral hearing loss and other symptoms as compression of the brainstem increases), or vascular incident. Damage to the vestibular component of the VIII nerve may result disturbances of equilibrium arising from loss of information concerning position in space.

The **crossed olivocochlear bundle (COCB)** arises from a region near the **medial superior olive (MSO)** of the olivary complex. Fibers descend, and most of them decussate near the fourth ventricle, and communicate with **outer hair cells**. The **uncrossed olivocochlear bundle (UCOB)** originates near the **lateral superior olive** of the olivary complex, with most of the fibers projecting ipsilaterally to the **inner hair cells** of the cochlea. It is believed that the olivocochlear bundle can be controlled through cortical activity and may be active in signal detection within noise.

Auditory Pathway. The auditory pathway to the cerebral cortex is illustrated in Figure 9–33. Dendrites of VIII nerve fibers synapsing on cochlear hair cells become depolarized following adequate mechanical stimulation via the cochlear traveling wave. Axons of the bipolar cells of the VIII vestibulocochlear nerve project to the cochlear nucleus, which is functionally divided into the dorsal cochlear nucleus (DCN), anteroventral cochlear nucleus (AVCN), and posteroventral cochlear nucleus (PVCN) of the pons. (Some authors distinguish only two nuclei, the DCN and ventral cochlear nucleus.) Projections from the VIII nerve are arrayed **tonotopically** within the cochlear nucleus, reflecting the organization of the cochlear partition. That is, there is an orderly array of fibers representing the information processed within the cochlea, from low to high frequency. This order is maintained throughout the auditory nervous system.

Projections from the cochlear nucleus take the form of **acoustic striae**. The **dorsal acoustic stria** arises from the DCN, coursing around the inferior cerebellar peduncle. It decussates, bypasses the superior olivary complex (SOC) and lateral lemniscus, making synapse at the inferior colliculus (IC). Fibers of the **ventral acoustic stria** course anterior to the inferior cerebellar peduncle and terminate in the contralateral superior olivary nuclei. The **intermediate acoustic stria** arises from the PVCN and terminates at the ipsilateral superior olivary complex.

FIGURE 9–33. Course of the vestibulocochlear nerve and auditory pathway.

The **medial superior olive (MSO)** and **lateral superior olive (LSO,** also known as the **s-segment)** are major auditory nuclei of the superior olivary complex within the pons. Localization of sound in the environment is processed primarily at this level. High frequency information at the LSO will provide the binaural intensity cue for location of sound in space, while low frequency information projected to the MSO will provide the interaural phase (frequency) cue for localization. In addition, the crossed and uncrossed olivocochlear bundles arise from cells peripheral to the MSO and LSO nuclei.

As you can see from the schematic of the auditory pathway, fibers from the SOC ascend to the lateral lemniscus and inferior colliculus, structures apparently involved in localization of sound. You may also notice that there are ample decussations throughout the pathway, following cochlear nucleus synapse. Indeed, the auditory pathway is primarily crossed, although a small ipsilateral component is retained. Unilateral deafness will result from cochlea or VIII nerve damage, but not from unilateral damage to the auditory pathway above the level of the auditory nerve. Although much hearing function will be retained as a result of the redundant pathway, interaction of the two ears is essential for localization of sound in space, and damage to the brainstem nuclei will result in loss of discrimination function. Of course, complete bilateral sectioning of the pathway would result in complete loss of auditory function.

Within the diencephalon, the **medial geniculate body (MGB)**, a thalamic nucleus, is the final auditory relay. The **auditory radiation** (also known as the **geniculotemporal radiation**) projects from the MGB to **Heschl's gyrus** (area 41) of the temporal lobe. This segment of the dorsal surface of the superior temporal convolution is partially hidden in the Sylvian fissure, and projections to the auditory cortex retain tonotopic organization. The adjacent area 42 is an auditory association area, which projects to other areas of the brain, as well as to the contralateral auditory cortex via the corpus callosum.

IX Glossopharyngeal Nerve (GSA, GVA, SVA, GVE, SVE)

The IX glossopharyngeal nerve serves both sensory and motor functions (see Figure 9–34). The motor component arises from the nucleus ambiguus and inferior salivatory nucleus of the medulla, while axons of the sensory component terminate in the medulla at the **solitary tract nucleus** and **spinal tract nucleus** of the V trigeminal. The rootlets emerge in the ventrolateral aspect of medulla, converge, and exit the skull through the jugular foramen of the temporal bone. The nerve courses deep to the styloid process of the temporal bone and beside the stylopharyngeus muscle. It enters the base of the tongue after penetrating the superior constrictor muscle. The nerve has **superior** and **inferior (petrosal) ganglia**.

The *special visceral afferent* function of the nerve mediates sensation from taste receptors of the posterior one-third of the tongue and a portion of the soft palate, with this information delivered to the solitary tract nucleus. Impulses from **baroreceptors** within the carotid sinus convey information concerning arterial pressure within the common carotid artery to the same nucleus. The *general visceral afferent* component provides sensation of touch, pain, and temperature from the pos-

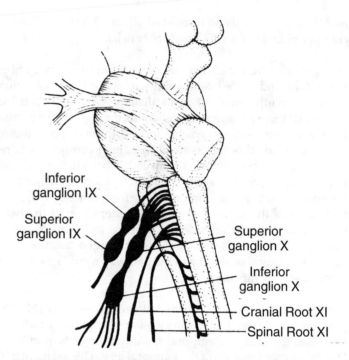

FIGURE 9–34. Relation of IX glossopharyngeal nerve to vagus and accessory nerves.

terior one third of the tongue, as well as from the faucial pillars, upper pharynx, and Eustachian tube to the inferior ganglion.

General somatic afferent information from the region behind the auricle and external auditory meatus is transmitted by the superior branch of IX glossopharyngeal to the nucleus of the spinal trigeminal via the superior ganglion.

Efferent innervation by IX glossopharyngeal includes *special visceral efferent* activation of the stylopharyngeus and superior constrictor muscles by means of the nucleus ambiguus. *General visceral efferent* innervation of the parotid gland for salivation arises from the inferior salivatory nucleus via the otic ganglion.

X Vagus Nerve (GSA, GVA, SVA, GVE, SVE)

The vagus nerve is both complex and important. Let us examine both motor and sensory components of this nerve. The vagus arises from the lateral medulla oblongata and exits from the skull through the jugular foramen along with the IX glossopharyngeal and XI accessory nerves.

The vagus is served by several nuclei and ganglia. The dorsal vagal nucleus (dorsal motor nucleus) gives rise to visceral efferent fibers for

Lesions of IX Glossopharyngeal Nerve

The IX glossopharyngeal nerve works in concert with the X vagus, making its independent function difficult to determine. Damage to the IX nerve will result in paralysis of the stylopharyngeus muscle, and may result in loss of general sensation (**anesthesia**) for the posterior one third of the tongue and pharynx, although the vagus may support these functions as well. The cooperative innervation with the vagus results in little effect on the pharyngeal constrictors, although reduced sensation of the auricle and middle ear may indicate IX damage. IX damage may also cause reduced or absent gag reflex, although absence of the reflex does not guarantee that a lesion exists.

parasympathetic innervation and receives information from the inferior vagal ganglion. The solitarius tract and nucleus serve taste, whereas the nucleus ambiguus provides motor innervation to laryngeal musculature and mucosa. As with the glossopharyngeal nerve, the vagus has inferior (nodose) and superior ganglia.

The *general visceral efferent* component of the vagus arises from the dorsal motor nucleus of X, providing parasympathetic motor innervation of intestines, pancreas, stomach, esophagus, trachea and bronchial smooth muscle and mucosal glands, kidneys, liver, and the heart. This branch is responsible for inhibiting heart rate. The striated muscles of the larynx as well as most pharyngeal and palatal muscles are innervated by the *special visceral efferent* portion of the vagus, served by the nucleus ambiguus.

The *general somatic afferent* component of the vagus delivers pain, touch, and temperature sense from the skin covering the ear drum, posterior auricle, and external auditory meatus to the superior vagal ganglion, and subsequently to the spinal nucleus of V trigeminal. It is this innervation that triggers nausea or vomiting when the eardrum is touched by external stimuli.

Pain sense from the mucosal lining of the lower pharynx, larynx, thoracic and abdominal viscera, esophagus, and bronchi is conveyed by means of the *general visceral afferent* component with soma in the inferior ganglion, with axons terminating in the caudal nucleus solitarius and dorsal vagal nucleus. Sensations of nausea and hunger are mediated by the vagus. This GVA component supports maintenance of heart beat, blood pressure (via baroreceptors), and respiration (stretch receptors in the lung signal fully distended tissue to terminate inspiration), and digestion.

Taste sense from the epiglottis and valleculae is mediated by the *special visceral afferent* component of vagus with soma of these afferent fibers residing in the inferior ganglion (Gilman & Winans, 1982). Axons from this component terminate in the caudal nucleus solitarius.

These functions are served through four important branches of the vagus. The auricular branch arises from the superior ganglion, while the pharyngeal and recurrent laryngeal, and superior laryngeal branches arise from the inferior ganglion.

The right **recurrent laryngeal nerve** courses under and behind the subclavian artery and ascends between the trachea and the esophagus. The left recurrent laryngeal nerve loops under the aortic arch to ascend between the trachea and esophagus. After entering the larynx between the cricoid and thyroid cartilages, tracheal and esophageal branches provide GVA innervation to the laryngeal mucosa beneath the vocal folds, and SVE innervation serves the intrinsic muscles of the larynx and the inferior pharyngeal constrictor. The auricular branch conveys sensory information from the tympanic membrane and external auditory meatus.

The **pharyngeal branch** of vagus mediates the SVA taste sense and GVA sensation from the base of the tongue and upper pharynx. It also mediates SVE innervation of the upper and middle pharyngeal constrictors, palatopharyngeus, palatoglossus, salpingopharyngeus, levator veli palatine, and musculus uvulae. The only soft palate muscle not innervated by the vagus is the tensor veli palatini.

The **superior laryngeal nerve** has both internal and external branches. The internal branch enters the larynx through the thyrohyoid membrane, receiving GVA information from the laryngeal region above the vocal folds. The external branch provides SVE innervation of the cricothyroid muscle.

XI Accessory Nerve (SVE)

The XI accessory nerve consists of both cranial and spinal components. It provides *special visceral efferent* innervation directly to the sternocleidomastoid and trapezius muscles and works in conjunction with the vagus to innervate the intrinsic muscles of the larynx, pharynx, and soft palate. The exception to this is the tensor veli palatini that is innervated by the V trigeminal, and the cricothyroid muscles that are innervated by the superior laryngeal nerve of vagus.

The cranial root arises from the caudal portion of the nucleus ambiguus, where it is joined by the spinal root, to exit through the jugular foramen with the vagus. On exiting the skull, the internal branch of the accessory nerve joins the inferior ganglion of vagus. The accessory nerve serves both recurrent laryngeal and pharyngeal nerves of the vagus.

Lesions of X Vagus Nerve

The X vagus is the most extensive of the cranial nerves, presenting an important constellation of clinical manifestations. Damage to the pharyngeal branch will result in deficit in swallowing, potential loss of gag through interaction with the IX glossopharyngeal nerve, and hypernasality due to weakness of the velopharyngeal sphincter (all velopharyngeal muscles are innervated by the vagus with the exception of the tensor veli palatine, which is innervated by the trigeminal). Unilateral pharyngeal branch damage will result in failure to elevate the soft palate on the involved side (asymmetrical elevation), producing hypernasality. Bilateral lesion will produce absent or reduced (but symmetrical) movement of the soft palate producing hypernasality, **nasal regurgitation** (loss of food and liquid through the nose), dysphagia, and paralysis of the pharyngeal musculature.

Lesions of the superior laryngeal nerve may result in loss of sensation of the upper larynx mucous membrane and stretch receptors, as well as paralysis of the cricothyroid muscle. Recurrent laryngeal nerve damage will alter sensation below the level of the vocal folds and stretch receptor information from the intrinsic muscles. Unilateral RLN lesion typically results in a flaccid vocal fold on the side of lesion accompanied by hoarse and breathy voice. In bilateral lesion, the vocal folds may rarely be paralyzed in the adducted position, which is life-threatening because of airway occlusion. More commonly the vocal folds are paralyzed in the paramedian position, compromising the airway by risk of aspiration. Paralysis in the adducted position will result in **laryngeal stridor**, harsh, distressing phonation upon inspiration and expiration. Paralysis in the paramedian position may permit limited breathy and hoarse phonation with limited pitch range due to loss of tensing ability of the vocalis. Vocal intensity range will be extremely limited by the loss of adductory ability.

The spinal root emerges from the first five spinal segments between the dorsal and ventral rootlets, ascending enter the skull through the foramen magnum and to join the cranial accessory nerve prior to exiting the skull (see Figure 9–35). The spinal root makes up external root of the accessory nerve, and innervates the sternocleidomastoid and trapezius muscles.

FIGURE 9-35. Spinal accessory nerve origins. (From data of Netter, 1973.)

XII Hypoglossal (GSE)

As the name implies, this nerve provides the innervation to motor function of the tongue. This *general somatic efferent* nerve arises from the hypoglossal nucleus of the medulla, exits the skull through the hypoglossal canal, and courses with the vagus. The hypoglossal nerve descends and branches to innervate all intrinsic muscles of the tongue, and all of the extrinsic muscles of the tongue except the palatoglossus, which is innervated via XI accessory nerve through the pharyngeal plexus.

Each hypoglossal nucleus is served primarily by the contralateral corticobulbar tract, which means that *left* upper motor neuron damage will result in *right* tongue weakness. Damage to the lower motor neu-

Lesions of XI Accessory Nerve

Lesion to the XI accessory nerve may have an effect on the trapezius and sternocleidomastoid muscles. Unilateral lesion affecting the sternocleidomastoid will result in the patient being unable to turn his or her head away from the side of the lesion. (The left sternocleidomastoid rotates the head toward the right side when contracted.) Lesions resulting in paralysis of the trapezius will result in restricted ability to elevate the arm and a drooping shoulder on the side of the lesion.

rons will result in ipsilateral deficit, because the fibers of the corticobulbar tract decussate prior to reaching the hypoglossal nucleus. Thus, left UMN damage or right LMN damage will affect muscles of the right side of the tongue. When the tongue is protruded, it will point to the side of the paralyzed muscles, because contraction of the posterior genioglossus is bilaterally unequal.

In summary, **cranial nerves** are extremely important to the speech-language pathologist.

■ Cranial nerves may be **sensory**, **motor**, or **mixed sensory-motor**, and are categorized based on their function as being **general** or **specialized** and as serving **visceral** or **somatic** organs or structures.
■ The **I olfactory nerve** serves the sense of smell, and the **II optic nerve** communicates visual information to the brain.
■ The **III oculomotor**, **IV trochlear**, and **VI abducens nerves** provide innervation for eye movements.
■ The **V trigeminal** innervates muscles of **mastication** and the **tensor veli palatini**, and communicates sensation from the face, mouth, teeth, mucosal lining, and tongue.
■ The **VII facial nerve** innervates muscles of **facial expression**, and the sensory component serves taste of the anterior two thirds of the tongue.
■ The **VIII vestibulocochlear** nerve mediates auditory and vestibular sensation.
■ The **IX glossopharyngeal nerve** serves the **posterior tongue taste** receptors, as well as somatic sense from the tongue, fauces, pharynx and eustachian tube.
■ The **stylopharyngeus** and **superior pharyngeal constrictor** muscles receive motor innervation via this nerve.
■ The **X vagus** is extremely important for autonomic function as well as somatic motor innervation.
■ Somatic sensation of **pain**, **touch**, and **temperature** from the region of the **ear drum** is mediated by the vagus, as well as **pain** sense from **pharynx**, **larynx**, **esophagus** and many other regions.

Lesions of XII Hypoglossal Nerve

Lesions affecting the XII hypoglossal will have a profound impact on articulation function and speech intelligibility. This nerve provides efferent innervation of intrinsic and extrinsic muscles of the tongue, as well as afferent proprioceptive supply. Unilateral LMN lesion will result in loss of movement on the side of lesion. Muscular weakness and atrophy on the affected side will result in deviation of the tongue toward the side of the lesion (function of the normal contralateral genioglossus will cause this). **Fasciculations**, or abnormal involuntary twitching or movement of muscle fibers, may occur prior to atrophy, arising from damage to the cell body. At rest the tongue may deviate toward the unaffected side as a result of the tonic pull of the normal styloglossus muscle. Upper motor lesion may result in muscle weakness and impaired volitional movements with accompanying spasticity.

◼ The **recurrent laryngeal nerve** and **superior laryngeal nerves** supply motor innervation for the intrinsic muscles of the larynx.

◼ The **XI accessory nerve** innervates the **sternocleidomastoid** and **trapezius** muscles, and collaborates with the vagus in activation of palatal, laryngeal and pharyngeal muscles.

◼ The **XII hypoglossal** nerve innervates the **muscles** of the **tongue** with the exception of the **palatoglossus**.

Anatomy of the Cerebral Cortex

Meningeal Linings

The central nervous system is invested with a triple-layer lining serving important protective and nutritive functions.

dura mater: L., tough mother

There are three meningeal linings covering the brain. The **dura mater** is a bi-layered, tough lining, which is the most superficial of the meningeal linings (see Figure 9–36). It is composed of an outer layer which is more inelastic than the inner layers and through which the meningeal blood vessels course. The potential space between the layers is called the **epidural space**. The **arachnoid** is a lacelike covering through which many blood vessels for the brain pass. The innermost layer of the meninges is the **pia mater**, a thin, membranous covering that closely follows the contour of the brain. The major arteries and veins serving the surface of the brain course within this layer.

arachnoid mater: L., spider mother; the arachnoid mater looks like a spiderweb

pia mater: L., pious mother; the pia mater is so-named because of its gentle but faithful attachment to the cerebral cortex

The dura mater makes four major infoldings, separating large structures of the brain. The **falx cerebri** separates the two cerebral hemi-

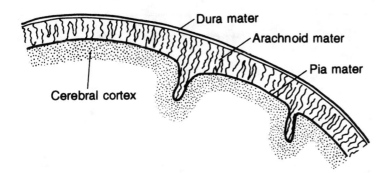

FIGURE 9–36. Schematic of the meningeal linings of the brain.

spheres as a vertical sheathe of dura, and the **falx cerebelli** performs the same function for the cerebellar hemispheres (see Figure 9–37).

The **tentorium cerebelli** is a horizontal dural shelf at the base of the skull that divides the cranium into superior (cerebral) and inferior (cerebellar) regions. The **diaphragma sella** forms a boundary between the pituitary gland and the hypothalamus and optic chiasm. The dura mater encircles the cranial nerves as they exit the brainstem.

At the foramen magnum the meningeal linings become continuous with the **spinal meningeal linings**. The spinal meninges are broadly similar to those of the brain, with some exceptions. The dura of the brain adheres to the bone, but that of the spinal cord does not adhere to the vertebrae. As with the brain meninges, cerebrospinal fluid flows through the subarachnoid space. Likewise, the pia mater closely follows the surface of the spinal cord, but serves an anchoring function as well. The cord is attached to the dura by means of 22 pairs of **denticulate ligaments** arising from the pia, and the dura extends laterally to encapsulate the dorsal root ganglion. At the inferior cord, the pia is continuous with the filum terminale, terminating on the first segment of the coccyx.

The Ventricles and Cerebrospinal Fluid

The central nervous system is bathed in **cerebrospinal fluid (CSF)** which provides a cushion for the delicate and dense neural tissue as well as some nutrient delivery and waste removal. Examining the system of **ventricles** and canals through which the cerebrospinal fluid flows will help you as we describe the cerebral cortex and subcortical structures. You will want to refer to Figure 9–38 for this discussion.

The ventricles are remnants of the embryonic neural tube. The ventricular system of the brain is made up of four cavities: right and left lateral ventricles and the third and fourth ventricles. Within each of these ventricles is a **choroid plexus** which produces **cerebrospinal**

Hematoma

A **hematoma** is a pooling of blood, typically arising from breakage of a blood vessel. **Subdural hematoma** involves intracranial bleeding beneath the dura mater, caused by rupture of cortical arteries or veins, usually the result of trauma to the head. Pressure from the pooling blood displaces the brain, shifting and compressing the brainstem, forcing the temporal lobe under the tentorium cerebelli, and compressing cerebral arteries. This critically dangerous condition may not be immediately recognized, because it may take several hours before pooling blood compresses the brain sufficiently to produce symptoms such as reduced consciousness, hemiparesis, pupillary dilation, and other symptoms associated with compressed cranial nerves. **Epidural hematoma**, hematoma occurring above the dura mater, may result in a patient being initially lucid, but displaying progressively decreasing levels of consciousness, reflecting compression of the brain.

Hematomas are characterized by location of insult. **Frontal epidural hematomas** arise from blows to the frontal bone and may result in personality changes. **Posterior fossa epidural hematomas** arise from blows to the back of the head, producing visual and coordination deficits.

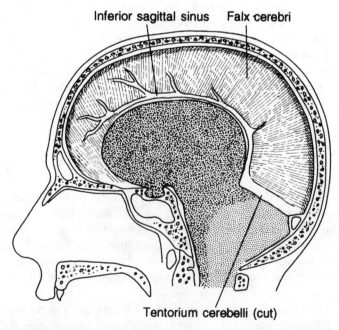

Inferior sagittal sinus   Falx cerebri

Tentorium cerebelli (cut)

FIGURE 9–37. The falx cerebri separates the left and right cerebral hemispheres.

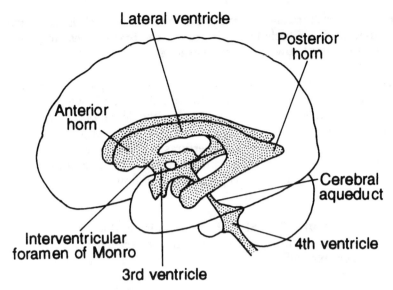

FIGURE 9-38. Ventricles of the brain.

fluid, although the plexus of the lateral ventricles produces the bulk of the fluid. The arrangement of these cavities provides a very good buffer for a delicate brain.

The paired **lateral ventricles** are the largest of the ventricles, composed of four spaces bounded superiorly by the corpus callosum and extending into each of the lobes of the cerebrum. They are shaped somewhat like horseshoes opened toward the front, but with posterior horns attached. The **anterior horn** projects into the frontal lobe to the genu of the corpus callosum. The medial wall is the septum pellucidum, and the inferior margin is the head of caudate nucleus. The **central portion**, located within the parietal lobe, includes the region between the interventricular foramen of Monro to the splenium, with the superior border being the corpus callosum, medial boundary being the septum pellucidum, and the inferior being portions of the caudate nucleus. The **posterior** or **occipital** horn extends into the occipital lobe to a tapered termination, with its superior and lateral surfaces being the corpus callosum. The **inferior horn** extends into the temporal lobe, curving down behind the thalamus to terminate blindly behind the temporal pole. The hippocampus marks the lower margin of the inferior horn. The lateral ventricles communicate with the third ventricle via the **interventricular foramen of Monro**.

The **third ventricle** is the unpaired medial cavity between the left and right thalami and hypothalami. The roof of the third ventricle is the tela choroidea, and the ventricle extends inferiorly to the level of the optic chiasm. The prominent **interthalamic adhesion** (massa intermedia or intermediate mass) bridges the ventricle, connecting the two thalami. Communication with the lateral ventricles is by means of paired interventricular foramina, and the third ventricle is connected to the fourth ventricle by means of the **cerebral** or **mesencephalic aqueduct** (also known as the sylvian aqueduct).

The **fourth ventricle** is shaped roughly like a diamond, projecting upward from the central canal of the spinal cord and lower medulla. The floor of the ventricle is the margin of the dorsal pons and upper medulla. The cerebellum forms the roof of the fourth ventricle. The ventricle has three openings or **apertures**, the **median aperture (foramen of Magendie)** and the paired left and right **lateral apertures (foramina of Luschka)** which permit CSF to flow into the subarachnoid space, to be described.

Circulation of CSF. CSF is the clear, fluid product of the choroid plexus in each of the ventricles. It provides an excellent cushion to protect the brain against trauma and also serves a transport function, as mentioned previously. The volume of CSF in the nervous system is approximately 125 ml which is replenished every 7 hours. The fluid is under a constant pressure which changes with body position and can be the cause of life-threatening conditions should something occlude the pathway for CSF.

Circulation of CSF begins in each of the lateral ventricles, coursing through the interventricular foramina of Monro to the third ventricle. From there, the fluid flows through the minute cerebral aqueduct to the fourth ventricle, where it drains into the subarachnoid space through the foramina of Luschka and Magendie to the cerebellomedullary cistern and to freely circulate around the brain and spinal cord. CSF then can course around the cerebellum and cerebrum to exit through the arachnoid granulation in sinuses of the dura mater and be absorbed by the venous system. Alternately, the CSF will course downward through the foramen magnum and subarachnoid space around the spinal cord.

In summary, the **cerebral cortex** is protected from physical insult by **cerebrospinal fluid** and the **meningeal linings**, the **dura, pia**, and **arachnoid mater**.

■ The meninges provide support for delicate neural and vascular tissue, with the dura dividing into regions that correspond to the regions of the brain supported by it.
■ The **spinal meningeal linings** similarly protect the spinal cord from movement trauma.
■ Cerebrospinal fluid originating within the **ventricles** of the brain and circulating around the spinal cord **cushions** these structures from trauma associated with rapid acceleration.

Cerebral Cortex

The **cerebrum** consists of two **cerebral hemispheres** or roughly equal halves of the brain. **Cortex** actually means "bark," referring to the bark or outer surface of a tree, and the cerebral cortex is the outer surface of the brain. The cortex is made up of six cell layers that have functional significance. The six layers are the outermost **molecular layer**, the **external granular layer** (which is primarily involved in sensory function), the **external pyramidal layer** (which is primarily involved in motor function), the **internal granular layer** (sensory), the **internal pyramidal layer** (motor), and the deepest layer, the **multiform** or **polymorphic layer**. In the early part of this century, Brodmann identified regions of the brain that were similar based on the preponderance of cell types, and his definition of these regions remains the primary means of identifying locations on the cortex. Figure 9–39 will assist you as we discuss landmarks of the superficial cortex.

As you can see in this figure, the **cerebral longitudinal fissure** separates the left and right cerebral hemispheres. The convoluted surface of the brain is a very beneficial product of development. Early in development the cerebral cortex has few of these furrows and bulges, but the brain growth outstrips the skull growth, causing the cerebral cortex to double in on itself. The result of this is greatly increased surface area, translating as more neural horsepower. You can think of the surface as a topographical map with mountains and valleys. The mountains (**convolutions**) in this case are called **gyri** (singular, **gyrus**) and the infolding valleys that separate the gyri are called **sulci** (singular, **sulcus**) or **fissures**, if deeper or more pronounced. These sulci, fissures, and gyri provide the major landmarks for navigating the cerebral cortex.

We divide the cerebral cortex into six lobes. Four of them are reasonably easy to see and are named after the bones with which they are associated, but two of these lobes require some thought and imagination. The six lobes are the frontal, parietal, occipital, temporal, insular, and limbic lobes.

Two prominent sulci serve as benchmarks in our study of the cerebral cortex. The **lateral sulcus (Sylvian fissure)** divides the temporal lobe from the frontal and anterior parietal lobes. The **central sulcus (Rolandic sulcus; Rolandic fissure)** separates the frontal and parietal lobes entirely. The central sulcus is the very prominent vertical groove running from the cerebral longitudinal fissure to the lateral sulcus Sylvian fissure), terminating in the inferior parietal lobe. As you can see in the sagittal section, this sulcus does not extend far down the medial surface. The areas of the temporal, parietal and frontal lobes along the lateral sulcus which overly the insular cortex are known as the **temporal operculum, fronto-parietal operculum**, and **frontal operculum**, as will be discussed. The broad outlines of the four prominent lobes are displayed in Figure 9–39.

Frontal Lobe. The frontal lobe is the largest of the lobes, making up one-third of the cortex. This lobe predominates planning and initiation of voluntary motion, as we shall see in Chapter 10. It is the anterior-most portion of the cortex, bounded posteriorly by the central sulcus.

FIGURE 9-39. a. Landmarks of the cerebral hemisphere. Shown is left hemisphere.

The inferior boundary is the lateral sulcus, and the medial boundary is the longitudinal fissure.

Three gyri run parallel to the longitudinal fissure. The **superior frontal gyrus** borders the longitudinal fissure and is separated from the **middle frontal gyrus** by the **superior frontal sulcus**. The **inferior frontal gyrus** is divided into three parts by the lateral sulcus: the **pars orbitale, pars triangularis,** and **pars opercularis (Broca's area)**. Of these, the pars opercularis is of vital importance in speech-language pathology, being the site in the dominant hemisphere responsible for speech motor control. The anterior-most prefrontal regions and the inferior orbital regions are associated with some aspects of memory, emotion, and intellect.

Anterior to the central sulcus is the prominent **precentral gyrus**, also referred to widely as the **motor strip** of the cortex. This is the site of initiation of voluntary motor movement, and fibers from this region and supplementary motor areas give rise to the corticospinal and corticobulbar tracts. Although we will discuss this region in the next chapter, you should be aware that it serves the voluntary motor function of the entire body, and the areas of the motor strip serving regions of the body have been well mapped.

homunculus: *L., little man*

b

FIGURE 9-39. b. Brodmann map of lateral and medial cerebrum.

Figure 9–40 shows the regions of the body served by portions of the motor strip. Regions of representation are not restricted to the superior and lateral surfaces, but continue into the medial-most regions of the cortex as well. As you can see, the face, head, and laryngeal regions are on the far lateral edge. If you compare this with the location of Broca's area on the side view of the hemisphere in the previous figure,

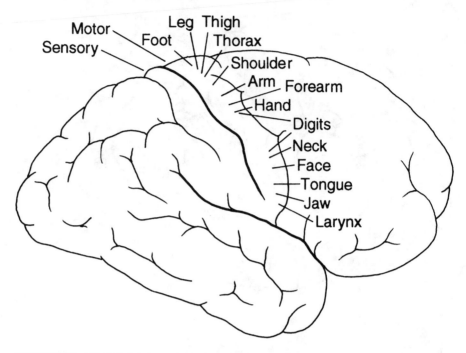

FIGURE 9-40. Right hemisphere, displaying regions of motor cortex governing motor activation of specific body regions.

you will see that these two regions are in close proximity. We will say more about the organization of this region in the next chapter.

Parietal Lobe. The parietal lobe is less neatly defined than the frontal lobe. Functionally, it is the primary reception site for somatic sense. The anterior boundary of the parietal lobe is the central sulcus, and the inferior boundary is the lateral sulcus. To define the posterior boundary, one must identify the parieto-occipital sulcus and draw an imaginary line to the preoccipital notch.

The sensory counterpart to the motor strip is the **postcentral gyrus**. This area receives somatic sensation from various body regions, somatotopically arrayed with a similar distribution to that of the motor strip. Virtually all contralateral somesthetic sensation that reaches consciousness will terminate in this region. Posterior to the postcentral gyrus is the **postcentral sulcus**, providing the anterior margin for the **superior** and **inferior parietal lobules** (that are separated by the intraparietal sulcus).

The inferior parietal lobule is one of the cortical **association areas**, integrating information related to vision (from the occipital lobe), audition (from the temporal lobe), and somatic sense (from the parietal lobe). This inferior lobule is divided into the **supramarginal** and **angular**

gyri. The angular gyrus is particularly important for comprehension of written material.

Temporal Lobe. The temporal lobe is the site of auditory reception and is extraordinarily important for auditory and receptive language processing. It is bordered by the lateral sulcus medially, projecting back to the parietal and occipital lobes posteriorly.

The **superior temporal gyrus** runs posteriorly to the angular gyrus of the parietal lobe, and is separated from the **middle temporal gyrus** by the **superior temporal sulcus**. On the upper medial surface of the superior temporal gyrus is **Heschl's gyrus**, Brodmann area 41, the center for auditory reception. Lateral to this is area 42, a higher order processing region. The posterior portion of the superior temporal gyrus is the functionally defined region known as **Wernicke's area**. Damage to this area of the dominant hemisphere results in disturbances of language, often profound. The inferior temporal gyrus lies within the middle fossa of the skull.

Occipital Lobe. The occipital lobe is the posterior limit of the brain, and is the primary visual reception site. This lobe rests on the tentorium cerebelli, with its anterior margin being the parieto-occipital sulcus, as discussed previously. The **calcarine sulcus** and **parieto-occipital sulcus** mark the boundaries of the wedge-shaped **cuneus**. Lateral to the calcarine sulcus is the **lingual gyrus**, and medial to it is the cuneus, adjacent to the cingulate gyrus. The regions surrounding the calcarine sulcus are the primary reception areas of the visual cortex.

cuneus: L., wedge

Insula. The insular cortex, or **island of Reil**, is not visible without deflecting the temporal lobe. The **circular sulcus** surrounds this oval-shaped lobe placed deep in the lateral sulcus. The **central sulcus of insula** divides the insula into anterior short gyri and a posterior long gyrus. The frontal, temporal, and parietal opercula overly the insula.

insula: L., island

To summarize, the **cerebrum** is divided into two grossly similar, mirror-image **hemispheres** which are connected by means of the massive **corpus callosum**.

- ■ The **gyri** and **sulci** of the hemisphere provide important landmarks for lobes and other regions of the cerebrum.
- ■ The **temporal lobe** is the site of **auditory reception** and **Wernicke's area**.
- ■ The temporal lobe is the prominent lateral lobe separated from the parietal and frontal lobes by the **lateral fissure**.
- ■ The anterior-most region is the **frontal lobe**, the site of most voluntary **motor activation** and the important speech region known as **Broca's area**.
- ■ Adjacent to the frontal lobe is the **parietal lobe**, the region of **somatic sensory reception**.

■ The **occipital lobe** is the most posterior of the regions, and is the site of **visual input** to the cerebrum.

■ The **insular lobe** is revealed by deflecting the temporal lobe and lies deep in the **lateral sulcus**.

■ The **operculum** overlies the insula, and the functionally defined **limbic lobe** includes the **cingulate gyrus, uncus, parahippocampal gyrus**, and other deep structures.

Medial Surface of Cerebral Cortex

corpus callosum: *L., hard body*

genu: *L., knee*

Viewing a sagittal section of the brain reveals a number of extremely important landmarks (see Figure 9–41). The **corpus callosum** is the large, dominating structure immediately inferior to the cerebral gray matter. It is the superhighway of the brain, providing communication concerning sensation and memory among the diverse regions of the two hemispheres by means of myelinated fibers. The corpus callosum makes up the roof of the lateral ventricles and the floor of the cerebral longitudinal fissure. The corpus callosum is divided into the rostrum, genu, body, and splenium. Fibers coursing through the **genu** serve the anterior frontal lobes, whereas fibers of the **body** (or **trunk**) serve the remainder of the frontal lobes and the parietal lobes. The **splenium** provides intercommunication for the temporal and occipital lobes.

a

FIGURE 9–41. a. Medial surface of the cerebral cortex.

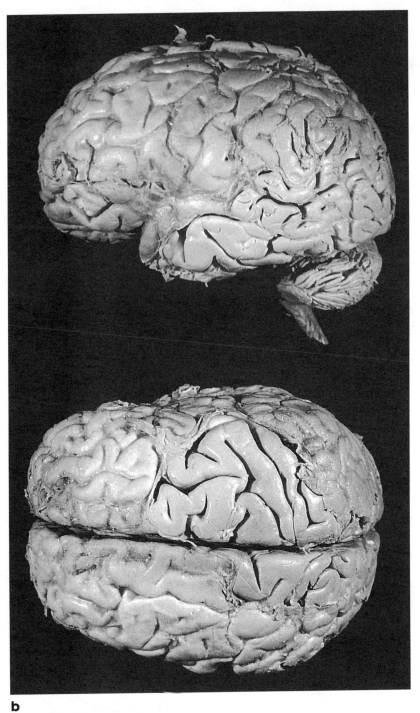

b

FIGURE 9-41. **b.** Photo of cerebral cortex. (After data and view of Carpenter, 1978.)

In the superior aspect of the medial cortex is the **paracentral lobule**, which is the reflected union of the precentral and postcentral gyri. Posterior to the paracentral lobule is the **precuneus**, which is separated from the **cuneus** by the **parieto-occipital sulcus**.

Limbic Lobe. The limbic lobe is not an anatomically distinct region, but one arising from functional relationships associated with motivation, sex drive, emotional behavior, and affect. The limbic lobe includes the uncus (formed by the amygdala), parahippocampal gyrus, cingulate gyrus, olfactory bulb and tract, as well as the hippocampal formation and the dentate gyrus, structures we shall discuss again.

Inferior Surface of Cerebral Cortex. Figure 9–42 shows the inferior cerebral cortex. The anterior portion is the **orbital surface** of the frontal lobe, and the inferior of the temporal lobe. The posterior undersurface is the that of the occipital lobe. The **olfactory sulcus** is superior to the olfactory tract and bulb.

The **parahippocampal gyrus** is medial-most portion of the cerebral cortex. This gyrus and the prominence known as the **uncus** combine

Olfactory tract

Uncus

Parahippocampal gyrus

FIGURE 9–42. Inferior surface of the cerebral cortex.

with the lateral olfactory stria, to make up the primary olfactory cortex, also known as the **pyriform lobe**.

Myelinated Fibers

The gray matter of the cortex represents masses of neuron bodies, but they interact through the **white matter** of the neuron, myelinated fibers. These fibers make up the communication link among the neurons, and without them there would be no neural function. In diseases that cause **demyelination** of the fibers, dysfunction of the areas served is virtually guaranteed.

There are three basic types of fibers. We have already discussed the tracts running to and from the cortex to brainstem and spinal cord, and these are made up of **projection fibers**, connecting the cortex with distant locations. The second type, **association fibers**, provides communication between regions of the same hemisphere. The **cingulum**, for instance, connects frontal and parietal lobes with the temporal lobe and parahippocampal regions. **Commissural fibers** make up the third type, and we have already mentioned the corpus callosum, a major group of commissural fibers. This type of fiber runs from one location on a hemisphere to the corresponding location on the other hemisphere.

The **corona radiata** is a mass of projection fibers running from and to the cortex (see Figure 9–43). It condenses as it courses down, forming an "L" shape as it reaches a location known as the **internal capsule**. The **anterior limb** of this separates the caudate nucleus and putamen of the basal ganglia, and serves the frontal lobe. The **posterior limb** includes the **optic radiation**, fibers projecting to the calcarine sulcus for vision. Nearly all of the afferent fibers within the corona radiata arise from the thalamus, the major sensory relay of the brain. The point of juncture of the anterior and posterior limbs is called the **genu**. Efferent fibers from the cortex make up the motor tracts.

There are both long and short association fibers. The **short association fibers** connect neurons of one gyrus to the next, traversing the sulcus. The **long association fibers** interconnect the lobes of the brain within the same hemisphere. The **uncinate fasciculus** connects the orbital portion, inferior, and middle frontal gyri with the anterior temporal lobe. The extremely important **arcuate fasciculus** permits the superior and middle frontal gyri to communicate with the temporal, parietal, and occipital lobes. A lesion of the arcuate fasciculus can result in conduction aphasia, in which expressive and receptive language remain essentially intact but the individual will be unable to repeat information presented auditorily. The **cingulum**, the white matter of the cingulate gyrus, connects the frontal and parietal lobes with the parahippocampal gyrus and temporal lobe.

Amyotrophic Lateral Sclerosis

There are a number of **demyelinating diseases**, conditions that cause degeneration of the brain myelin. **Amyotrophic lateral sclerosis**, a form of motor neuron disease, is a progressive, demyelinating condition of unknown etiology with a typical course of 2 to 5 years from date of diagnosis to death. Patients, typically in their fourth to fifth decade of life, experience initial weakness in a limb, with fatigue and cramping. As the disease progresses, limb function is lost, although sensory function typically is retained. Motor symptoms indicate both upper and lower motor neuron degeneration, thereby sometimes producing symptoms of spasticity alternating with flaccidity. As the myelin deteriorates, it is replaced with a sclerosis or a covering of hardened tissue that markedly increases neural conduction time. In the later stages of the disease, the patient experiences difficulty with respiration, requiring alteration of posture to accommodate reduced ability to work against gravity. The patient eventually will experience dysphagia and paralysis of muscles of speech while retaining full cognitive function.

Internal capsule

Pons

Medulla

Pyramidal decussation

FIGURE 9–43. Corona radiata as it passes through the internal capsule. (From data of Carpenter, 1978.)

We have already discussed one of the groups of commissural fibers, the corpus callosum. Another important group of fibers makes up the **anterior commissure**. The anterior commissure crosses between hemispheres to connect the right and left olfactory areas, as well as portions of the inferior and middle temporal gyri.

Anatomy of the Subcortex

Basal Ganglia. The basal ganglia (or basal nuclei) are a group of cell bodies intimately related to control of background movement and initiation of movement patterns. The ganglia included under the broader term of basal ganglia include the caudate nucleus (including head, body, and tail), the putamen, and the globus pallidus. Some consider the amygdaloid body (or amygdala) to be part of the basal ganglia, but it is generally included within the limbic system. Functionally, the subthalamic nuclei and substantia nigra may be included as well due to their central role in basal ganglia activity.

caudate nucleus: L., caudatus, tail

globus pallidus: L., white globe

Visualizing the basal ganglia is somewhat of a challenge. The relationship of the parts may be seen in Figure 9–44. The **head of caudate nucleus** is anteriorly placed, the **body** courses up and back, and the **tail** curves down. The **amygdaloid body** is adjacent to the tail, but does not fuse with it. The **globus pallidus** and **putamen** attach to and reflect back on the caudate body.

putamen: L., shell

The combination of globus pallidus and putamen is referred to as the **lentiform** or **lenticular nucleus** because their combined nuclei are lens-

lentiform nucleus: L., lentis, lens

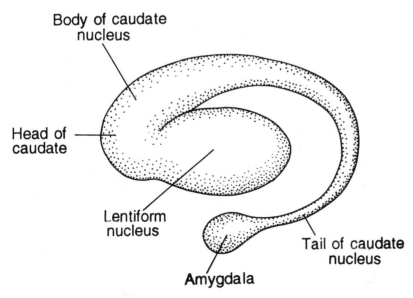

FIGURE 9–44. Components of the basal ganglia. (After Netter, 1973.)

amygdaloid body: L.,
amygdalinus, *almond*

corpus striatum: *L.,*
striped body

shaped. The putamen and caudate nucleus together are referred to as the **striatum**. The **corpus striatum** includes the striatum (putamen and caudate) and globus pallidus. (The corona radiata forming the internal capsule perforate the caudate and putamen, giving a striped appearance, and thus the term "striated body.")

Within the brain, the lentiform nucleus (globus pallidus and putamen) is lateral to the internal capsule, and the caudate is medial to the internal capsule. The head of caudate protrudes into the anterior horn of the lateral ventricle. The body makes up a portion of the floor of the lateral ventricle and is lateral to the superior thalamus. The amygdaloid body lies in the roof of the inferior horn of the lateral ventricle. Lesions to the basal ganglia result in extrapyramidal dysfunction, including hyperkinetic and hypokinetic dysarthrias.

Hippocampal Formation. The hippocampal formation is strongly implicated in memory function, and is part of the rhinencephalon. It communicates with the hypothalamus, which is related to visceral function and emotion, and to portions of the temporal lobe associated with memory function. As you can see from Figure 9–45, the hippo-

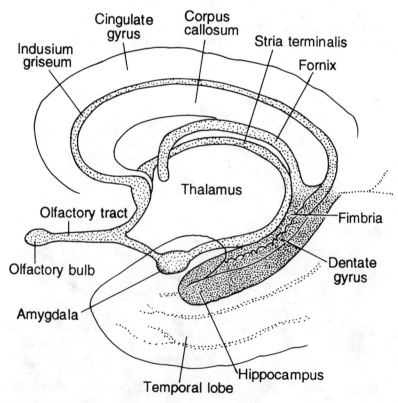

FIGURE 9–45. Orientation of the hippocampal formation. (From data of Netter, 1973.)

campal formation includes the parahippocampal gyrus and makes up a portion of the floor of the inferior horn of the lateral ventricle.

The **pes hippocampus** ("foot") is the anterior projection of the hippocampus, and the **fimbria** of hippocampus is a medial layer of white fibers that are continuous with the fornix. The **fornix** is a near-circle of myelinated fibers terminating in the **mammillary body**, and which provides most of the communication between the hippocampus and the hypothalamus. It contains commissural fibers which permit communication with the opposite hippocampus.

pes hippocampus: L., foot of hippocampus

mammillary body: L., mamillia, nipple

fornix: L., arch

fimbria: L., fringe

The **dentate gyrus** (dentate fascia) lies between the fimbria of hippocampus and the parahippocampal gyrus, and continues as the indusium griseum. The **indusium griseum** is a layer of cell bodies overlaying the corpus callosum and becoming continuous with the cingulate gyrus.

dentate: L., dens, tooth

Diencephalic Structures. The diencephalon is composed of the thalamus, epithalamus, hypothalamus, and subthalamus. This is a small and compact region.

Thalamus. The paired thalami are the largest structures of the diencephalon and are the final, common relay for sensory information directed toward the cerebral cortex. All sensation, with the exception of olfaction, passes through the thalamus, making it an exceedingly important region of the brain. Of those sensations, only pain (and possibly temperature) sense is consciously perceived at the thalamus, but that pain cannot be localized without cortical function.

The **reticular activating system** arises from the thalamus and is the functional system responsible for arousing the cortex, and perhaps for focusing cortical regions to heightened awareness. In addition, the thalamus is the primary bridge for information from the cerebellum and globus pallidus to the motor portion of the cerebral cortex. Each of the nuclei which communicate with a cortical region also receives efferent, corticothalamic projections from the same region.

The thalami form a portion of the lateral walls of the third ventricle, and are separated from the globus pallidus and putamen by the internal capsule. Fibers from the thalamus project to the cortex via the internal capsule and corona radiata. The thalamus is composed of 26 nuclei in three regions defined by the internal medullary lamina.

Thalamic nuclei may be organized into functional categories. **Specific thalamic nuclei** communicate with specific regions of the cerebral cortex, while **association nuclei** communicate with association areas of the cortex. **Subcortical nuclei** have no direct communication with the cerebral cortex.

Epithalamus. The most prominent structures of the epithalamus include the **pineal body**, which is a gland involved in development of gonads, the **habenular nuclei** and **habenular commissure**, the **striae medularis**, and the **posterior commissure**. The habenular nuclei receive input from the septum, hypothalamus, brainstem, raphe nuclei, and ventral tegmental area via the habenulopeduncular tract and stria medullaris. Connections with the thalamus, hypothalamus, and septal area from the habenular nuclei are via the habenulopeduncular tract (fasciculus retroflexus), terminating in the interpeduncular nucleus, which projects to the those structures. The posterior commissure consists of decussating fibers of the superior colliculi, nuclei associated with visual reflexes.

Subthalamus. The major landmark of the subthalamus is the **subthalamic nucleus**, a lentiform structure on the inner surface of the internal capsule. Many fibers project through the subthalamus en route to the thalamus. The subthalamus receives input from globus pallidus and the motor cortex and is involved in control of striated muscle. Lesions to it have been known to produce the violent, uncontrolled flailing movements of arms and legs known as **ballism**. Unilateral lesion produces **hemiballism** of the contralateral side.

Hypothalamus. The hypothalamus makes up the floor of the third ventricle. Although it is comprised of numerous nuclei, it is generally divided into preoptic, mammillary, and tuberal regions (see Figure 9–46). The hypothalamus provides the organizational structure for the **limbic system**. Through interaction with the other components of this system (cingulate gyrus, septal area, parahippocampal gyrus, amygdala, and hippocampal formation), the hypothalamus regulates reproductive behavior and physiology, desire or perception of need for food and water, perception of satiation, control of digestive processes, and metabolic functions including maintenance of water balance and body temperature. Damage to the hypothalamus can result in loss of appropriate autonomic responses, such as heart rate acceleration and sweating, shivering when cold, or even moving to a warmer environment when cold. Damage to the **satiety center** will result in voracious eating, whereas damage to the **feeding center** will result in starvation and dehydration. This structure is involved in the behavioral manifestations associated with emotion (tearing, heart rate acceleration, sweating, goose-flesh, flushing, mouth dryness), although it is assumed that cortical function is an important intermediary in normal emotional response.

In summary, the structures underlying the cerebral cortex are vital to modification of information arriving at or leaving the cerebral cortex.

■ The **basal ganglia** are subcortical structures involved in control of **movement**, while the **hippocampal formation** of the inferior temporal lobe is deeply implicated in **memory** function.

■ The **thalamus** of the **diencephalon** is the final relay for **somatic sensation** directed toward the cerebrum, and other diencephalic structures.

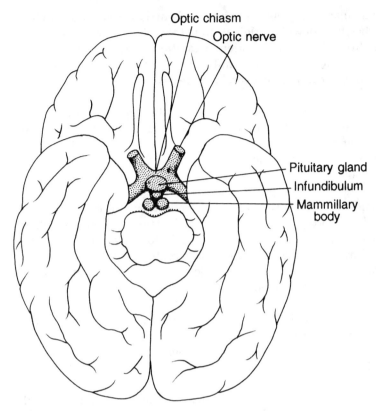

FIGURE 9-46. Structures of the hypothalamus visible from inferior cerebral cortex.

■ The **subthalamus** interacts with the globus pallidus to control **movement**, and the **hypothalamus** controls many bodily functions and desires.

■ The regions of the cerebral cortex are interconnected by means of a complex network of **projection fibers**, connecting the cortex with other structures, **association fibers**, which connect regions of the same hemisphere; and **commissural fibers**, which provide communication between corresponding regions of the two hemispheres.

Cerebrovascular System

Although the brain makes up only 2% of the body weight, it consumes an enormous 20% of the oxygen transported by the vascular system to meet the high metabolic requirements of nervous tissue. The vascular system of the brain (the **cerebrovascular system**) maintains the constant circulation required by the nervous system. Disruption of this supply for a few seconds will begin cellular changes in neurons, and longer vascular deprivation results in devastating effects.

The vascular supply of the brain arises from the carotid and vertebral branches, both of which originate from the aorta. The **carotid division** arises from left and right **internal carotid arteries** which enter the brain lateral to the optic chiasm. The internal carotid arteries give rise to the **anterior** and **middle cerebral arteries**.

The **anterior cerebral artery** courses along the superior surface of the corpus callosum within the medial longitudinal fissure (see Figure 9–47). It branches to supply the medial surface of the frontal and parietal lobes, corpus callosum, basal ganglia, and the anterior limb internal capsule.

The middle cerebral artery courses laterally along the inferior surface of the brain and through the lateral (Sylvian) fissure. It provides blood to the lateral surface of the hemispheres, including the temporal lobe, motor strip, Wernicke's area, sensory reception regions, and association areas. One branch of the middle cerebral artery serves the basal ganglia and internal capsule.

The **vertebral division** arises from the vertebral arteries which ascend on the anterior surface of the medulla oblongata. The vertebral artery branches, forming the descending **anterior** and **posterior spinal arteries**. The left and right vertebral arteries continue to ascend the ventral surface of the brainstem, joining at the superior medulla to form the **basilar artery**. The **superior cerebellar** and **anterior inferior cerebellar arteries** branch from the basilar artery to serve those locations of the cerebellum. (The **posterior inferior cerebellar artery** arises from the vertebral artery prior to this branching.) At the superior ventral pons the basilar artery divides to become the left and right **posterior cerebral arteries**.

The **posterior cerebral artery** serves the inferior temporal and occipital lobes, the medial occipital lobe and primary visual cortex, upper midbrain, diencephalon, and cerebellum.

Circle of Willis. The cerebrovascular system of the brain contains many redundancies to ensure constant blood supply to the brain. The most prominent of these is the **circle of Willis**, a series of **anastomoses** (points of communication between arteries) which completely encircles the optic chiasm. If you will again look at Figure 9–47, you can see that the anterior cerebral arteries are connected by means of the **anterior communicating artery**, and the **posterior communicating artery** connects the middle cerebral artery with the posterior cerebral artery. This connects the vertebral and carotid systems, helps equalize locally high or low blood pressure, and promotes equal distribution of blood.

The anterior and posterior spinal arteries supply the spinal cord. The single anterior spinal artery descends in the anterior medial fissure of

INFERIOR VIEW

Ant. cerebral **a.**

Middle cerebral a.

Post. cerebral a.

Basilar a.

Temporal lobe (cut)

Middle vertebral a.
Ant. spinal a.

Internal carotid a.

Ant. inf. cerebellar a.

Post. inf. cerebellar **a.**

CIRCLE OF WILLIS

Anterior communicating a.

Anterior cerebral a.

Basilar a.
Superior cerebellar a.
Posterior cerebral a.
Posterior communicating a.

Anterior cerebral a.

MEDIAL VIEW

Middle cerebral a.

Internal carotid a.

LATERAL VIEW

FIGURE 9–47. Major vascular supply of the cerebral cortex.

the spinal cord, giving off **radicular arteries** which serve the anterior spinal cord and anterior funiculus. The left and right posterior spinal arteries descend in similar fashion, also giving off radicular arteries. Blood from the posterior spinal arteries serves the posterior funiculi and posterior horns, while that of the anterior spinal artery serves the anterior spinal cord. Radicular arteries from anterior and posterior arteries serve spinal nerves. Anastomoses with the vertebral, posterior intercostal, lumbar, and sacral arteries provide a safeguard against vascular accident.

Venous Drainage. The blood supply for the brain requires a return route for blood that has circulated and exchanged its nutrients. The **venous system** is the system of blood vessels called veins which provide the means of draining carbon-dioxide-laden blood to the lungs for re-oxygenation.

Venous drainage is accomplished by means of a series of superficial and deep cisterns. Superficial drainage empties into the superior sagittal sinus and transverse sinus. Deep drainage is by means of the inferior sagittal sinus, the straight sinus, transverse sinuses and sigmoid sinus. Blood returns to the general blood stream by means of the jugular veins, and spinal cord drainage is by means of radicular veins.

Obstruction of the cerebrovascular supply typically occurs in one of two ways. A **thrombus** is a foreign body (such as a clot of blood or bubble of air) that obstructs a blood vessel, and that obstruction is called a **thrombosis**. If the thrombus breaks loose from its site of formation and floats through the blood stream it becomes an **embolus**, or floating clot. An **embolism** is an obstruction of a blood vessel by that foreign body brought to the point of occlusion by blood flow. **Aneurysm** is a dilation or ballooning of a blood vessel due to weak walls. When an intracranial aneurysm ruptures, the blood is released into the space surrounding the brain, in most cases, because most aneurysms occur in arteries as opposed to capillaries. The pressure associated with both development of the ballooning aneurysm and the sudden release of blood into the cranial cavity is life-threatening, with sites of neural damage being related to the location of the rupture.

Occlusion of the anterior cerebral artery is infrequent, resulting in hemiplegia, loss of some sensory function, and personality change (see Figure 9–48). Occlusion of the middle cerebral artery is the most common and can result in severe disability due to the critical nature of the areas served. In addition to severe unilateral or bilateral motor and sensory deficit, left hemisphere damage to Broca's area, Wernicke's area, and association areas may produce profound aphasia. Posterior cerebral artery occlusion produces variable deficit which may include memory dysfunction.

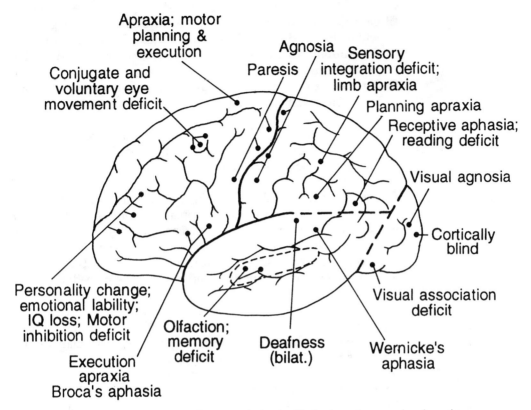

FIGURE 9–48. General deficits associated with lesions to cerebral cortex.

In summary, the **cerebrovascular system** is the literal life-blood of the brain.

■ The **anterior cerebral arteries** serve the medial surfaces of the brain, while the **middle cerebral artery** serves the lateral cortex, including the temporal lobe, motor strip, Wernicke's area, and much of the parietal lobe.

■ The **vertebral arteries** branch to form the anterior and posterior spinal arteries, with ascending components serving the ventral brainstem.

■ The **basilar artery** gives rise to the **superior** and **anterior inferior cerebellar arteries** to serve the cerebellum, while the **posterior inferior cerebellar artery** arises from the **vertebral** artery.

■ The basilar artery divides to become the **posterior cerebral arteries**, serving the inferior temporal and occipital lobes, upper midbrain, and diencephalon.

■ The **circle of Willis** is a series of communicating arteries that provides redundant pathways for blood flow to regions of the cerebral cortex, equalizing pressure and flow of blood.

■ Obstruction of the blood supply is always critical: A foreign body within the blood vessel (**thrombus**) creates an obstruction to blood flow (**thrombosis**), or becomes an **embolus** when released into the blood stream.

■ An **aneurysm** is a ballooning of a blood vessel, and rupture of an aneurysm results in blood being released into the region of the brain.

■ The **middle cerebral artery** is the most common site of occlusion, resulting in significant language and speech deficit if the occlusion involves the dominant cerebral hemisphere.

Cerebellum. The cerebellum is the largest component of the hind-brain, resting within the posterior cranial fossa, immediately inferior to the posterior cerebral cortex. The cerebellum is responsible for coordinating motor commands with sensory inputs to control movement, and it communicates with the brainstem, spinal cord, and cerebral cortex by means of superior, middle, and inferior cerebral peduncles.

From behind, one can see that the cerebellum is composed of two hemispheres and is prominently invested with horizontal grooves. As you can see from the posterior view of Figure 9–49, the **primary fissure** separates the cerebellar **cortex** into two lobes (by the way, you now realize that the term "cortex" is not specific to the cerebral cortex). The **anterior lobe** is often referred to as the superior lobe, and the **middle lobe** is known also as the inferior lobe. The **vermis** separates the two hemispheres and aids in defining the **intermediate** and **lateral** cerebellar regions of the posterior surface.

vermis: *L., worm*

To view the cerebellum from the front one must remove it from the brainstem. The surface from the front reveals the third lobe of the cerebellum, the **flocculonodular lobe**, made up of the right and left **flocculi** and central **nodulus**. The prominent **middle cerebellar peduncle** is between the **superior** and **inferior cerebellar peduncles**.

paleocerebellum: *Gr.,* **paleo,** *old cerebellum*

neocerebellum: *Gr.,* neo, *new cerebellum*

The cerebellum may be divided functionally into three regions. The flocculonodular lobe is functionally referred to as the **vestibulocerebellum** (or archicerebellum), while the **spinocerebellum** (or paleocerebellum) is the anterior lobe and the portion of the posterior lobe associated with the arm and leg. The posterior lobes and the intermediate vermis make up the **neocerebellum** (or **pontocerebellum**).

The inner cerebellum is faintly reminiscent of the cerebral cortex. The outer cortex is a dense array of neurons, and beneath this is a mass of white communicating axons. At the center of the white fibers are a series of nuclei serving as relays between the cerebellum and the communicating regions of the body.

The cerebellar cortex is composed of three layers, the outer **molecular layer**, the intermediate **Purkinje layer**, and the deep **granular layer**

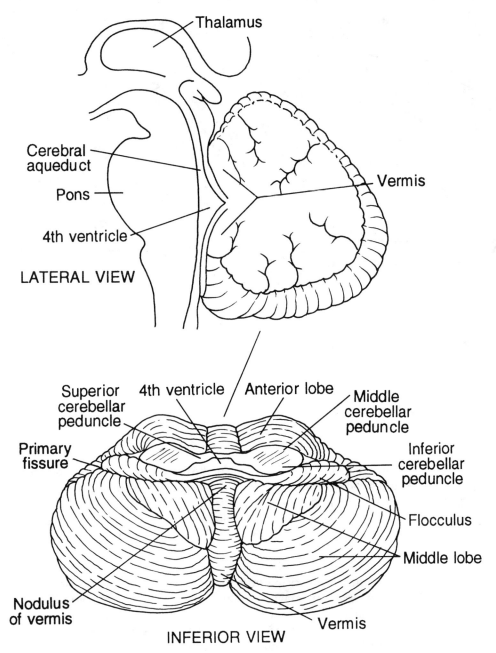

FIGURE 9–49. Cerebellum as seen in sagittal section and from beneath. (After views and data of Poritsky, 1992.)

(see Figure 9–50). The outer molecular layer contains **Golgi**, **basket**, and **stellate cells**, and the intermediate layer contains **Purkinje cells**. Purkinje cells are large neurons forming the boundary between the molecular and granular layers of the cortex. Axons of the 15 million Purkinje cells project to the central cerebellar nuclei. Excitation of

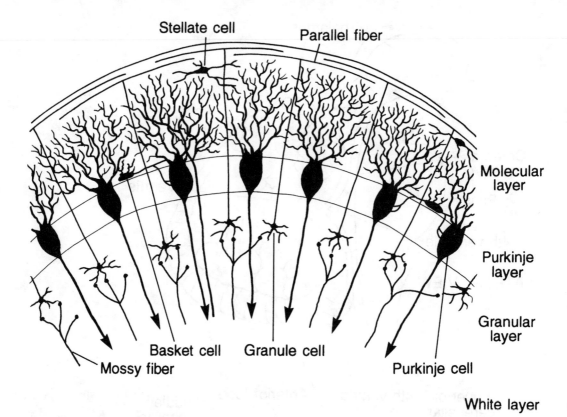

FIGURE 9–50. Cellular layers of the cerebellar cortex.

Purkinje cells causes inhibition of the nucleus with which it communicates. Golgi cells project their dendrites into the molecular layer and their axons into the granular layer. Their soma receive input from both climbing fibers and Purkinje cells, and the axons synapse with granule cell dendrites. Basket cells and stellate cells arborize to communicate with Purkinje cells.

Climbing fibers arising from the inferior olivary nuclei pass through the inner granular layer to communicate with the Purkinje cells. These fibers are strongly excitatory to Purkinje cells. Granule cells within this inner layer project axons to the outer layer where they divide into a "T" form. The branches course at roughly right angles to the base of the axon, synapsing with the dendritic arborization of the Purkinje cells. Activation of these granule cells excites basket and stellate cells but inhibits Purkinje cells. Projections from noncerebellar regions (spinal cord, brainstem, cerebral cortex) terminate in mossy fibers.

There are four pairs of nuclei within the cerebellum, all of which receive input from the Purkinje cells of the cortex (see Figure 9–51). The **dentate nucleus** has the appearance of serrated sac, opening medially.

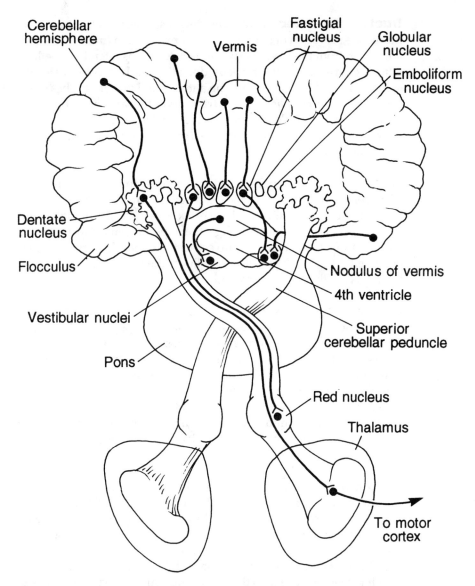

FIGURE 9-51. Cerebellar nuclei and interaction between cerebellum and cerebral cortex. (After view and data of Poritksy, 1992.)

Projections from this nucleus route through the superior cerebellar peduncle to synapse in the ventrolateral nucleus of the thalamus and from there ascend to the cerebral cortex by means of thalamocortical fibers. The **emboliform** and **globose nuclei** (collectively referred to as the **nucleus interpositus**) project to the red nucleus, providing input to the rubrospinal tract. The **fastigial nucleus** communicates with the vestibular nuclei of the brainstem, the reticular formation of the pons and medulla, and inferior olive.

Tracts of the Cerebellum. The **dorsal spinocerebellar tract** communicates sensation of temperature, proprioception (muscle spindle), and touch from the lower body and legs to the ipsilateral cerebellum. Afferents arise from the nucleus dorsalis (Clarke's column) in the spinal cord and project to both the anterior and posterior lobes of the cerebellum. The **cuneocerebellar tract** serves the same function for the arms and upper trunk, originating in the external cuneate nucleus of the cervical region, and entering the cerebellum through the inferior cerebellar peduncle.

The **ventral spinocerebellar tract** transmits proprioception information (golgi tendon organs) and pain sense from the legs and lower trunk to the ipsilateral cerebellar cortex. Fibers decussate within the spinal cord, ascend, enter through the superior cerebellar peduncle, and then decussate again to project to the cortex. The **rostral spinocerebellar tract** is the cervical parallel of the ventral spinocerebellar tract, serving the upper trunk and arm region.

Pontocerebellar fibers from the pontine nuclei provide the greatest input to the cerebellum as they cross midline and ascend as the middle cerebellar peduncle to terminate as mossy fibers. **Olivocerebellar fibers** from the inferior olivary and medial accessory olivary nucleus of the medulla project to the contralateral cerebellum, terminating as climbing fibers. The olive receives input from the spinal cord, cerebral cortex, and red nucleus, as well as visual information. All other tracts of the cerebellum terminate on mossy fibers. The **vestibulocerebellar** tract provides input from the vestibular nuclei to the flocculonodular lobe via the inferior peduncles.

The **corticopontine** projection is an important feedback system for control of voluntary movement. Projections from parietal, occipital, temporal, and frontal lobes (including the motor cortex) synapse on pontine nuclei, projecting via pontocerebellar fibers to the opposite cerebellar cortex. The mossy fiber terminations synapse with granule cells, the branches of which synapse with Purkinje cell dendrites. The Purkinje cells synapse with the dentate nucleus which projects back to the cerebellar cortex as well as to the motor cortex of the cerebrum via the superior cerebellar peduncle and thalamus. In this way the command for voluntary movement can be modified relative to body position, muscle tension, muscle movement, and so on.

Cerebellar Peduncles. The superior cerebellar peduncle (brachium conjunctivum) arises in the anterior cerebellar hemisphere, coursing through the lateral wall of the fourth ventricle to decussate within the pons at the level of the inferior colliculi. Many tracts are served by this peduncle. **Dentatothalamic** fibers arise from the dentate nucleus and synapse in the opposite red nucleus and thalamus. The ventral spinocerebellar tract ascends within this peduncle, and fibers from the fastigial nucleus descend in conjunction with this peduncle as they course to the lateral vestibular nucleus. The **middle cerebellar peduncle** (brachium pontis) is made up of fibers projecting from the contralateral pontine nuclei. The **inferior cerebellar peduncle** (restiform body) communicates input from the spinocerebellar tracts to the cerebellum, exiting the brainstem at the upper medulla.

Cerebellar Function. Cerebellar function may be reasonably partitioned according to the portions of the cerebellum. The flocculonodular lobe (archicerebellum) is the oldest component and is responsible for orientation of the body in space. It receives input from the vestibular nuclei of the brainstem, and damage to this portion of the cerebellum will result in trunk ataxia, staggering, and generally reduced response to motion (as in reduced vestibular responses or motion sickness).

The newer anterior (superior) lobe (the paleocerebellum) exerts moderating control over antigravity muscles. Damage can result in increased stretch reflexes of support musculature. The "young" posterior (inferior) lobe (neocerebellum) is responsible for stopping or damping movements, especially those of the hands. Damage to this lobe will result in problems with fine movements, dysmetria (inability to control the range of movement), tremor associated with voluntary movement, and trouble with performing alternating movement tasks (such as oral diadochokinetic tasks). One can see gait deficits and hypotonia as well.

The cerebellum is a vital "silent partner" in integration of body movement with the internal and external environment of the body. Although it is incapable of initiating movement, it is intimately related to control of the rate and range of movement, as well as the force with which that movement is executed.

To summarize, the **cerebellum** is responsible for **coordinating motor commands** with sensory inputs, communicating with the brainstem, cerebrum, and spinal cord.

- The cerebellum is divided into **anterior, middle,** and **flocculonodular** lobes, and communicates with the rest of the nervous system via the **superior, middle,** and **inferior cerebral** peduncles.
- The **flocculonodular** lobe coordinates position in space via the **vestibular** nuclei.
- The **anterior lobe** coordinates **postural adjustment** against gravity, and the **posterior lobe** mediates **fine motor** adjustments.
- The **cerebellar cortex** consists of an **outer molecular layer**, a **Purkinje layer**, and a deep **granular layer**.
- The **Golgi, basket, stellate,** and **Purkinje cells** are responsible for coordinating input received from the nervous system.

Four pairs of nuclei are found in the cerebellum.

■ The sack-like **dentate nucleus** project output through the **superior cerebellar peduncle** to **red nucleus**, **thalamus**, and ultimately the **cerebral cortex**.

■ The **emboliform** and **globose nuclei** project to **inferior olive** via the **red nucleus**, with information ultimately reaching the **contralateral cerebellar hemisphere**.

■ The **fastigial nucleus** communicates with the **vestibular nuclei**.

Several tracts provide conduit to and from the cerebellum.

■ The **dorsal spinocerebellar** and **cuneocerebellar tracts** communicate proprioception (muscle spindle), temperature, and touch sense from the lower and upper body to the cerebellum.

■ The **ventral spinocerebellar** and **rostral spinocerebellar tracts** mediate ipsilateral proprioceptive information (golgi tendon organ) and pain sense from the lower and upper body.

■ The **olivocerebellar tract** mediates information received at the olivary complex from the spinal cord, cerebral cortex, red nucleus, and visual and cutaneous senses, and provides communication between cerebellar hemispheres.

■ The **superior cerebellar peduncle** enters the pons at the level of the inferior colliculi, serving the dentate nucleus, red nucleus, and thalamus.

■ The **middle cerebellar peduncle** consists of projections from the pontine nuclei, and the **inferior cerebellar peduncle** receives input from the spinocerebellar tracts, exiting at the upper medulla.

This overview of neuroanatomy should give you some feel for the complexity of this system. The interaction of all of these systems provides us with the smooth motor function required for speech, as well as the cognitive and linguistics processes required for comprehension of the spoken word and formulation of a response. The next chapter will examine some of those processes.

CHAPTER SUMMARY

The **nervous system** is a complex, hierarchical structure. Voluntary movement, sensory awareness, and cognitive function are the domain of the **cerebral cortex**. The communication links of the nervous system are **spinal nerves**, **cranial nerves**, and **tracts** of the brainstem and spinal cord. Several organizational schemes characterize the nervous system. The **autonomic** and **somatic nervous systems** control involuntary and voluntary functions. One may divide the nervous system into **central** and **peripheral** nervous systems. **Developmental** characterization separates the brain into **prosencephalon** (**telencephalon** and **diencephalon**), the **mesencephalon** (**midbrain**), and the **rhomben-cephalon** (**metencephalon** and **myelencephalon**). Monopolar, bipolar, or multipolar **neurons** communicate through synapse by means of **neurotransmitter substance**. Responses may be **excitatory** or **inhibitory**. **Glial cells** provide the fatty sheath for **myelinated** axons, as well as support structure for neurons.

The **spinal cord** is comprised of **tracts** and **nuclei**. The 31 pairs of **spinal nerves** serve the limbs and trunk. **Sensory nerves** have cell bodies in **dorsal root ganglia** and **motor neuron** bodies lie within the spinal cord. **Upper motor neurons** have their cell bodies above the segment at which the spinal nerve originates. **Lower motor neurons** are the final neurons in the efferent chain. **Efferent tracts**, such as the corticospinal tract, transmit information from the brain to the spinal nerves. Afferent tracts such as the **spinothalamic tract**, transmit information concerning the physical state of the limbs and trunk to higher brain centers. The **corticobulbar tract** is of particular interest to speech-language patholo-gists because of it serves **motor cranial nerves** for speech.

The **brainstem** is divided into **medulla**, **pons**, and **midbrain**. It is more highly organized than the spinal cord and mediates higher level body functions such as vestibular responses. The **pyramidal decussation** of the medulla is the point at which the motor commands originating in one hemisphere of the cerebral cortex cross to serve the opposite side of the body. The IX, X, XI, and XII cranial nerves emerge at the level of the **medulla**. The **pons** contains four cranial nerve nuclei, the V, VI, VII, and VIII nerves. The **midbrain** contains the important cerebral pedun-cles, and gives rise to the III and IV cranial nerves. The **reticular for-mation** is a phylogenetically old set of nuclei essential for life function. The pons and midbrain set the stage for communication with the high-er levels of the brain, including the **cerebellum** and **cerebrum**. This communication link permits not only **complex motor** acts, but **con-sciousness**, **awareness**, and **volitional** acts.

Cranial nerves are extremely important to the speech-language pathologist. Cranial nerves may be **sensory**, **motor**, or **mixed** sensory-motor, and are categorized based on their function as being **general** or **specialized**, and as serving **visceral** or **somatic** organs or structures. The **V trigeminal** innervates muscles of mastication and the tensor veli palatini, and communicates sensation from the face, mouth, teeth, mucosal lining, and tongue. The **VII facial** nerve innervates muscles of facial expression, and the sensory component serves taste of the anterior two thirds of the tongue. The **VIII vestibulocochlear** nerve mediates auditory and vestibular sensation. The **IX glossopharyngeal** nerve serves the posterior tongue taste receptors, as well as somatic sense from the tongue, fauces, pharynx, and eustachian tube. The sty-lopharyngeus and superior pharyngeal constrictor muscles receive motor innervation via this nerve. The **X vagus** serves autonomic and somatic functions, mediating pain, touch, and temperature from the ear drum and pain sense from the pharynx, larynx, and esophagus. The **recurrent laryngeal** nerve and **superior laryngeal** nerves supply motor innervation for the intrinsic muscles of the larynx. The **XI accessory** nerve innervates the sternocleidomastoid and trapezius muscles, and collaborates with the vagus in activation of palatal, laryngeal, and pharyngeal muscles. The **XII hypoglossal** nerve innervates the muscles of the tongue with the exception of the palatoglossus.

The **cerebral cortex** is protected from physical insult by **cerebrospinal fluid** and the **meningeal linings**, the **dura, pia,** and **arachnoid mater**. Cerebrospinal fluid originating within the **ventricles** of the brain and circulating around the spinal cord cushions these structures from trauma associated with rapid acceleration. The **cerebrum** is divided into two **hemispheres** connected by the **corpus callosum**. The **gyri** and **sulci** of the hemisphere provide important landmarks for lobes and other regions of the cerebrum. The **temporal lobe** is the site of auditory reception, the **frontal lobe** is responsible for most voluntary motor activation, and of the important speech region known as **Broca's area**. The **parietal lobe** is the region of somatic sensory reception. The **occipital lobe** is the site of visual input to the cerebrum. The **insular lobe** is revealed by deflecting the temporal lobe, and lies deep in the lateral sulcus. The **operculum** overlies the insula. The functionally defined **limbic lobe**, includes the cingulate gyrus, uncus, parahippocampal gyrus, and other deep structures.

The **basal ganglia** are subcortical structures involved in control of movement, and the hippocampal formation of the inferior temporal lobe is deeply implicated in memory function. The **thalamus** of the diencephalon is the final relay for somatic sensation directed toward the cerebrum and other diencephalic structures. The **subthalamus** interacts with the globus pallidus to control movement, and the **hypothalamus** controls many bodily functions and desires. The regions of the cerebral cortex are interconnected by means of a complex network of **projection fibers**, connecting the cortex with other structures, **association fibers**, which connect regions of the same hemisphere, and **commissural fibers**, which provide communication between corresponding regions of the two hemispheres.

The **anterior cerebral arteries** serve the medial surfaces of the brain, and the **middle cerebral artery** serves the lateral cortex, including the temporal lobe, motor strip, Wernicke's area, and much of the parietal lobe. The **vertebral arteries** branch to form the anterior and posterior spinal arteries, with ascending components serving the ventral brainstem. The **basilar artery** gives rise to the superior and anterior inferior cerebellar arteries to serve the cerebellum, while the **posterior inferior cerebellar artery** arises from the vertebral artery. The basilar artery divides to become the **posterior cerebral arteries**, serving the inferior temporal and occipital lobes, upper midbrain, and diencephalon. The circle of Willis is a series of communicating arteries that provides redundant pathways for blood flow to regions of the cerebral cortex, equalizing pressure and flow of blood.

The **cerebellum** coordinates motor and sensory information, communicating with the brainstem, cerebrum, and spinal cord. It is divided into **anterior, middle,** and **flocculonodular** lobes and communicates with the rest of the nervous system via the superior, middle, and inferior **cerebral peduncles**. Position in space is coordinated via the flocculonodular lobe, and adjustment against gravity is mediated by the anterior lobe. The posterior lobe mediates fine motor adjustments. The superior cerebellar peduncle enters the pons and serves the **dentate nucleus, red nucleus,** and **thalamus**. The middle cerebellar peduncle communicates with the pontine nuclei, while the inferior cerebellar peduncle receives input from the spinocerebellar tracts.

Study Questions

1. The _____ governs voluntary actions.

2. The _____ is responsible for coordinating movement

3. _____ is the sense of muscle and joint position sense

4. _____ are groups of cell bodies in the PNS with functional unity.

5. _____ sense is the sense of the body in motion

6. Special senses include _____, _____, _____, _____, and _____ _____

7. The _____ system includes the cerebrum, cerebellum, subcortical structures, brainstem, and spinal cord

8. The _____ system consists of the 12 pairs of cranial nerves and 31 pairs of spinal nerves, as well as the sensory receptors

9. The _____ system governs involuntary activities of involuntary muscles

10. The _____ nervous system governs voluntary activities.

11. Information directed toward the brain is termed _____

_____ while information directed from the brain is termed

_____

12. Developmental divisions: Identify the division referred to by each statement.

a. _____ refers to the "extended" or "telescoped" brain, and includes the cerebral hemispheres, the white matter immediately beneath it, the basal ganglia, and the olfactory tract

b. _____ refers to the olfactory bulb, tract, and striae; pyriform area; intermediate olfactory area; hippocampal formation; and fornix.

c. _____ includes the thalamus, hypothalamus, pituitary gland (hypophysis), and optic tract.

d. _____ refers to the midbrain

e. _____ includes the pons and cerebellum.

f. _____ refers to the medulla

13. On the figure below identify the parts of the neuron indicated.

a. _____

b. _____

c. _____

d. _____

e. _____

f. _____

g. _____

h. _____

i. _____

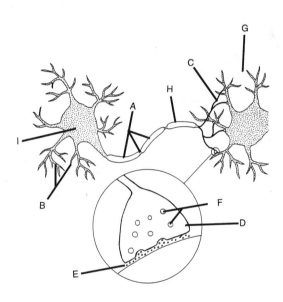

14. On the figure below identify the parts of the cerebrum indicated.

a. _____ lobe

b. _____ lobe

c. _____ lobe

d. _____ lobe

e. _____ gyrus

f. _____ gyrus

g. _____ sulcus

h. _____ sulcus

15. On the figure below identify the parts of the surface of the cerebrum.

a. _____gyrus

b. _____

c. _____gyrus

d. _____area

e. _____area

f. _____gyrus

g. _____gyrus

h. _____sulcus

16. On the figure below identify the components of the ventricle system indicated.

a. _____

b. _____

c. _____

d. _____

17. On the figure below identify the arteries and structures indicated.

a. _____artery

b. _____artery

c. _____artery

d. _____artery

e. _____artery

f. _____artery

g. _____artery

h. _____artery

i. _____

Study Question Answers

1. The <u>CEREBRUM</u> governs voluntary actions.

2. The <u>CEREBELLUM</u> is responsible for coordinating movement

3. <u>PROPRIOCEPTION</u> is the sense of muscle and joint position sense

4. <u>GANGLIA</u> are groups of cell bodies in the PNS with functional unity.

5. <u>KINESTHETIC</u> sense is the sense of the body in motion

6. Special senses include <u>OLFACTION</u>, <u>VISION</u>, <u>GUSTATION</u>, and <u>AUDITION</u>.

7. The <u>CENTRAL NERVOUS SYSTEM</u> includes the cerebrum, cerebellum, subcortical structures, brainstem, and spinal cord

8. The <u>PERIPHERAL NERVOUS SYSTEM</u> consists of the 12 pairs of cranial nerves and 31 pairs of spinal nerves, as well as the sensory receptors

9. The <u>AUTONOMIC NERVOUS SYSTEM</u> governs involuntary activities of involuntary muscles

10. The <u>SOMATIC NERVOUS SYSTEM</u> nervous system governs voluntary activities.

11. Information directed toward the brain is termed <u>AFFERENT</u> while information directed from the brain is termed <u>EFFERENT</u>.

12. Developmental divisions: Identify the division referred to by each statement.

    a. <u>TELENCEPHALON</u> refers to the "extended" or "telescoped" brain, and includes the cerebral hemispheres, the white matter immediately beneath it, the basal ganglia, and the olfactory tract

    b. <u>RHINENCEPHALON</u> refers to the olfactory bulb, tract, and striae; pyriform area; intermediate olfactory area; hippocampal formation; and fornix.

    c. <u>DIENCEPHALON</u> includes the thalamus, hypothalamus, pituitary gland (hypophysis), and optic tract.

    d. <u>MESENCEPHALON</u> refers to the midbrain

    e. <u>METENCEPHALON</u> includes the pons and cerebellum.

    f. <u>MYELENCEPHALON</u> refers to the medulla

13. On the figure below identify the parts of the neuron indicated.

    a. <u>AXON</u>

    b. <u>DENDRITE</u>

c. <u>TELODENDRIA</u>

d. <u>TERMINAL END BOUTON</u>

e. <u>SYNAPTIC CLEFT</u>

f. <u>SYNAPTIC VESICLES</u>

g. <u>POSTSYNAPTIC NEURON</u>

h. <u>MYELIN SHEATH</u>

i. <u>SOMA</u>

14. On the figure below identify the parts of the cerebrum indicated.

a. <u>FRONTAL</u> lobe

b. <u>TEMPORAL</u> lobe

c. <u>OCCIPITAL</u> lobe

d. <u>PARIETAL</u> lobe

e. <u>PRECENTRAL</u> gyrus

f. <u>POSTCENTRAL</u> gyrus

g. <u>CENTRAL</u> sulcus

h. <u>LATERAL</u> sulcus

15. On the figure below identify the parts of the surface of the cerebrum.

a. <u>CINGULATE GYRUS</u>

b. <u>CORPUS CALLOSUM</u>

c. <u>SUPERIOR TEMPORAL GYRUS</u>

d. <u>WERNICKE'S AREA</u>

e. <u>BROCA'S AREA</u>

f. <u>PRECENTRAL GYRUS</u>

g. <u>HESCHL'S GYRUS</u>

h. <u>CENTRAL SULCUS</u>

16. On the figure below identify the components of the ventricle system indicated.

a. <u>LATERAL VENTRICLE</u>

b. <u>THIRD VENTRICLE</u>

c. <u>FOURTH VENTRICLE</u>

d. <u>CEREBRAL AQUEDUCT</u>

17. On the figure below identify the arteries and structures indicated.

    a. <u>ANTERIOR CEREBRAL ARTERY</u>

    b. <u>MIDDLE CEREBRAL ARTERY</u>

    c. <u>POSTERIOR CEREBRAL ARTERY</u>

    d. <u>ANTERIOR COMMUNICATING ARTERY</u>

    e. <u>SUPERIOR CEREBELLAR ARTERY</u>

    f. <u>INTERNAL CAROTID ARTERY</u>

    g. <u>BASILAR ARTERY</u>

    h. <u>VERTEBRAL ARTERY</u>

    i. <u>CIRCLE OF WILLIS</u>

REFERENCES

Bateman, H. E., & Mason, R. M. (1984). *Applied anatomy and physiology of the speech and hearing mechanism.* Springfield, IL: Charles C. Thomas.

Bhatnagar, S. C., & Andy, O. J. (1995). *Neuroscience for the study of communicative disorders.* Baltimore, MD: Williams & Wilkins.

Bowman, J. P. (1971). *The muscle spindle and neural control of the tongue.* Springfield, IL: Charles C. Thomas.

Carpenter, M. B. (1978). *Core text of neuroanatomy* (2nd ed.). Baltimore, MD: Williams & Wilkins.

Chusid, J. G. (1979). *Correlative neuroanatomy and functional neurology* (17th ed.). Los Altos, CA: Lange Medical Publications.

Cotman, C. W., & McGaugh, J. L. (1980). *Behavioral neuroscience.* New York: Academic Press.

Darley, F. L., Aronson, A. E., & Brown, J. R. (1975). *Motor speech disorders.* Philadelphia, PA: W. B. Saunders.

Filskov, S. B., & Boll, T. J. (1981). *Handbook of clinical neuropsychology.* New York: John Wiley & Sons.

Ganong, W. F. (1981). *Review of medical physiology.* Los Altos, CA: Lange Medical Publications.

Gelfand, S. A. (1990). *Hearing.* New York: Marcel Dekker.

Gilman, S., & Winans, S. S. (1982). *Manter and Gatz's essentials of clinical neuroanatomy and neurophysiology.* Philadelphia, PA: F. A. Davis.

Kandel, E. R., Schwartz, J. H., & Jessell, T. M. (1991). *Principles of neural science.* Norfalk, CT: Appleton and Lange.

Kuehn, D. P., Lemme, M. L., & Baumgartner, J. M. (1989). *Neural bases of speech, hearing, and language.* Boston, MA: College-Hill Press.

McMinn, R. M. H., Hutchings, R. T., & Logan, B. M. (1994). *Color atlas of head and neck anatomy.* London: Mosby-Wolfe.

Moore, K. L. (1988). *The developing human.* Philadelphia, PA: W. B. Saunders Company.

Netsell, R. (1986). *A neurobiologic view of speech production and the dysarthrias.* San Diego, CA: College-Hill Press.

Netter, F. H. (1983a). *The CIBA collection of medical illustrations. Vol. 1. Nervous system. Part I. Anatomy and physiology.* West Caldwell, NJ: CIBA Pharmaceutical Company.

Netter, F. H. (1983b). *The CIBA collection of medical illustrations. Vol. 1. Nervous system. Part II. Neurologic and neuromuscular disorders.* West Caldwell, NJ: CIBA Pharmaceutical Company.

Netter, F. H. (1989). *Atlas of human anatomy.* West Caldwell, NJ: CIBA Pharmaceutical Company.

Noback, C. R., & Demarest, R. J. (1977). *The nervous system.* New York: McGraw-Hill.

Nolte, J. (1993). *The human brain.* St. Louis, MO: Mosby Year Book.

Poritsky, R. (1992). *Neuroanatomy: A functional atlas of parts and pathways.* St. Louis, MO: Mosby-Year Book.

Rohen, J. W., & Yokochi, C. (1993). *Color atlas of anatomy.* New York: Igaku-Shoin.

Twietmayer, A., & McCracken, T. (1992). *Coloring guide to regional human anatomy.* Philadelphia: Lea & Febiger.

Wood, P. J., & Criss, W. R. (1975). *Normal and abnormal development of the human nervous system.* Hagerstown, MD: Harper & Row.

Williams, P., & Warrick, R. (1980). *Gray's anatomy* (36th Brit. ed.). Philadelphia, PA: W. B. Saunders.

Yost, W. A., & Nielsen, D. W. (1977). *Fundamentals of hearing.* New York: Holt, Rinehart and Winston.

Zemlin, W. R. (1988). *Speech and hearing science. Anatomy and physiology.* Englewood Cliffs, NJ: Prentice-Hall.

CHAPTER

10

Neurophysiology

There is perhaps no greater challenge than to examine the nervous system. While extraordinary advances over the past 30 years have vastly expanded our understanding of the workings of the brain, we still have a great deal to learn. We will set out in this chapter to provide at least some of the pieces to a puzzle. Above all, knowledge of how the nervous system functions is the key to successful treatment by speech-language pathologists. All therapy works within the limits of the client's nervous system, because behavior, motivation, learning, and especially speech and language function depend on the ability to process information and respond to it. We hope that this introduction to nervous system physiology will tempt you to spend your life examining it.

We will approach our discussion of nervous system function from the "bottom-up," looking first at the simplest responses of the system (communication between neurons) and working our way up to the all-important functions of the cerebral cortex. The single neuron response and reflex arc associated with the spinal cord represent the basic level of information processing, the brainstem structures provide control of balance and other high-level reflexes. The diencephalon supports attention to stimulation and basic (but highly organized) responses to danger. The cerebellum provides exquisite integration of sensory information and motor planning, but the cerebrum is the site of consciousness, planning, ideation, and cognition. When you are caught off guard by a loud noise, your lower neural processes will register the noise, cause you to orient to it, cause you to flinch, and even possibly to move away from it. Only your cerebrum evaluates the input to determine the nature and meaning of the noise.

THE NEURON

Neuron Function

The nervous system is composed of billions of neurons whose singular function is to communicate. The communication between neurons occurs at the synapse, the junction between neurons through which neurotransmitter substance is released. The product of that release is excitation or inhibition of the following neuron, but there is a great deal that goes on before we can talk about the synapse itself. We must address energy gradients, electrical charge, and membrane permeability.

The analogy of a water tower will help explain gradients. Engineers build water towers to hold water so that you can turn on your tap for a drink or a shower. Water is pumped up into the tower, using electrical energy, and the energy expended to do that is stored in the elevated water. Because the energy has the potential of being expended, it is referred to as **potential energy**. There is a **gradient** of pressure between the tank and your faucet, and the water will flow from the point of higher pressure to the point of lower pressure. You know that water will not naturally flow up the pipe to the tower, but it will flow quite freely if you break a pipe in your house. That sets the stage for discussing the passage of ions through the membraneous wall of a neuron. Gradients will be established between inside and outside of the cell, and ions have a tendency to flow to equalize that "pressure." We have pumps that move ions to increase that gradient, and we have faucets that we turn on to let those ions flood in.

In neurons, the gradient is established using electrical charge and molecule density rather than pressure, but the analogy with the water tower holds. You may remember from playing with magnets that the positive poles of two magnets repel each other, but opposite poles attract. **Ions** are atoms that have either lost or gained an **electron** (negative particle), causing them to acquire either a positive or negative charge. This means that positive ions will be repelled by positive ions but will be attracted by negative ions. Likewise, if there is a high concentration of molecules on one side of a membrane (a high **concentration gradient**), the molecules will tend to migrate to equalize the concentration. Movement of a charged particle produces an electrical current, an important point to remember because current is a prime mover in activating the cell membrane.

The notion of ions passing through membranous walls assumes the physical quality of **permeability**, which is the ease with which ions may pass through a membrane. The membranous wall of a neuron is semipermeable, meaning that *some* ions may pass through it, given appropriate circumstances. Ions may pass into or out of a healthy neuron wall through passive or active mechanisms.

Ions in higher concentration are held back from crossing the neural membrane by special proteins that serve as gate-keepers. **Voltage-sensitive proteins** are those that open when they receive adequate electrical stimulation. There also are **channel proteins** that allow specific ions to pass through the membrane.

The second mechanism for moving ions (**ion transport**) is active pumping. You will recall that, in the water tank analogy, something had to pump water up into the tank. To do so required an *active* process that used energy. There are ion pumps whose role is to move sodium (Na) and potassium (K) ions against the gradient (i.e., pump them "up hill"). The energy used by these **sodium-potassium pump** proteins is in the form of adenosine triphosphate, or ATP, a product of the mitochondria of the cell. The pumps operate continually, moving three sodium ions out for every two potassium ions in. We now have the pieces we need to "fire" a neuron.

Figure 10–1 shows a neuron at rest. The minus signs inside the neuron indicate that there is a negative charge, arising from the relatively smaller number of positive ions within the **intracellular space** (the space within individual cells) than outside in the **interstitial space** (the space between cells). At rest there is a potential difference of -70 mV, a gradient that will promote ion movement if a channel opens to permit that movement. This charge is referred to as the **resting membrane potential (RMP)**. At rest, there are 30 times as many K^+ ions inside as outside, and 10 times as many Na^+ ions outside as inside. K^+ is leaking continually out of the cell and is continually pumped back in by the sodium-potassium pumps. If the membrane were to permit free ion flow, the chemical gradient would drive Na^+ into the cell and K^+ out of the cell. The smaller number of charged particles within the cell drives the potential difference to -70 mV.

An **action potential (AP)** is a change in electrical potential that occurs when the cell membrane is stimulated adequately to permit ion exchange between intra- and extracellular spaces. When a critical threshold of stimulation is reached, the Na^+ ion gates open up, causing the large number of ions to flood the intracellular space, raising the intracellular potential to $+50$ mV over the course of about 1 millisecond (this is a net change of at about 120 mV). This equalization of the ion gradient is called **depolarization**, and for about 0.5 millisecond no amount of stimulation of that region of the membrane will cause it to depolarize again. This phase of depolarization, termed the **absolutely refractory period**, is the time during which the cell membrane cannot be stimulated to depolarize. During the absolutely refractory period, the K+ channels open up and K+ ions flow out of the intracellular space. The sodium gates will spontaneously close and become inactivated (**sodium inactivation**) and the sodium-potassium pump removes

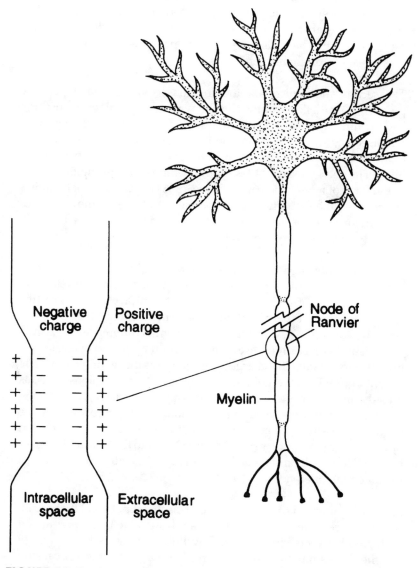

FIGURE 10–1. A quiescent neuron, showing equilibrium of membrane potential.

most of the Na^+ ions while increasing the intracellular concentration of K^+ ions. Potassium channels are slower than sodium channels, and the outflow of K^+ ions actually promotes restoration of the RMP, because it increases the relative positivity of the extracellular fluid and, thus, the negativity of the intracellular fluid.

The **relatively refractory period** is a period during which the membrane may be stimulated to excitation again, but only with greater than typical stimulation. This period follows the absolutely refractory period. This period lasts from 5–10 milliseconds.

The critical limit at which the membrane channels break down is approximately –50 mV. That is, portions of cell membrane may be depolarized, but if ion movement is insufficient to elevate the membrane potential the 20 mV from –70 to –50 mV, an action potential will not occur. If stimulation does not result in sufficient ion transfer to reach this level, an action potential will not be triggered and the RMP will be restored by the ongoing action of the ion pump.

This whole cycle from RMP to AP and back to RMP takes about 1 millisecond in most neurons, and this is a defining time period. This means that a neuron may respond every 1/1000 of a second, or 1000 times per second. Even if it is stimulated 2000 times per second, it will not be able to respond.

An action potential would do no good at all if it did not propagate, because no information would be passed to the next neuron or to a motor fiber. **Propagation** refers to spreading effect of wave action, much as the wave generated by throwing a rock in a pond spreads out from the stone's point of contact with the water. The action potential is also propagated in a wave of depolarization. When the membrane undergoing the local polarization reaches the critical limit, ions flow rapidly across the membrane, as discussed. Because the adjacent membrane contains voltage-sensitive protein channels, the current flow stimulates those regions to depolarize as well. In this manner the depolarization spreads along the membrane, ultimately reaching the terminal of the axon. This regeneration of the action potential along the entire length of the axon will produce precisely the same voltage difference.

The neuron responds in an all-or-nothing manner. That is, it either depolarizes or it does not. If it fails to depolarize, no action potential is generated and no information is conveyed. If the critical threshold for depolarization is reached, an action potential will be produced and information will be transmitted. The neuron acts like a light switch in this sense, and the only variation in information is in the frequency with which the neuron is "turned on," referred to as **spike rate** or **rate of discharge**.

The node of Ranvier is described in Chapter 9.

Propagation of the action potential is facilitated by axon diameter and myelin. Fibers with larger diameters propagate at a much higher rate than smaller fibers, and myelin further speeds up propagation. Figure 10–2 shows that myelin is laid down on the axon in "donuts" with nodes of exposed membrane between them. Voltage-sensitive channels are found within the membrane of the **nodes of Ranvier**, but generally are absent in the myelinated regions. The myelin insulates the fiber so that even if there were channels they would serve no function because ions could not pass through them.

Thus, the membrane becomes depolarized at one node, and the effect of that depolarization is felt at the next node where the membrane depolarizes as well. The propagating action potential is "passed" from node to node, and this jumping is referred to as **saltatory conduction**. Clearly, in long fibers, many precious milliseconds can be saved by skipping from node to node.

When the impulse reaches the terminal point on the axon, a highly specialized process is initiated. The synaptic vesicles within the terminal end buttons contain a neurotransmitter substance that will permit

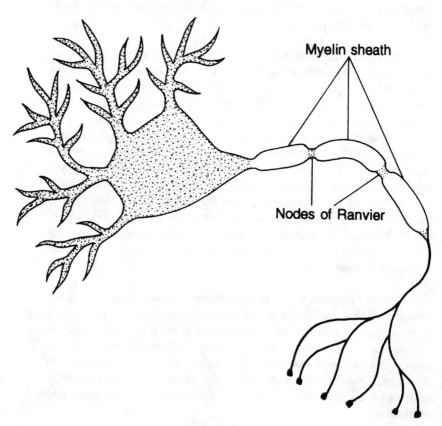

FIGURE 10-2. Myelin sheath and nodes of Ranvier.

communication between the two neurons. A **neurotransmitter** is a substance that is released from the terminal end button of an axon and causes either excitation or inhibition of another neuron or excitation of a muscle fiber. When the action potential reaches the terminal point, the vesicles are stimulated to migrate to the membrane wall where they will dump their neurotransmitter through the membrane into the synaptic cleft (see Figure 10–3).

The neurotransmitter travels across the cleft very quickly (100 microseconds) and is dumped into the cleft to activate receptor proteins on the **postsynaptic neuron**, and that activation triggers ion channels to open. The neurotransmitter and receptor must match or activation will not occur. That is, the neurotransmitter is a key and the receptor is a lock: If the key does not fit, the gate will not open.

The neurotransmitter may have either an excitatory or inhibitory effect on the neuron. Excitatory effects increase the probability that a neuron will depolarize, whereas inhibition decreases that probability. Excitatory stimulation generates an **excitatory postsynaptic potential (EPSP)**, whereas inhibitory synapses produce **inhibitory postsynaptic poten-**

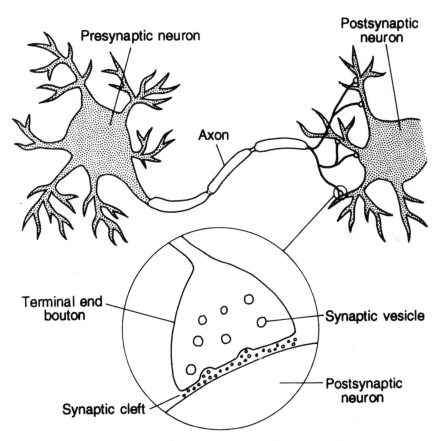

FIGURE 10-3. Expanded view of synapse between two neurons.

tials. Excitation causes depolarization, whereas inhibition causes **hyperpolarization**, greatly elevating the threshold of firing. Generally, inhibitory synapses are found on the soma. Synapses on the dendrite will usually be excitatory. Synapses on the axon tend to reduce the amount of neurotransmitter substance released into the synaptic cleft, thereby modulating neurotransmitter flow.

The EPSP actually begins as a micropotential, only depolarizing the membrane by about 3 mV. If there is a sufficient number of miniature EPSP depolarizations, the sum of their depolarization will reach the critical threshold and an action potential will be generated, as before. You may think of this as voting by neurons: There are thousands of synapses on a neuron from hundreds or thousands of neurons making synapse on a single neuron, and they "vote" to cause an action potential in the postsynaptic neuron by depolarizing a small portion of the receptive membrane. If there are sufficient numbers of depolarizations, there will be an action potential. This is referred to as spatial summation. **Spatial summation** refers to the quality of some neurons wherein they require many near-simultaneous synaptic activations, representing many points of contact arrayed over the surface of the neuron. Likewise, there can be **temporal summation**, in which a smaller number of regions depolarize virtually simultaneously.

Single neurons may take input from thousands of other neurons to produce a single response, a process called **convergence**. In this configuration, a mass of information is distilled into a single response. In contrast, **divergence** occurs when the axon of one neuron makes synapse with many thousands of other neurons. Its single piece of information is transmitted to a vast array of other neurons.

The neurotransmitter substance released into the synaptic cleft does not go to waste. As soon as it is released, enzymes specific to it break it down for resynthesis of the neurotransmitter within the neuron.

In summary:

■ Communication between neurons of the nervous system occurs at the **synapse**.
■ **Neurotransmitter** passing through the **synaptic cleft** will either **excite** or **inhibit** the postsynaptic neuron.
■ If a neuron is excited sufficiently, an **action potential** will be generated.
■ Stimulation of neuron membrane to **depolarize** causes exchange of ions between the extracellular and intracellular space, and the ion movement results in a large and predictable change in voltage across the membrane.
■ The **resting membrane potential** is the electrical potential measurable prior to excitation.

- The **absolutely refractory period** after excitation is an interval during which the neuron may not be excited to fire, whereas it may fire during the **relatively refractory period,** given adequate stimulation.
- Because an **action potential** always results in the same neural response, the neuron is capable of representing differences in input only through rate of response.
- **Myelinated** fibers conduct the wave of depolarization more rapidly than demyelinated fibers, primarily due to **saltatory conduction.**

Muscle Function

A similar process occurs at the **neuromuscular junction**, the point where nerve and muscle communicate. In this case the product of the communication will be a muscle twitch rather than an action potential. The basic unit of skeletal muscle control is the **motor unit**, consisting of the motor neuron, its axon, and the muscle fibers it innervates.

Figure 10–4 shows a neuromuscular junction, looking very much like an axon. In this case, however, there is a **terminal endplate** on the axon, with a synaptic cleft as before. The neurotransmitter, **acetylcholine**, is dumped into the active zone, and a **miniature end plate potential (MEPP)** will be generated. If there are sufficient numbers of MEPPs, a muscle action potential will be generated.

You know that movement requires muscular effort, and muscle can only contract, shortening the distance between two points. This is a good opportunity to examine that function at the microscopic level.

If you were to look at a cotton rope, you would see that the rope is actually made up of smaller ropes, wrapped in a spiral. Further examination would reveal that those smaller spiral ropes were made up of individual strings, and your microscope would show you that those strings were made of cotton fibers that had been spun into thread. There are successively smaller elements from which the rope is made, and they all have similar orientation and structure. The same is true for muscle.

As you can see from Figure 10–5, skeletal (striated) muscle is a long ropelike structure that is made up of strands of muscle fiber, each running the length of the muscle and having many nuclei. Fibers are made up of long **myofibrils**, and myofibrils are composed of either **thin** or **thick myofilaments**.

Thin myofilaments are composed of a pair of **actin** protein strands coiled around each other to form a spiral or helix, and twin strands of tropomyosin laced with molecules of troponin wrap around this helix. Thick filaments are composed of myosin molecules arranged in staggered formation. These two components are key players in movement:

Myasthenia Gravis

Myasthenia gravis is a neuromuscular disease with its primary effect on the neuromuscular junction. It appears that an individual's autoimmune system develops an immune response to the neurotransmitter receptor of the neuromuscular junction, building antibodies that block the receptor. Blocked receptors are unable to respond to neurotransmitter substance, so that, as the disease progresses, greater numbers of receptors become blocked and increasingly fewer ion channels can be activated to depolarize a neuron.

The individual with myasthenia gravis will complain of extreme fatigue as the day progresses: He or she may feel reasonably well in the morning, but become exhausted by noon. The speech-language pathologist is quite often the first person to suspect myasthenia gravis because the individual notices that speech has become more difficult and people are having difficulty understanding what he or she says. Reduced velar function is often an early sign, producing hypernasal speech with reduced intelligibility.

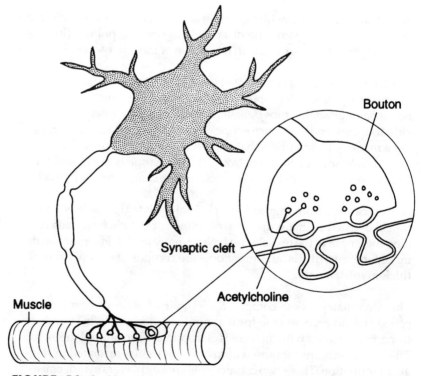

FIGURE 10-4. Neuromuscular junction between neuron and muscle fiber.

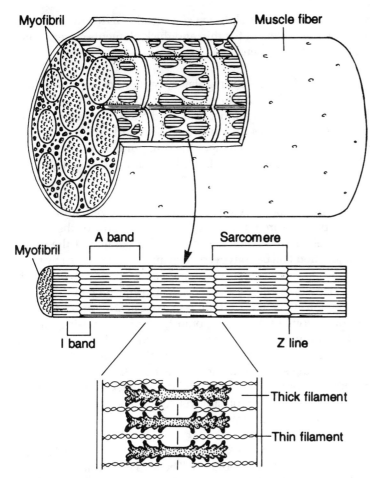

FIGURE 10–5. Exploded view of muscle fiber components. Each muscle fiber is made up of thin and thick filaments. After view of Campbell, 1987.)

The actin and myosin filaments will slide past each other during muscle contraction, with arms reaching from the myosin to the actin. The tropomyosin and troponin will facilitate the bridging arms, as you shall see.

When the myofilaments group together to form muscle myofibrils, a characteristic striated appearance is seen. This is the product of alternating dark and light myofilaments. Each of these combined units is known as a **sarcomere**, and this is the building block of striated muscle. An area known as the **Z line** marks the sarcomere margin, and the thin filaments are bound at this point, while the thick filaments are centered within the sarcomere, much like overlapping bricks in a wall. The **A band** is the region of overlap between thin and thick fibers at rest, and the **H zone** in the center of the sarcomere is a region with only thick filaments.

The two myofilaments will slide across each other as the muscle shortens, bringing the centers of the thin and thick filaments closer together. Here is how that happens.

When the muscle is at rest, the regulatory proteins of tropomyosin on the thin filaments block the binding sites, prohibiting formation of cross bridges. Tropomyosin must be moved out of the way to free up the actin and binding sites, and that function is performed by calcium. When calcium is present, it changes the configuration of the proteins, revealing the binding site on the thin filaments and facilitating development of cross bridges.

At rest, calcium is found within the **sarcoplasmic reticulum** of the muscle cytoplasm (sarcoplasmic reticulum is a form of the cellular endoplastic reticulum). An action potential generated at the neuromuscular junction will be conveyed deep into the muscle cell by transverse tubules that are in contact with the sarcoplasmic reticulum. The AP depolarizes the membrane of the sarcoplasmic reticulum, permitting calcium ions to be released. Presence of calcium causes the morphology of tropomyosin and troponin to change, exposing binding sites and permitting myosin to bridge from the thick filaments to the thin filaments. ATP provides the energy to the arm, which reaches across to a binding site on the thin filaments, pulls, and releases even as other arms are pulling and releasing. When the AP stops, calcium is taken back up into the sarcoplasmic reticulum, and the binding site is once again hidden and contraction ceases.

This seems like a lot of work to contract a muscle, and it is. Work requires energy, and ATP supplies it. The actual contraction is much like pulling yourself up a mountainside using a rope. You grab the rope and pull, hand-over-hand, drawing yourself upward. Your arms are like the myosin arms; the rope is like the thin filament of actin, and you are the thick filament. This is the **sliding filament model** of muscle contraction.

In this process, the center of the sarcomere (the H zone) will disappear as the sarcomere shortens. There are about 350 heads on each thick filaments that can bridge across to the thin filaments, and each bridge can perform its hand-over-hand act five times per second.

This still does not tell us how muscle does its job. When the AP is generated and the sarcoplasmic reticulum releases calcium, there is an all-or-none response, and the muscle twitches. From your study, you already know that muscles come in all sizes, from the massive to the minute. Further, muscles must perform vastly different functions, from gross, slow movement to quick, precise action. How do we manage this?

The answer to this question lies largely in allocation of resources. For fine movement, only a limited number of muscle fibers need to be recruited for movement, whereas heavy lifting will clearly require recruitment of many fibers. The neuromotor innervation accounts for much of this, because each muscle fiber is innervated by one motor neuron, but each motor neuron may innervate a large number of muscle fibers. The more motor neurons that are activated, the greater the number of fibers that will contract. Use of many motor nerves to activate muscle is called **multiple motor unit summation**.

Another mechanism of control is a functional difference between how various muscles act. **Slow twitch** muscle fibers remain contracted five times longer than **fast twitch fibers**, perhaps because calcium remains in the cytoplasm for longer periods. Slow twitch fibers typically are found in muscles that must contract for long periods of time, such as those used to support your body against gravity. Fast twitch muscles are used to meet rapid contraction requirements. It may surprise you to know that the rapidly moving tongue tip is supplied with fast twitch fibers, but slow-moving deep tongue muscles have slow twitch fibers. One neuron may innervate thousands of slow twitch fibers, but neurons serving fast twitch fibers may only innervate 10 or 20 muscle fibers. This difference in innervation ratio permits extremely fine control: If you need to tense the vocal folds quickly for pitch change, you want to be able to precisely control the fraction of a millimeter required to keep your voice from going sharp while singing. This control comes from being able to activate progressively more motor units in fine steps. On the other hand, maintaining an erect posture requires less precision and more stamina.

To summarize:

■ Activation of a muscle fiber causes release of calcium into the environment of **thick myofilaments,** revealing the binding sites on the **thin filaments** that permit **cross bridging** from the thick filaments.
■ The action of the bridging causes the myofilaments to slide past each other, thereby shortening the muscle.
■ **Slow twitch** muscle fibers remain contracted longer than **fast twitch** fibers, with the former being involved in maintenance of posture and the latter in fine and rapid motor function.

Muscle Spindle Function

We touched on the activities of the muscle spindle in Chapter 9, but let us discuss its function more thoroughly. If you examine Figure 10–6, you will see the major players in posture and motor control in general. It is sobering to realize that the lowest level of motor response (the stretch reflex) is intimately related to the highest levels of motor response requiring extraordinary skill and dexterity, such as fine motor control of the fingers. Discussion of the muscle spindle will provide the background necessary to talk about higher level motor control.

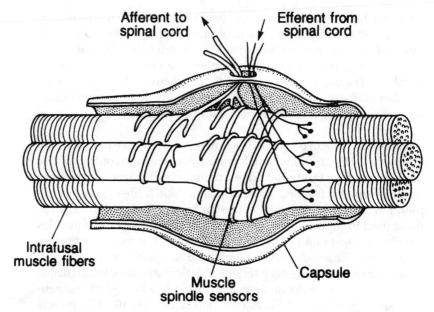

FIGURE 10-6. Schematic representation of a muscle spindle.

The role of the muscle spindle is to provide feedback to the neuromotor system about muscle length and thus information about motion and position. Before we explain that function let us examine the structure of this important sensory element.

There are two basic types of striated muscle fibers with which we must be concerned. **Extrafusal muscle fibers** make up the bulk of the muscles discussed over the past several chapters. Deep within the structure of the muscle is another set of muscle fibers, referred to as **intrafusal muscle fibers**. These fibers have a parallel course to the extrafusal fibers and would not really be obvious on gross examination of a muscle. Close examination would reveal short intrafusal fibers that attach to the muscle and are capable of sensing changes in the length of the muscle. At or near the **equatorial region** of the intrafusal muscle fiber are the stretch sensors themselves, with the combination of muscle and sensor known as the **muscle spindle**, so named because of its spindle shape.

The intrafusal fibers may be classified as being either **thin** or **thick.** Thick muscle fibers typically are outfitted with a capsule that contains nuclear bag fibers, and thin muscle fibers will house nuclear chain fibers. **Nuclear bag fibers** are groups of stretch receptors collected in a cluster at the equatorial region of the intrafusal muscle fiber. **Nuclear chain fibers**, in contrast, are a row of stretch sensors in the equatorial region. These two configurations have different functions, as we shall see. The placement of the capsules in the equatorial region is important, because that portion of these fibers is noncontractile.

The muscle spindle has both afferent and efferent innervation. The afferent component conveys the sensation of muscle length change to the central nervous system, while the efferent system sends nerve impulses that cause the intrafusal fibers to contract. The innervation pattern is important and deserves your attention. **Nuclear bag fibers** send information to the CNS by means of **Group Ia primary** afferent fibers, wrapping around the capsule in a spiral formation. Group Ia fibers are large, and when the muscle is stretched, the nuclear bag changes shape. That distortion causes the nerve to fire, sending information to the spinal cord. Bags surrounding nuclear chain fibers may have primary Ia afferents as well, but may instead have **Group II secondary** afferent fibers. These are smaller fibers conveying a functionally different response, although they also respond to stretch of muscle.

The term **nuclear bag fiber** *refers to the portion of the muscle spindle that is formed by a cluster of stretch sensors situated on the equatorial region of the muscle fiber.*

Extrafusal (general skeletal muscle) and intrafusal (muscle spindle) muscle fibers have distinctly different innervation. Extrafusal muscle is innervated through **alpha** motor fibers, which are larger in diameter than the **gamma** (or **fusimotor**) efferent fibers of the intrafusal muscle.

As you can see, there is a great deal of physical differentiation going on with this sensory system. There are two types of sensors, two types of afferent fibers delivering information to the CNS, and a specialized efferent system (gamma efferents) that can cause the intrafusal muscle to contract.

The muscle spindle responds to both phasic and tonic muscle lengthening. **Phasic lengthening** refers to the period during which a muscle is undergoing a *change in length* (acceleration). This information is transduced by the nuclear bag fibers and conveyed via Group Ia afferents to the CNS. **Tonic lengthening** refers to a muscle that is maintained in a lengthened condition, and this information is conveyed via the nuclear chain fibers by means of either type of afferent. It turns out that both pieces of information are essential for motor control.

Figure 10–7 will help us discuss how this system helps you control your muscles. The best way to describe how the spindle works is to think of posture control. If you were to pay close attention to your body as you stand in line in the post office, you would notice that you sway ever so slightly. That slight movement you feel is a trigger for the intrafusal system.

When you lean a little, some of your leg muscles stretch. When they do so, the spindle sends notice to the motor neuron within the spinal column that the muscle has changed position. The motor neuron with which it synapses immediately activates the extrafusal muscle mass to contract, thereby counteracting that "accidental" stretching that occurred in response to gravity. Notice that you passively stretched the muscle spindle fibers and then the muscles of your leg with which

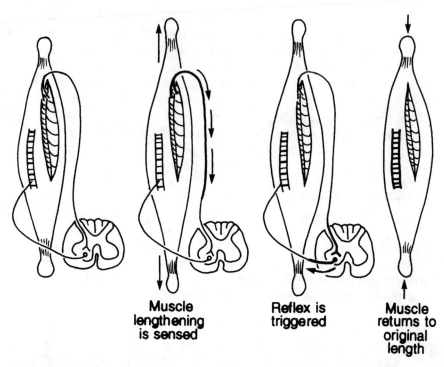

FIGURE 10-7. Schematic representation of muscle spindle function to control muscle length.

those spindles are associated contracted to return the muscle to its original length.

One more thing to note in Figure 10–7 is that this afferent synapses with another neuron. In the drawing, the spindle within the flexor is sending its information centrally. The afferent makes **inhibitory** synapse with extensors associated with the same joint, so that you are not only actively contracting flexors but also actively inhibiting contraction of extensors.

What if you move your legs purposefully? How do the muscle spindles oppose *that* movement? When a new posture is reached, the intrafusal muscle contracts to adjust the tension on the spindle, accommodating the new posture. Likewise, the muscle spindle afferent information is delivered to cerebral cortex and to the cerebellum. When voluntary movement is initiated, both alpha and gamma systems are activated. There is speculation that the gamma system receives information from the cortex concerning the desired or *target* muscle length, and thus the gamma system provides feedback to the cortex when this length has been achieved. Thus, the gamma system may be a regulatory mechanism for voluntary movement, and damage to this system has devastating effects.

Lesions and the
Gamma Efferent System

To appreciate the effects of lesions to the extrapyramidal system, it might help to do a quick exercise. Do this: Reach across the desk top to pick up a pencil. As you do this, pay attention to what your muscles are doing. Even as you reach for the pencil, your elbow rotates to accommodate the needs of your arm and hand to make contact with the object. As you get close to the target, your fingers start to close and the rate of movement of your arm slows down. For all of this to happen, your brain must know how fast your muscles are changing length as well as where the target is located in space relative to your hand and body. Contraction of extensors obviously is important, but your brain must also contract flexors to help control extensor contraction lest the movement be ballistic.

Damage to the cerebellum will reduce activation of the fusimotor system. Because this system maintains muscle tone through mild, constant muscle contraction, muscles in a patient with lesions to the cerebellum will lose tone and become flaccid. In contrast, loss of the moderating control by the cerebrum through lesion will cause hypertonia in antigravity musculature and extensors, because the stretch reflexes are unrestrained. In this condition, the alpha system is either disabled or not well coordinated with the gamma system due to the lesion, and spasticity results.

Lesions and conditions of the basal ganglia will have various effects, among them the rigidity of Parkinson's disease. In this condition, intrafusal systems for both extensors and flexors are unrestrained, resulting in simultaneous contraction of antagonists and rigidity. Other basal ganglia lesions will result in general hypertonicity.

Golgi Tendon Organs

Another type of sensor, which is less well-understood, is the Golgi tendon organ (GTO), a sensor located at the tendon which is sensitive to the degree of tension on the muscle. If the muscle is passively stretched, it takes a great deal to excite a GTO. However, if a muscle is contracted, the GTO is quite sensitive to the tension placed on it.

The GTO probably works in close conjunction with the muscle spindle. The muscle spindle will be active any time a muscle is *lengthened*, while the GTO will be sensitive to the *tension* placed on the muscle. If a muscle is tensed isometrically, lengthening will be minimal but the

GTO will be quite sensitive to the tension placed on it by contraction. Likewise, if a muscle is passively stretched, the muscle spindle will respond but the tendon organ will not.

Other Sensation and Sensors

There are a host of other receptors, as we discussed in the last chapter. Sensory receptors are nerve endings that have become specialized to **transduce** (change) energy from one form to another.

When one of these sensors is stimulated, it sends information concerning that stimulation to the CNS for processing. You will not be aware of stimulation unless a **threshold** of stimulation is reached. This threshold varies from sensor to sensor, and even from individual to individual. A stimulus capable of eliciting a response from a given receptor is termed the **adequate stimulus**. The receptor converts the energy exciting it into electrochemical energy, producing what is referred to as a **receptor potential** or **generator potential**, depending on how far the information is being transferred. The magnitude of the potential is related to that of the stimulus, and it typically will be constant until the stimulus is removed.

Sensors vary in morphology and function, but fall into the general classes of encapsulated and nonencapsulated. Encapsulated sensors tend to be pressure sensitive, transducing pressure applied to the skin into electrochemical energy sensed by the nervous system. Some sensors are **rapidly adapting**, in that they respond only to *change* in stimulation. These sensors are particularly well suited for transduction of vibration, whereas **slowly adapting** sensors will respond better to long-duration stimulation. Pain, temperature, and some mechanoreceptors are simply unshielded nerve endings that respond when stimulated by one or several different stimuli. The sensation of joint position in space apparently is the product of many of these encapsulated and nonencapsulated sensors.

To summarize:

■ **Muscle spindles** provide feedback to the neuromotor system about muscle length, tension, motion, and position.
■ Muscle spindles running parallel to intrafusal muscle fibers sense lengthening of muscle, whereas **golgi tendon** organs sense muscle tension.
■ **Nuclear bag fibers** convey information concerning acceleration, whereas the **nuclear chain fibers** are responsive to sustained lengthening.
■ When a muscle is passively stretched a **segmental reflex** is triggered, through which the **extrafusal muscles** paralleling the muscle spindles are activated, thereby shortening the muscle.

- **Golgi tendon organs** apparently respond to the tension of musculature during active contraction.
- There are many other receptor types, but the common thread is that they all transduce internal or external environment information into electrochemical impulses.
- When a sensor is stimulated beyond its threshold for response, it sends information concerning that stimulation to the CNS for processing.

HIGHER FUNCTIONING

We have been discussing responses that occur at the lowest levels of the nervous system and often do not even reach consciousness. Although it is essential for your brain to know what your tongue muscles are doing, it is obvious that there is more to speech than movement of muscles.

We will take a regional approach to review of the function of the cerebral cortex. Neuroscience has a long history of lively discussion about how the brain functions. Some see the brain as an organ with strict localization of function. Although it is clear that regions of the cerebral cortex, such as the motor strip, are highly specialized for specific functions, other regions of the cortex are less well defined. To further confound things, the developing brain is **plastic**. The brains of infants who receive trauma are more likely to overcome damage to function than adults receiving the same trauma. This and other evidence has led to theories of **equipotentiality**, which state that the brain functions as a whole. One could strike a balance with the notion of **regional equipotentiality**. There seems to be a functional unity by regions, but the degree of functional loss to an individual receiving trauma also is related to the total volume of damaged tissue. Our discussion will focus on functional regions and association pathways of the brain and interconnections among regions.

The cortex appears to be organized around regions of **primary** activity for a given area, including the primary receptive area for somatic sense, primary motor area, primary auditory cortex, and primary region of visual reception (see Figure 10–8). Adjacent to these are **higher order areas of processing**. That is, there are secondary, tertiary, and even quaternary areas of higher order processing adjacent to the primary receptive areas for sensation. There also are higher order areas of processing for motor function, as we shall see. Beyond the higher order areas of processing are **association areas** in which the highest form of human thought occurs. That is, we receive information from our senses at primary reception areas and we extract the information received and put it together with other information associated with the modality at higher order areas of processing. This information is passed to association areas for the highest level of cognitive processing.

FIGURE 10-8. Brodman area map of lateral and medial cerebrum.

The **primary reception area for vision** (VI) is located within the calcarine fissure of the occipital lobe (area 17). At that location, precise maps of information received at the retinae are projected. The **secondary visual processing region** is considered to be area 18 of the occipital lobe, with even higher level processing regions found in the temporal lobe (area 20, 21) and occipital lobe (area 19 and the region anterior to it). Area 7 of the parietal lobe performs higher level processing of visual information as well. Because higher level processing sites seem to be concerned with feature extraction, the precise visual field map projected onto the primary cortex is generally not found at those higher level processing sites.

Somatic sense is received by the parietal lobe, with the primary reception area (SI) being the postcentral gyrus (areas 1, 2, and 3). Again, studies have repeatedly demonstrated that body sense is projected somatotopically along this strip, but this projection is much less apparent at the secondary sites. The opercular portion of the parietal lobe is considered to be the higher order processing region, as is area 5 of the parietal lobe (Kupfermann, 1991).

Auditory information is tonotopically projected at Heschl's gyrus (41) of the temporal lobe (AI), whereas the superior temporal gyrus (area 22) performs higher level processing of the auditory input. There is some retention of the tonotopic nature of the received signal at the higher level processing region.

Three regions of the brain play central roles in **motor function**, but to discuss these areas we must clarify the three phases of the voluntary motor act. First, to perform a voluntary motor task, you must identify a target, such as making the tongue tip contact the alveolar ridge. Next, you must develop a plan to achieve the target behavior. Finally, you must execute the plan, a process requiring the movement of muscles with accurate timing, force, and rate.

These three functions appear to be governed by three different regions of the cerebral cortex. First, the target must be identified, and this is a function of the posterior parietal lobe. The posterior parietal lobe (areas 5, 7, 39, and 40) processes information about somatic sensation related to **spatial orientation**, including integration of information about position of body parts in space and visual information. Inputs to these parietal regions arise from the thalamus: The venteroposterolateral thalamic nucleus (VPLo) projects body sense information from distant receptors, the caudal ventrolateral thalamic nucleus (VLc) and VPLo project cerebellar information to the posterior parietal regions, and the VLc and ventral anterior nucleus (VA) project information from the basal ganglia to the posterior parietal lobe. In this way, the posterior parietal lobe receives a complete "body map" of the location and condition of all body parts, including the speech articulators.

The second area, **premotor region** (area 6), anterior to the motor strip appears to be involved in planning the action. The premotor region takes information from the parietal lobe (areas 1, 2, and 3) concerning the immediate location of muscles and joints and integrates that information with a plan of action. In addition, the **supplementary motor area** (**SMA**: superior and medial portions of area 6) is involved in even more complex acts, including speech initiation. The SMA is strongly involved in the preparatory speech act, as well as in the decision to initiate the act. If an individual is only told to mentally rehearse, the SMA will be activated without the premotor region being involved.

*The cochlea and the brainstem nuclei serving it have a **tonotopic** array, which is the correlate of the spatiotopic array seen in the motor strip. High-frequency sounds are resolved at the basal end of the cochlea, whereas low-frequency sounds are resolved at the cochlea apex. Frequency is spread out in an orderly, sequential array along the basilar membrane of the cochlea, and this tonotopic arrangement is seen in the projections at nearly all levels of the auditory pathway.*

Finally, the precentral gyrus or **motor strip** (MI) found in area 4 is responsible for execution of voluntary movement. The motor strip neurons make up half of the pyramidal tract, the major motor pathway. Commands to muscles from the motor strip include information concerning the degree of force and timing of contraction.

Motor System Lesions

Damage to regions of higher function reflect the specialized nature of these locations. A lesion to the motor strip will result in muscular weakness and loss of motor function on the side of the body opposite the lesion. **Dysarthria** is a speech disorder arising from paralysis, muscular weakness, and dyscoordination of speech musculature. The type of dysarthria is broadly defined by the site of lesion.

Flaccid dysarthria arises from damage to lower motor neurons (LMN) or their cell bodies. Thus, flaccid dysarthria reflects damage to the cranial nerves serving speech muscles. As we discussed in Chapter 9, focal lesions to cranial nerves have focal effects on the musculature they serve, and this is manifested in the various subtypes of flaccid dysarthria that one will see clinically. For instance, damage to the VII facial nerve will result in facial paralysis, whereas damage to the V trigeminal will produce paralysis of the muscles of mastication. Damage to the recurrent laryngeal nerve of the X vagus will result in flaccid dysphonia. In all cases, the result will be a flaccid paralysis, manifested as a muscular weakness and **hypotonia** (low muscle tone). If the cell body is involved in the lesion, there may also be **fasciculations** or twitching movements of the affected articulator. In addition, because the damage occurs distal to the interneurons serving the reflex arc (which is a central phenomenon within the brainstem or spinal cord), reflexive responses mediated by the nerve are either reduced or absent. You can normally elicit a jaw jerk reflex by pulling down on a slack jaw, but this reflex may be reduced or absent in flaccid dysarthria if the V trigeminal is involved.

Specific cranial nerve functions and disorders are discussed in Chapter 9.

Spastic dysarthria arises from bilateral damage to upper motor neurons (UMN) of the pyramidal (direct) and extrapyramidal (indirect) motor pathways. The direct pathway generally is excitatory, being involved with execution of skilled motor acts. The indirect pathway generally is inhibitory, controlling background activities such as maintenance of muscle tone, posture, and agonist contraction to control the trajectory for movement.

Bilateral UMN damage results in an inability to execute skilled movements (paralysis) and muscle weakness. Damage to the extrapyramidal system results in loss of inhibition of reflexes, or **hyperreflexia**, as well as increased muscle tone, or **hypertonia**. Thus, the jaw jerk reflex mentioned in the discussion of flaccid dysarthria would now be very easily triggered, to the point that the individual could not control the response.

The person with spastic dysarthria has reduced force of contraction of muscles from the pyramidal lesion, and this is further confounded by easily elicited reflexive contractions arising from attempting to use the articulators. That is, attempts by the affected individual to lower his or her jaw will result in reflexive contraction of the muscles that elevate the jaw, thereby foiling the attempt. Therapy obviously will be directed toward regaining control over those reflexes!

When a unilateral lesion occurs in the region of facial muscle control, the result is **unilateral upper motor neuron dysarthria** (UUMN) (Duffy, 1995). The effects of UUMN dysarthria are less devastating than those of a bilateral lesion. UUMN results in spastic signs on the side contralateral to the lesion for the tongue and lower facial muscles, because they have unilateral (contralateral) innervation, whereas other articulatory muscles are bilaterally innervated.

Ataxic dysarthria arises from damage to the cerebellum or to the brainstem vestibular nuclei, or both. Because the cerebellum is responsible for coordination of motor activity, ataxic dysarthria is characterized by loss of coordination, deficits in achieving an articulatory target, and problems in coordinating rate, range, and force of movement. Speech in ataxic dysarthria will be distorted because irregular articulation results from **overshoot** (moving an articulator beyond its target) and **undershoot** (moving an articulator an insufficient distance to reach the target). **Dysdiadochokinesia**, a deficit in the ability to make repetitive movements, is a dominant characteristic, as is **dysprosody**, or deficit in maintenance of the intonation and linguistic stress of speech.

Hyperkinetic and hypokinetic dysarthria are the result of damage to different regions of the extrapyramidal system. **Hyperkinetic dysarthria** is characterized by extraneous, involuntary movement of speech musculature *in addition to* movement produced voluntarily. That is, in hyperkinetic dysarthria, articulators move without voluntary muscular contraction, and this is overlaid on the speech act. Hyperkinesias are seen primarily in damage to the basal ganglia circuitry, especially that responsible for inhibiting movement.

Damage to the subthalamic nucleus, which inhibits the globus pallidus, results in uncontrolled flailing known as **ballism**. If damage to the basal ganglia results in a decrease in the neurotransmitter acetylcholine (ACh) or an increase in dopamine (DA), extraneous **choreiform** movements (involuntary twitching and movement of muscles) will result, such as those seen in Huntington's disease. Hyperkinesias take a number of forms, ranging from **tics** (rapid movement of small groups of muscle fibers) and **tremors** (rhythmic contractions) to

athetosis (slow, writing movements) and **dystonia** (involuntary movement to a posture, with the posture being held briefly).

Hypokinetic dysarthria is characterized by paucity of movement, most often caused by Parkinson's disease. The disease arises from damage to the substantia nigra, the cell mass responsible for production of dopamine (DA). Dopamine is used by the basal ganglia to balance ACh, and a shortage of DA results in inhibited initiation of motor function, reduction of range of movement, co-contraction of agonists and antagonists (resulting in **rigidity**), and a characteristic pill-rolling tremor of the hands. Speech in Parkinson's disease will be rushed, with reduced duration of speech sounds, reduced vocal intensity, and reduced fluctuation in fundamental frequency.

Mixed dysarthrias arise from damage to more than one of the controlling systems. **Mixed spastic-flaccid dysarthria** is found in amyotrophic lateral sclerosis, a disease that attacks the myelin of UMN and LMN fibers. **Mixed spastic-ataxic dysarthria** results from damage to the UMN and cerebellar control circuitry, as often seen in multiple sclerosis. **Mixed hypokinetic-ataxic-spastic dysarthria** is found with the degeneration of Wilson's disease (hepatolenticular degeneration). Generally, one may see any combination of dysarthrias, based on the systems involved in the disease process (Duffy, 1995).

The dysarthrias are all characterized by some degree of loss of motor function accompanied by muscular weakness and dyscontrol. **Apraxia** is a dysfunction of motor planning in absence of muscular weakness or muscular dysfunction.

Damage to the premotor region results in gross apraxia for the motor function mediated by the area broadly served by the adjacent motor strip neurons. With damage to the SMA, an individual will have difficulty initiating speech, and the effect is bilateral. Damage to the premotor region near the facial projections of the motor strip (the area known as **Broca's area**) will result in apraxia of speech, also known as verbal apraxia. This apraxia will be characterized by significant loss of fluency and groping behavior associated with even the simplest articulations. The individual with premotor damage will not show the muscular weakness typical of an individual with motor strip damage, but the ability to contract the musculature voluntarily is impaired.

If an individual has damage to the posterior parietal cortex, the result will be difficulty focusing on the target of action. This individual will have difficulty locating objects in space and may even ignore or neglect the side of the body served by the damaged parietal lobe tissue because he or she cannot use that information. In addition, damage to the region of the supramarginal gyrus will result in verbal apraxia affecting long and complex sequences, as compared with damage to the speech premotor region, which results in deficits of simple articulatory gestures.

One may also experience **oral apraxia**, which is a deficit in the ability to perform nonspeech oral gestures, such as imitatively puffing up the cheeks or blowing out a candle.

Afferent Inputs

The motor strip is populated by giant Betz cells, and this area receives input from the thalamus, sensory cortex, and premotor area. Regions involved in fine motor control (such as those activating facial regions or the fingers) are very richly represented. There is heavy sensory input to this motor region, underscoring the notion that control of movement is strongly influenced by information about the ongoing state and position of the musculature. Some muscle spindle afferents terminate in the motor strip, and spinal reflexes are modified and controlled, at least in part, by activity from this region. The portion of the motor strip serving a particular part of the body will receive tactile and proprioceptive information from the same body region, providing an effective path for modification of the motor plan even as it is being executed.

The premotor region appears to be involved in preparation for movement, anticipation of movement, and organization of skilled movement. It receives somatic sensory information from the parietal lobe, as well as sensory information from the thalamus, and projects its output to the motor strip. Afferent parietal information to the supplementary motor area also supports its involvement in active planning and rehearsal of the motor act, as well as decision making about movement. Broca's area (regions 44 and 45 of the frontal lobe) uses parietal lobe information to perform a high-level planning function for movement of the speech articulators for speech function, as will be discussed.

Association Regions

Association areas are considered to provide the highest order of information processing of the cerebral cortex. It appears that higher order integration areas extract detailed information from the signal input to the primary areas, whereas association areas permit that information to flow among the various processing sites, effectively connecting modalities. These regions are involved in intellect, cognitive functions, memory, and language.

There are three major association areas of interest: The temporal-occipital-parietal association cortex (TOP), the limbic association cortex, and the prefrontal association cortex.

The **temporal-occipital-parietal region** is of the utmost importance to speech-language pathologist, because it includes the areas associated with language in humans. This region includes portions of the temporal, parietal, and occipital lobes (areas 39, 40, and portions of 19, 21, 22, and 37). It receives input from auditory, visual, and somatosensory regions, permitting the integration of this information into language function.

The **limbic association area** (regions 23, 24, 38, 28, and 11) includes regions of the parahippocampal gyrus and temporal pole (temporal lobe), cingulate gyri (parietal and frontal lobes), and orbital surfaces (inferior frontal lobe). The limbic system is involved with motivation, emotion, and memory, making it an ideal association area. Clearly, memory function is served by reception of information from diverse sensory inputs.

The **prefrontal association area** (anterior to area 6) is involved with integration of information in preparation for the motor act, as well as higher level cognitive processes. The premotor regions, consisting of the premotor gyrus and supplemental motor area appear to be vital to initiation of motor activity, whereas the prefrontal region anterior to these regions is involved in the motor plan. According to Kupferman (1991), the premotor region receives input from the primary sensory reception areas or low-order processing regions, while the prefrontal regions derive their input from the higher order regions. Both premotor and prefrontal regions project to the motor strip, permitting both low-order and abstract sensory perceptions to influence the motor act. Broca's area (regions 44 and 45), the frontal operculum, and the insula also are involved in motor programming. These regions share qualities of both the prefrontal association region and the premotor gyrus, because damage to them results in both motor planning and higher level language deficit, including word-retrieval problems.

In addition to this, the orbitofrontal region (the region on the underbelly of the cerebrum that overlays the orbit region) is involved in limbic system function, as well as motor planning memory associated with delayed execution.

To summarize:

■ The complexity of higher functions of the brain is reflected in the inability to assign precise locations for specific functions.
■ General regions, such as **Wernicke's area**, can be ascribed broad function, and this view facilitates examination of brain function and dysfunction.
■ A broad view of brain function classifies regions of the cerebrum as primary, higher order, and association regions.

- **Primary** sensory and motor regions include the **primary reception area** for somatic sense, **primary motor area, primary auditory cortex,** and **primary** region of **visual reception**.
- Adjacent to these are higher order areas of processing, apparently responsible for extracting features of the stimulus.
- **Association** areas are the regions of highest cognitive processing, integrating sensory information with memory.
- The **prefrontal area** appears to be involved in higher function related to motor output (such as inhibition of motor function and the ability to change motor responses), whereas the **temporal-occipital-parietal association area** is involved in language function.
- The limbic association **area** integrates information relating to affect, motivation, and emotion.
- **Flaccid dysarthria** results from damage to LMN, whereas UMN lesions result in spastic dysarthria.
- **Ataxic dysarthria** arises from cerebellar damage.
- **Hyperkinetic dysarthria** is the result of damage to inhibitory processes of the extrapyramidal system, whereas **hypokinetic dysarthria** results from lesion to excitatory mechanisms.
- **Apraxia** arises from lesion to the regions associated with preparation and planning for the motor act, specifically the supramarginal gyrus of the parietal lobe, Broca's area, and the SMA.

Hemispheric Specialization

Despite the gross similarities between the two cerebral hemispheres, the brain is essentially asymmetrical, and the functional and anatomic asymmetries underlie basic processing differences of extreme importance to speech-language pathologists. When researchers have examined large numbers of brains, they have found that the lateral fissure is slightly longer on the left hemisphere than on the right, and the area of primary auditory reception (the planum temporale, or Heschl's gyrus) is larger on this side as well. This anatomical asymmetry supports an extremely rich body of functional asymmetry between the two hemispheres.

If you write with your right hand, you may count yourself among the broad majority of individuals who exhibit functional dominance for language and speech in the left hemisphere. Motor pathways decussate as they descend, and auditory pathways decussate in ascension, with the result being that your right hand (and right ear) are dominated by activities of the left hemisphere.

decussate: L., decussare, to make an X. To decussate means to cross over

The two hemispheres continually work in concert with each other, being anatomically connected via the corpus callosum. Virtually all right-handed individuals will show language function in the left hemisphere, while 30% of left-handers will either have their language function within the right hemisphere or have it shared between the two hemispheres. Thus, one will speak of the "dominant hemisphere" for language as being, typically, the left hemisphere, knowing full well that there is a group for whom the reverse is true. With that in mind, let us examine some of the hemispheric differences that have been found.

A great deal of the information we have gained concerning hemispheric specialization has come from treatment of seizure disorders. These disorders often involve the temporal lobe that, as you shall soon see, is imminently involved with language function. When surgical procedures are planned to alleviate seizures, the neurosurgeon will do everything possible to spare the speech and language regions. To learn where these regions are, he or she may electrically stimulate regions of the brain to determine their location prior to removing a portion of the cortex, a procedure known as **brain mapping**. The physician also may inject the carotid artery of one or the other of the hemispheres with amytal sodium, a barbiturate, thereby incapacitating the hemisphere. In this way the surgeon can determine which hemisphere is dominant for language function. Among the surgical procedures used to terminate seizures is severing of the communication link between the two cortices, the corpus callosum.

Individuals in whom the corpus callosum has been severed have provided a great deal of the evidence concerning hemispheric specialization. Auditory information presented to the right ear is processed predominantly by the left hemisphere, and left ear information is received by the right hemisphere. By careful examination of responses, researchers have found that short-duration acoustic information (such as consonants, transitions, and stop consonant bursts) is processed most efficiently by the left hemisphere in right-handed individuals. The left hemisphere seems to be specialized for the process of analysis, favoring discrete, sequential, rapidly changing information. Spoken and written language perception and production are clearly favored by this hemisphere, whereas the "nondominant" right hemisphere favors more spatial and holistic elements, such as face recognition, speech intonation, melody, and perception of form. This is not to say that the right hemisphere has nothing to say. It has been demonstrated that it has a reasonably large vocabulary (dominated by nouns), but rudimentary grammar. Although expressive abilities are quite limited, the right hemisphere can follow commands and demonstrate knowledge of verbal information through gesture and pointing using the left hand.

Thus, in the majority of individuals, language processing is lateralized to the left hemisphere, and speech production is controlled by the same hemisphere. Interpretation of the intention of the speaker as presented through intonation and facial expression is processed by the right hemisphere. As you shall soon see, damage to the two hemispheres produces markedly different deficits.

Lesion Studies

Aphasia

A primary source of information concerning function of the cerebral cortex in humans comes from lesion studies. Researchers have examined the behavioral outcome of accidental or surgical lesions in individuals, thus developing our understanding of cortical function.

Of particular interest to our field are the regions associated with speech and language. We have long known that damage to Wernicke's area (posterior area 22) typically results in the disruption of language known as **aphasia**. Similarly, we have come to recognize that damage to Broca's area (areas 44 and 45) severely disrupts the oral manifestation of language: speech. Through cortical mapping and precise lesion studies, researchers have described these conditions and sites of lesions more precisely, providing us with some insight into how the cerebral cortex functions.

As you know, Heschl's gyrus of the temporal lobe has the primary responsibility for auditory reception, the region adjacent to it in the superior temporal gyrus is a higher order processing region, and the parahippocampal gyrus is involved with memory. Portions of the inferior and middle temporal gyri are regions of higher level integration of visual information. Wernicke's area is posterior to this, technically comprised of the posterior superior gyrus of the temporal lobe, but we know that language function involves a markedly larger area, generally including the temporal-occipital-parietal association areas.

Damage to Heschl's gyrus often results in cortical deafness, the inability to hear information that has passed through the lower auditory nervous system. Lesions of the higher order processing region adjacent to AI will produce a deficit in processing complex auditory information, and if the lesion involves the inferior temporal lobe (area 28), the individual may experience a memory deficit associated with visual information.

With the notion of the auditory and visual input function of the temporal lobe in mind, let us examine lesions involving Wernicke's area. **Wernicke's aphasia** is referred to as a "fluent aphasia," because individuals with this condition have relatively normal flow of speech. Their expressive language may have relatively normal syntactic structure, but the content of their productions will be markedly reduced. They will often substitute words or create entirely new words. If you think of the proximity to the auditory reception areas and the discussion of auditory integration, it will not surprise you that the individual with Wernicke's aphasia will have a great deal of difficulty understanding what he or she hears and will not be able to accurately repeat speech of others.

The condition known as **Broca's aphasia** is a stark contrast to Wernicke's aphasia. Broca's aphasia arises not only from lesions to Broca's area (areas 44 and 45), but also from lesions of the operculum of the frontal and parietal regions, the insula, and the supramarginal gyrus of the parietal lobe. That is, Broca's aphasia arises from lesions of areas served by the upper division of the middle cerebral artery. Broca's area is involved with the planning of the speech, and the aphasia associated with it is far from fluent. Although the individual with Broca's aphasia generally will retain comprehension of auditory or visual input, the patient's expressive abilities may be severely impaired. Length and complexity of utterances will be markedly reduced, and speech may require extreme effort.

Wernicke's and Broca's areas communicate directly with each other by means of the arcuate fasciculus, providing a very strong link between the receptive component of language and its expression. When these fibers or the supramarginal gyrus of the parietal lobe have been damaged the patient will show signs of **conduction aphasia**. This individual will have good comprehension of speech or written material, relatively fluent spontaneous speech, but impaired ability to repeat utterances heard. There also will be phoneme substitutions.

If damage to the brain includes Wernicke's and Broca's areas and areas below the brain, the result may be **global aphasia**. In this condition, both expressive and receptive abilities are severely impaired. Speech is halting and nonfluent at best, with poverty of grammatical structures and significant comprehension deficit. Gesture and facial expressions may be the primary means of communication for this individual.

You can see how these areas of deficit fit together. Damage to regions of the temporal lobe will tend to cause receptive language problems depending on the location, whereas damage to the frontal speech regions may leave receptive abilities intact but cause a deficit in expression of language (speech).

We have been conveniently ignoring the fact that the cerebral cortex is firmly attached to subcortical structures, including the basal ganglia and thalamus. Improvement in brain imaging techniques has revealed that damage to many of these areas results in language impairment, although these reports emphasize the importance of not assuming a strict localizationist stance. Damage to the thalamus may have a significant impact on attention, but also has resulted in a type of aphasia that includes difficulty naming objects (**anomia**), generation of novel words (**neologisms**), and word or sound substitutions. Damage to the basal ganglia has resulted in nonfluent aphasia as well if there is damage to the putamen or caudate nucleus. It is likely that the hierarchical nature of the brain involves using these phylogenetically older structures to integrate information necessary for expression and reception, and that disruption of the pathways always results in some deficit.

Apraxia

Sometimes lesions can result in **primary oral** or **primary verbal apraxia**, a deficit in the ability to program the articulators for nonspeech (oral apraxia) or speech production (verbal apraxia) in the absence of muscular weakness or paralysis. Apraxia often co-occurs with aphasia and is viewed by many to be a component of Broca's aphasia. Errors in apraxia will tend to be phoneme substitution errors, although they will be much less predictable than articulation errors arising from other causes. Because the person with apraxia often has good comprehension, he or she will be quite aware of the errors and will struggle to correct them. This struggle will result in loss of speech fluency (and a great deal of frustration for the speaker). As the desired articulatory configuration becomes more complex (as in producing consonant clusters instead of singletons), the client's speech difficulty will increase.

At least two regions are involved in apraxia. If damage is restricted to the frontal lobe in the region of Broca's area, the individual will have difficulty producing even the simplest gestures with the articulators (referred to as executive apraxia). Damage to the supramarginal gyrus of the parietal lobe results in difficulty sequencing more complex articulatory gestures (planning apraxia).

Other Deficits

Not all lesions affect language directly. Left frontal lobe lesions often result in altered decision-making ability and difficulty changing strategies in problem solving. There is often a loss of response inhibition, and social skills are lost. Control of emotion may be compromised by frontal lobe lesions, resulting in emotional lability (excessive and uncontrollable emotional response) or reduced emotion. Personality characteristics are often altered by frontal lobe lesion. If the parahippocampal region of the cerebral cortex is involved, there may be difficulty learning complex tasks and remembering information received through sensory modalities. Penfield and Roberts (1959) found that removal of both hippocampi produced profound long-term memory deficit, whereas much milder problems arose from unilateral lesion. Removal of the left hippocampus results in difficulty remembering verbal information.

Although right hemisphere lesions generally do not result in aphasia, they do have linguistic and social significance. Lesions to this hemisphere may result in loss of the ability to process information contained in intonation of speech, so that nuance is lost. Communication of emotion, intent, and humor may be impaired in this individual. Individuals with right-hemisphere lesions often will make linguistically inappropriate responses, most likely arising from the inability to process these pragmatic functions.

To summarize:

■ The **hemispheres** of the brain display clear functional differences.
■ The **left hemisphere** in most individuals is dominant for language and speech, processes brief duration stimuli, and performs detailed analysis.
■ The **right hemisphere**, in contrast, appears to process information in a more holistic fashion, preferring spatial and tonal information.
■ **Face recognition** appears to be a right-hemisphere function.
■ Lesion studies have shown that damage to **Wernicke's area** in the dominant hemisphere usually results in a receptive language deficit with relatively intact speech fluency, whereas damage to **Broca's area** results in loss of speech fluency manifested as Broca's aphasia.
■ Damage to the **arcuate fasciculus** connecting these two regions will result in **conduction aphasia**, and damage to all of these regions will produce **global deficit**.
■ **Verbal dyspraxia** may result from damage to Broca's area, but also has been seen with lesions to the supramarginal gyrus, supplementary motor area, frontal operculum, and insula.
■ **Nondominant hemisphere lesions** often result in deficit in **pragmatics**, especially related to monitoring facial responses of communication partners, information carried in the intonation of speech, and communicative nuance.
■ **Frontal lobe lesions** may result in deficits in judgment and response inhibition, whereas damage to the **hippocampus** will affect short-term memory, especially as it relates to auditory information.

Motor Control for Speech

The production of speech is an extraordinarily complex process. We tend to view area 4 as the "prime mover," but it would be more accurate to view it as place where the very complex planning, programming, and preparation reach fruition. Movement is initiated at the motor strip, but only after it has been conceived, and after the steps involved for muscle activity have been prepared. To further confound things, control of speech musculature must be precisely coordinated, a process involving afferent input from the muscles.

Input to the motor strip arises from the premotor regions that are involved in preparation of the motor act. The premotor gyrus and supplemental motor area receive input concerning state of the musculature from the postcentral gyrus, and it appears that knowledge of articulator position in space is established here. In addition, Broca's area (areas 44 and 45) communicates with the TOP by means of the arcuate fasciculus and is intimately involved in articulatory planning. The prefrontal association area receives input from diffuse sensory integration regions of the cerebrum, and this information is used to make decisions concerning execution of the motor act (such as inhibiting a response). Prefrontal and premotor regions project to the precentral gyrus, as does Broca's area, so that both immediate planning and cognitive strategies associated with speech influence the output.

The primary motor cortex (MI) receives information concerning the state of muscles, tendons, and tissue through several means. The sensory cortex (SI) receives this information in a well-organized fashion. Area 3 receives muscle afferent information from group Ia fibers terminating in the thalamus and from mechanoreceptors of the skin that are apparently very important for speech muscles of the face. Area 1 receives mechanoreceptor input as well, and area 2 receives joint sense. This information is all directed to the MI, either directly or via other SI areas, assumedly to modulate the motor command based on current status.

This sensory information obviously is not the only information processed by MI. The premotor region (lateral area 6) is involved in organization of the motor act for skilled, voluntary movement, and its output is directly routed to MI in both hemispheres. It receives somatic and visual information and apparently integrates this into its motor plan. The SMA (which is located in medial area 6) appears to be involved in the programming of speech and other sequential movements, as well as control of some reflexes. The SMA receives information concerning tactile, auditory, and visual senses. It should be remembered that information from the cerebellum and basal ganglia is exchanged with MI, SMA, and the premotor region as well. Indeed, lesions of the SMA or basal ganglia can result in akinesia (loss of the ability to initiate movement), and lesions of the premotor cortex may result in apraxia (dysfunction in ability to program movement). Loss of regions of MI will result in paralysis or weakness of involved muscle groups, reduction in fine motor control, and spasticity arising from the unmodulated reflexes.

Thus, the motor impulse that is initiated by MI is really the end product of planning (Broca's area and SMA area 6) and programming (Broca's area and premotor area 6), with the strategic formulations arising from areas 8, 9, and 10 of the frontal lobe. The motor areas are influenced by the current state of the musculature of the body via somatosensory afferents to SI, the thalamus, and the cerebellum. The afferent information concerning the tissues being acted on will help the MI area modify its output to accommodate fine motor control.

In this way, the motor impulse initiated by the motor strip is the end product of planning and programming, with the strategic formulations arising from the prefrontal region. The motor areas are influenced by the current state of the musculature of the body.

Clearly, the execution of speech involves extensive interaction of the areas of the brain in a rapidly coordinated fashion. Studies have revealed that we are amazingly versatile in overcoming obstacles to

A bite block is a device used to stabilize the mandible. Often made of hard acrylic or dental impression material, the bite block is used to eliminate the contribution of the mandible to tongue movement for diagnostic and therapeutic purposes. For an excellent discussion on preparation and use of the bite block, see Dworkin (1994).

speech production (this is good news for the budding speech-language pathologist). Try this: Say "Sammy is a friend of mine." Now place your pencil between your molars on side of your mouth, bite down lightly, and say it again a few times. Were you able to produce intelligible speech? Although the pencil interfered with some dental or labial productions, on the whole you were not only intelligible, but accurate. If the program for the individual articulators was "written in stone," you would not have been able to tolerate this aberration (use of a "bite block"), and your speech would have been unintelligible. Through this sort of examination we realize that you probably develop an internal standard of what you want your speech to sound like, and then do whatever is necessary to match that standard. Thus, your role as a speech-language pathologist could well include helping your client develop that internal standard, and conditions that alter that internal model will inevitably alter the output.

CHAPTER SUMMARY

Communication between neurons of the nervous system occurs at the **synapse**, and **neurotransmitter** passing through the **synaptic cleft** will either excite or inhibit the postsynaptic neuron. When sufficiently stimulated an **action potential** will be generated, causing membrane depolarization and exchange of ions between the **extracellular** and **intracellular** space. **Ion movement** results in a large and predictable change in voltage across the membrane. **Resting membrane potential** is the relatively stable state of the neuron at rest, while the **absolutely refractory period**, after excitation is an interval during which the neuron may not be excited to fire. During the **relatively refractory period** a neuron may be stimulated to fire, given increased stimulation. Neurons are capable of representing differences in input only through **rate** of response. **Myelinated fibers** conduct the wave of depolarization more rapidly than **demyelinated fibers**, primarily due to saltatory conduction.

Muscle is comprised of thick and thin **myofilaments** that slide across each other during contraction. **Activation** of a muscle fiber causes release of calcium into the environment of **thick myofilaments**, revealing the binding sites on the **thin filaments** that permit cross bridging from the thick filaments. **Muscle shortening** is the product of repeated contraction of the cross bridges. **Slow twitch** muscle fibers remain contracted longer than **fast twitch fibers**, with the former being involved in maintenance of posture and the latter in fine and rapid motor function.

Muscle spindles provide feedback to the neuromotor system about muscle length, tension, motion, and position. Muscle spindles running parallel to intrafusal muscle fibers are sensors for muscle length, whereas **golgi tendon organs** sense muscle tension. **Nuclear bag fibers** convey information concerning acceleration and **nuclear chain fibers**

respond to sustained lengthening. When a muscle is passively stretched, a **segmental reflex** is triggered. Extrafusal muscles paralleling the muscle spindles are activated and the muscle is shortened. Golgi tendon organs apparently respond to the tension of musculature during active contraction.

Higher function of the brain defies a strict localization approach to functional organization. General regions, such as Wernicke's area, can be ascribed broad function, and this view facilitates examination of brain function and dysfunction. Brain function may be classified into regions of **primary, higher order,** and **association regions**. **Primary sensory** and **motor regions** include the primary reception area for somatic sense, primary motor area, primary auditory cortex, and primary region of visual reception. **Higher order** areas of processing are apparently responsible for extracting features of the stimulus. **Association areas** are the regions of highest cognitive processing, integrating sensory information with memory. The **prefrontal area** appears to be involved in higher function related to motor output, while the **temporal-occipital-parietal** association is involved in spoken and written language function. The **limbic association** area integrates information relating to affect, motivation, and emotion.

Dysarthria is a speech disorder resulting from damage to the motor execution system of the central nervous system and, resulting in muscular weakness and reduction in motor control. **Flaccid dysarthria** results from damage to LMN, whereas UMN lesions result in **spastic dysarthria**. **Ataxic dysarthria** arises from cerebellar damage. **Hyperkinetic dysarthria** is the result of damage to inhibitory processes of the extrapyramidal system, whereas **hypokinetic dysarthria** results from lesion to excitatory mechanisms. **Apraxia** arises from lesion to the regions associated with preparation and planning for the motor act, specifically the supramarginal gyrus of the parietal lobe, Broca's area, and the SMA. Apraxia is a deficit in **motor planning**, existing without muscular weakness or paralysis.

The hemispheres of the brain display clear functional differences. Language and speech, brief duration stimuli, and detailed information are processed in the **left hemisphere** in most individuals. The **right hemisphere** appears to process information in a more holistic fashion, preferring spatial and tonal information. Lesions to **Wernicke's area** in the dominant hemisphere results in a receptive language deficit with relatively intact speech fluency, whereas damage to **Broca's area** results in loss of speech fluency. Damage to the **arcuate fasciculus** connecting these two regions will result in **conduction aphasia**, and damage to all of these regions will produce **global deficit**. **Verbal dyspraxia** may result from damage to Broca's area, the supramarginal gyrus, supplementary motor area, frontal operculum, and insula. **Right hemisphere lesions** often result in deficit in pragmatics, misinterpretation of information carried in the speech intonation, and communicative nuance.

Frontal lobe lesions often result in impaired judgment and failure to inhibit responses, whereas damage to the **hippocampus** will affect short-term memory.

Movement is initiated at the **motor strip**, but there is a great deal of planning that occurs prior to that point. The **premotor regions**, including Broca's area, are involved in planning for the motor act, and project that plan to the motor strip. The **prefrontal association** area also provides input to the motor strip concerning higher cognitive elements of the speech act, and the lowest levels of information (information about muscle stretch and tension) are also fed to the motor strip.

Study Questions

1. _____ is a change in electrical potential that occurs when a cell membrane is stimulated adequately toe permit ion exchange between intra- and extracellular space.

2. The _____ period is the time during which the cell membrane cannot be stimulated to depolarize.

3. The _____ is a period during which the membrane may be stimulated to excitation again, but only with greater than typical stimulation.

4. The _____ of the axon myelin promote saltatory conduction.

5. The substance known as _____ is discharged into the synaptic cleft, stimulating the postsynaptic neuron.

6. Activation of a muscle fiber causes release of calcium into the environment of _____ myofilaments.

7. _____ twitch muscle fiber remain contracted longer than _____ twitch fibers.

8. _____ spindles provide feedback to the neuromotor system about muscle length, tension, motion and position.

9. Higher cognitive processing occurs generally in _____ _____ areas.

10. The _____ area is involved in language function.

11. _____ dysarthria from damage to LMN, while UMN lesions result in spastic dysarthria.

12. _____ dysarthria is the result of damage to inhibitory processes of the extrapyramidal system.

13. _____ arises from cerebellar damage.

14. _____ arises from lesion to the regions associated with preparation and planning for the motor act, specifically the supramarginal gyrus of the parietal lobe, Broca's area, and the SMA.

15. The _____ area of the cerebrum appears to be involved in higher function related to motor output (such as inhibition of motor function and the ability to change motor responses), whereas the temporal-occipital-parietal association area is involved in language function.

16. The _____ area integrates information relating to affect, motivation, and emotion.

17. The _____ hemisphere in most individuals is dominant for language and speech, processes brief duration stimuli, and performs detailed analysis.

18. The _____ hemisphere appears to process information in a more holistic fashion, preferring spatial and tonal information.

19. Damage to _____ area in the dominant hemisphere usually results in a receptive language deficit with relatively intact speech fluency.

20. Damage to _____ area in the dominant hemisphere often results in loss of speech fluency manifested as Broca's aphasia.

21. Damage to the _____ fasciculus will result in conduction aphasia, and damage to all of these regions will produce global deficit.

Study Question Answers

1. ACTION POTENTIAL is a change in electrical potential that occurs when a cell membrane is stimulated adequately toe permit ion exchange between intra- and extracellular space.

2. The ABSOLUTELY REFRACTORY PERIOD is the time during which the cell membrane cannot be stimulated to depolarize.

3. The RELATIVELY REFRACTORY PERIOD is a period during which the membrane may be stimulated to excitation again, but only with greater than typical stimulation.

4. The NODES OF RANVIER of the axon myelin promote saltatory conduction.

5. The substance known as <u>NEUROTRANSMITTER</u> is discharged into the synaptic cleft, stimulating the postsynaptic neuron.

6. Activation of a muscle fiber causes release of calcium into the environment of <u>THICK</u> myofilaments.

7. <u>SLOW</u> twitch muscle fiber remain contracted longer than <u>FAST</u> twitch fibers.

8. <u>MUSCLE</u> <u>SPINDLES</u> provide feedback to the neuromotor system about muscle length, tension, motion and position.

9. Higher cognitive processing occurs generally in <u>ASSOCIATION</u> areas.

10. The <u>TEMPORO-OCCIPITAL-PARIETAL</u> <u>ASSOCIATION</u> area is involved in language function.

11. <u>FLACCID DYSARTHRIA</u> from damage to LMN, whereas UMN lesions result in spastic dysarthria.

12. <u>HYPERKINETIC DYSARTHRIA</u> is the result of damage to inhibitory processes of the extrapyramidal system.

13. <u>ATAXIC DYSARTHRIA</u> arises from cerebellar damage.

14. <u>APRAXIA</u> arises from lesion to the regions associated with preparation and planning for the motor act, specifically the supramarginal gyrus of the parietal lobe, Broca's area, and the SMA.

15. The <u>PREFRONTAL</u> area of the cerebrum appears to be involved in higher function related to motor output (such as inhibition of motor function and the ability to change motor responses), while the temporal-occipital-parietal association area is involved in language function.

16. The <u>LIMBIC</u> <u>ASSOCIATION</u> area integrates information relating to affect, motivation, and emotion.

17. The <u>LEFT</u> <u>HEMISPHERE</u> in most individuals is dominant for language and speech, processes brief duration stimuli, and performs detailed analysis.

18. The <u>RIGHT</u> <u>HEMISPHERE</u> appears to process information in a more holistic fashion, preferring spatial and tonal information.

19. Damage to <u>WERNICKE'S</u> area in the dominant hemisphere usually results in a receptive language deficit with relatively intact speech fluency.

20. Damage to <u>BROCA'S</u> area in the dominant hemisphere often results in loss of speech fluency manifested as Broca's aphasia.

21. Damage to the <u>ARCUATE</u> fasciculus will result in conduction aphasia, and damage to all of these regions will produce global deficit.

REFERENCES

Bechera, A., Tranel, D., Damasio, H., Adolphs, R., Rockland, C., & Damasio, A. R. (1995). Double dissociation of conditioning and declarative knowledge relative to the amygdala and hippocampus in humans. *Science, 269,* 1115–1118.

Bowman, J. P. (1971). *The muscle spindle and neural control of the tongue.* Springfield, IL: Charles C. Thomas.

Carpenter, M. B. (1978). *Core text of neuroanatomy* (2nd ed.). Baltimore, MD: Williams & Wilkins.

Chusid, J. G. (1979). *Correlative neuroanatomy and functional neurology,* (17th ed.). Los Altos, CA: Lange Medical Publications.

Collins, M. J. (1989). Differential diagnosis of aphasic syndromes and apraxia of speech. In Square-Storer (Ed.), *Acquired apraxia of speech in aphasic adults* (pp. 87–114). London: Taylor and Francis.

Cotman, C. W., & McGaugh, J. L. (1980). *Behavioral neuroscience.* New York: Academic Press.

Crary, M. A. (1993). *Developmental motor speech disorders.* San Diego, CA: Singular Publishing Group.

Darley, F. L., Aronson, A. E., & Brown, J. R. (1975). *Motor speech disorders.* Philadelphia, PA: W. B. Saunders.

Dworkin, J. P. (1994). *Motor speech disorders: A treatment guide.* St. Louis, MO: C. V. Mosby.

Filskov, S. B., & Boll, T. J. (1981). *Handbook of clinical neuropsychology.* New York: John Wiley & Sons.

Ganong, W. F. (1981). *Review of medical physiology.* Los Altos, CA: Lange Medical Publications.

Gelfand, S. A. (1990). *Hearing.* New York: Marcel Dekker.

Ghez, C. (1991). Voluntary movement. In E. R. Kandel, J. H. Schwartz, & T. M. Jessell, (Eds.), *Principles of neural science* (3rd ed., pp. 609–625). Norwalk, CT: Appleton & Lange.

Gilman, S., & Winans, S. S. (1982). *Manter and Gatz's essentials of clinical neuroanatomy and neurophysiology.* Philadelphia, PA: F. A. Davis.

Kandel, E. R., Siegelbaum, S. A., & Schwartz, J. H. (1991). Synaptic transmission. In E. R. Kandel, J. H. Schwartz, & T. M. Jessell, (Eds.), *Principles of neural science* (3rd ed.) Norwalk, CT: Appleton & Lange.

Kelly, J. P. (1991). The neural basis of perception and movement. In E. R. Kandel, J. H. Schwartz, & T. M. Jessell, (Eds.), *Principles of neural science* (3rd ed.). Norwalk, CT: Appleton & Lange.

Kuehn, D. P., Lemme, M. L., & Baumgartner, J. M. (1989). *Neural bases of speech, hearing, and language.* Boston: College-Hill Press.

Kupferman, I. (1991). Localization of higher cognitive and affective functions: The association cortices. In E. R. Kandel, J. H. Schwartz, & T. M. Jessell, (Eds.), *Principles of neural science* (3rd ed.). Norwalk, CT: Appleton & Lange.

Mayeux, R., & Kandel, E. R. (1991). Disorders of language: The aphasias. In E. R. Kandel, J. H. Schwartz, & T. M. Jessell, (Eds.), *Principles of neural science* (3rd ed.). Norwalk, CT: Appleton & Lange.

Netter, F. H. (1983). *The CIBA collection of medical illustrations. Vol. 1. Nervous system. Part I. Anatomy and physiology* West Caldwell, NJ: CIBA Pharmaceutical Company.

Netter, F. H. (1983). *The CIBA collection of medical illustrations. Vol. 1. Nervous system. Part II. Neurologic and neuromuscular disorders.* West Caldwell, NJ: CIBA Pharmaceutical Company.

Noback, C. R., & Demarest, R. J. (1977). *The nervous system.* New York: McGraw-Hill.

Noback, C. R., Strominger, N. L., & Demarest, R. J. (1991). *The human nervous system.* Philadelphia, PA: Lea & Febiger.

Nolte, J. (1993). *The human brain.* St. Louis, MO: Mosby Year Book.

Penfield, W., & Roberts, L. (1959). *Speech and brain–mechanisms.* Princeton, NJ: Princeton University Press.

Poritsky, R. (1992). *Neuroanatomy: A functional atlas of parts and pathways.* St. Louis: Mosby Year-Book.

Raymond, J. L., Lisberger, S. G., & Mauk, M. D. (1996). The cerebellum: A neuronal learning machine. *Science. 272,* 1126–1131,

Square-Storer, P., & Roy, E. A. (1989). The apraxias: Commonalities and distinctions. In P. Square–Storer (Ed.), *Acquired apraxia of speech in aphasic adults (pp. 20–63).* London: Taylor and Francis.

Twietmeyer, A., & McCracken, T. (1992). *Coloring guide to regional human anatomy.* Philadelphia: Lea & Febiger.

Wood, P. J., & Criss, W. R. (1975). *Normal and abnormal development of the human nervous system.* Hagerstown, MD: Harper & Row.

Williams, P,. & Warrick, R. (1980). *Gray's anatomy,* (36th British ed.). Philadelphia, PA: W. B. Saunders.

Yost, W. A., & Nielsen, D. W. (1977). *Fundamentals of hearing.* New York: Holt, Rinehart and Winston.

Zemlin, W. R. (1988). *Speech and hearing science: Anatomy and physiology.* Englewood Cliffs, NJ: Prentice-Hall.

APPENDIX

Anatomical Terms

Anatomical position:	Upright, palms forward, eyes directly ahead, feet together
Anterior:	Toward the front of the body or subpart
Asthenia:	Weakness
Bifurcation:	A fork; split into two parts
Caudal:	Towards the tail or coccyx
Central:	Relative to the center of a structure
Cranial:	Toward the head
Deep:	Further from the surface
Distal:	Further from the trunk or thorax; further from the attached end
Dorsal:	Pertaining to the back of the body or posterior surface
Extension:	Straightening or moving out of the flexed position
External:	Toward the exterior of a body
Flexion:	The act of bending
Frontal plane:	Divides body into anterior and posterior halves

Horizontal plane:	Divides body or body part into upper and lower halves
Inferior:	The lower point; nearer the feet
Insertion:	Distal attachment of a muscle
Internal:	Enclosed or on the interior
Lateral:	Away from the midline of the body or subpart
Medial/Mesial:	Toward the midline of the body or subpart
Origin:	Proximal attachment of a muscle
Palmar:	Pertaining to the palm of the hand
Peripheral:	Relative to the periphery or away from the center
Plantar:	Pertaining to the sole of the foot
Posterior:	Toward the back of the body or sub-part
Prone:	Body in horizontal position with face down
Proximal:	Closer to the trunk or thorax; nearer to the attached end
Radial:	Pertaining to the radius bone
Sagittal plane:	Divides body or body part into right and left halves
Superior:	The upper point; nearer the head
Superficial:	Near to the surface
Supine:	Body in horizontal position with face up
Ventral:	Pertaining to the belly or anterior surface

APPENDIX

Useful Combining Forms

ab-	Away from	-cule	Implies something very small
ad-	Toward	com-	With or together with
-algia	Pain	con-	With or together with
amphi-	On both sides	contra-	Opposite
-a-	Without; lack of	cor-	Heart
an-	Without; lack of	circum	Around
ana	Up	corp-	Body
angio-	Blood vessels	crus-	Cross; leg-like part
ante-	Before	crur-	Cross; leg-like part
antero-	Before	cryo-	Cold
apo-	Away from	-cule	Implies something very small
arthr-	A joint	-culus	Diminutive form of a noun
bi-	Two	-culum	Diminutive form of a noun
blast-	Germ	-cyte	Cell
brachy-	Short	de-	Away from
brady-	Slow	dextro-	Right
capit-	Head, or toward the head end	-dynia	Pain
-carpal	Wrist	dys-	Bad; with difficulty
-cele	Tumor	e-	Out from
cephalo-	Head, or toward the head end	ec-	Out of
-cle	Implies something very small	ecto-	On the outer side; toward the surface

-ectomy	Excision	-oma	Morbid condition of a part, often a tumor
-emia	Blood		
endo-	Toward the interior; within	oro-	Mouth
ento-	Toward the interior; within	ortho	Straight
ep-	Upon or above something else	-osis	Condition
epi-	Upon or above something else	osseo-	A hardened or bony part, but not strictly
etio-	Cause or origin		
ex-	Out of, toward the surface	osteo-	Bone
extra-	Outside	palato-	Palate
extero-	Aimed outward or nearer to the surface	para	Beside; partial
		patho-	Abnormal in some way
-gen	Producing	-pathy	Disease
-genic	Producing	-penia	Poverty
hemi-	Half	ped-	Child
hyper-	Above; increased, or too much of something	ped-	Foot
		per	Through; passing through; before
hypo-	Below; decreased, or too little of something		
		peri	Around
idio-	Peculiar	-plasty	Molding, forming
-ilos	Diminutive form of noun	-poiesis	Making
infra-	Below	-phage	Eating
inter-	Between	-phagia	Eating
intero-	Aimed inward or farther from the surface	-pher-	Bearing or carrying
		-plasia	Growth
intra-	Within	-plastic	Capable of being molded
intro-	Into	poly-	Many
ipsi-	Same	post-	After; behind
iso-	Equal	postero-	Behind
-itis	Inflammation or irritation	pachy-	Thick
-ium	Diminutive form of noun	pre-	Before; in front of
latero-	Side	pro-	Before; in front of
lepto-	Thick	proto-	Primitive; simple form
leuco-	White	quadra-	Four
levo-	Left	quadri-	Four
macro-	Large	-rrhea	A flowing
medio-	Middle	-raphy	Suturing or stitching
megalo-	Large	re-	Back or again; curved back
meso-	Middle	retro-	Backward, toward the rear
meta-	After; mounted or built upon	scirrho-	Hard
micro-	Small	sclero-	Hard
mono-	Single	-sclerosis	Hardening
morph-	Form	scolio-	Curved
my-	Pertaining to muscle	semi-	Half
myelo-	Pertaining to spinal cord	sinistro-	Left
myo-	Pertaining to muscle	soma-	Pertaining to the body
naso-	Nose	somato-	Pertaining to the body
neo-	New	steno-	Narrow
neuro-	Nerve	strepto-	Swift
oculo-	Eye	sub-	Under

sup-	Under; moderately	-tomy	Cutting
super-	Above; excessively	trans-	Beyond or on the other side
supra-	Above, upon	tri-	Three
sym-	With or together	-trophy	Growth, usually by expanding
syn-	With or together	-trophic	Related to nourishment
tachy-	Swift; fast	-tropy	Implies seeking or heading for something
-tarsal	Ankle		
telo-	Far from, toward the extreme	uni-	One
tetra-	Four		

APPENDIX

Muscles of Respiration

THORACIC MUSCLES OF INSPIRATION

Primary Inspiratory Muscle

Muscle: **Diaphragm**

Origin: Xiphoid process of sternum, inferior margin of the rib cage (ribs 7–12), corpus of L1, transverse processes of L1–L5

Course: Fibers course up and medially

Insertion: Central tendon of diaphragm

Innervation: Phrenic nerve arising from cervical plexus of spinal nerves C3, C4, C5

Function: Depresses central tendon of diaphragm, enlarges vertical dimension of thorax, distends abdomen

539

Accessory Thoracic Muscles of Inspiration

Muscle:	**External intercostal**
Origin:	Inferior surface of ribs 1–11
Course:	Down
Insertion:	Upper surface of rib immediately below
Innervation:	Intercostal nerves: thoracic intercostal nerves arising from T2 through T6 and thoracoabdominal intercostal nerves from T7 through T11
Function:	Elevate rib
Muscle:	**Levator costarum, longis**
Origin:	Transverse processes of T7 through T11
Course:	Down and obliquely out
Insertion:	Bypass the rib below the point of origin, inserting rather into the next rib
Innervation:	Dorsal rami (branches) of the intercostal nerves arising from spinal nerves T2 through T12
Function:	Elevate rib cage
Muscle:	**Levator costarum, brevis**
Origin:	Transverse processes of vertebrae C7 through T11
Course:	Course obliquely down and out
Insertion:	Tubercle of the rib below
Innervation:	Dorsal rami (branches) of the intercostal nerves arising from spinal nerves T2 through T12
Function:	Elevate rib cage
Muscle:	**Serratus posterior superior**
Origin:	Spinous processes of C7 and T1 through T3
Course:	Course down and laterally
Insertion:	Just beyond the angles of ribs 2 through 5

Innervation: Ventral intercostal portion of the spinal nerves T1 through T4 or T5

Function: Elevate rib cage

Accessory Muscles of Neck

Muscle: **Sternocleidomastoid**

Origin: Mastoid process of temporal bone

Course: Down and in

Insertion: Superior manubrium sterni; clavicle

Innervation: XI Accessory, spinal branch arising from spinal cord in the regions of C2 through C4 or C5

Function: Elevate sternum and, by association, rib cage

Muscle: **Scalenus anterior**

Origin: Transverse processes of vertebrae C3 through C6

Course: Down

Insertion: Superior surface of rib 1

Innervation: C4 through C6

Function: Elevate rib 1

Muscle: **Scalenus medius**

Origin: Transverse processes of vertebrae C2 through C7

Course: Down

Insertion: Superior surface of the first rib

Innervation: Cervical plexus derived from C3 and C4 and spinal nerves C5 through C8

Function: Elevate rib 1

Muscle: **Scalenus posterior**

Origin: Transverse processes of C5 through C7

Course: Down

Insertion: Second rib

Innervation: Spinal nerves C5 through C8

Function: Elevate rib 2

Muscle: **Trapezius**

Origin: Spinous processes of C2 to T12

Course: Fan laterally

Insertion: Acromion of scapula and superior surface of clavicle

Innervation: XI Accessory, spinal branch arising from spinal cord in the regions of C2 through C4 or C5

Function: Elongates neck, controls head

Muscles of Upper Arm and Shoulder

Muscle: **Pectoralis major**

Origin: Sternal head: length of sternum at costal cartilages; clavicular head: anterior clavicle

Course: Fanlike laterally, converging at humerus

Insertion: Greater tubercle of humerus

Innervation: Superior branch of the brachial plexus (spinal nerves C4 through C7 and T1)

Function: Elevate sternum, and subsequently increase transverse dimension of rib cage

Muscle: **Pectoralis minor**

Origin: Anterior surface of ribs 2 through 5 near chondral margin

Course: Up and laterally

Insertion: Coracoid process of scapula

Innervation: Superior branch of the brachial plexus (spinal nerves C4 through C7 and T1)

Function: Increases transverse dimension of rib cage

Muscle: **Serratus anterior**

Origin: Ribs 1 through 9, lateral surface of thorax

Course: Up and back

Insertion: Inner vertebral border of scapula

Innervation: Brachial plexus, long thoracic nerve from C5 through C7

Function: Elevate ribs 1–9

Muscle: **Subclavius**

Origin: Inferior surface of clavicle

Course: Oblique and medial

Insertion: Superior surface of rib 1 at chondral margin

Innervation: Brachial plexus, lateral branch, from fifth and sixth spinal nerves

Function: Elevate rib 1

Muscle: **Levator scapulae**

Origin: Transverse processes of C1 through C4

Course: Down

Insertion: Medial border of scapula

Innervation: C3 through C5 of cervical plexus

Function: Neck support, elevates scapula

Muscle: **Rhomboideus major**

Origin: Spinous processes of T2 through T5

Course: Down and laterally in

Insertion: Scapula

Innervation: Spinal C5 from the dorsal scapular nerve of upper root of brachial plexus

Function: Stabilize shoulder girdle

Muscle: **Rhomboideus minor**

Origin: Spinous processes of C7 and T1

Course: Down and laterally in

Insertion: Medial border of scapula

Innervation: Spinal C5 from the dorsal scapular nerve of upper root of brachial plexus

Function: Stabilize shoulder girdle

Muscle: **Internal intercostal**

Origin: Inferior margin of ribs 1–11

Course: Down and lateral

Insertion: Superior surface of the rib below

Innervation: Intercostal nerves: thoracic intercostal nerves arising from T2 through T6 and thoracoabdominal intercostal nerves from T7 through T11

Function: Depress ribs 1–11

Muscle: **Innermost intercostal**

Origin: Inferior margin of ribs 1–11; sparse or absent in superior thorax

Course: Down and lateral

Insertion: Superior surface of the rib below

Innervation: Intercostal nerves: thoracic intercostal nerves arising from T2 through T6 and thoracoabdominal intercostal nerves from T7 through T11

Function: Depress ribs 1–11

Muscle: **Transversus thoracis**

Origin: Inner thoracic lateral margin of sternum

Course: Laterally

Insertion: Inner chondral surface of ribs 2–6

Innervation: Thoracic intercostal nerves and thoracoabdominal intercostal nerves and subcostal nerves derived from T2 through T2 spinal nerves

Function: Depress rib cage

Posterior Thoracic Muscles

Muscle: **Subcostal**

Origin: Inner posterior thorax; sparse in upper thorax; from inner surface of rib near angle

Course: Down and lateral

Insertion: Inner surface of second or third rib below

Innervation: Intercostal nerves of thorax, arising from the ventral rami of the spinal nerves

Function: Depress thorax

Muscle: **Serratus posterior inferior**

Origin: Spinous processes of T11, T12, L1 through L3

Course: Up and laterally

Insertion: Lower margin of the ribs 7–12

Innervation: Intercostal nerves from T9 through T11 and subcostal nerve from T12

Function: Contraction of these muscles would tend to pull the rib cage down, supporting
              expiratory effort

ABDOMINAL MUSCLES OF EXPIRATION

Anterolateral Abdominal Muscles

Muscle: **Transversus abdominis**

Origin: Posterior abdominal wall at the vertebral column via the thoracolumbar fascia of
              the abdominal aponeurosis

Course: Lateral

Insertion: Transversus abdominis aponeurosis and inner surface of ribs 6 through 12, inter-
              digitating at that point with the fibers of the diaphragm; inferior-most attachment
              is at the pubis

Innervation: Thoracic and lumbar nerves from the lower spinal intercostal nerves (derived
              from T7 to T12) and first lumbar nerve, iliohypogastric and ilioinguinal branches

Function: Compress abdomen

Muscle: **Internal oblique abdominis**

Origin: Inguinal ligament and iliac crest

Course: Fans medially

Insertion: Cartilaginous portion of lower ribs and the portion of the abdominal aponeurosis lateral to the rectus abdominis

Innervation: Thoracic and lumbar nerves from the lower spinal intercostal nerves (derived from T7 to T12) and first lumbar nerve, iliohypogastric and ilioinguinal branches

Function: Rotates trunk, flexes trunk, compresses abdomen

Muscle: **External oblique abdominis**

Origin: Osseous portion of the lower seven ribs

Course: Fans downward

Insertion: Iliac crest, inguinal ligament, and abdominal aponeurosis lateral to rectus abdominis

Innervation: Thoracoabdominal nerve arising from T7 through T11 and subcostal nerve from T12

Function: Bilateral contraction flexes vertebral column and compresses abdomen, unilateral contraction results in trunk rotation

Muscle: **Rectus abdominis**

Origin: Originates as four or five segments at pubis inferiorly

Course: Up to segment border

Insertion: Xiphoid process of sternum and the cartilage of rib 5–7, lower ribs

Innervation: T7 through T11 intercostal nerves (thoracoabdominal) subcostal nerve from T12 (T7 supplies upper segment, T8 supplies the second, T9 supplies remainder)

Function: Flexion of vertebral column

Posterior Abdominal Muscles

Muscle: **Quadratus lumborum**

Origin: Iliac crest

Course: Fans up and in

Insertion: Transverse processes of the lumbar vertebrae and inferior border of rib 12

Innervation: Thoracic nerve T12 and L1 through L4 lumbar nerves

Function: Bilateral contraction fixes the abdominal wall in support of abdominal compression

MUSCLES OF UPPER LIMB:

Muscle:	**Latissimus dorsi**
Origin:	Lumbar, sacral, and lower thoracic vertebrae
Course:	Up fanlike
Insertion:	Humerus
Innervation:	For respiration, stabilizes posterior abdominal wall for expiration
Function:	Brachial plexus, posterior branch; Fibers from the regions C6 through C8 form the long subscapular nerve

APPENDIX

D

Muscles of Phonation

INTRINSIC LARYNGEAL MUSCLES

Muscle: **Lateral cricoarytenoid**

Origin: Superior-lateral surface of the cricoid cartilage

Course: Up and back

Insertion: Muscular process of the arytenoid

Innervation: X vagus, recurrent laryngeal nerve

Function: Adducts vocal folds, increases medial compression

Muscle: **Transverse arytenoid**

Origin: Lateral margin of posterior arytenoid

Course: Laterally

Insertion: Lateral margin of posterior surface, opposite arytenoid

Innervation: X vagus, recurrent laryngeal nerve

Function: Adduct vocal folds

Muscle: **Oblique arytenoid**

Origin: Posterior base of the muscular processes

Course: Obliquely up

Insertion: Apex of the opposite arytenoid

Innervation: X vagus, recurrent laryngeal nerve

Function: Pull the apex medially

Muscle: **Posterior cricoarytenoid**

Origin: Posterior cricoid lamina

Course: Up and out

Insertion: Posterior aspect of the muscular process of arytenoid cartilage

Innervation: X vagus, recurrent laryngeal nerve

Function: Abduct vocal folds

Muscle: **Cricothyroid**

Origin: Pars recta: anterior surface of the cricoid cartilage beneath the arch; pars oblique: cricoid cartilage lateral to the pars recta

Course: Pars recta: up and out; pars oblique: obliquely up

Insertion: Pars recta: lower surface of the thyroid lamina;

               Pars oblique: thyroid cartilage between laminae and inferior horns

Innervation: External branch of superior laryngeal nerve of X vagus

Function: Depress thyroid relative to cricoid, tense vocal folds

Muscle: **Thyrovocalis (medial thyroarytenoid)**

Origin: Inner surface, thyroid cartilage near notch

Course: Back

Insertion: Lateral surface of the arytenoid vocal process

Innervation: X vagus, recurrent laryngeal nerve

Function: Tense vocal folds

Muscle: **Thyromuscularis (lateral thyroarytenoid)**

Origin: Inner surface of thyroid cartilage near the notch

Course: Back

Insertion: Muscular process and base of arytenoid cartilage

Innervation: X vagus, recurrent laryngeal nerve

Function: Relaxes vocal folds

Muscle: **Superior thyroarytenoid**

Origin: Inner surface of thyroid cartilage near the angle

Course: Back

Insertion: Muscular process of arytenoid

Innervation: X vagus, recurrent laryngeal nerve

Function: Relaxes vocal folds

EXTRINSIC LARYNGEAL, INFRAHYOID AND SUPRAHYOID MUSCLES

Hyoid and Laryngeal Elevators

Muscle: **Digastricus, anterior and posterior**

Origin: Anterior: inner surface of the mandible, near symphysis; posterior digastricus: mastoid process of temporal bone

Course: Medial and down

Insertion: Hyoid, by means of intermediate tendon

Innervation:	Anterior: V trigeminal nerve, mandibular branch, via the mylohyoid branch of the inferior alveolar nerve; Posterior: VII, digastric branch
Function:	Anterior belly: draw hyoid up and forward; Posterior belly: draw hyoid up and back; together: elevate hyoid
Muscle:	**Stylohyoid**
Origin:	Styloid process of temporal bone
Course:	Medially down
Insertion:	Corpus hyoid
Innervation:	Motor branch of the VII facial nerve
Function:	Elevates and retracts the hyoid bone
Muscle:	**Mylohyoid**
Origin:	Mylohyoid line, inner surface of mandible
Course:	Fanlike to median fibrous raphe and hyoid
Insertion:	Corpus of hyoid
Innervation:	Alveolar nerve, V trigeminal, mandibular branch
Function:	Elevates the hyoid or depresses mandible
Muscle:	**Geniohyoid**
Origin:	Mental spines, inner surface of mandible
Course:	Back and down
Insertion:	Corpus, hyoid bone
Innervation:	XII hypoglossal nerve and C1 spinal nerve
Function:	Elevate hyoid bone, depress mandible
Muscle:	**Hyoglossus**
Origin:	Greater cornu hyoid
Course:	Up
Insertion:	Side of tongue

Innervation: Motor branch of the XII hypoglossal

Function: Elevate hyoid; depress tongue

Muscle: **Genioglossus**

Origin: Inner surface of mandible, mental spines

Course: Up and back

Insertion: Tongue and corpus hyoid

Innervation: Motor branch of XII hypoglossal

Function: Elevate hyoid; depress, retract, protrude tongue

Muscle: **Thyropharyngeus of inferior pharyngeal constrictor**

Origin: Posterior pharyngeal raphe

Course: Down, fanlike laterally

Insertion: Thyroid lamina and inferior cornu

Innervation: X vagus, recurrent laryngeal nerve (external laryngeal branch) and X vagus, superior laryngeal nerve (pharyngeal branch) and XI accessory

Function: Elevate larynx and constrict pharynx

Hyoid and Laryngeal Depressors

Muscle: **Sternohyoid**

Origin: Manubrium sterni and clavicle

Course: Superiorly

Insertion: Inferior margin of hyoid corpus

Innervation: Ansa cervicalis from spinal C1–C3

Function: Depresses hyoid

Muscle: **Omohyoid, superior and inferior heads**

Origin: Superior: corpus hyoid; inferior: upper border, scapula

Course: Superior: down; inferior: down and laterally

Insertion: Via intermediate tendon to hyoid

Innervation: Superior: superior ramus of ansa cervicalis from C1; inferior: ansa cervicalis, spinal C2 and C3

Function: Depress hyoid

Muscle: **Sternothyroid**

Origin: Manubrium sterni

Course: Up and out

Insertion: Oblique line, thyroid cartilage

Innervation: Spinal nerves C1, C2, and C3

Function: Depress thyroid cartilage

Muscle: **Thyrohyoid**

Origin: Oblique line, thyroid cartilage

Course: Up

Insertion: Greater cornu, hyoid

Innervation: XII Hypoglossal nerve and fibers from spinal C1

Function: Depress hyoid or elevate thyroid

APPENDIX

Muscles of Face, Soft Palate, and Pharynx

FACIAL MUSCLES

Muscle: **Risorius**

Origin: Posterior region of the face along the fascia of the masseter

Course: Forward

Insertion: Orbicularis oris at corners of mouth

Innervation: Buccal branch of the VII facial nerve

Function: Retracts lips at the corners

Muscle: **Buccinator**

Origin: Pterygomandibular ligament

Course: Forward

Insertion: Orbicularis oris at corners of mouth

Innervation: Buccal branch of the VII facial nerve

Function: Movement of food onto the grinding surfaces of the molars; oropharynx constriction

Muscle: **Levator labii superioris**

Origin: Infraorbital margin of the maxilla

Course: Down and in to the upper lip

Insertion: Mid-lateral region of the upper lip

Innervation: Buccal branches of the VII facial nerve

Function: Elevation of the upper lip

Muscle: **Zygomatic minor**

Origin: Facial surface of the zygomatic bone

Course: Downward

Insertion: Mid-lateral region of upper lip

Innervation: Buccal branches of the VII facial nerve

Function: Elevation of the upper lip

Muscle: **Levator labii alaeque nasi superioris**

Origin: Frontal process of maxilla

Course: Vertically along the lateral margin of the nose

Insertion: Mid-lateral region of the upper lip

Innervation: Buccal branches of the VII facial nerve

Function: Elevation of the upper lip

Muscle: **Zygomatic major (zygomaticus)**

Origin: Lateral to the zygomatic minor on zygomatic bone

Course: Obliquely down

Insertion: Corner of the orbicularis oris

Innervation: Buccal branches of the VII facial nerve

Function: Elevates and retracts angle of mouth

Muscle: **Depressor labii inferioris**

Origin: Mandible at the oblique line

Course: Up and in

Insertion: Lower lip

Innervation: Mandibular marginal branch of facial nerve

Function: Dilates orifice by pulling lip down and out

Muscle: **Depressor anguli oris (triangularis)**

Origin: Lateral margins of mandible on oblique line

Course: Course fanlike up

Insertion: Orbicularis oris and upper lip at corner

Innervation: Mandibular marginal branch of the facial nerve

Function: Depresses corners of mouth and helps to compress upper lip against lower lip

Muscle: **Mentalis**

Origin: Region of the incisive fossa of mandible

Course: Down

Insertion: Skin of the chin below

Innervation: Mandibular marginal branch of the facial nerve

Function: Elevates and wrinkles chin and pulls lower lip out

Muscle:	**Platysma**
Origin:	Fascia overlaying pectoralis major and deltoid
Course:	Up
Insertion:	Corner of the mouth, region below symphysis mente, lower margin of the mandible, and skin near the masseter
Innervation:	Cervical branch of the VII facial nerve
Function:	Depression of the mandible

Intrinsic Tongue Muscles

Muscle:	**Superior longitudinal**
Origin:	Fibrous submucous layer near the epiglottis, the hyoid, and from the median fibrous septum
Course:	Fans forward and outward
Insertion:	Lateral margins of the tongue and region of apex
Innervation:	XII hypoglossal nerve
Function:	Elevates, assists in retraction, or deviate tip of tongue
Muscle:	**Inferior longitudinal**
Origin:	Root of the tongue and corpus hyoid
Course:	Forward
Insertion:	Apex of the tongue
Innervation:	XII hypoglossal nerve
Function:	Pulls tip of the tongue downward, assists in retraction, deviates tongue
Muscle:	**Transverse muscles of the tongue**
Origin:	Median fibrous septum
Course:	Laterally
Insertion:	Side of the tongue in the submucous tissue

Innervation: XII hypoglossal nerve

Function: Provides a mechanism for narrowing the tongue

Muscle: **Vertical muscles of the tongue**

Origin: Base of the tongue

Course: Vertically

Insertion: Membranous cover

Innervation: XII hypoglossal nerve

Function: Pull tongue down into the floor of mouth

Extrinsic Tongue Muscles

Muscle: **Genioglossus**

Origin: Inner mandibular surface at symphysis

Course: Fans up back and forward

Insertion: Tip and dorsum of tongue and corpus hyoid

Innervation: XII hypoglossal nerve

Function: Anterior fibers retract tongue; posterior fibers protrude tongue; together, anterior and posterior fibers depress tongue

Muscle: **Hyoglossus**

Origin: Length of greater cornu and lateral body of hyoid

Course: Upward

Insertion: Sides of tongue between styloglossus and inferior longitudinal muscles

Innervation: XII hypoglossal nerve

Function: Pulls sides of tongue down

Muscle: **Styloglossus**

Origin: Anterolateral margin of styloid process

Course: Forward and down

Insertion: Inferior sides of the tongue

Innervation: XII hypoglossal nerve

Function: Draw the tongue back and up

Muscle: Chondroglossus

Origin: Lesser cornu hyoid and corpus

Course: Up

Insertion: Interdigitates with intrinsic muscles of the tongue medial to hyoglossus

Innervation: XII hypoglossal nerve

Function: Depresses the tongue

Mandibular Elevators and Depressors

Muscle: Masseter

Origin: Zygomatic arch

Course: Down

Insertion: Ramus of the mandible and coronoid process

Innervation: Anterior trunk of mandibular nerve arising from the V trigeminal

Function: Elevate mandible

Muscle: Temporalis

Origin: Temporal fossa of temporal and parietal bones

Course: Converging downward and forward, through the zygomatic arch

Insertion: Coronoid process and ramus

Innervation: Temporal branches arising from the mandibular nerve of V trigeminal

Function: Elevates the mandible and draws it back if protruded

Muscle: **Medial pterygoid (internal pterygoid)**

Origin: Medial pterygoid plate and fossa

Course: Down and back

Insertion: Mandibular ramus

Innervation: Mandibular division of the V trigeminal nerve

Function: Elevates the mandible

Muscle: **Lateral pterygoid (external pterygoid)**

Origin: Lateral pterygoid plate and greater wing of sphenoid

Course: Back

Insertion: Pterygoid fovea of the mandible

Innervation: Mandibular branch of the V trigeminal nerve

Function: Protrudes the mandible

Muscle: **Digastricus, anterior belly**

Origin: Inner surface of mandible at digastricus fossa, near the symphysis

Course: Medially and down

Insertion: Intermediate tendon to juncture of hyoid corpus and greater cornu

Innervation: Mandibular branch of V trigeminal nerve via the mylohyoid branch of the inferior alveolar nerve

Function: Pulls hyoid forward; depresses mandible if in conjunction with digastricus posterior

Muscle: **Digastricus, posterior belly**

Origin: Mastoid process of temporal bone

Course: Medially and down

Insertion: Intermediate tendon to juncture of hyoid corpus and greater cornu

Innervation: Digastric branch of the VII facial nerve

Function:	Pulls hyoid back; depresses mandible if in conjunction with anterior digastricus
Muscle:	**Mylohyoid**
Origin:	Mylohyoid line, inner mandible
Course:	Back and down
Insertion:	Median fibrous raphe and inferiorly to hyoid
Innervation:	Alveolar nerve, arising from the V trigeminal nerve, mandibular branch
Function:	Depress the mandible
Muscle:	**Geniohyoid**
Origin:	Mental spines of the mandible
Course:	Medially
Insertion:	Corpus hyoid
Innervation:	XII hypoglossal nerve and C1 spinal nerve
Function:	Depresses the mandible

MUSCLES OF THE VELUM

Muscle:	**Levator veli palatini (levator palati)**
Origin:	Apex of petrous portion of temporal bone and the medial wall of the Eustachian tube cartilage
Course:	Down and forward
Insertion:	Palatal aponeurosis of soft palate, lateral to musculus uvulae
Innervation:	Pharyngeal plexus from the XI accessory and X vagus nerves
Function:	Elevates and retracts the posterior velum
Muscle:	**Musculus uvulae**
Origin:	Posterior nasal spines of the palatine bones and palatal aponeurosis
Course:	Run the length of soft palate
Insertion:	Mucous membrane cover of the velum

Innervation: Pharyngeal plexus of XI accessory and X vagus nerves

Function: Shortens the soft palate

Muscle: **Tensor veli palatini (tensor veli palati)**

Origin: Scaphoid fossa of sphenoid, sphenoid spine, and lateral Eustachian tube wall

Course: Course down, terminates in tendon which passes around pterygoid hamulus, then is directed medially

Insertion: Palatal aponeurosis

Innervation: Mandibular nerve of V trigeminal

Function: Tenses and flattens soft palate; assists in dilating Eustachian tube

Muscle: **Palatoglossus**

Origin: Anterolateral palatal aponeurosis

Course: Down

Insertion: Sides of posterior tongue

Innervation: Pharyngeal plexus from the XI accessory and X vagus nerves

Function: Elevate tongue or depress soft palate

Muscle: **Palatopharyngeus**

Origin: Anterior hard palate midline of soft palate

Course: Laterally and down

Insertion: Posterior margin of the thyroid cartilage

Innervation: Pharyngeal plexus from XI accessory and pharyngeal branch of X vagus nerve

Function: Narrows pharynx, lowers the soft palate

MUSCLES OF PHARYNX

Muscle: **Superior pharyngeal constrictor**

Origin: Pterygomandibular raphe

Course: Posteriorly

Insertion: Median raphe of pharyngeal aponeurosis

Innervation: XI accessory nerve and X vagus via pharyngeal plexus

Function: Pulls the pharyngeal wall forward and constricts pharyngeal diameter

Muscle: **Middle pharyngeal constrictor**

Origin: Horns of the hyoid and stylohyoid ligament

Course: Up and back

Insertion: Median pharyngeal raphe

Innervation: XI accessory nerve and X vagus via pharyngeal plexus

Function: Narrows the diameter of the pharynx

Muscle: **Inferior pharyngeal constrictor: cricopharyngeus**

Origin: Cricoid cartilage

Course: Back

Insertion: Orifice of esophagus

Innervation: XI accessory nerve and X vagus via pharyngeal plexus

Function: Constricts superior orifice of esophagus

Muscle: **Inferior pharyngeal constrictor: thyropharyngeus muscle**

Origin: Oblique line of thyroid lamina

Course: Up and back

Insertion: Median pharyngeal raphe

Innervation: XI accessory nerve and X vagus via pharyngeal plexus

Function: Reduces the diameter of the lower pharynx

Muscle: **Salpingopharyngeus**

Origin: Lower margin of Eustachian tube

Course: Down

Insertion: Converges with palatopharyngeus

Innervation: X vagus and spinal accessory nerve via the pharyngeal plexus

Function: Elevates lateral pharyngeal wall

Muscle: **Stylopharyngeus**

Origin: Styloid process

Course: Down

Insertion: Into pharyngeal constrictors and posterior thyroid cartilage

Innervation: Muscular branch of IX glossophyarngeal nerve

Function: Elevates and opens the pharynx

APPENDIX

Sensors

GENERAL CLASSES

Interoceptors: Monitor events within the body (e.g., distension of stomach, blood pH)

Exteroceptors: Respond to stimuli outside of body (touch, hearing, vision)

Proprioceptors: Monitor change in body position or position of its parts (body position sense) (e.g., muscle and joint sensors, vestibular sensation)

SPECIFIC TYPES

Teloreceptors: Respond to stimuli separate from body (hearing, vision)

Contact receptors: Respond to stimuli that touch body (e.g., tactile, pain, deep and light pressure, temperature)

Chemoreceptors: Respond to chemical change (smell, taste, pH, etc.)

Photoreceptors: Respond to light changes (vision)

Thermoreceptors: Respond to heat

Mechanoreceptors: Respond to mechanical force (touch, muscle length and tension, auditory, vestibular receptors, etc.)

Nociceptors: Pain sensors

CLASSES OF SENSATION

Somatic sense: Related to pain, temperature, mechanical stimulation of somatic structures (skin, muscle, joints)

Kinesthesia: Sense of motion

Special senses: Senses mediating specific exteroceptive information such as vision, audition, olfaction

APPENDIX

Cranial Nerves

CLASSES OF CRANIAL NERVES

GSA **General Somatic Afferent:** Related to pain, temperature, mechanical stimulation of somatic structures (skin, muscle, joints)

GVA **General Visceral Afferent:** From receptors in visceral structures (e.g., digestive tract)

GVE **General Visceral Efferent:** Autonomic efferent fibers

GSE **General Somatic Efferent:** Innervates skeletal (striated) muscle

SSA **Special Somatic Afferent:** Special senses—sight, hearing, equilibrium

SVA **Special Visceral Afferent:** Special senses of smell, taste

SVE **Special Visceral Efferent:** Innervation of muscle of branchial arch origin: larynx, pharynx, face

CRANIAL NERVES, SOURCES, AND FUNCTIONS

I. Olfactory

SVA: sense of smell

Source: mitral cells of olfactory bulb

II. Optic

SSA: Vision

Source: rod and cone receptor cells synapse with bipolar interneurons which synapse with multipolar ganglionic neuron; optic nerve is axon of multipolar ganglionic neurons; nerve becomes myelinated after exit eye socket and entrance into cranium; left and right nerves decussate at chiasm and project as optic tract to lateral geniculate body; projects to occipital cortex via optic radiations; left nasal nerve portion and right temporal nerve portion join after chiasm; left temporal nerve portion and right nasal aspect of nerve join after chiasm; visual field result is that left nasal and right temporal visual fields (right portion of image) project to left cerebral cortex; left temporal and right nasal visual fields (left portion of image) project to right cerebral cortex).

III. Oculomotor

GSE: All extrinsic ocular muscles except superior oblique and lateral rectus

Source: Oculomotor nucleus

GVE: Light and accommodation reflexes

Source: Edinger-Westphal nucleus

IV. Trochlear

GSE: Superior oblique muscle of eye (turns eye down when eye is adducted)

Source: Trochlear nuclei

VI. Abducens

GSE: Lateral rectus muscle for ocular abduction

Source: abducens nucleus

V. Trigeminal

GSA: Exteroceptive afferent for pain, thermal, tactile from face, forehead, mucous membrane of mouth and nose, teeth cranial dura; proprioceptive (deep pressure, kinesthesis) from teeth, gums, temporomandibular joint, stretch receptors of mastication

Source: Sensory nucleus of Trigeminal

SVE: To muscles of mastication, tensor tympani, tensor veli palatini

Source: Motor nucleus of trigeminal

Components of V Trigeminal:

Ophthalmic branch: Sensory only

  GSA: From cornea, iris, upper eyelid, front of scalp

Maxillary branch: Sensory only

  GSA: From lower eyelid, nose, palate, upper jaw

Mandibular branch: Sensory and motor

  GSA: From lower jaw and teeth, mucosa, cheeks, temporomandibular joint, anterior two thirds of tongue

  SVE: To muscles of mastication (internal & external pterygoid, temporalis, masseter), tensor tympani

VII. Facial

SVE: to facial muscles of expression, platysma, buccinator

Source: Motor nucleus of VII

SVA: Taste, anterior two thirds of tongue

Source: Solitary nucleus

GSA: Cutaneous sense of EAM and skin of ear

Source: Trigeminal nuclei

GVE: Lacrimal gland (tears); mucous membrane of mouth and nose

Source: superior salivatory and lacrimal nuclei

VIII. Vestibulocochlear

SSA: vestibular and cochlear sensation

Cochlear (auditory) portion: sensors are hair cells; cell bodies in spiral ganglion; axons are VIII nerve, auditory portion; low frequency (apical) fibers terminate at ventral cochlear nucleus (VCN) and high frequency fibers (basal) terminate at dorsal cochlear nucleus (DCN); transfer of auditory sensation to central nervous system

Source: Spiral ganglion

Vestibular portion: from semicircular canals, utricle, saccule; project to vestibular nuclei of medulla and subsequently to all levels of brainstem, spinal cord, cerebellum, thalamus, and cerebral cortex; maintenance of extensor tone, anti-gravity responses, balance, sense of position in space; coordinated eye/head movement through projection to III Oculomotor, IV Trochlear, VI Abducens cranial nerves;

Source: Vestibular ganglion

IX. Glossopharyngeal

GVA: somatic (tactile, thermal, pain sense) from posterior one third of tongue, tonsils, upper pharynx, Eustachian tube, mastoid cells

Source: Solitary nucleus

SVA: Taste, posterior one third of tongue

Source: Inferior salivatory nucleus

GSA: somatic sense of EAM and skin of ear

Source: Trigeminal nuclei

SVE: Innervation of stylopharyngeus, superior pharyngeal constrictor

Source: Inferior salivatory nucleus

GVE: Parotid gland

Source: Inferior salivatory nucleus

X. Vagus

GSA: Cutaneous sense from external auditory meatus

Source: Trigeminal nuclei

GVA: Sensory from pharynx, larynx, trachea, esophagus, viscera of thorax, abdomen

Source: Solitary nucleus

SVA: Taste buds near epiglottis and valleculae

Source: Solitary nucleus

GVE: To parasympathetic ganglia, thorax, and abdomen

Source: Dorsal motor nucleus of X

SVE: Striated muscle of larynx and pharynx

Source: Nucleus ambiguus

XI. Accessory

SVE, Cranial portion: Joins with X Vagus to form recurrent laryngeal nerve to innervate intrinsic muscles of larynx

Spinal portion—innervates sternocleidomastoid and trapezius

Source: Cranial portion: Nucleus ambiguus of medulla

SVE: Spinal portion: Anterior horn of C1 through C5 spinal nerves; unite and ascend; enter skull via foramen magnum; exit with vagus at jugular foramen

XII. Hypoglossal

GSE: Muscles of tongue

Source: Nucleus of Hypoglossal nerve

Clinical Note: Lesion of LMN produces ipsilateral damage (tongue deviates to side of damage).

APPENDIX

ANIMA
Software for Anatomy and Physiology
of Speech and Language

David G. Drumright
J. Anthony Seikel
Douglas W. King

To the Student

We hope that you will find the ANIMA (Anatomy of Speech and Language) software labs useful in your coursework. The software is designed to provide you with a hands-on experience in physiological principles, as well as to give a review of anatomical material.

There are 44 lessons of varying length, 7 of which are major quizzes. All lessons have quiz questions built into their structure. Lessons are designed to permit you to move forward and backward through the material (including questions) to promote learning. For regular lessons, you are able to improve your scores by restudying the material and retaking individual quiz items. This option is not available in the seven major quizzes.

To encourage security and discourage copying, each copy of the book includes one Anima disk. This is the Key Disk, which can be used to install the Anima files on any computer. After running the INSTALL program, the same disk becomes your key and your grade-carrying disk. Anima will not run without a properly validated key disk in a floppy drive; you must enter your ID (name or number) and password at the time of installation, and thereafter use the same ID and password to start the program. This method gives you full possession of your grades. You can use the key disk in any computer where Anima is installed; your grades always go onto the key disk, not into the computer. (At grade-recording times like midterm or final, your instructor will collect key disks and use them to record your grades, just like collecting lab notebooks.)

If you don't have your own computer, you must still use INSTALL at the start of the semester to "personalize" the key disk; you may then use it in any computer where Anima has been installed.

After installation, each time you start up Anima your key disk must be present; you first enter your name and password. The program then gives you two choices: start lesson or see grades.

When you choose START, you'll see a list of the 44 lessons; select whichever one is next, or whichever is scheduled by your instructor, and proceed from there. Each lesson is arranged in a series of "pages" with various activities on each page. Note especially the top part of the screen, which stays constant while the text and figures change below. The top section is where your "progress report" appears. A typical lesson will involve several "learning pages" with text, animations and figures, in which you click the mouse on locations or buttons to learn the names of anatomical features. After several learning pages, you'll find a graded page, which repeats some of the identifications, but with an added indication of right or wrong. When a question is being graded, a large question mark will appear in the upper "progress report" area; after you answer, the question mark will turn to a happy face or an unhappy face, and the numbers in the progress report will be updated.

The Proceed button moves you forward through the "learning pages." After a page containing graded questions, the program will turn the page automatically to the next learning page. At any time, though, you can turn back by hitting the Back button, which lives in the upper right corner. This enables you to repeat the learning pages until you get the answers right.

The exception to this arrangement comes in the seven unit tests, which are clearly identified in the opening list. These test lessons are entirely graded, and the "page-turning" is forced by your answers, with no Proceed button and no Back button.

When you finish each lesson, the result of your performance on the graded questions is written onto your key disk, and your score then shows in a box. If you want to see all of your grades to date, insert the key disk, start up Anima, enter your name and password as with normal running, but select Grades instead of Start. This will give you a more complicated screen, with an upper list box holding the lessons and a lower list box which holds your name to start with. To see only one lesson, click on its line in the upper box; the grade report from that lesson will appear in the lower box. To see all of them, click the 'See All Grades' button; the reports from all 44 lessons (including the ones you haven't worked yet) will appear in the lower list box.

INSTALLATION INSTRUCTIONS

Hardware and Software Requirements

ANIMA runs under Windows 3.1, WFW 3.11, or Windows 95, requiring about 10 MB of disk space. Memory requirements are the same as those for Windows, and a color monitor is required.

To install ANIMA, insert the key disk into a floppy slot. (To avoid writing a lot of alternatives we'll assume here that you're using floppy drive A: and that your destination directory is C:\ANATOMY.) Start up Windows if you are not in Windows already, and then run the INSTALL program.

In Win 3.1, this means selecting the File menu in Program Manager, and then selecting Run under that menu. (Using keyboard, that's Alt-F-R.) In Win 95, you Run something by hitting the Start button and then selecting Run. In either case, you'll then see a blank for 'Command Line.' Fill in A:INSTALL and hit Enter.

The INSTALL program gives you four initial choices:

1. Full Install: This choice personalizes the key disk and also copies all the Anima files into a chosen directory on the hard disk of the computer.

INSTALL first asks you for a directory. It will not stop you from using an existing directory, because you might have a good reason for doing that, but that's still generally unwise.

INSTALL checks to be sure that the directory is on a usable hard disk, with enough free space to hold the files.

If directory is OK, it then asks you for name or ID. This can be either a name or a number. The actual letters or numbers are critical, but spacing, punctuation and capitalization are not. At this initial stage, you should enter the name or ID in the form you want to appear on grade records. Later on, during each actual use of Anima, some sloppy typing will be forgiven. For example, if you enter "Jane P. Smith" in the INSTALL program, Anima will show the name exactly that way in grade records, and will let you get by with "jane p smith" or even "jANE PsMITH" but not "Jane Smith" as identification.

Similarly, if you start with the Social Security number 123-12-1234, Anima will later accept variations like 123121234 but not 223-12-1234.

After the name entry, INSTALL asks for a short password. Form is a bit more critical here. Capitalization still doesn't matter, but the password must consist of only letters and numbers, with no spaces or punctuation. INSTALL will ask you to try something different if your entry breaks that rule.

The password should be thought of as a single word or any series of letters and digits resembling a single word (like XPZ14R). Weird combinations like X%$7-Q*U will not work. In actual use, capitalization is open but spacing and punctuation are not: If you entered XPZ14R during the INSTALL, you could then use xpz14R but not XPZ 14R.

Once you've given a name and a usable password, INSTALL starts to expand and copy the Anima executable and lesson files from the floppy into your destination directory on the hard disk. (You get a last chance to say Go or Stop before the copying starts.) Copying takes around 1 to 5 minutes depending on the computer's speed.

When copying is done, INSTALL proceeds to personalize the floppy disk with your name and password. *Note:* What ends up on the computer itself has no "identity." That's all in the key disk. Any student with a valid key disk may use any installed setup of Anima, but Anima won't run at all without a key disk.

2. Only Make Key: This is the choice to use if you don't have your own computer; you will still need to personalize a key disk so that you can run Anima on a computer where it's fully installed. The steps within INSTALL are identical to full installation except that no directory is requested and no copying happens. If you later acquire access to a computer, you can still do a "Full Install" using the same key disk; at that time your entry of name and password during the Install will serve to verify, not create, the key.

3. Remove Installation: You could certainly remove the hard-disk files by ordinary deletion, so this action is provided as a convenience for (preferably immediate) undoing of an installation that went into the wrong directory or onto the wrong computer. What INSTALL required from you here is the same as on a Full Installation, because you have to know what directory you intend to remove, and you must also verify the name and password. (In other words, you can't create a new key disk while Uninstalling.) If the directory contains other files and/or other subdirectories, INSTALL will remove only its own products; other files will remain, and any subdirectory that contains something other than the Anima files also will remain.

4. Quit Now: Mostly self-explanatory. There are several chances to Quit during the INSTALL. Any hit on a Quit button will leave no changes to either the key disk or the hard disk; in effect, nothing has happened. But once you have said Go at the copying stage, INSTALL proceeds automatically to copy all the files and personalize the key disk. After that, there's no undoing the key disk, but you can use the Remove installation choice to undo the installation in the computer.

After doing a Full Install, you will still need to create the desktop icon. There is too much variation among different Win versions and optional desktop managers to perform this step automatically. If your Windows setup uses a nonstandard desktop, which is true of many campus computers, you'll have to do whatever is usual in that system to create a desktop icon. Here are instructions for standard Win 3.1 and for creating a visible and usable icon in Win 95. We'll assume here for simplicity that you installed Anima in the C:\ANATOMY directory.

In standard Win 3.1:

1. Put the focus in whatever group you want. (This may not be necessary if your Win screen is arranged on one "level"; or you may want to create a new group first to hold ANIMA.)
2. Select File-New on the Program Manager menu.
3. In the "New Program Object" dialog, select "New Item."
4. In the "Program Item Properties" dialog: Put ANIMA (or a short name of your own choosing, perhaps more meaningful to you) in the "Description" box.
5. Click on the "Command Line" box. Type C:\ANATOMY\ANIMA.EXE in that box and hit Enter.
6. Click on the Working Directory box. Put C:\ANATOMY in that box and hit Enter.
7. From there, just click OK until you're back to the regular Win desktop.

In Win 95:

You may want to create a program icon in the supposedly standard way (completely hidden and unavailable, reachable only through the arcane labyrinth that branches off from the Start button). Indeed you may want to do it that way, but we won't tell you how. If you want to use Anima effectively, you should instead create what Win 95 mysteriously terms a "shortcut."

1. Put the mouse in an unoccupied spot on the desktop (not on any icon) and click the right

button. This brings up a menu with "Arrange Icons" on top. Click on "New" in that box.

2. This brings up a menu with "Folder" on top. Click on "Shortcut" in that menu.

3. This leads to a larger box with a blank for "Command Line." Fill in the full pathname of the Anima program, as in C:\ANATOMY\ANIMA.EXE and then hit Enter or click "Next."

4. This leads to a box where you specify the name you want. Fill in "Anima" or any other short name that seems appropriate, and hit Enter or click "Finish."

5. After that, our little skull icon will appear on the desktop; use the mouse to drag it to wherever you want.

SUMMARY OF LESSONS

LESSON 1: Inspiration, Expiration, Pressure, Airflow

TOPICS: Introduction to respiratory system, respiration, inspiration, expiration, trachea, pharynx, oral cavity, nasal cavity, alveoli, gas exchange, bronchial tree, bronchiole, Boyle's law, negative and positive pressure, airflow

LESSON 2: Vertebrae and Vertebral Column

TOPICS: Lungs, gas exchange, respiration, muscular activity and lung inflation, framework of respiration: thorax, ribs, vertebral column, vertebrae, classes of vertebrae and landmarks, sternum, ribs

LESSON 3: Rib Cage Components

TOPICS: Sternum and landmarks, clavicle, scapula, chondral portion, osseous portion, qualities of cartilage, types of ribs, torque, elasticity, rib cage elevation, thorax volume change

LESSON 4: Pectoral and Pelvic Girdles

TOPICS: Pectoral girdle, clavicle, scapula, sternum, pubic bone, ischium, ilium and landmarks, pubic symphysis

LESSON 5: Preview of Muscular Action of Inspiration

TOPICS: Rib cage expansion, vertical and transverse dimensions, diaphragm and action, accessory muscles of inspiration, pressure change, Boyle's law applied

LESSON 6: Respiratory Passageway in Detail

TOPICS: Orientation to lungs/rib cage, respiratory passageway, trachea, bronchial divisions, lobes, segments, terminal bronchioles, alveoli (ducts, sacs), mediastinum, lung landmarks, capillary bed

LESSON 7: Details of Lung Parts

TOPICS: Respiratory system components, diameters and surface area, respiratory zones, conducting passageways, capillary bed

LESSON 8: Pleural Linings and Pleural Linkage

TOPICS: Movements of respiration review, diaphragm and thorax, pleural linings, linkage, mucosal fluid, intrapleural space, mediastinum

LESSON 9: Quiz on Vertebrae and Lungs (Lessons 1–8)

TOPICS: This lesson is a quiz over the details of trachea and lungs.

LESSON 10: Muscles of Inspiration

TOPICS: Thorax movement, primary and accessory muscles of inspiration: diaphragm and attachments and actions, central tendon, hiatuses

LESSON 11: Accessory Muscles of Respiration: Intercostals

TOPICS: Vertical and transverse dimensions, diaphragm, rib cage elevation, rib movement, volume increase, rib course, external and internal intercostal muscles, interchondral portion of internal intercostals, sternal and vertebral differences, intercostal nerves

LESSON 12: Accessory Muscles of Inspiration

TOPICS: Posterior thoracic muscles, levatores costarum muscles brevis and longis, serratus posterior, intercostal nerves, sternocleidomastoid, XI accessory nerve, scalenus anterior, medius, and posterior, pectoralis major and pectoralis minor, levator scapulae, latissimus dorsi, rhomboideus major, rhomboideus minor, trapezius

LESSON 13: Expiration

TOPICS: Passive and active expiration, torque, elasticity, gravity, elevation of the rib, cartilaginous portion of the rib cage, torque, restoring forces, elastic cartilage, elevation of rib cage against gravity, volume changes, Boyle's law revisited, interosseous portion of internal intercostal muscles, movement of rib cage, transversus thoracis, abdominal muscles, action of abdominal compression, transversus abdominis, internal oblique abdominis, external oblique abdominis, rectus abdominis, transversus abdominis, linea alba, linea semilunaris.

LESSON 14: Physiology of Respiration

TOPICS: Diaphragm, accessory muscles of inspiration, vertical and transverse dimension of thorax, torque, elasticity, and gravity, spirometer, volume, pressure, manometer, respiratory rate, respiratory cycle, minute volume, tidal volume, gender differences, age changes in respiratory rate, physical changes in development and aging, volumes and capacities, quiet tidal volume, inspiratory reserve volume, expiratory reserve volume, residual volume, dead air space, vital capacity, functional residual capacity, total lung capacity, inspiratory capacity, effects of posture

LESSON 15: Pressures of Respiration

TOPICS: Intraoral pressure, subglottal pressure, alveolar pressure, subglottal pressure, intrapleural pressure, atmospheric pressure, pressures and volume changes, Draper et al. data, EMG and diaphragm and accessory muscles, effect on volume, checking action, respiratory cycle for speech/nonspeech, relaxation pressure, tissue forces, lung elasticity, muscle action, thoracic recoil

LESSON 16: Quiz on Respiration (Lessons 10–15)

This lesson is a quiz over the muscles and actions of respiration.
[*Note:* Some figures in the respiration section are modified from data and views of Des Jardins (1984), Draper, Ladefoged, and Whitteridge, (1959); Netter (1989); Pappenheimer et al. (1950); Rahn, Otis, Chadwick, and Fenn (1946); Spector (1956); Twietmeyer and McCracken (1992); and Hixon (1973)]

LESSON 17: The Framework of the Larynx

TOPICS: Larynx, thyroid cartilage: superior cornu, inferior horn of thyroid, laminae, notch, oblique line; cricoid cartilage: cricoid facets, joints, cricothyroid joint, cricoarytenoid joint; arytenoid cartilages: facets, muscular process, vocal process, apex, muscular attachment, orientation of cartilages; corniculate cartilages; epiglottis; hyoid bone; greater and lesser cornua, corpus

LESSON 18: The Inner Larynx

TOPICS: Ventricular folds, laryngeal ventricle, true vocal folds, vestibule, aryepiglottic folds, conus elasticus, tissues of vocal folds, vocal ligament, thyrovocalis and thyromuscularis muscles and attachments, epiglottis, vocal fold rotating, tensing, relaxing, recurrent laryngeal nerve, glottis, cartilaginous and membranous portion of vocal fold margin

LESSON 19: Intrinsic Muscles of the Larynx

TOPICS: Functions of intrinsic laryngeal muscles, adduction, abduction, relaxation of the vocal folds, vocal fold tensors, rotation, gliding, medial compression, recurrent laryngeal nerve, superior laryngeal nerve, cricothyroid

LESSON 20: Extrinsic Muscles of the Larynx

TOPICS: Laryngeal elevation and depression, digastricus anterior and posterior, stylohyoid, mylohyoid, geniohyoid, geniohyoid, sternothyroid, thyrohyoid, omohyoid

LESSON 21: Quiz on Larynx (Lessons 17–20)

TOPICS: This lesson is a quiz over the cartilages and muscles of the larynx.

LESSON 22: Vibrations

TOPICS: Oscillation, elastic restoring forces, stiffness, inertia, mass, periodicity, period, frequency, Hertz

LESSON 23: Laryngeal Function for Nonspeech and Speech

TOPICS: Protection of airway, coughing, throat clearing, increased abdominal pressure, lifting, abdominal and thoracic fixation, dilation, phonation, vocal attack (glottal, simultaneous, breathy), vocal fold movements (rock, rotate, glide), pitch change, tonic contraction for sustained phonation, aerodynamic-myoelastic theory, modal phonatory register, vertical and anterior-posterior modes of oscillation [*Note:* Some figures are modified from data and views of Langley, Telford, and Christensen (1969); Netter (1989); Shprintzen and Bardach (1995); Titze (1994); and Williams and Warrick (1980).]

LESSON 24: The Articulatory/ Resonatory System

TOPICS: Articulation, mobile and immobile articulators, source-filter theory of vowel production, vocal tract, oral cavity, nasal cavity, pharynx, cavities as resonators, turbulence, voicing, mandible, velum, pharynx, alveolar ridge, hard palate, teeth

LESSON 25: Quiz on Laryngeal Action (Lessons 22–24)

TOPICS: This lesson is a quiz over vibrations and the function of the larynx.

LESSON 26: Bones of the Face

TOPICS: Mandible, symphysis mente, mental foramen, corpus, angle, ramus, condylar process, temporomandibular joint, coronoid process, mandibular notch, teeth, dental alveoli, alveolar arch, mylohyoid line, mandibular foramen, maxillae, hard palate, dental ridge, clefting of lip and hard palate, frontal process infra-orbital margin, infraorbital foramen, zygomatic process of maxilla, nasal crest, nasal notch, alveolar process, alveoli, maxillary sinus, palatine process, hard palate, intermaxillary suture, incisive foramen, premaxillary suture, premaxilla, palatine bones, posterior nasal cavities, posterior nasal spine, nasal crest, horizontal plate, perpendicular plates, nasal septum, vomer, cartilaginous septum, perpendicular plate of ethmoid bone, zygomatic bone, frontal process, temporal process, zygomatic arch, orbital margin, maxillary process

LESSON 27: Bones of the Cranial Skeleton

TOPICS: Ethmoid bone, perpendicular plate, bony septum, crista galli, cribriform plates, sphenoid bone, corpus, greater wings of sphenoid, lesser wings of sphenoid, and pterygoid processes, hypophyseal fossa, lateral pterygoid plates, medial pterygoid plates, pterygoid hamulus, frontal bone, zygomatic processes, orbital portion, nasal portion, parietal bones, squamosal suture, sagittal suture, lambdoidal suture, wormian bones, sagittal suture, coronal suture, occipital bone, foramen magnum, condyles, basilar part, temporal bone, mastoid process, external auditory meatus, mandibular fossa, squamosal portion, styloid process

LESSON 28: Teeth

TOPICS: Mastication, upper and lower adult dental arches, orientation, root, gingival line, crown, neck, dental enamel, dentin, pulp, cementum, locational terms, distal, mesial, medial, buccal surface, lingual surface, occlusal surface, central incisors, lateral incisors, cuspids, bicuspids, molars, occlusion, dental development, deciduous arch

LESSON 29: Dental Orientation and Occlusion

TOPICS: Function of teeth, cutting, tearing, chewing, occlusion, Class I occlusion, Class II occlusion, Class III occlusion, malocclusion, relative micrognathia, torsiversion, labioverted, linguaverted, distoverted, mesioverted, infraverted, supraverted, persistent open bite, persistent closed bite

LESSON 30: Quiz on Facial Bones and teeth (Lessons 26–29)

TOPICS: This lesson is a quiz over the bones of the face and the teeth.

LESSON 31: Cavities of the Vocal Tract

TOPICS: Oral cavity, faucial pillars, hard palate, rugae, median raphe, soft palate, uvula, anterior, posterior faucial pillars, palatine, tonsils, buccal cavity, pharyngeal cavity, oropharynx, laryngopharynx, nasopharynx, pharyngeal protuberance, nasal choanae, orifice of eustachian tube, torus tubarius, salpingopharyngeus muscle, adenoids, nasal cavities, nasal septum, turbinates

LESSON 32: Muscles of the Face and Mouth

TOPICS: Orbicularis oris, cupid's bow, columella nasi, philtrum, risorius muscle, buccinator, pterygomandibular ligament, levator labii superioris alaeque nasi, levator labii superioris, zygomatic minor, levator anguli oris, zygomatic major, depressor labii inferioris, mentalis, platysma, action of facial muscles on lips

LESSON 33: Physiology of Articulation

TOPICS: Nonspeech functions of articulators, mastication, deglutition, stages of mastication and deglutition, oral preparatory stage, the oral stage, pharyngeal stage, esophageal phase, articulators, upper and lower lip function, force, velocity, mandible movement, tongue movements, extrinsic and intrinsic muscle function, velum

LESSON 34: Muscles of the Mouth

TOPICS: Tongue, median fibrous septum, dorsum, tip, oral surface, pharyngeal surface, median sulcus, lingual papillae, terminal sulcus, foramen cecum, lingual tonsils, lingual frenulum, intrinsic muscles, extrinsic muscles, superior longitudinal muscle, inferior longitudinal muscle, transverse intrinsic muscles, vertical muscles, genioglossus, hyoglossus, palatoglossus, styloglossus

LESSON 35: Muscles of Mastication

TOPICS: Mastication, masseter, temporalis, medial pterygoid muscle, lateral pterygoid muscle, digastricus anterior, mylohyoid, platysma, geniohyoid

LESSON 36: Muscles of the Soft Palate

TOPICS: Velum, elevation, tension, depression, levator veli palatini muscle, musculus uvulae, tensor veli palatini, palatoglossus, palatopharyngeus, superior, middle, inferior pharyngeal constrictors, salpingopharyngeus, stylopharyngeus

LESSON 37: Quiz on Muscles and Cavities of Mouth (Lessons 31–36)

This lesson is a quiz over the tissue of the face and mouth.
[*Note:* Some figures are modified from data and views from Bateman (1977); Bateman and Mason (1984); Langley, Telford, and Christensen, (1969); Netter (1989); Shprintzen and Bardach, (1995); Telford and Christensen (1969); Williams and Warrick (1980).]

LESSON 38: The Neuron

TOPICS: Central and peripheral nervous systems, neurons, glial cells, soma, dendrite, axon, axon hillock, myelin sheath, nodes of ranvier, telodendria, terminal end boutons, synaptic vesicles, neurotransmitter substance, interneurons, motor (efferent) neurons, sensory (afferent) neurons

LESSON 39: Anatomy of Spinal Cord

TOPICS: Spinal cord, myelin sheath, tracts, foramen magnum, conus medullaris, filum terminale, spinal nerves, dermatomes, dorsal root ganglion, ventral root fibers, segmental spinal reflex arc, synapse

LESSON 40: Brainstem

TOPICS: Anterior spinothalamic tract, decussation, corticospinal tract, medulla, pyramidal decussation, anterior and lateral corticospinal tracts, corticobulbar tract, cranial nerves, brainstem, nuclei, obex, fourth ventricle, pons, middle cerebellar peduncle, superior and inferior cerebellar peduncles, third ventricle, cerebral aqueduct, midbrain, cerebral peduncles, dorsal motor nucleus

LESSON 41: Cranial Nerves

TOPICS: V trigeminal, ophthalmic, maxillary, and mandibular nerves and functions, VII facial nerve and functions, VIII vestibulocochlear nerve, auditory pathway, olivocochlear bundle, IX glossopharyngeal, X vagus nerve, superior and recurrent laryngeal nerves, XI accessory nerve, XII hypoglossal

LESSON 42: Cerebral Cortex and Lobes of the Brain

TOPICS: Cerebrum, cerebral hemispheres, Brodmann classifications, sulcus, gyrus, cerebral longitudinal fissure, frontal, parietal, occipital, temporal, insular, and limbic lobes, lateral sulcus, superior, middle, and inferior temporal gyri, Heschl's gyrus, Wernicke's area, hippocampus, central fissure, precentral gyrus, premotor region, Broca's area, parietal lobe, supramarginal and angular gyri, occipital lobe, insular lobe

LESSON 43: Inner Parts of Brain

TOPICS: Corpus callosum, commissural fibers, projection fibers, corona radiata, short and long association fibers, arcuate fasciculus, meningeal linings, cerebrospinal fluid, ventricles, choroid plexus, interventricular foramen of Monro, cerebral aqueduct, basal ganglia, thalamus, hypothalamus, cerebellum

LESSON 44: Quiz on the Nervous System (Lessons 38–43)

This lesson is a quiz over the nervous system, spinal cord and brain parts.
[*Note:* Some figures in the neurology section are modified from data and views of Carpenter (1978), Gilman and Winans (1982), Netter (1983a, 1983b, 1989), Poritsky, (1992).]

REFERENCES

Bateman, H. E. (1977). *A clinical approach to speech anatomy and physiology.* Springfield, IL: Charles C. Thomas.

Bateman, H. E., & Mason, R. M. (1984). *Applied anatomy and physiology of the speech and hearing mechanism.* Springfield, IL: Charles C. Thomas.

Carpenter, M. B. (1978). *Core text of neuroanatomy.* (2nd ed.). Baltimore, MD: Williams & Wilkins.

Des Jardins, T. (1984). *Clinical manifestations of respiratory disease.* Chicago, IL: Year Book Medical Publishers.

Draper, M., Ladefoged, P., & Whitteridge, D. (1959). Respiratory muscles in speech. *Journal of Speech and Hearing Research, 2,* 16–27.

Gilman, S., & Winans, S. S. (1982). *Manter and Gatz's essentials of clinical neuroanatomy and neurophysiology.* Philadelphia, PA: F. A. Davis.

Hixon, T. J. (1973). Respiratory function in speech. In F. D. Minifie, T. J. Hixon, & F. Williams, (Eds.), *Normal aspects of speech, hearing, and language.* Englewood Cliffs, NJ: Prentice-Hall.

Langley, L. L., Telford, I. R., & Christensen, J. B. (1969). *Dynamic anatomy and physiology.* New York: McGraw-Hill

Netter, F. H. (1983). *The CIBA collection of medical illustrations.* Vol. 1. *Nervous system.* Part I. *Anatomy and physiology* West Caldwell, NJ: CIBA Pharmaceutical Company.

Netter, F. H. (1983). *The CIBA Collection of medical illustrations.* Vol. 1. *Nervous system.* Part II. *Neurologic and neuromuscular disorders.* West Caldwell, NJ: CIBA Pharmaceutical Company.

Netter, F. H. (1989). *Atlas of human anatomy.* West Caldwell, NJ: CIBA Pharmaceutical Company.

Pappenheimer, J. R., Comroe, J. H., Cournand, A., Ferguson, J. K. W., Filley, G. F., Fowler, W. S., Gray, J. S., Helmholtz, H. F., Otis, A.

B., Rahn, H., & Riley, R. L. (1950). Standardization of definitions and symbols in respiratory physiology. *Federation proceedings, Federation of the American Society for Experimental Biology*, 602–605.

Poritsky, R. (1992). *Neuroanatomy: A functional atlas of parts and pathways*. St. Louis, MO: Mosby-Year Book.

Rahn, H., Otis, A., Chadwick, L. E., & Fenn, W. (1946). The pressure-volume diagram of the thorax and lung. *American Journal of Physiology, 146*, 161–178.

Spector, W. S. (1956). *Handbook of biological data*. Philadelphia, PA: W. B. Saunders.

Shprintzen, R. J., & Bardach, J. (1995). *Cleft palate speech management*. St. Louis, MO: C. V. Mosby.

Titze, I. R. (1994). *Principles of voice production*. Englewood Cliffs, NJ: Prentice-Hall.

Twietmeyer, A., & McCracken, T. (1992). *Coloring guide to regional human anatomy*. Philadelphia: Lea & Febinger.

Williams, P., & Warrick, R. (1980). *Gray's anatomy (36th Brit. ed.)*. Philadelphia, PA: W. B. Saunders.

GLOSSARY

-a-	Without; lack of
-ab-	Away from
Abdomen	Region of the body between the thorax and pelvis
Abdominal viscera	Organs of the abdominal region
Abdominal fixation	Process of impounding air within the lungs through inhalation and forceful vocal fold adduction which results in increased intra-abdominal pressure.
Abduction	To draw a structure away from midline
Absolutely refractory period	Period following depolarization of a cell membrane during which stimulation will not result in further depolarization
Acetylcholine	Neurotransmitter involved in communication between several classes of neurons and between nerve and muscle
Actin	One of two muscle proteins
Action potential (AP)	Electrical potential arising from depolarizing a cell membrane
Ad-	Combining form meaning toward
Adduct	To draw two structures closer together or to move toward midline
Adduction	Process of drawing two structure closer together or moving a structure toward midline
Adenoids	Lymphoid tissue within the nasopharynx
Adequate stimulus	Stimulation of sufficient intensity or frequency to cause a response

Adipose	Connective tissue impregnated with fat cells
Afferent	Carrying toward a central location; generally, sensory nerve impulses
Agonists	Muscle contracted for purpose of a specific motor act (as contrasted to the antagonist)
Ala	Wing-like structure
-algia	Combining form meaning pain
Alpha motor neurons	Motor neurons involved in activation of the majority of skeletal musculature
Alveolar pressure	Air pressure measured at the level of the alveolus in the lung
Alveolus	Small cavity; as in alveolus of lung, the air sac wherein gas exchange occurs
Ambulation	Walking
Amphi-	On both sides
Amphiarthrodial	Bony articulation in which bones are connected by cartilage
An-	Without; lack of
Ana	Up
Anastomoses	Communication between two vessels or structures
Anatomical position	Erect body, with palms, arms, and hands face forward
Anatomical dead space	Space within the conducting passageway of the respiratory system that is not involved in exchange of gasses
Anatomy	The study of structure of an organism
Aneurysm	Abnormal dilation or ballooning of a blood vessel (typically an artery)
Angio-	Blood vessels
Angiology	Science dealing with blood vessels and the lymphatic system
Anomia	Inability to remember names of objects
Ansa	Structure that forms a loop or arc
Antagonist	A muscle that opposes the contraction of another muscle (the agonist)
Ante-	Before
Anterior	In front of; before
Antero-	Before
Antrum	An incompletely closed cavity
Apex	Peak; extremity

Aphasia	Acquired language disorder, typically arising from cerebrovascular accident
Apical	Referring to the apex of a structure
Apo-	Away from
Aponeurosis	Sheet-like tendon
Appendicular skeleton	The skeleton including upper and lower extremities
Applied anatomy	The subdiscipline of anatomy concerned with diagnosis, treatment, and surgical intervention
Approximate	To bring closer together
Areolar	Loose connective tissue
Arm	The upper extremity including the region from the elbow to the shoulder
Arthr-	A joint
Arthrology	The study of joints
Articulation	The point of union between two structures
Articulators	In speech production, the moveable and immobile structures used to produce the sounds of speech
Articulatory system	In speech science, the system of structures involved in shaping the oral cavity for production of the sounds of speech
Ascending pathways	Sensory pathways of the nervous system
Association fibers	Neurons which transmit information between two regions of the same cerebral hemisphere
Asthenia	Weakness
Astrocytes	A form of neuroglial cell
Ataxia	Deficit in motor coordination
Atlas	The first cervical vertebra
Atmospheric pressure	Pressure of the atmosphere generated by its weight, approximately 760 mm Hg
Attrition	Wearing away
Audition	Hearing
Auditory evoked potentials	Electrical potentials arising from auditory stimulation
Auditory tube	Eustachian tube; aerating tube connecting nasopharynx and middle ear
Autonomic	Independently functioning
Autonomic nervous systems	Portion of nervous system controlling involuntary bodily functions

Axial skeleton	Portion of the skeleton including the trunk, head, and neck
Axis	Imaginary line representing the point around which a body pivots
Axoaxonic synapses	Synapses between two axons
Axodendritic synapses	Synapses involving axon and dendrite
Axon	The process of a neuron that conducts information away from the soma or body
Babinski reflex	Dorsiflexion of the great toe and spreading of other toes upon stimulation of the ventral surface of the foot
Baroreceptors	Pressure sensors
Basal ganglia	Nuclei deep within the cerebral hemispheres, involved in movement initiation and termination, and including the caudate nucleus, lentiform nucleus, amygdala, and claustrum
Base	The lower or supporting portion of a structure
Bellies	The fleshy portion of a muscle
Bernoulli effect	The effect which dictates that, given a constant volume flow of air or fluid, at a point of constriction there will be a decrease in air pressure perpendicular to the flow and an increase in velocity of the flow.
Bi-	Two
Bifurcate	Two-forked; to split into two parts or channels
Bite block	A structure used experimentally or clinically to eliminate movement of the mandible during articulatory tasks
Blast-	Germ
Bolus	A ball or lump of masticated food ready to swallow
Boyle's law	The law stating that, given a gas of constant temperature, an increase in the volume of the chamber in which the gas is contained will cause a decrease in air pressure
Brachy-	Short
Brady-	Slow
Brain mapping	Procedure of identifying functional regions of the cerebral cortex by electrical stimulation during speech, reading, or other tasks
Brevis	Short; brief
Broca's aphasia	Aphasia characterized by loss of fluency and reduced paucity of vocabulary, usually arising from lesion to Brodmann areas 44 and 45 of the dominant cerebral hemisphere (Broca's area)

Broca's area	Brodmann areas 44 and 45 of the dominant cerebral hemisphere, responsible for motor planning for speech and components of expressive language
Brodmann areas	Regions of the cerebral hemisphere, identified by numeric characterization based upon functional and anatomical organization
Bronchi	The two major branches from the trachea leading to right and left lungs
Bronchial tree	Network of bronchi and bronchial tubes
Bronchial tube	Divisions of the respiratory tree below the level of the mainstem bronchi
Bronchioles	Small divisions of bronchial tree
Buccal cavity	Cavity lateral to the teeth, bounded by the cheek
Buccal	Pertaining to the cheek
Bulb	Pertaining to the brainstem
Bulbar	Pertaining to the brainstem
Capillaries	Minute blood vessel
Capit-	Combining form meaning head, or toward the head end
Caput	The head
Caries	Decay of soft or bony tissue
-carpal	Combining form: wrist
Cartilage	Connective tissue embedded in matrix, capable of withstanding significant compressive and tensile forces
Cartilaginous joints	Joint in which cartilage serves to connect two bones
Cartilaginous	Constructed of cartilage
Caudal:	Toward the tail or coccyx
-cele	Combining form: tumor
Cementum	Thin layer of bone joining tooth and alveolus
Central nervous system	Brain and spinal cord components
Central	Relative to the center of a structure
Cephalo-	Combining form: head, or toward the head end
Cerebrospinal fluid	Fluid originating in the choroid plexuses of the ventricles, and providing cushion to brain structures

Cerebrovascular system	Vascular system serving the nervous system
Channel proteins	Specialized proteins in cell membrane that allow specific ions to pass through the membrane
Checking action	The use of muscles of inspiration to impede the outward flow of air during respiration for speech
Chemoreceptors	Sensory organ that is sensitive to properties of specific chemicals
Chondral	Pertaining to cartilage
Cilia	Hair-like processes
Circum	Around
Class I malocclusion	Malocclusion in which there is normal orientation of the molars, but there is an abnormal orientation of the incisors
Class I occlusion	Relationship between upper and lower dental arches in which the first molar of the mandibular arch is one-half tooth advanced of the maxillary molar
Class II malocclusion	Relationship between upper and lower dental arches in which the first mandibular molars are retracted at least one tooth from the first maxillary molars
Class III malocclusion	Relationship between upper and lower dental arches in which the first mandibular molar is advanced farther than one tooth beyond the first maxillary molar
-cle	Combining form: implies something very small
Clinical eruption	Eruption of teeth into the oral cavity
Cm	Centimeter
Coarticulation	The overlapping effect of one sound upon another
Com-	Combining form: with or together with
Commissural fibers	Neural fibers that run from one location on a hemisphere to the corresponding location on the other hemisphere
Comparative anatomy	Study of homologous structures of different animals
Compressive strength	The ability to withstand crushing forces
Con-	Combining form: with or together with
Conduction aphasia	Aphasia due to lesion of the arcuate fasciculus
Conduction velocity	Rate of conduction of impulse through a neuron
Condyle	Rounded prominence of a bone
Contra-	Combining form: opposite
Contracture	Permanent contraction of a muscle

Contralateral	Originating on the opposite side
Convergence	Coming together toward a common point
Convolutions	Turns; infoldings
Cor-	Combining form: heart
Cornu	Horn
Coronal section	A section dividing the body into front and back halves
Corp-	Combining form: body
Corpus	Body
Cortex	Outer covering
Cough	Forceful evacuation of the respiratory passageway, including deep inhalation through widely abducted vocal folds, tensing and tight adduction of the vocal folds, and elevation of the larynx, followed by forceful expiration
Cranial nerves	The twelve pairs of nerves arising from the brain
Cranial	Toward the head
Craniostosis	Premature ossification of cranial sutures
Cranium	The portion of the skull containing the brain
Crown	The highest point of a structure
Crur-, crus	Combining form, meaning cross; leg-like part
Crux	Cross
Cryo-	Combining form: cold
-cule	Combining form: implies something very small
-culum, -culus	Combining form: diminutive form of a noun
Cycle of vibration	Point in a vibratory cycle at which the function begins to repeat itself
Cycle of respiration	Completion of both inspiration and expiration phases of respiration
-cyte	Combining form: cell
Cytology	Science dealing with structure of cells
De-	Away from
Dead space air	The air within the conducting passageways that cannot be involved in gas exchange
Decibel	The logarithmic expression of the ratio of two sound pressures or powers to express acoustic level
Deciduous dental arch	The dental arch containing the ten temporary teeth

Deciduous	Shedding
Decussate	To cross over
Deep	Further from the surface
Defecation	Evacuation of bowels
Deglutition	Swallowing
Dendrite	The process of a neuron that transmits information to the cell body
Dendrodendritic synapse	Synapse between two dendrites
Dentate	Referring to tooth; notched; tooth-like
Dentin	Osseous portion of the tooth
Depolarization	Neutralizing of polarity difference between two structures
Dermatome	Region of body innervated by a given spinal nerve
Descending pathways	Motor pathways of the central nervous system
Developmental anatomy	Study of anatomy with reference to growth and development to birth
Dextro-	Right
Diffusion	Migration or mixing of one material (e.g., liquid) through another
Digestive system	The system of organs and glands involved in digestion of food and liquids
Dilate	To open or expand an orifice
Dissection	The process of separating tissues of a cadaveric specimen
Distoverted	Tilted away from midline
Divergence	To become progressively farther apart
Dorsal	Pertaining to the back of the body or distal
Dorsum	Posterior side of a structure
-dynia	Pain
Dys-	Bad; with difficulty
Dysmetria	Deficit in control of the range of movement of a structure, such as a limb or the tongue
E-	Out from
Ec-	Out of
Ecto-	On the outer side; toward the surface
-ectomy	Excision

Efferent	Carrying away from a central point
Elasticity	The quality of a material that causes it to return to its original position after being distended
Electrophysiology	The study of electrical phenomena associated with cellular physiology
Ellipsoid	Shaped like a spindle
Embolism	The obstruction of a blood vessel by an object or clot
Embolus	An object within a blood vessel that has been carried by the blood stream
Embryonic development	In humans, the stage between the second and eighth weeks of gestation
-emia	Referring to blood
En passant	In passing
Enamel	The hard outer surface of the tooth
Encephalon	The brain
Endo-	Toward the interior; within
Ensiform	Sword-like
Ento-	Toward the interior; within
Ep-, epi-	Upon or above something else
Epimysium	Sheathe of connective tissue around skeletal muscle
Equilibrium	A condition of balance
Equipotentiality	Having equal electrical charge
Esophageal reflux	Introduction of gastric juices into the pharyngeal region through the esophagus
Etio-	Pertaining to cause or origin
Eversion	Turning outward
Ex-	Out of, toward the surface
Expiration	Process of evacuating air from the lungs during respiration
Extension	Straightening or moving out of the flexed position
External	Toward the exterior of a body
Extero-	Aimed outward or nearer to exteroceptors
Extra-	Outside
Eye tooth	Cuspid
Facet	A small surface

Fasciculus	A small bundle
Fibroblasts	Germinal cell of connective tissue
Final common pathway	The lower motor neuron serving a muscle or a muscle bundle
Fissures	A relatively deep groove
Flexion	The act of bending, often upon the ventral surfaces
Foramen	An opening or passageway
Fossa	A depression, groove, or furrow
Fovea	A pit
Frenum	A small band of tissue connecting two structures, one of which is mobile
Frenulum	A small frenum; often synonymous with frenum
Frontal	Anterior; pertaining to the front
Frontal plane:	Divides body into anterior and posterior
Function	The process or action of a structure
Functional unity	Structures which demonstrate similarities in function
Funiculus	Small, cord-like structure
Fundamental frequency	The lowest frequency of vibration of the vocal folds or of a harmonic series
Ganglion	Mass of nerve cell bodies lying outside of the central nervous system
-gen	Producing
General visceral efferent	The autonomic efferent fibers serving viscera and glands
General visceral afferent	Nerves that transmit sensory information from receptors in visceral structures, such as the digestive tract
General somatic efferent	Nerves providing innervation of skeletal muscle
General somatic afferent	Sensory nerves which communicate sensory information from skin, muscles, and joint, including pain, temperature, mechanical stimulation of skin, length and tension of muscle, and movement and position of joints
-genic	Producing
Genu	Knee
Gingiva	Gum tissue
Glia	Support tissue of the brain
Glottal fry	Phonatory mode characterized by low fundamental frequency and syncopated beat

Glottal	Referring to the glottis
Glottis	The space between the true vocal folds
Gooseflesh	Autonomic skin response resulting in erection of skin papillae
Gray matter	Cell bodies of neurons
Gross anatomy	Study of the body and its parts as visible without the aid of microscopy
Gustation	Sense of taste
Gyrus	Outfolding of tissue in cerebral cortex
Habitual pitch	The perceptual correlate of vocal fundamental frequency habitually used by an individual
Hard palate	The bony portion of the roof of the mouth, made up of the palatal processes of the maxillae and the horizontal plates of the palatine bones
Head	Proximal portion of a bone
Hemi-	Half
Hemiballism	Hyperkinetic condition involving involuntary and uncontrollable flailing of extremities of the right or left half of the body
Hemispheric specialization	The concept that one cerebral hemisphere is more highly specialized for a given task or function (e.g., language) than the other hemisphere
Hertz	Cycles per second
Heschl's gyrus	Area 41 of the temporal lobe; the primary reception area for auditory sense
Hg	Mercury
Hiatus	Opening
Histology	Study of tissue through microscopy
Homunculus	Literally, "little man"; referring to the spatiotopic array of fiber distribution along the central sulcus, representing body parts served by cortical region
Horizontal plane	Divides body or part into upper and lower portions
Hyaline cartilage	Smooth cartilage covering the ends of bones at articulations
Hyper-	Above; increased, or too much of something
Hyperextension	Extreme extension
Hyperpolarization	The condition wherein the threshold for depolarization is elevated, requiring increased stimulation to discharge
Hypo-	Below; decreased, or too little of something

Hypotonia	Low muscle tone
Hypoxic	Oxygen deficiency
Idio-	Peculiar
-ilos	Diminutive form of noun
Incisors	Anterior four teeth of dental arch
Indirect system	Extrapyramidal system of central nervous system, responsible for control of background movement, equilibrium, and muscle tone
Inertia	The tendency for a body at rest to remain at rest, and for a body in motion to remain in motion
Inferior	The lower point; nearer the feet
Infra	Below
Infraverted	In dentition, an inadequately erupted tooth
Inhibition	In nervous system function, the process of reducing the ability of a neuron to discharge through synaptic action
Innervation	Stimulation by means of a nerve
Insertion	The relatively mobile point of attachment of a muscle
Inspiration	Inhalation; drawing air into the respiratory system
Inspiratory reserve volume	The volume of air that can be inhaled after a tidal inspiration
Inspiratory capacity	The maximum inspiratory volume possible after tidal expiration
Intensity	Magnitude of sound, expressed as the relationship between two pressures or powers
Inter-	Between
Interchondral	The region between the cartilaginous portion of the anterior rib cage
Intercostal	Between the ribs
Internal	Within the body
Intero-	Aimed inward or farther from the surface
Interoceptors	Sensory receptor activated by stimuli from within the body (as opposed to exteroceptor)
Interstitial	Space between cells or organs
Intonation	The melody of speech, provided by variation of fundamental frequency during speech
Intra-	Within
Intracellular	Within the cell

Intrafusal muscle fibers	Muscle to which the muscle spindle is attached
Intraoral	Within the mouth
Intraosseous eruption	Eruption of tooth through bone
Intrapleural pressure	Pressure measured within the pleural linings of the lungs
Intro-	Into
Ions	A particle carrying positive or negative charge
Ipsi-	Same
Ipsilateral	Same side
Iso-	Equal
-itis	Inflammation or irritation
-ium	Diminutive form of noun
Joint	Articulation
Kinesthesia	Including sense of range, direction, and weight
Labioverted	Tilted toward the lip
Laminae	A flat membrane or layer
Laryngologists	Specialist in the study of vocal pathology
Laryngoscope	Instrument of visualization of the larynx and associated structures
Lateral	Away from the midline of the body
Latero-	Side
Leg	1. The lower anatomical extremity, particularly the region between the knee and ankle. 2. A device used for raising grain from ground level to the top of a bin, consisting of a continuous flexible belt with a series of metal buckets or scoops.
Lepto-	Thick
Lesion	A region of damaged tissue or a wound
Leuco-	White
Levo-	Left
Ligaments	Fibrous connective tissue connecting bones or cartilage
Limbic system	The central nervous system structures responsible for mediation of motivation and arousal, including the hippocampus, amygdala, dentate gyrus, cingulate gyrus, and fornix
Lingual	Referring to the tongue
Linguaverted	Tilted toward the tongue
Lobe	A well-defined region of a structure

Loudness	The psychological correlate of sound intensity
Lower motor neuron	The final common neurological pathway leading to the muscle, including the anterior horn cell of spinal cord, nerve roots, and nerves
Lumbar puncture	Insertion of aspiration needle into subarachnoid region of spinal cord, usually below L4
Lymphoid tissue	Tissue comprising lymphatic organs, including tonsils and adenoids
Macro-	Large
Manometer	Device for measuring air pressure differences
Mass	That characteristic of matter that gives it inertia
Mastication	Chewing
Maximum phonation time	The duration in seconds that an individual is capable of sustaining phonation
Meatus	Passageway
Mechano receptors	Sensory receptors sensitive to mechanical stimulation such as pressure upon the skin
Medial	Toward the midline of the body or subpart (syn. mesial)
Medial compression	The degree of force that may be applied by the vocal folds at their point of contact
Median	Middle
Mediastinal	Referring to the middle space; in respiration, referring to the organs separating the lungs
Medio-, medius	Middle
Megalo-	Large
Membranous glottis	The anterior three-fifths of the vocal fold margin; the soft tissue of the vocal folds (note that the term "glottis" is loosely used here, because glottis is actually the space between the vocal folds
Meningeal infection	Infection of the meningeal linings of the brain and spinal cord
Meninges	The membranous linings of the brain and spinal cord
Mesencephalon	The midbrain
Mesial	Toward the midline of the body or subpart (syn. medial)
Mesioverted	Tilted toward the midline
Meso-	Middle
Meta-	After; mounted or built upon
Metencephalon	Embyronic portion of brain from which cerebellum and pons originate

Micro-	Small
Microns	One thousandth of a millimeter; one millionth of a meter
Microscopic anatomy	Study of structure of the body by means of microscopy
Minute volume	The volume of air exchanged by an organism in 1 minute
Mitochondria	Microscopic cellular structures which provide the energy source for a cell
ml	Milliliters; one thousandth of a liter, equal to one centimeter
mm	Millimeter; one thousandth of a meter
Modal register	The vocal register used during normal conversation (i.e., that vocal register used most frequently)
Molars	The posterior three teeth of the mature dental arch, used for grinding
Mono-	Single
Monoloud	Without variation in vocal loudness (the perception of vocal intensity)
Monopitch	Without variation in vocal pitch (the perception of frequency)
Morph-	Form
Morphology	Study of the form of a structure without regard to function
Motor unit	The lower motor neuron and muscle fibers it innervates
Motor strip	The precentral gyrus of the frontal lobe; the point at which execution of voluntary motor acts is initiated
Motor endplate	Point of contact between motor neuron and muscle fiber
Motor neurons	Neurons that innervate muscle
Mucus	Viscous fluid secreted by mucous tissue and glands
Mucous	Tissue which secretes mucus
Multipolar neurons	Neurons possessing more than two processes
Muscle	An aggregation of muscle fibers with functional unity
My-	Pertaining to muscle
Myelencephalon	Portion of embryonic brain giving rise to the medulla oblongata
Myelin	Fatty sheath surrounding axons of some nerves
Myelo-	Pertaining to spinal cord
Myo-	Pertaining to muscle
Myoelastic-aerodynamic theory	Theory of vocal fold function that accounts for phonation through the lawful interplay of tissue mass, elasticity, and aerodynamic principles

Myology	The study of muscles and their parts
Naris	Nostril (plural, nares)
Naso-	Nose
Nasopharynx	The region of the pharynx posterior to the nasal cavity and superior to the velum
Neck	Constricted portion of a structure
Neo-	New
Neologisms	New word; in pathology, novel word coined by individual, but without meaning shared with listener
Nerve	Bundle of nerve fibers outside the central nervous system that has functional unity
Neuraxis	The axis of the nervous system, representing the embryonic brain axis
Neuro-	Nerve
Neurology	Study of the nervous system
Neuromotor dysfunction	Dysfunction in motor ability arising from lesion within the nervous system or the neuro-motor junction
Neuromuscular junction	The point of contact between a muscle fiber and the nerve innervating it
Neuron	A nerve cell
Neurotransmitters	Substance that is released into synaptic cleft upon excitation of a neuron
Neutroclusion	Normal molar relationship between upper and lower dental arches
Nodes of ranvier	Regions of myelinated fibers in which there is no myelin
Nucleus	An aggregate of neuron cell bodies within the central nervous system
Oblique	Diagonal
Occlusal surface	The surfaces of teeth within opposing dental arches that make contact
Occlusion	State of being closed
Oculo-	Eye
Olfaction	The sense of smell
-oma	Morbid condition of a part, often a tumor
Optimal pitch	The perceptual characteristic representing the ideal or most efficient frequency of vibration of the vocal folds

Oral cavity	The region extending from the orifice of the mouth in the anterior, and bounded laterally by the dental arches and posteriorly by the fauces
Oral diadochokinesis	A task involving repetition of movements requiring alternating contraction of antagonists muscles associated with speech (lips, mandible, tongue)
Organelles	A specialized structure of a cell (e.g., mitochondria)
Organs	Tissue of the body with functional unity
Origin	Proximal attachment of a muscle; point of attachment of a muscle with relatively little movement
Oro-	Mouth
Oropharynx	The region of the pharynx bounded posteriorly by the faucial pillars, superiorly by the velum, and inferiorly by the epiglottis
Ortho	Straight
Oscillation	Predictably repetitive movement
-osis	Condition
Osseo-	A hardened or bony part
Ossified	The process of tissue turning into bone
Osteo-	Bone
Osteology	Study of the structure and function of bones
Overbite	The vertical overlap of maxillary incisors over the mandibular incisors when molars are occluded
Overjet	Vertical overlap of maxillary incisors over mandibular incisors
Pachy-	Thick
Palatine tonsils	Lymphoid tissue between the fauces.
Palato-	Palate
Palmar	Pertaining to the palm of the hand
Palpate	To examine by means of touch
Para	Beside; partial
Pars	Part
Patho-	Abnormal in some way
Pathological anatomy	Study of parts of the body with respect to the pathological entity
-pathy	Disease
Ped-	Foot; child

-penia	Poverty
Per	Through; passing through; before
Perfusion	Migration of fluid through a barrier
Peri	Around
Pericardium	The membranous sac surrounding the heart
Perimysium	The sheathe surrounding muscle bundles
Period	The time required to complete one cycle of vibration or movement
Periodic	Having predictable repetition
Peripheral nervous system	That portion of the nervous system including spinal and cranial nerves
Peripheral	Relative to the periphery or away from
Permeability	The quality of penetrability
Persistent open bite	The condition wherein the incisors of upper and lower dental arches show a vertical gap, due to malocclusion of the posterior arch which prohibits anterior contact
Persistent closed bite	The condition wherein supraversion of the anterior dental arch prohibits the posterior teeth from occlusion
Pes	A foot-like structure
-phage, phagia	Eating
Pharyngeal tonsil	The mass of lymphatic tissue within the nasopharynx; a.k.a. adenoids
Pharynx	The respiratory passageway from the larynx to the oral and nasal cavities.
-pher-	Bearing or carrying
Phonation	The voiced tone produced by the vibrating vocal folds
Phonatory system	The system including the laryngeal structures through which phonation is achieved
Photoreceptors	Sensory receptors for visual stimulation
Physiological dead space	In respiration, ventilatory capacity that is wasted. In non-pathological conditions, physiological dead space is the same as anatomical dead space
Physiology	The study of function of the body and its components
Pitch	The psychological (perceptual) correlate of frequency of vibration
Pitch range	The perceptual correlate of the range of fundamental frequency variation possible for an individual

Plantar grasp reflex	Grasping by the toes upon light stimulation of the sole of the foot
Plantar	Pertaining to the sole of the foot
-plasia	Growth
-plastic	Capable of being molded
-plasty	Molding, forming
Pleural	Pertaining to the pleurae of the lungs
Pleurisy	Inflammation of the pleural linings of the lungs
Plexus	A network of nerves
-poiesis	Making
Poly-	Many
Post-	After; behind
Post-synaptic neuron	The neuron receiving input
Posterior	Toward the rear
Postero-	Behind
Potential energy	Energy which may be expended
Pre-	Before; in front of
Pre-motor area	The region of the cerebral cortex anterior the precentral gyrus (area 6)
Pressure	The derived measure representing force expended over an area
Primary verbal apraxia	Deficit in planning the speech act, resulting in inconsistent phonemic distortions and substitutions with oral groping behaviors for voluntary verbal motor acts, but in absence of muscular weakness or paralysis
Primary oral apraxia	Deficit in planning the nonspeech act, resulting in difficulty with imitating or producing voluntary nonspeech oral gestures but in absence of muscular weakness or paralysis
Pro-	Before; in front of
Process	A prominence of an anatomical structure
Projection fibers	Neural tracts running to and from the cerebral cortex connecting it with distant locations.
Pronate	To place in the prone position
Prone	Body in horizontal position with face down
Proprioception	The awareness of weight, posture, movement, position in space
Prosencephalon	In embryology, the forebrain, from which the telencephalon and diencephalon will arise

Proto-	Primitive; simple form
Protuberance	A bulge or prominence above a structure's surface
Proximal	Closer to the trunk or thorax; nearer to pubic bone,
Pulse register	Glottal fry; the vocal register characterized by low fundamental frequency, with syncopated vibration of vocal folds
Quadra-, quadri	Four
Quiet tidal volume	The volume of air exchanged during one cycle of quiet respiration
Radial	Pertaining to the radius bone
Ramus	A branch or division
-raphy	Suturing or stitching
Rate of discharge	Of a neuron, the rate at which the neuron depolarizes
Re-	Back or again; curved back
Reciprocal	Interchangeable
Reflex	Motor acts that are involuntary responses to stimulation
Relative micrognathia	The hypoplasia of the mandible relative to the maxilla
Residual volume	In respiration, the volume of air remaining after a maximum exhalation
Resonatory system	The portion of the vocal tract through which the acoustical product of vocal fold vibration resonates (usually the oral, pharyngeal, and nasal cavities combined; sometimes referring only to the nasal cavities and nasopharynx)
Respiration	The process of exchange of gas between an organism and its environment
Respiratory system	The physical system involved in respiration, including the lungs, bronchial passageway, trachea, larynx, pharynx, oral, and nasal cavities
Respiratory physiology	The study of function in respiration
Resting lung volume	The volume of air remaining within the lungs after quiet tidal expiration (a.k.a., expiratory reserve volume)
Retro-	Backward, toward the rear
Rhinorrhea	Liquid discharge from the nose
Rhombencephalon	Embryonic division of the brain from which the pons, cerebellum, and medulla oblongata ultimately arise
Rima glottidis	Space between the vocal folds; glottis
Rima vestibuli	The space between the false (ventricular) vocal folds
Root	The part of an organ hidden within other tissues

Rostrum	A beaked or hooked structure
-rrhea	A flowing
Ruga, rugae	Folds or creases of tissue
Sagittal plane	Divides body or body part into right and left
Scirrho-, sclero	Hard
-sclerosis	Hardening
Scolio-	Curved
Segmental	Divided into segments
Sellar	Saddle-like
Semi-	Half
Sensation	Awareness of body conditions sensed
Septum	A divider
Short association fibers	Neurons of the cerebrum connecting regions within the same hemisphere
Sinistro-	Left
Sinus	A cavity or passageway
Skeletal muscle	Striated or voluntary muscle
Slow twitch	Muscle fibers displaying a slow modal response
Smooth muscle	Visceral muscle
Soft palate	The musculotendinous structure separating the oropharynx and nasopharynx; a.k.a. velum
Soma	A cell body
Somatic muscle	Skeletal muscle; striated muscle
Somato-	Pertaining to the body
Somesthetic	Pertaining to awareness of body sensation
Sound wave	The acoustical manifestation of physical disturbance in a medium
Spatiotopic	The physical array of many of the regions of the cerebral cortex which defines the specific region of the body represented (e.g., the pre- and postcentral gyri).
Special somatic afferent	Cranial nerves that serve the special body senses such as vision and hearing
Special senses	Olfaction, audition, and vision
Special visceral efferent	Cranial nerves that innervate striated muscle of branchial arch origin, including the larynx, pharynx, soft palate, face, and muscles of mastication.

Special visceral afferent	Cranial nerves that provide information from the special visceral senses of taste and smell
Spheroid	Shaped like a sphere
Spike rate	Rate of discharge of a neuron
Spinal nerves	Nerves arising from the spinal cord
Spinal cord segment	A segment of the spinal cord corresponding to a vertebral region
Spinal column	The vertebral column
Spinal cord	The nerve tracts and cell bodies within the spinal column
Spirometer	Device used to measure respiratory volume
Steno-	Narrow
Stereognosis	Ability to recognize objects through tactile sensation
Strepto-	Swift
Stress	In speech, the product of relative increase in fundamental frequency, vocal intensity, and duration
Striated	Striped
Strohbass	Glottal fry; a.k.a., pulse register
Sub-	Under
Subglottal	Beneath the glottis
Subglottal pressure	Air pressure generated by the respiratory system beneath the level of the vocal folds
Sulcus	A groove
Sup-	Under; moderately
Super-	Above; excessively
Superficial	Near to the surface
Superior	The upper point; nearer the head
Supination	To place in the supine position
Supine	Body in horizontal position with face up
Supra-	Above, upon
Supraverted	Turning up
Surface anatomy	Study of the body and its surface markings, as related to underlying structures
Surfactant	A chemical agent that reduces surface tension
Suture	The demarcation of union between two structures through immobile articulation

Sym-	With or together
Symphysis	The type of union of two structures that were separated in early development, resulting in an immobile articulation
Syn-	With or together
Synapse	The junction between two communicating neurons
Synaptic vesicles	The saccules within the end bouton of an axon that contain neurotransmitter substance
Synaptic cleft	The region between two communicating neurons into which neurotransmitter is released
Synergists	A muscle in conjuction with another muscle to facilitate movement
Synovial fluid	The fluid within a synovial joint
System	A functionally defined group of organs
Systematic anatomy	Descriptive anatomy
Tachy-	Swift; fast
Tactile	Referring to the sense of touch
-tarsal	Ankle
Teleceptors	Sensory receptors responsive to stimuli originating outside of the body
Telencephalon	Embryonic structure from which cerebral hemispheres and rhinencephalon develop
Telo-	Far from, toward the extreme
Telodendria	The terminal arborization of an axon
Tendon	Connective tissue attaching muscle to bone or cartilage
Tensile strength	The quality of a material which provides resistance to destructive pulling forces
Teratogen	An agent that causes abnormal embryonic development
Tetra-	Four
Thermoreceptors	Sensors responsive to temperature
Thorax	The part of the body between the diaphragm and the 7th cervical vertebrae
Thrombosis	Formation of a blood clot in the vascular system
Thrombus	An obstructing blood clot
Tidal volume	That volume inspired and expired during normal, quiet respiration
Tissue recoil	The property of tissue that causes it to return to its original form after distension and release

-tomy	Cutting
Tonic	Pertaining to muscular contraction
Torque	Rotary twisting
Torsiversion	Rotating a tooth about its long axis
Torso	The trunk of the body
Total lung capacity	Sum of tidal volume, inspiratory reserve volume, expiratory reserve volume, and residual volume
Tracts	In the central nervous system, a bundle of nerve fibers
Trans-	Beyond or on the other side
Transduce	To change from one form of energy to another
Transverse	At right angles to the long axis
Tremor	Minute, involuntary repetitive movements
Tri-	Three
Trifurcate	To divide into three parts
-trophic	Related to nourishment
-trophy	Growth, usually by expanding
-tropy	Implies seeking or heading for something
Trunk	The body excluding head and limbs
Tubercle	A small rounded prominence on bone
Turbulence	Disturbance within fluid or gas caused by irregularity in passageway
Uni-	One
Upper extremity	The arm, the forearm, wrist, and hand
Vascularized	To become vascular
Vasoconstriction	Decrease in diameter of blood vessel
Velum	Soft palate
Ventilation	Air inhaled per unit time
Ventral	Pertaining to the belly or anterior surface
Ventricular system	System of cavities and passageways of the brain and spinal cord through which cerebrospinal fluid passes
Venules	A minute vein
Viscera	Internal organs within a cavity
Visceral	Pertaining to internal organs

Vital capacity	The total volume of air that can be inspired after a maximal expiration
Vocal jitter	Cycle-by-cycle variation in fundamental frequency of vibration
Vocal fundamental frequency	Primary frequency of vibration of the vocal folds
Vocal intensity	Sound pressure level associated of a given speech production
Voiced	Speech produced using the vibrating vocal folds
Voiceless phonemes	Phonemes produced without the use of vocal folds
Waveform	Graphic depiction of change in amplitude of vibration over time
Wet spirometer	Device used for measurement of respiratory volumes

INDEX